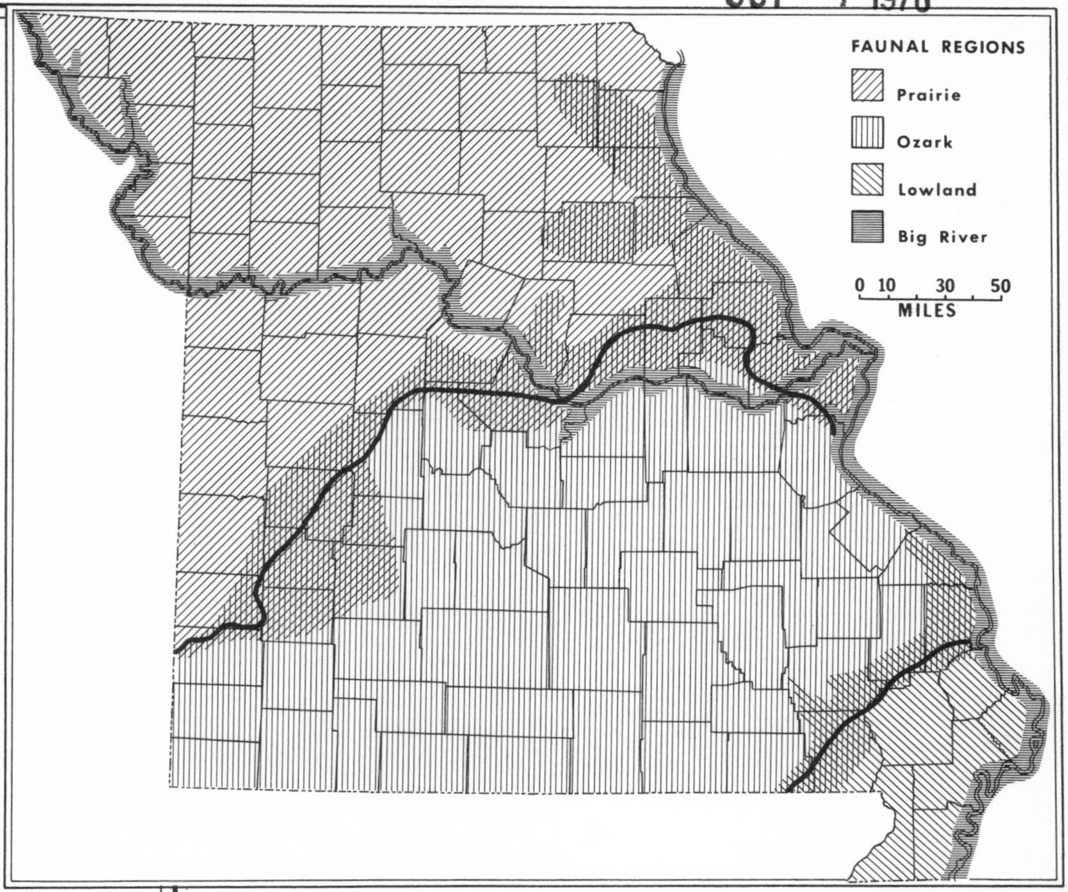

FAUNAL REGIONS
Prairie
Ozark
Lowland
Big River
0 10 30 50
MILES

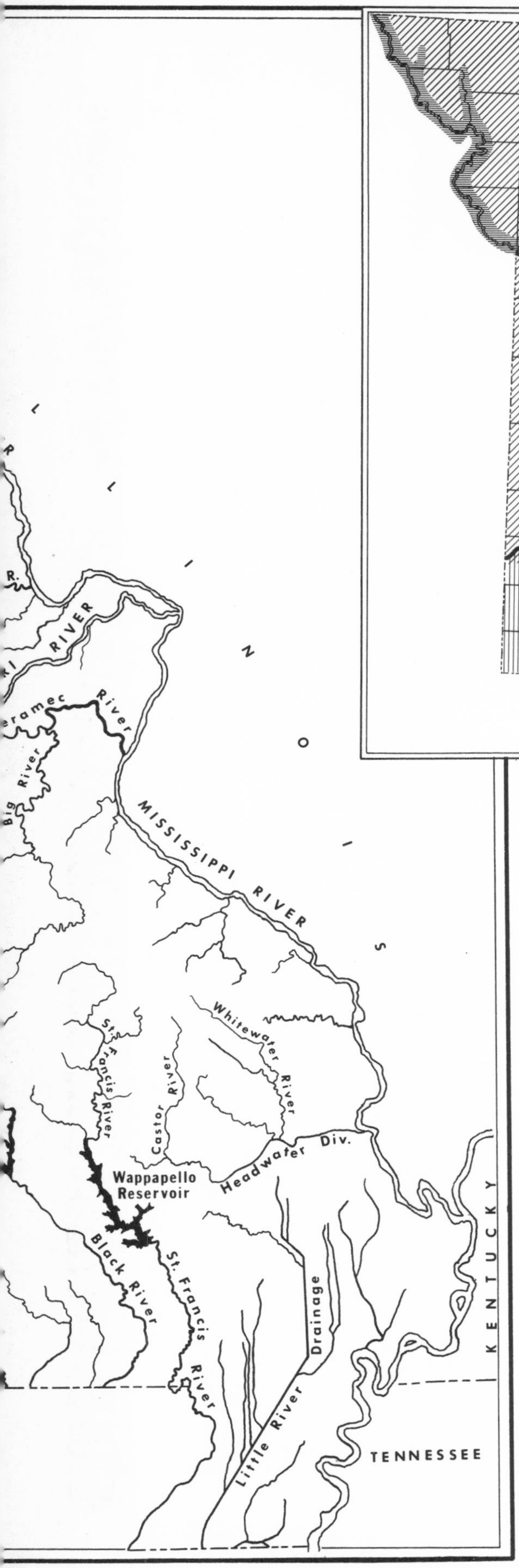

Missouri Faunal Regions and River Drainages

The Fishes of Missouri

The Fishes of Missouri

by
William L. Pflieger

Mark Sullivan • Editor

Lynne Taylor • Artist

Published by

Missouri Department of Conservation

1975

Printing and binding by
Western Publishing Co.

Table of Contents

Color Plates

Foreword

Several books have appeared in recent years describing the fishes of states near Missouri. But since the kinds of fishes and the conditions under which they live differ from state to state, none of these can properly serve as a reference for Missouri. The purpose of this book is to acquaint the reader with the nearly 200 kinds of fishes found in Missouri; to provide keys, descriptions, and illustrations for identifying them; and to make available information on their distribution, life ways, and importance to man.

So that the book will be useful to readers with varied backgrounds and interests, an effort has been made to adopt a style that is nontechnical, but which permits an accurate and reasonably complete treatment of the subject. Special terms have been kept to a minimum. Those which seem essential for clarity or conciseness are defined where first used or in a glossary at the back of the book. The information on each species follows a uniform arrangement, and subheadings have been used so that information on a particular topic can be more easily located. Literature citations have been included to give credit for information not my own and to suggest sources for further information. These are indicated by small superscript numbers that refer to the numbered list of references at the back of the book. A distribution map, which indicates locations where specimens have been collected, and a small inset range map are included to show the distribution of each species in Missouri and the total range in North America.

A separate report on fish distribution in Missouri has been published previously.[1] Preparation of that report permitted a more thorough treatment and the inclusion of much information not appropriate to a general purpose handbook.

Much is known about Missouri fishes, but even more remains to be learned. Important details are still to be discovered about the biology of the most common species, and almost nothing is known about many others. Present distribution of Missouri fishes is rather well documented, but significant changes can be expected in the future if present trends continue. It is hoped that this book will stimulate further studies to uncover new facts about the fishes of Missouri.

William L. Pflieger

Acknowledgements

This book could not have been written without the contributions of many individuals. Information on fish distribution in Missouri was acquired over a period of more than three decades through the efforts of numerous collectors. The contributions of these individuals were acknowledged in a technical report on fish distribution[1] and will not be repeated here. George V. Harry deserves special mention because of his very thorough survey of Missouri fishes conducted in the early 1940s. Mr. Harry generously made the results of his studies available when I first became interested in Missouri fishes.

The Missouri Department of Conservation has supplied funds, equipment and personnel for conducting field work since the study began, and defrayed the cost of publication of this book. The bulk of my studies have been carried out as an employe of the Department, and have been financed in part through the Dingell-Johnson Program (Project F-1-R). For their interest in and support of this project I am indebted to Carl R. Noren, director; Paul G. Barnickol, assistant director; Charles A. Purkett, Jr., Chief of Fisheries Division; John L. Funk and Joe G. Dillard who served successively as Superintendent of Fisheries Research; and to Dr. G.B. Herndon, formerly Chief of Fisheries Section, whose early interest led to publication of this book.

The following biologists provided specimens or information resulting from their studies: William Dieffenbach, Richard Duchrow, Stephen Eder, Otto Fajen, George Fleener, James Fry, John Goddard, Willis Hanson, John Robinson, Perry Robinson, Thomas Russell, Frank Ryck, Spencer Turner, and Fred Vasey. Conservation Agents throughout the state provided many fish specimens and reports, as well as valuable advice and assistance in the field.

I owe a special debt to Mark Sullivan for editing the manuscript, for his many valuable suggestions concerning design of the book, and for handling the intricate details of publication. The format for the illustrated keys was suggested by Charles W. Schwartz who prepared many of the illustrations for the key to the families of Missouri fishes. All other illustrations for the keys and chapter headings are by Lynne Taylor. Jim Keller prepared the layout of the book, added labels to the illustrated keys, and prepared overlays for the distribution maps. Rebecca Turk drafted the drainage and faunal region maps. Lynne Beasley and Rebecca Turk assisted in preparing the manuscript for publication. Debbie Ellis and Connie McPherson typed the final draft of the manuscript. Color photographs of fishes were supplied by the following individuals: Charles A. Purkett, Jr. (Niangua darter, orangethroat darter, and freshwater drum), James R. Whitely (orangespotted sunfish and crystal darter), and Don Wooldridge (shovelnose sturgeon, bowfin, and channel catfish). Photographs of fish habitats were furnished by Don Wooldridge (Table Rock Reservoir and Chariton River), and Russ Reagan (Mississippi River). Other photographs are by the author.

Elizabeth R. Schwartz offered many suggestions for simplifying and improving the keys. Reeve M. Bailey, University of Michigan, reviewed an early draft of the keys and pointed out certain inaccuracies and weaknesses. Frank B. Cross, University of Kansas, and Jamie E. Thomerson, Southern Illinois University, read the manuscript and offered valuable suggestions. Charles Taber, Southwest Missouri State College, provided significant new distribution records for the taillight shiner, Niangua darter, and redfin darter.

My wife, Jo Ann, assisted in many ways, and has been a constant source of encouragement.

Introduction to the Fishes

Missouri is home to nearly 200 kinds of fishes, perhaps more than are found in any other area of similar size and shape on the North American continent. They range in size from the pygmy sunfish and least darter, which mature at a length of an inch or less, to the paddlefish and blue catfish which reach weights of over 100 pounds. Some rank among the most colorful of all animals. Darters may be appropriately referred to as the "hummingbirds of the fish world" because of the brilliant and varied colors of the breeding dress of the males. Some minnows, topminnows, and sunfish are scarcely less brightly colored. In Missouri, fish live almost everywhere there is water, but each type of water has its own characteristic species. The Ozark cavefish lives in the limpid pools of underground streams, while the sicklefin chub is found only in the muddy, turbulent waters of the Missouri and lower Mississippi rivers. Some Missouri fish may complete their entire life in a short stretch of stream, or perhaps even in a single pool. Others make long journeys. The American eel and Alabama shad migrate between Missouri and the sea. In this introductory section I will try to bring together some of the more interesting and unusual facts about Missouri fishes and present certain general information that cannot be properly treated elsewhere in the book.

Place in the Animal Kingdom

Fish are members of a major subdivision of the Animal Kingdom, the "vertebrates", which includes frogs, salamanders, lizards, snakes, birds, and mammals. A common feature of all vertebrates, found in no other animal group, is a backbone, or vertebral column. Animals without backbones, the invertebrates, include such groups as insects, spiders, snails, and worms. Crayfish and jellyfish, in spite of their names, are invertebrates rather than fish. No one knows exactly how many kinds of fish there are, but it is certain that there are nearly as many as all other vertebrates combined. Even the most conservative estimates indicate more than 15,000 species.

As a rule, fish are easily recognized because they possess a certain combination of characteristics not found in other animals. But since difficulties occasionally arise as to whether or not a particular animal is a fish, we need to briefly consider these characteristics. Fish are vertebrates that live in water, "breathe" by means of gills, and have fins instead of legs. With such obvious exceptions as catfish, most also have the body covered with scales. The majority of fishes found in Missouri are so obviously "fish-like" in appearance that they are seldom confused with anything else. Lampreys and the eel remotely resemble snakes, but the presence of fins and a smooth slimy skin immediately indicates that they are not. Some fish-like characters are also found in other animals that live in the water, and these animals are occasionally confused with fish. Certain salamanders have gills and fins for at least part of their life, but all have one or two pairs of legs. In some, the legs are very small and could be overlooked. Tadpoles, as every youngster knows, are not fish but the young of frogs. Perhaps the easiest way to tell tadpoles from fish is that in tadpoles the head and body form a single, broad unit that narrows very abruptly into the tail. In fish, the head and body taper so gradually into the tail that it is not easy to tell where one ends and the other begins. No discussion of animals that look like fish would be complete without mentioning whales, though this is a bit far afield for a book on the fishes of Missouri. Whales are descendents of land-dwelling mammals that took up life in the oceans, and, like all mammals, they breathe by means of lungs. The internal structure of their fin-like forelimbs is quite different from that of the fins of fishes, and their "tail fin" is flattened from top to bottom rather than from side to side as in a fish.

Names and Classification

Man customarily gives names to the objects about him and classifies or groups these objects according to their properties. Naming is essential to communication, and classifying objects in this manner is a great aid to learning and remembering facts about them. The most satisfactory system for naming and classifying objects is one that has wide acceptance. Biologists have adopted a standard system for naming and classifying plants and animals that is in use throughout the world. This system is designed to ensure that all living things will have universally accepted names, and to provide a convenient and logical arrangement for all that is known about them. Since we shall be making use of this system, a brief explanation of it is in order.

The fundamental unit or building block of this system is the *species.* We all intuitively recognize species among the more familiar animals. Thus, we easily recognize that the domestic cat is different from the tiger, though they share many basic similarities. But the differences are not always so clear cut, and it is necessary to have criteria for deciding doubtful cases. Briefly, a species is a group of individuals that share a common inheritance through interbreeding and, as a consequence, are more similar to each other in structure and habit than they are to individuals of other species. Individuals of different species interbreed rarely or not at all. If interbreeding does occur, the resulting offspring are sterile or, for other reasons not entirely understood, these offspring fail to pass their inheritance on to future generations. In this way the species are kept distinct.

Every species has been given a *scientific* name which consists of two words written in Latin or latinized form. The first word is the generic name and is always capitalized. This part of the scientific name is the same for all species that make up a group or *genus* having certain characteristics in common. The second word in the scientific name is never capitalized and is different for each species in a particular genus. This is the *specific* name. Sometimes the scientific name is followed by the name of the person or persons who first described and named the species. It is customary to do this at least once each time the scientific name is used in a publication, and I have done so at the beginning of the species accounts. If the describer's name is in parentheses it means that the species has been shifted from one genus to another at some time after the original description.

Individuals from different parts of a species' range sometimes differ in certain minor characteristics. These differences are often recognized by describing and naming two or more *subspecies,* each of which occupies a definite part of the species' range. When this is done, a third word is added to the scientific name. The differences between subspecies often are so slight that they can be recognized only by a specialist. We will generally ignore subspecies for this reason, except to point out a few of the more striking examples.

In the standard classification system individuals are classified into species. These are in turn classified into genera, which are joined together into larger groups called *families,* and so on up to the most inclusive of all groups, the Plant Kingdom and the Animal Kingdom. The units that make up a particular group at any level in the classification have more in common with each other than with the units included in any other group at that level. In this way the diversity of nature is organized into a system that is more readily understood. It is much easier to learn and remember a particular fact if we can see how it relates to other facts within a logical framework.

Each species of fish, in addition to its scientific name, has one or more *common* names. These are the names in everyday use and have the advantage of being more familiar than scientific names. Unfortunately, the same species sometimes comes to be known by different common names in different parts of its range, or the same common name is applied to two or more different species. Thus, the rock bass, *Ambloplites rupestris,* is almost universally known as the goggle-eye in the Missouri Ozarks. Goggle-eye is a very descriptive name, but it is also commonly used for the warmouth, *Lepomis gulosus,* a common fish in southeast Missouri. The common names used in this book are those recommended by the American Fisheries Society in the third edition of *A List of Common and Scientific Names of Fishes from the United States and Canada* (Special Publication No. 6). I have also included for each species a list of common names used locally in Missouri, so that the reader can associate the recommended common name with the name he may be accustomed to using.

Distribution and Habitat

Though fishes are found almost everywhere there is permanent water, each species has its own *distribution* or *range.* Some are wide-ranging; others have a more limited distribution. A few, such as the Niangua darter, occur nowhere else in the world except Missouri. The largemouth bass is a wide-ranging species. Its native range included most of the United States east of the Great Plains and, with man's help, it now occurs over nearly all of this country and in many other countries as well.

Since fish are aquatic animals, they are distributed according to stream systems. Often a species that is widespread and abundant in one stream system is absent from other nearby stream systems, even though the habitat seems suitable. This results because fish cannot readily move from one stream system to another. Continuous waterways are required and, from a fish's point of view, streams only a few miles apart by an overland route might as well be hundreds, or even thousands of miles apart. Thus, a fish in James River in Webster County, Missouri, would have to swim over 1,500 miles to get into the Niangua River of the same county. Streams extend their drainages headward as they erode the areas they drain. In so doing they sometimes "capture" streams of other systems, thus diverting their flow and all the fishes that are present from one system to another. As a result of such rare events, species become established in two separate stream systems. As time passes, the separate populations may slowly change or evolve into different subspecies or species. That this has happened many times is indicated by the common occurrence of different but closely related fishes in adjacent stream systems. Thus, the bleeding shiner and Missouri saddled darter, two common fishes in the Niangua River and other streams of the northern Ozarks, are represented in the James River by two close relatives, the duskystripe shiner and Arkansas saddled darter. In discussing fish distribution I will refer repeatedly to various Missouri streams and reservoirs. These are named on a map inside the front cover of this book.

Within its range, a species is not found everywhere. Rather, it occurs in certain natural settings that are its *habitat.* The successful fisherman is one who has learned to recognize the habitat of the species he seeks. He knows that the smallmouth bass lives in clear, permanent-flowing streams where there is enough current to create rocky or gravelly pools, while its close relative the largemouth is more likely to be found in some sluggish backwater, oxbow lake, or reservoir. In general, the species of a single group such as a genus or family occupy similar habitats. Nearly all members of the sunfish family, for example, prefer quiet water. Even the smallmouth bass avoids the swifter currents. In contrast, most darters prefer flowing waters and many are characteristic of swift-flowing riffles. Missouri has few natural lakes, and most of our native fish are characteristic of stream habitats. Even those that prefer lakes and other non-flowing waters commonly occur in the quieter sections of streams.

Habitat conditions vary greatly from one section of Missouri to another. The streams differ with respect to such conditions as gradient or rate of fall, volume and constancy of flow, current velocity, water clarity, development of riffles and pools, and nature of bottom materials. These conditions are determined by climate, local relief or topography, soil and bedrock types, vegetative cover, and man's use of the regions through which the streams flow.

Few species of Missouri fishes are statewide in occurrence and none is uniformly distributed over the state. Rather, each has its own pattern of distribution that is related to its special requirements. Species with similar requirements have similar patterns of distribution. Conversely, species with different requirements have patterns of distribution that are largely complementary. As a result, four principal fish faunal regions, each characterized by a particular assemblage of fish species, can be recognized in Missouri: Ozark, Lowland, Prairie, and Big-river. These regions are shown on a map inside the front cover of this book. The following discussion is presented to give a general picture of them and to indicate the fishes that are characteristic of each.

Ozark Faunal Region

Geologically, this region is an elevated plain that was uplifted near the beginning of the Pleistocene ice age more than a million years ago and has since been deeply eroded by the streams that drain it. Much of the Ozarks has been carved into a complex system of rugged hills, but extensive areas of relatively level topography remain along the major stream divides. Granite rock as old as the earth itself outcrops at the surface of the southeastern Ozarks, but limestone laid down by an ancient sea underlies most of the remainder of

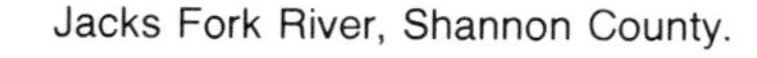
Jacks Fork River, Shannon County.

the region. The limestone contains large quantities of chert or flint that remains behind as coarse, angular rock fragments when the surrounding limestone is dissolved away. The thin, stony soil derived from the limestone does not favor the development of an intensive agriculture, and large areas of the Ozarks are forested or devoted to pasture.

Ozark streams occupy narrow, steep-sided valleys, and in places are bordered by sheer, limestone bluffs that sometimes rise 150 feet or more above the stream bed. The streams themselves typically consist of a series of short pools and well defined riffles. Chert gravel washed down from the surrounding slopes is the most abundant bottom type. Rubble and bedrock are not uncommon, and limestone boulders that have fallen away during bluff formation partly block the channel in places. Ozark streams are the clearest in the state because much of the water that enters them is first filtered through unconsolidated deposits of chert. The Ozarks is a region of many springs which provide an abundant and reliable source of water for the streams. The largest springs have a flow equal to that of a small river. A stream may double in size below the entrance of such a spring and remain cool enough for a considerable distance to support trout and other coldwater fishes. Aquatic plants of several kinds occur in Ozark streams. Water cress, *Nasturtium,* is abundant about the mouths of springs and along small streams that receive much spring flow. Beds of water willow, *Justicia,* occur in riffle areas and along rocky shores. Also common along rocky shores is spatterdock or yellow pond lily, *Nuphar.* Submergent plants, including coontail, *Ceratophyllum;* water milfoil, *Myriophyllum;* and pond weeds, *Potamogeton;* abound in quiet pools and backwaters.

The Ozark Faunal Region supports a large and complex assemblage of fishes. Sixty-five species, or just over one-third of all Missouri fishes, have their distribution centered in the Ozarks. Fourteen of these are unique to the Ozark Region, occurring nowhere else in the world.

Greer Spring, Oregon County.

Table Rock Reservoir, Stone County.

Minnows (22 species) and darters (17 species) are the dominant groups of small fishes in Ozark streams. The most common and widespread minnows are: southern redbelly dace, hornyhead chub, rosyface shiner, bleeding shiner, striped shiner, wedgespot shiner, bigeye shiner, Ozark minnow, largescale stoneroller, and central stoneroller. The streamline chub, telescope shiner, duskystripe shiner, and whitetail shiner are abundant in certain drainages. Common and widespread darters in Ozark streams are: banded darter, greenside darter, rainbow darter, orangethroat darter, and fantail darter. The bluestripe darter, stippled darter, Niangua darter, and Missouri saddled darter are unique to the Ozark Region of Missouri. The northern studfish and blackspotted topminnow are the most common killifishes in Ozark streams. Three species of madtom catfishes are characteristic of Ozark streams. The slender madtom is widespread, while the Ozark madtom and checkered madtom are restricted to the southern Ozarks. Two species of sculpins are the dominant fishes in many Ozark spring branches. Brook lampreys (four species) are restricted in Missouri to the Ozark Region, but are uncommon and localized in distribution.

Suckers and sunfishes are the dominant groups of large fishes in Ozarks streams. The northern hog sucker, black redhorse, and golden redhorse comprise the bulk of the suckers in most streams. The aggregate weight of suckers is often greater than that of all other large fishes combined. The longear sunfish is one of the most abundant and generally distributed Ozark stream fishes. The smallmouth bass and rock bass are other common members of the sunfish family in Ozark streams. The walleye is characteristic of the larger rivers.

Several large hydroelectric and flood control reservoirs have been constructed in the Ozarks in recent years and have profoundly affected the fish populations of impounded stream sections. Most of the characteristic Ozark fishes virtually disappear with impoundment and are replaced by wide-ranging fishes that are characteristic of the pools of streams. Some of these species were present in the streams before impoundment. Others were introduced from elsewhere by man. The brook silverside and gizzard shad are the principal forage fishes in Ozark reservoirs. The Mississippi silverside and threadfin shad are abundant in a few reservoirs where they have been introduced. The channel catfish, bluegill, spotted bass, largemouth bass, crappies (two species), white bass, and walleye are the principal game fishes in Ozark reservoirs. The muskellunge, northern pike, and striped bass have been introduced on an experimental basis. The carp is the most abundant species of large nongame fish.

Wolf Bayou, Pemiscot County.

Lowland Faunal Region

This region of southeast Missouri is a flat, lowland plain set off from adjacent uplands of the Ozarks by a steep, rocky bluff that marks a sudden change in elevation. Elevations of 1,400 feet or more occur in the Ozarks, but much of the Lowlands is less than 300 feet above sea level. The monotony of the lowland plain is broken only by Benton Hills and Crowley's Ridge, two prominent topographic features that extend in a curved line from the Mississippi River in northeastern Scott County, southwestward to the St. Francis River in Dunklin County. Bedrock is exposed at the surface only along the margin of the Ozarks and at a few places in Crowley's Ridge. Elsewhere it is covered to great depths by clay, sand, and gravel deposited by the Mississippi and Ohio rivers as they shifted their courses back and forth across the Lowlands. In places these deposits are as much as 2,700 feet deep.

Before settlement the Lowlands were covered by cypress swamps and drained by streams that entered from the Ozark Region to the north. During wet seasons almost all of the Lowlands were under water. Flood waters of the Mississippi River sometimes swept the Lowlands as far west as the St. Francis River. It was not until the early 1900's that serious efforts were made to clear and drain the swamps. Today the swamps are largely gone and the Lowlands are intensively cultivated.

Approximately 1,200 miles of ditches, constructed to drain the swamps, are the principal habitat for fishes in this region. The major ditches are large enough to be designated as small rivers. They are nearly uniform in depth, with considerable current throughout. Cover is sparse and aquatic vegetation is confined primarily to the shorelines. Some of the smaller ditches have no perceptible current, while others are fairly swift. Submerged aquatic vegetation, especially coontail, *Ceratophyllum;* water milfoil, *Myriophyllum;* and various pondweeds, *Potamogeton;* are often abundant. The sands and gravels underlying the Lowlands act as a vast reservoir for water that falls as rain or snow. This water is slowly released into the ditches and, as a result, their flow is very constant. Erosion is minimized by low relief and the ditches run clear much of the time. Sand and small gravel are the principal bottom type in areas of current; silt and organic debris predominate in quiet areas.

The fish fauna of the Lowlands is not as diverse as that of the Ozarks, but is no less distinctive. Twenty-five species are either confined to the Lowlands or occur only occasionally elsewhere in Missouri. Many fishes characteristic of the Gulf Coastal Plain reach the northern limit of their range in the Lowlands of southeastern Missouri.

Minnows and darters are well represented, but are less dominant numerically than in the Ozarks. Common minnows in the Lowlands are: ribbon shiner, ironcolor shiner, weed shiner, blacktail shiner, and bullhead minnow. The principal species of darters are: dusky darter, sand darters (3 species), slough darter, and cypress darter. The tadpole madtom and freckled madtom

Mingo Swamp, Stoddard County.

are common small catfishes. Other small fishes characteristic of the Lowlands are: pirate perch, starhead topminnow, mosquito fish, and banded pygmy sunfish.

No single group of large fishes is dominant in the Lowlands. Characteristic species include: gars (3 species), bowfin, eel, carp, buffalofishes (3 species), spotted sucker, warmouth, spotted sunfish, flier, crappies (2 species), and largemouth bass. Certain species are common in both the Ozarks and Lowlands. These include: grass pickerel, blackspotted topminnow, spotted bass, and longear sunfish.

The fauna of the Lowlands was greatly altered by drainage of the swamps. Probably, species characteristic of standing waters—pugnose minnow, ironcolor shiner, starhead topminnow, pirate perch, pygmy sunfish, flier, and slough darter—were abundant in the swamps. Other species that are characteristic of flowing waters—ribbon shiner, blacktail shiner, bullhead minnow, brindled madtom, spotted bass, stargazing darter, and dusky darter—are now more widespread.

Prairie Faunal Region

This region may be broadly characterized as a flat to rolling plain, nearly as high in elevation as parts of the adjacent Ozark Region. That part of the Prairie Region north of the Missouri River has been subjected to the leveling action of glaciation.

Little River Drainageway, Pemiscot County

A flat plain, known as the Audrain Prairies, extends northward from Audrain County along the Missouri-Mississippi drainage, but breaks off abruptly into hilly country along streams to the east, south and west. Much of northwestern Missouri has a gently rolling to undulating surface, while south of the Missouri River the prairie is nearly as level as the Audrain Prairies. Shales and thin sandstones are the principal bedrocks underlying the Prairies, but limestones similar to those under parts of the Ozarks predominate to the east along the Mississippi and lower Missouri rivers. In places the bedrock is covered to considerable depths by glacial till, and along the Missouri and Mississippi rivers loess, wind-blown dust, has been deposited to depths of as much as 150 feet. The soils are deeper and less stony than those of the Ozarks. The region originally was covered by prairie grasses, broken by timber in the more hilly sections. Today, nearly all of the grassland and much of the timber are gone and the Prairie Region is nearly as intensively cultivated as the Lowlands.

The major streams of the Prairies occupy broad, flat valleys that slope gradually and, in places, almost imperceptibly into the surrounding uplands. Originally those streams meandered back and forth across their valleys and left many oxbow lakes and sloughs as they shifted their courses. Most streams have now been channelized and are straight and nearly uniform in depth. Silt, sand, and gravel are the principal bottom types. Only a few highly mineralized springs are present, and stream flow is less constant in the Prairie Region than elsewhere in the state. The water is turbid much of the time, due to erosion of clay from the fine-textured soils. Aquatic vegetation is generally sparse, but water willow, *Jus-*

Chariton River, Adair County.

ticia, occurs wherever rocky bottoms are present.

In general, there is a transition from west to east and from north to south in the characteristics of the streams. Streams in northwest Missouri conform most closely to the description given above, while streams to the south and east approach Ozark streams in their characteristics. A similar transition occurs in the fish fauna, resulting in a complex mixing of Prairie and Ozark species along the border between the two regions.

The fish fauna of most streams in the Prairie Faunal Region is less varied than in other faunal regions. This results because prairie streams are subject to widely fluctuating environmental conditions, and only fishes tolerant of these fluctuations can persist. Because the characteristic Prairie species can live in a variety of situations, they are less restricted in distribution than fishes of other regions. Some penetrate well into the Ozarks along its northern and western border, and others occur in the Lowlands. Eighteen species have their distribution centered in the Prairie Faunal Region.

South Fork of Salt River, Audrain County.

Clear Creek, Clay County.

Minnows are the dominant group of small fishes. The most common species are: golden shiner, cheek chub, suckermouth minnow, bigmouth shiner, red shiner, redfin shiner, sand shiner, and fathead minnow. The darter group is poorly represented in Prairie streams. The johnny darter is the only species that is very widespread. The stonecat is the characteristic madtom of Prairie streams. Certain small fishes are not widespread, but are particularly characteristic of the Prairie Region. These are: common shiner, Topeka shiner, ghost shiner, brassy minnow, plains killifish, trout-perch, and blackside darter.

The most common large nongame fishes are: gizzard shad, carp, river carpsucker, quillback, and white sucker. Catfishes are one of the more important groups of large fishes in Prairie streams. The principal catfishes are the black bullhead, channel catfish, and flathead catfish. The most common representatives of the sunfish family are: green sunfish, orangespotted sunfish, bluegill, largemouth bass, and white crappie.

Certain fishes that are otherwise restricted to the Ozarks occur in the eastern part of the Prairie Region, along with the more typical Prairie species. Among these are: bigeye shiner, golden redhorse, smallmouth bass, slenderhead darter, orangethroat darter, and fantail darter.

Big-river Faunal Region

The Missouri and Mississippi rivers support a distinct assemblage of fishes that sets them apart as a separate faunal region. Certain fishes found in these rivers occur nowhere else in Missouri, and many others are most abundant in the Missouri and Mississippi. Because the fishes in these rivers and the lower reaches of their principal tributaries are so distinct, these streams are treated as a separate faunal region. They drain a vast area before reaching Missouri and their character as a habitat for fishes is not determined to any great degree by local conditions. Rather, it is a reflection of conditions over all the areas that they drain. To understand these rivers as a fish habitat it is necessary to consider these conditions.

The Missouri River originates at the confluence of the Gallatin, Madison, and Jefferson rivers in southwestern Montana and flows for about 2,500 miles in an easterly and southeasterly direction, joining the Mississippi River just north of St. Louis. It is the longest river on the North American continent. The lower 570 miles of the Missouri River lie entirely within or form the western boundary of Missouri. At its headwaters it is a clear mountain stream. As it flows eastward and southeastward it receives silt-laden tributaries from the Badlands of Wyoming and the Dakotas. Farther downstream its silt load is increased by drainage from the intensively cultivated prairies of the Dakotas, Nebraska, Iowa, Kansas, and Missouri. Because of this, it is one of the most turbid large streams on the continent. Most of the region drained by the Missouri River is arid or semi-arid. As a result, it contributes only about 12% of the total flow of the Mississippi Basin, though it has about one-third of the drainage area. The Missouri River was formerly subject to wide fluctuations in flow, with peaks in spring and early summer. Several large reservoirs now in place on the upper Missouri have reduced peak discharges and stabilized the flow. These reservoirs have also markedly reduced turbidity all the way to the river's mouth.

In its original condition the Missouri River occupied a wide, braided channel with many islands and backwaters. The location of the channel changed with every flood, and bank erosion was continuous. In recent years the river has been confined to a single, relatively narrow channel by the installation of wing dikes and revetments. Channel shifting and bank erosion have been almost eliminated, and the quiet backwaters are largely gone. The current in most of the main channel is swift. Fine, shifting sand is the principal bottom type, with small gravel where the current is strongest and deep deposits of flocculent silt in protected areas along the shore. The main channel is of rather uniform depth, without the development of alternating shoals and pools.

The Mississippi River originates in northern Minnesota and flows about 2,400 miles in a southerly direction to the Gulf of Mexico. It forms the entire eastern border of Missouri, a distance of 494 miles. Along the border of Missouri it receives its two principal tributaries, the Missouri and Ohio rivers. The upper Mississippi, above the mouth of the Missouri, drains a region that is less arid than that drained by the Missouri River, and the flow is consequently greater and less subject to fluctuations. With only 32% as large a drainage area as the Missouri River, the flow is 18% greater. Compared to the Missouri, the upper Mississippi River is a clear stream. In its original condition it consisted of a series of alternating deep pools and shallow rapids, and it was a more placid stream than the Missouri. The contrast between the two streams has been heightened by the construction of a series of navigation pools on the Mississippi, of which six are in the Missouri section of the river. These have converted the river into a series of lakes, but areas with considerable current still occur downstream from the dams. Such areas have bottoms of sand, gravel, and rock. The bottoms of the navigation pools are mostly silt. Extensive beds of aquatic vegetation occur in protected areas of the pools.

Missouri River, Boone County.

Below the mouth of the Missouri River the Mississippi takes on much of the character of the Missouri. It has not been impounded and has a swift current. The turbidity is high, but is less than that of the Missouri. Gravelly and rocky bottoms are more prevalent than in the Missouri River. The Ohio River joins the Mississippi not far below Cape Girardeau and has a marked effect on the Mississippi. The Ohio drains an area of high rainfall and, with a drainage area only 30% as large as the Mississippi River at their junction, it has an average discharge that is 50% greater. Thus, the flow of the Mississippi River more than doubles below the mouth of the Ohio and dilution by the clear waters of the Ohio greatly reduces turbidity. Sand and gravel are the principal bottom types in the Mississippi River downstream from the mouth of the Ohio, with silt in the backwaters.

The assemblage of fishes occurring in the Missouri and Mississippi rivers is large and varied. In all, 30 species and one subspecies have their distribution centered in these two large rivers. Ten species have not been collected elsewhere in the state. The Missouri and Mississippi rivers are characterized as much by the fishes that avoid them as by those that are restricted to them. More than 40 species that occur in tributary streams are not yet known from the big rivers. An additional 23 species that are common in tributary streams have occurred only rarely in collections from the Missouri and Mississippi.

Minnows are the only abundant group of small fishes in the Big-river Region. The most common and generally distributed species are: silver chub, speckled chub, flathead chub, emerald shiner, river shiner, and the silvery minnows (3 species). The sturgeon chub, sicklefin chub, silverband shiner, and channel mimic shiner are strictly Big-river minnows, having been taken in Missouri only from the Missouri and Mississippi rivers. The appropriately named river darter is the only species of the darter group that is at all widespread in the large rivers.

The most abundant large fishes in the Missouri and Mississippi rivers are: shortnose and longnose gars, gizzard shad, carp, river carpsucker, buffalofishes (3 species), channel catfish, flathead catfish, white bass, and freshwater drum. The largemouth bass, bluegill, and crappies (2 species) are abundant in oxbows and backwaters. Other species that are particularly characteristic of the Big-river Region include: chestnut lamprey, shovelnose sturgeon, pallid sturgeon, paddlefish, skipjack herring, goldeye, blue sucker, and blue catfish.

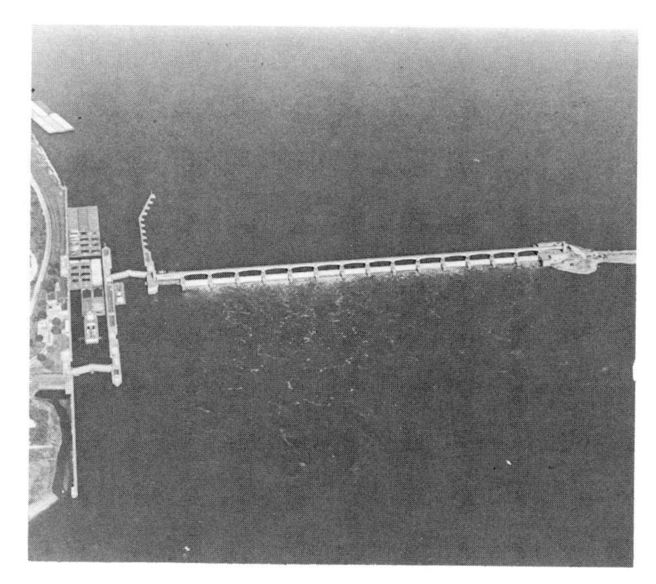

Mississippi River, Lock and Dam, Clarksville.

Though many fishes are rather uniformly distributed in the Missouri and Mississippi rivers, others are characteristic of certain sections. Five minnows—sicklefin chub, sturgeon chub, flathead chub, plains minnow, and western silvery minnow —that occur in the Missouri River also are found in the lower Mississippi River, but not in the Mississippi River above the mouth of the Missouri. Two madtoms—stonecat and freckled—and four darters—slenderhead, logperch, river and western sand—are fairly common in the Mississippi River but are very rare in the Missouri. The skipjack herring, threadfin shad, eastern silvery minnow, and Mississippi silverside are much more common in the Mississippi River downstream from the mouth of the Ohio than in other river sections.

Structure and Life Ways

Form and Function

The body form or shape of a fish is so intimately related to its way of life that the two are most readily understood by considering them together. Though fish come in many sizes and shapes, all are constructed on the same basic plan. The features shared by all are related to the special properties of water as a place to live; the modifications of the basic plan are those which fit each species for the particular life it leads. Water is a very different sort of place to live than air. To know fish better it is necessary to understand these differences and see how they relate to the life of fishes.

Because water is so dense, it resists movement of its inhabitants. Even staying in one spot is a challenge for animals that live in flowing waters. To move efficiently in water requires a certain form. The body of a fish is not sharply divided into head, trunk and tail as in most land animals. Rather, these body parts grade one into the other, forming a single unit with smooth contours that provide little resistance to water.

Fast-moving fishes, and those fitted for life in swift currents, are beautifully streamlined, like the fuselage of a jet airplane or the hull of a submarine. The skipjack herring and rosyface shiner are of this type. The speckled chub, northern hog sucker, and many darters that live in swift currents, but on the bottom, are shaped more like a car body, streamlined above and flat below. Sunfish that live in quiet water about thick growths of aquatic plants or other cover have deep, laterally flattened bodies and are built more for maneuverability than for speed. The eel has a long, snake-like body that is suited for crawling through crevices and for burrowing into the bottom.

Another result of high density is that an object immersed in water is supported to a much greater degree than an object in air. This largely counteracts the effects of gravity, and fish do not need strong supporting structures such as the limbs of land animals. Most fish have an internal gas-filled structure called a swim bladder, and can adjust the gas volume so that their density just equals that of water. While in water these fish are, for all practical purposes, "weightless", and can move up or down with little effort. The swim bladder is reduced or absent in fish such as darters and sculpins that live on the bottom in swift currents. They are denser than water and sink immediately to the bottom when they stop swimming.

Fish swim by contracting a series of block-like muscles called *myomeres* situated along the sides, assisted by the fins. When a fish is in a hurry it moves by alternately contracting the myomeres on opposite sides, causing a powerful sweep of the tail that drives the fish forward. The tail fin also acts as a rudder, and the dorsal and anal fins along the upper and lower surfaces of the body provide stability like the keel on a sailboat. The pectoral fins—those located just behind the gill openings—provide a braking action, and also function in climbing or diving. When slow progress is required the fins are the primary locomotor structures. The greatly enlarged pectoral fins of darters and sculpins can provide a sculling action, and slow movement in the bowfin and eel is accomplished by waves of motion along the very long dorsal and anal fins. When a fish is resting quietly it continually "backs" water with its pectoral fins to counteract the jetting action of respiratory currents from the gill openings. These respiratory currents assist to some extent in forward movement.

Most fish have scales embedded in the skin. These scales are of several basic types. Certain primitive fishes, such as sturgeons and gars, have hard, plate-like *ganoid* scales that are arranged in non-overlapping rows. More typical are thin, flexible *cycloid* and *ctenoid* scales which overlap like shingles on a roof. Cycloid scales, such as those of minnows and suckers, are smooth; ctenoid scales, such as those of sunfish and perch, have prickles, *ctenii,* on their exposed margins, and are rough to the touch. Catfish and some other groups lack scales and are covered by tough, leathery skin that can be stripped away like the hide of a mammal. The skin of fishes secretes a slimy coating of *mucus* that reduces friction with the water and protects against infections by bacteria and other parasites. Removal of large patches of mucus through injury or rough handling can result in infection and death.

Fish come in many color shades and patterns, but fall into several basic types depending on where they live. Fish that swim about in open water away from the bottom are often a rather uniform brown or olive-green above, fading to silvery or yellowish-white on the belly. The fish is thus made inconspicuous when viewed either from above, against the predominantly brown or green background of the stream bottom, or from below, against the mirror-like background of the water's surface. Fish that live among rocks on the stream bottom or about thick growths of aquatic plants are commonly marked by prominent blotches, bars or stripes. These markings enhance the resemblance of the fish to its background, or disrupt the body outline by calling attention to one part. The dark saddle bars of the northern hog sucker and many other bottom-dwelling fish, and the iridescent spots and stripes of topminnows, are disruptive marks. Cavefish are noteworthy for the complete lack of external pigment and appear white with a pinkish hue where the blood shows through.

The markings of fish are normally very constant among individuals of a single species or subspecies, but may vary with size, sex, or season of the year. Thus, the young of gars have a bold, black stripe that disappears when a length of about 10 inches is attained. The males of many minnows, sunfish, and darters develop bright colors during the breeding season. Males of some species rival in beauty the most brilliantly colored birds and butterflies. These breeding colors, along with characteristic patterns of behavior, serve to advertise the presence of the male to other individuals of his own kind. Females are thus attracted to the spawning areas and other males are warned away in those species where the male guards a territory.

Free oxygen is an essential condition of existence for fish, just as for nearly all life. But instead of removing oxygen from air by means of lungs, fish use special structures called *gills* to extract oxygen dissolved in the water. The gills of fish are located on each side of the head beneath a bony flap called the gill cover. Each gill consists of a bony arch with many flexible filaments that are richly supplied with blood vessels. A fish "breathes" by opening its mouth and drawing in water. The mouth is then closed, forcing water over the gills and out through the slit-like opening behind the gill cover. Under ideal conditions a fish can remove 80% or more of the oxygen from the water. Such efficiency is essential, since the oxygen concentration in water is rarely more than 1%, compared to 21% for air. A fish out of water soon suffocates in spite of the high oxygen content of air. Out of water, the gill filaments collapse against each other, blocking the circulation of the air. Also, the gills soon dry out.

The oxygen content of air remains constant, but that of water may fluctuate drastically, dropping to near zero under certain conditions. Some fish that live where the oxygen concentration frequently reaches low levels are very tolerant of low oxygen, or are able to obtain oxygen from the air. In gars, the swim bladder is richly supplied with blood vessels and has an opening to the throat. Gars come to the surface at frequent intervals to renew the air supply in the swim bladder. In this way it functions in respiration much like the lungs of higher animals. This permits gars to live in waters unsuitable for many other fish. The eel can absorb oxygen through the skin as long as it remains moist, and is known to move overland at night from one body of water to another. Even in water the eel takes up over half of its oxygen through the skin.

The various senses—sight, hearing, taste, smell, and touch—by which animals are made aware of their surroundings are developed in fish just as in man, but the structures involved in perception differ in certain respects.

A fish's eye is basically like our own, but has no lid and thus cannot be shut. Because of the special optical properties of water, fish are near-sighted. But this works no great hardship, since turbidity and other factors greatly reduce the light available in water for distance vision. Many fish have good color vision, some exceeding man in the violet range of the spectrum. At distances greater than a few feet a fish's eye probably is effective only in detecting movement and contrasting shades of color. The eye is reduced in size in fish such as the shovelnose sturgeon and sicklefin chub that live in waters where vision is hampered by continuous high turbidity, and is absent in cavefish that live in continuous darkness. In fish such as the mooneye that feed actively in late evening or at night, the eye is unusually large so as to more effectively gather the available light. In others that have a similar activity pattern, such as catfish, the eyes are quite small. In all species where visual acuity is reduced, other senses are developed to a correspondingly higher degree.

Fishes can hear, although there is no external indication of an ear. The *inner ear,* which ultimately is the organ of hearing in all vertebrates, is present in fish. It functions in receiving underwater sounds, and in equilibrium. Hearing is best developed in minnows, suckers, and catfish, which have the inner ear connected to the swim bladder by a chain of small bones called *Weberian ossicles.* These bones transfer sound vibrations picked up by the swim bladder to the inner ear.

The sense of smell is highly developed in many fish. Experiments indicate that they can recognize different streams, or even certain locations in a stream, by smell alone. This is very important in homing and in guidance during migration. Smell also functions in detecting food, and probably in finding suitable mates. The nostrils of fish do not open into the throat, as in man, and are not used for breathing. Rather, they end in shallow pits which are the center for the sense of smell. In many fish each nostril has two openings and a continuous current of water can pass in one and out the other.

The sense of taste is of less importance to fish such as bass, which feed primarily by sight, than to catfish and other species that are less visually oriented. Generally, the sense of taste is best developed in fish that are active mostly at night, or that live in continuously turbid water. Such "taste feeders" commonly have taste buds developed over the external surfaces of the body and fins as well as in the mouth. Many taste feeders have thread-like barbels located about the mouth. These are sensitive to touch as well as taste, and fish having them recognize their food by its feel as well as by its taste.

The *lateral line system* of fish may be considered as a special sense not found in man and other land animals. This sense has been called "distant touch" and may be thought of almost as a form of underwater radar or sonar. Moving objects, such as prey or enemies, are detected by the disturbances they create, and fixed objects are detected when they reflect waves set up by movement of the fish itself. In this way the lateral line system supplements vision. The sensory structures for this system are in the *lateral line,* a series of open-ended tubes that extends along the side from the head to the tail, and the several branches of the lateral line that extend onto various parts of the head.

Social Organization and Movements

Though some fish lead a solitary existence, many are more or less gregarious, preferring to live in close proximity to others of their own kind. Most gregarious of all are fish that live in close-knit schools. Among Missouri fishes, schooling is most highly developed in the herrings, minnows, and suckers. Certain other species, such as the bullheads, the bowfin, and the largemouth bass, form schools when young, but not as adults.

A school is not merely a crowd of fish. It is a social grouping in which a definite organization is maintained. Schooling fish commonly sort themselves out so that all individuals in a school are of about the same size. The individuals maintain a definite orientation to one another and their movements are remarkably synchronized. A constant fish-to-fish distance is maintained. When an obstruction is approached or a predator appears, all turn in unison and swim off in a new direction.

Surprisingly, the school has no leader, and the manner in which this remarkable social organization is maintained has been a source of much speculation. It has been suggested that visual attraction of one individual for others of its kind keeps the school together and maintains the characteristic spacing. According to this explanation, individuals are attracted and move towards each other until a certain distance is reached, but are repelled if they approach too closely. Schooling must have certain advantages, since it has developed in many separate groups, but these advantages are not well understood. Experimental studies have suggested that schooling somehow promotes better growth and reduced mortality from predation and other factors.

Most fish of small streams lead a sedentary existence, confining their activities to a definite area or *home range.* An Indiana study[2] reveals that the home range of green sunfish, longear sunfish, and rock bass may include only 100 to 200 feet of stream. Less is known about the movements of fish in larger streams, but it is likely that these fish are less sedentary. The skipjack herring seems to be constantly on the move and probably does not have a well defined home range. Tagging studies of stream fish in Missouri suggest that some species consist of a sedentary group and a mobile group.[3] The reasons for this are not entirely understood, but it appears that individuals in stable habitats are more sedentary than individuals in unstable habitats. The carp shows this behavior. Some carp have been recaptured not far from the point of release, but one individual tagged in Boone County, Missouri, was recaptured 2½ years later below Gavins Point Dam, South Dakota, 674 stream miles away.[4]

Many fish make regular daily or seasonal movements. Even sedentary species have definite feeding and resting areas and follow a regular daily cycle of activity that includes movement between areas. Some species occur in one habitat during summer and a different habitat during winter. Usually the winter habitat is in quieter water or larger streams than the summer habitat. The longest movements that most fish make are associated with spawning activities. Paddlefish in Lake of the Ozarks move 50 miles or more up the Osage River to spawn. The American eel migrates to the Sargasso Sea, an area of the Atlantic Ocean northeast of Cuba, to spawn, and the Alabama shad moves up the Mississippi River from the Gulf of Mexico to spawn in the streams of Missouri and other inland states.

Foods and Feeding

Like all animals, fish must take into their bodies as food the substances that supply energy and raw materials for activities and growth. To effectively use the range of foods available, various fish have specialized with respect to diet and the structures associated with the capture and digestion of food. Some fish, *herbivores,* feed mainly on plants; others, *carnivores,* feed only on animals; many, *omnivores,* feed on both plants and animals.

The first food of nearly all fish consists of tiny plants and animals called *plankton* that live suspended in the water. Certain fish, including some of the largest species, continue to feed on plankton throughout life. Algae that grow attached to rocks and other submerged objects are important plant foods for several Missouri fish. Higher aquatic plants are of little importance as food for our fishes, though certain kinds found elsewhere feed almost exclusively on such material. The seeds, fruits, and flowers of terrestrial plants are commonly eaten when available. Insects, including both terrestrial and aquatic kinds, are a very important animal food for many fishes. Other invertebrates eaten include terrestrial and aquatic worms, snails, clams, and crustaceans. Large predatory fish will eat many kinds of vertebrates, but other fish are by far the most important food.

In fish there is a definite correlation between diet and the structures associated with the capture and digestion of food. Fish that feed exclusively on other animals have mouths that fit the size of their prey. Some, such as the sculpin, can ingest prey nearly as large as themselves. Most predatory fish are well endowed with teeth for seizing and holding prey. In gars and pikes these take the form of prominent canine teeth, while bass and catfish have pads of very small, closely-set teeth. Carnivorous minnows lack teeth in the mouth, but have sharp, hooked throat teeth that tear or fragment the food during its passage to the stomach. Herbivorous fishes generally have smaller mouths than their predatory relatives and possess teeth modified for scraping or grinding. The stoneroller, an herbivorous minnow, has a blade-like structure on the lower jaw for scraping algae from submerged objects, and has flattened grinding surfaces on its throat teeth. Many plankton-feeding fish have no teeth, but exhibit some means for straining their food from the water. The paddlefish typifies these. It has slender, closely-set structures on the gill arches that form a net for removing plankton from water passing through them as the fish swims about, mouth agape. The young of lampreys also have a straining device, but it brings in water and plankton by a pumping action of the gill region.

Plant food requires considerable time for digestion, and plant-eating fish have a long, many-looped intestine with no well defined stomach. An exception is the gizzard shad which has a thick-walled stomach that functions as a food grinder like the gizzard of a chicken. Fish that feed on animal life have a short intestine that is adequate for the rapid digestion of such material. Generally, there is a well defined stomach for temporary storage and partial digestion of the large food items often eaten.

Bottom-feeding fish, such as the stoneroller, commonly graze sheep-like in large schools. Sturgeons suck up large quantities of bottom material from which they selectively remove snails and other food and reject the rest. Carpsuckers and certain minnows take in large quantities of "bottom ooze" and mud from which they extract the algae and other organic material. Trout and many carnivorous minnows feed principally on insects and small invertebrates found floating at the water's surface or drifting with the current.

Predatory fish are often solitary. Some, such as the pikes, pounce on their hapless victims from ambush. Others, such as the gars, slowly stalk their prey. The skipjack herring and white bass depend on active pursuit to capture their food. Certain lampreys have the distinction of being the only parasites among Missouri fishes. Adults attach themselves to other fish with their sucking-disc mouth and feed on their host's body fluids through a hole made with their hard tongue. Brook lampreys are even more unusual; they do not feed at all once the adult stage is reached.

Reproduction

Like all higher animals, fishes start life as a single-celled structure, the egg. Development of the egg, with rare exceptions, can proceed only after it has been penetrated by another single cell called a sperm. Reproduction is the process by which the egg and sperm are brought together and the egg develops into an individual capable of an independent existence. Fishes have adopted a variety of interesting habits and adaptations for assuring reproductive success.

Compared to those of birds, fish eggs are quite small. They are, however, very large cells and are readily visible to the naked eye when mature. In most fishes the egg is fertilized externally after it has been released by the female. This is possible because the water in which fishes live provides a medium for the mobile sperm to seek out and penetrate the egg. Because fertilization must occur within a brief time span after exposure to water, the sperm and egg are released more or less simultaneously by the male and female while in close proximity. The mating act in fishes is referred to as spawning.

Fishes of temperate regions generally have a definite and rather restricted spawning season. The majority of Missouri fishes spawn in late spring or early summer, but one or more species may be found spawning at any given time between mid-March and late August. Early spring spawners include the least brook lamprey, grass pickerel, and walleye. Late spring and early summer spawners include the longnose gar, hornyhead chub, redhorse suckers, black basses, white bass, and most darters. Summer spawners include the red shiner, bluntnose minnow, and most sunfishes. The only winter spawners among our fishes are the rainbow trout and mottled sculpin; they spawn from late November into January.

Spawning in many fishes is preceded by movements or migrations. For most sunfishes this simply means moving into shallower parts of pools occupied throughout the year. Many large-stream or reservoir fishes, including the chestnut lamprey, longnose gar, redhorse suckers, white bass, and freshwater drum, "run" into tributaries to spawn. One of the most notable spawning runs in the state involves the movement of paddlefish into the upper Osage River from Lake of the Ozarks. The longest spawning movements by any Missouri fish are by the American eel, which spawns in the Sargasso Sea area of the Atlantic Ocean northeast of Cuba, and by the Alabama shad, which ascends the Mississippi River from the Gulf of Mexico to spawn in the larger streams of Missouri and other inland states.

The mosquitofish and threadfin shad may mature and spawn during the summer in which they were born. Many minnows spawn during their second summer of life. But most larger species will not mature until their third or fourth summer. The lake sturgeon is about 20 years of age before it spawns for the first time.

With the approach of the spawning season, maturing males of some fishes undergo a transformation in form and color so dramatic that they are scarcely recognizable as the same species. The breeding colors of some minnows, sunfishes, and darters rival in brilliance the most brightly colored birds and butterflies. Males of many minnows and suckers develop wart-like structures called breeding tubercles on the head, body, and fins. The male channel catfish develops a swollen head and thick, fleshy lips, giving him a bizarre appearance. Males of the bluntnose and fathead minnows develop a fleshy pad along the back. The most obvious change in females in most fishes is a ballooning of the abdomen as the eggs mature and enlarge. Changes in the coloration of females are generally slight, but the smallmouth bass and some other members of the sunfish family are exceptions. The sexes of the smallmouth bass are virtually indistinguishable until the female enters the nest to spawn. At that time she assumes a bold pattern of bars and blotches that contrast sharply with the uniform olive-brown of the male. Unlike most color transformations associated with spawning that develop over a period of days or weeks, those of the female smallmouth come and go as quickly as a blush.

Fishes practice varying degrees of parental care, from none at all beyond releasing the eggs at a time and place suitable for their development, to guarding the eggs and shepherding the young about for a time after they are free-swimming. The gizzard shad exemplifies those species that practice a minimum of parental care. Eggs of this species are released and fertilized by a mixed school of males and females as they swim near the shore line. The sticky eggs become attached to the first object they encounter and complete their development without further attention from the adults. Other species that broadcast their eggs in this manner include all members of the pike family, the carp, and the buffalofishes.

Many stream fish bury their eggs in gravelly riffles. Burying the eggs protects them from egg-eating predators, and the circulation of water through the gravel provides a source of oxygen for development. Spawning in the longnose gar and redhorse suckers is accompanied by violent vibrating motions that mix the eggs into the gravel as they are released and fertilized. In several darters, the female wriggles into the gravel and releases her eggs as she lies half-buried, with the male above. The chestnut lamprey excavates a pit-like depression in the riffle bottom where the eggs are deposited and then covered as the pit is refilled.

The hornyhead chub also digs a pit. Spawning occurs sporadically as the pit is refilled, and eventually a large mound of gravel, mixed with eggs, rises several inches above the stream bottom. Pit construction in the chestnut lamprey is a cooperative activity by several males and females, but the pit and mound of the hornyhead chub are all the work of one male. The male jealously guards his nest, but tolerates the presence of several other minnow species that also deposit their eggs in the growing mound. Often a veritable swarm of brightly colored bleeding shiners, Ozark minnows, and redbelly dace are present over a nest as the male chub moves among them, oblivious to their presence. The male chub abandons his nest long before the eggs hatch.

Males of the sunfish family fan out a saucer-shaped nest in quiet water, where the eggs are deposited, but not buried. The developing eggs and resulting offspring are guarded vigorously against all intruders. Catfish fan out a similar nest or deposit and guard their eggs in a hollow log or other natural cavity.

The bluntnose minnow and fantail darter stick their eggs to the underside of flat objects lying just off the bottom, and these are guarded by the male until hatching. Cavefish incubate their eggs in the gill chamber. The mosquitofish retains its eggs in the ovaries until hatching and the young are born alive. The mosquitofish is the only Missouri fish having internal fertilization, and the anal fin of the male is modified into a slender structure for transferring the sperm.

Parental care is carried to the ultimate in species that guard the young after they are free-swimming. The bowfin, black bullhead, and largemouth bass remain with their close-knit schools of fry until they are an inch or more in length.

Generally speaking, there is a correlation between the number of eggs produced by a species and the degree of parental care. Fishes that practice no parental care must produce large numbers of eggs to assure the survival of a few, while those that attend the eggs can get by with producing fewer eggs because a high percentage survive to hatching. The white bass abandons its eggs after spawning and a single large female may produce nearly a million eggs. In contrast, eggs of the fantail darter are guarded, and the female deposits only about 45 at a time. The size of the eggs is related more to the number produced than to the size of the adult fish. Eggs from a 3-inch fantail darter are larger than those from a white bass 15 inches long.

The eggs of fishes contain large quantities of food material in the form of yolk on which the developing individual depends until it can feed. Hatching in most fishes is followed by a larval stage during which the young complete a substantial part of their development. During this stage the larva is relatively quiescent, living off of the yolk contained in a large globular sac beneath the body. Often the mouth is not yet open, and the fins appear as more or less continuous folds along the midline of the body. Larval gars have an adhesive disc on the snout by which they attach to submerged objects for a time. In most species the larval stage is completed by the time the yolk sac is absorbed. In lampreys, the larval stage continues for years, during which the larvae lead a very different kind of life than the adults.

Growth and Longevity

Unlike birds and mammals that cease growing once maturity is reached, fishes have the potential for continued growth throughout life. Because fishes are cold-blooded animals, the growth rate follows a seasonal pattern in response to changes in temperature. This seasonal pattern results in the formation of a series of growth zones on fish scales, with each zone separated by a distinct line or break called an *annulus.* The annulus forms in winter when growth ceases, and the zone between successive annuli reflects the growth achieved in a single growing season. In catfish and other species that have no scales, annuli may be discerned on sections from fin spines, ear bones (otoliths), and other hard parts. Thus, a complete record of the growth of a fish is provided by its scales or other hard parts. Much has been learned concerning the rate of growth and longevity of fishes by studying this record.

Growth of fishes is most rapid in early life and may slow to an almost imperceptible rate in old age. Growth varies markedly from one population of a species to another. In streams, fish growth is generally slower in headwaters than farther downstream. Growth is more rapid in a newly established fish population than in the same population after it is well established. In a new impoundment, nutrients for food production are abundant and competition is minimal because the fish population has not reached carrying capacity. Acute overcrowding can result in slow growth and stunting, with few individuals attaining the adult size characteristic of the species. This invariably occurs in pond bluegill populations if sufficient bass or other predators are not present to keep their numbers in check.

Each species has its own characteristic growth potential. The longnose gar averages about 20 inches long by the end of its first year of life and may eventually reach a length of nearly 5 feet. The johnny darter scarcely exceeds an inch long at the end of its first year and is not known to achieve a length much greater than 3 inches. Perhaps the smallest Missouri fish is the least darter which does not exceed 1.8 inches in length. At the other end of the spectrum is the alligator gar. It is reported to reach a length of 10 feet and a weight of 300 pounds in the southern part of its range. The lake sturgeon is reported to achieve a similar size, but the largest reported from Missouri weighed 97 pounds. The largest authenticated records for any Missouri fish in recent times are a 117-pound blue catfish and a 110-pound paddlefish, both from the Osage River.

Generally, those species that achieve the largest size also live the longest. A lake sturgeon from Lake of the Woods, Ontario, is reported to have attained the venerable age of 152 years. The spawning run of paddlefish in the upper Osage River is composed mostly of individuals 14 to 21 years old, with some going up to 30 years or more.[5] About 4 to 6 years is the usual life span for most hook-and-line fishes, with occasional individuals living 10 years or more. Species the size of most minnows and darters rarely live more than 3 or 4 years. The speckled chub and brook silverside do not normally live beyond their second summer.

In many species there is a difference in growth rate and maximum size between males and females. The male is usually largest in species where he cares for the young or guards a spawning territory, while in species with a large egg production and no parental care the female achieves the largest size. Generally, the slowest-growing individuals in a population live longer than those with more rapid growth.

Importance to Man

Fish rank high as a source of food for man, and contribute much in a recreational way. Some are of considerable commercial importance; some are of special interest to the sportsman, and thus are indirectly of economic value; others are of no direct importance, but serve as food for more valuable species; all are a part of our rich heritage of native wildlife.

Commercial fishing was once an important occupation along the Missouri and Mississippi rivers, but is now at a relatively low level. The total commercial harvest from these two rivers by Missouri fishermen in 1970 amounted to 800,000 pounds of fish having an estimated live-weight wholesale value of about $157,000. Commercial fisheries statistics for the period 1945 to 1967 indicate a continuing downward trend in this activity.[6] Pollution and habitat destruction are primarily responsible for the decline. The commercial fishery in the Mississippi River below St. Louis has been nearly ruined by pollution, and here the decline over the period indicated was 92%. In the Missouri River, which has been extensively channelized, the decline was 86%. The upper Mississippi River has been less affected, and there the decline was only 29%. However, proposals now under consideration to deepen the channel for navigation could have a very detrimental effect on the fishery of the upper Mississippi River.

In Missouri the recreational value of fishes is very high. Nearly one million sport-fishing permits are sold each year. The 1965 National Survey of Fishing and Hunting revealed that each freshwater fisherman spends about $89 per year on his sport. The cost of fishing tackle and permits comprised only a small part of this amount. Also included were such items as bait, guides, boat rentals, food and lodging, and transportation. Many individuals not primarily interested in fishing participate in outdoor activities in which aquatic wildlife play a part. A one-year study conducted on the Platte River, a prairie stream in northwestern Missouri, revealed that 38% of the 96,500 trips made to this river by recreationists were for uses not directly related to hunting and fishing.[7] Float fishing has always been a popular pastime in the Ozarks, but increasing numbers of individuals are taking float trips simply for the purpose of enjoying nature. The aquatic and terrestrial wildlife observed on such a trip contribute much to the experience. According to figures compiled by the National Scenic Riverways, 120,000 floaters used a 160-mile section of Current River and Jacks Fork in 1972. Nonconsuming users require much the same equipment and accomodations as fishermen. Thus, both fishermen and nonconsuming users contribute significantly to the economy of Missouri as they engage in activities in which fish and other aquatic wildlife play a part. But even more important is the contribution these activities make to the well-being of the participant.

The Study of Fishes

Identifying Fishes with Keys and Other Aids

For the fisherman, knowing the species in his catch can provide an additional measure of satisfaction from his sport. For the student of fishes, accurate identification of the species under observation is an essential first step in learning new facts. One objective of this book is to provide keys, illustrations, and descriptions for identifying any fish likely to be encountered in Missouri waters.

Use of these aids for fish identification requires an understanding of terms applied to various structures of fishes, and of methods used in making certain counts and measurements. This information is provided in an alphabetized glossary and accompanying illustrations placed for easy reference at the back of the book.

In fish identification, much reliance is placed on counts of scales, fin rays, and fin spines. Also used are the presence or absence of certain structures, and the relative size and shape of various body parts. Often, *proportional measurements* are used to express the relative size of two body parts. Generally, fishes can be identified by external appearance, but sometimes internal structures must be examined. The reader may wonder why color differences are not used more widely for fish identification. One reason is that color may vary significantly among individuals of the same species, depending on age, sex, and stage of maturity. More importantly, most colors fade rapidly after death and thus are of value only in identification of living fish. Certain patterns do persist, or even become more apparent, after preservation, and these are used wherever they provide reliable characters for identification.

Large fishes can be studied without magnification, but a good hand lens or binocular microscope is required for examining structures of minnows and other small species. Dividers, such as can be obtained where engineering supplies are sold, are essential for precision in taking proportional measurements. Forceps are useful for spreading fins and removing specimens from jars. A scalpel or pair of small, pointed scissors is needed for cutting open specimens to examine internal structures. A dissecting needle and good quality ruler complete the equipment ordinarily needed for fish identification.

Many readers may be unfamiliar with the use of identification keys. The keys in this book consist of numbered couplets, with each couplet made up of sets of paired statements. These paired statements provide alternatives between which the reader must choose during the process of identifying a specimen. The contrasting conditions presented in each couplet are also illustrated in order to further facilitate the decision-making process.

When a fish entirely unknown is encountered, the following procedure is recommended for identifying it. First, key the unknown fish to family, using the illustrated "Key to the Families". Read the set of contrasting statements in couplet **1a** and **1b,** and study the accompanying illustrations. Choose the set of statements that best fits your specimen. If you choose 1a, your specimen is a member of the lamprey family. If you choose 1b, proceed to couplet 2a and 2b as directed. Follow the chain of numbers through the key until you come to the name of the family to which your specimen belongs. The family name will be accompanied by a page number where a discussion of the family begins. For families that contain more than one species, this discussion will include a key of the family. Follow the same procedure as in the key to the families until you reach the name of the species to which your fish belongs. The number in italics at the beginning of each set of statements in the keys corresponds to the number of the statement used in reaching that point in the key. If it becomes apparent that a wrong choice has been made at some preceding stage in the keying process, the number in parentheses makes it possible to refer back in the key until the point where the error was made is reached.

Using the Accounts and Maps

Most of this book is comprised of accounts, identification keys, and distribution maps for 25 fish families and 198 native or introduced fish species.

The family accounts are brief and include only such general information as is applicable to all members of the family. For all families containing more than one species a key to the Missouri species immediately follows the family account. To facilitate location of the species account, a page number accompanies each species name in the keys.

The species accounts follow a uniform arrangement, and subheadings are used so that information on a particular topic can be more easily located. The page and key couplet where the species is illustrated is indicated under the subheading "Illustration".

In the section headed "Description", a list of characters is given that can be used to confirm an identification obtained with the keys, or to identify a specimen by comparing descriptions if the reader is sufficiently familiar with the group to narrow the choice without using the keys. The particular combination of characters in the description will separate the species from all its relatives found in Missouri. The life colors of the species are described, along with any noteworthy variation that may occur with age, sex, or stage of sexual maturity. Tubercles and other structural features found only in breeding males are also described. An indication of the usual size range and the maximum size known for Missouri specimens completes the description. All length measurements in the species accounts are total length unless indicated otherwise.

Under the heading "Distribution and Habitat," the distribution of the species in Missouri is discussed in relation to fish faunal regions, streams and reservoirs, and counties. These geographic features are named on maps located on the inside front cover of the book. The map accompanying each species account is a "spot" distribution map on which each plotted symbol indicates a locality where the species has been collected. The present range of the species in Missouri is indicated by the shaded area on the map. Symbols plotted outside the shaded range indicate localities of former occurence where the species is no longer thought to be found.

Three different symbols are used to show changes in distribution over the time interval for which collections are available. Large open circles represent collections made prior to 1905, small open circles indicate collections made between 1905 and 1945, and black dots are collections made since 1945. The distribution of localities from which collections were made is shown in Figures 1 and 2. Records are available for more than 1,500 fish collections.

The small inset map shows the range of the species in North America. Except for introduced species, such as the carp and brown trout, only native range is indicated. Many hook-and-line species have been widely and successfully introduced outside their native range. Other species have been eliminated from a part of their native range as a result of habitat changes.

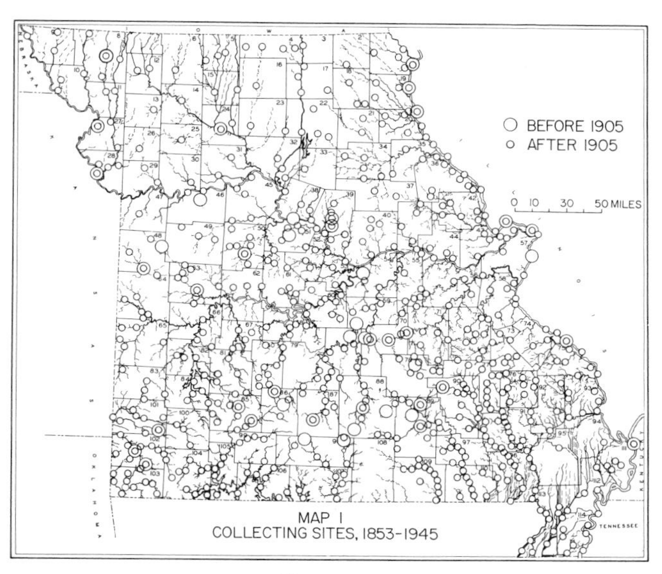

Figure 1

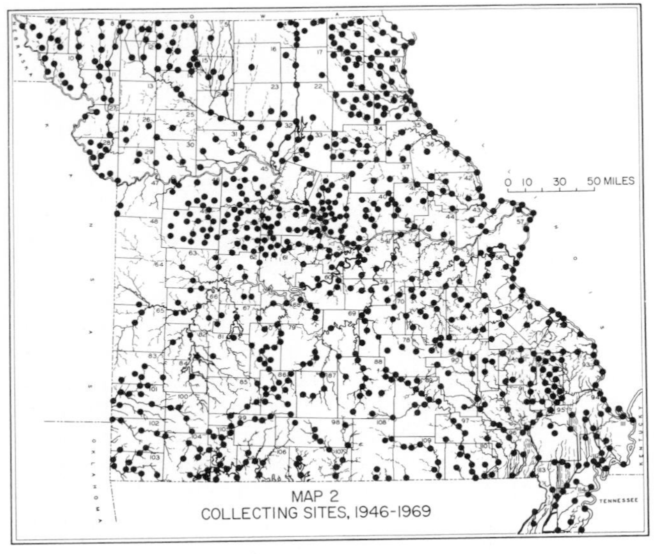

Figure 2

The "Habits and Life History" section is based on published studies, supplemented by observations by the writer over the past 14 years. Studies made in other states were used if no information was available on the species in Missouri. Literature citations are included to give credit for information not my own and to suggest sources for further information. Citations are indicated by small superscript numbers that correspond to the numbered list of references at the back of the book.

A section on "Importance and Angling" is included for species of direct benefit to man.

Collecting and Preserving

A wide variety of methods are used for collecting fishes, but our discussion will be limited to those most readily available to the general collector. Since all methods are in some degree selective for particular species, the collector interested in obtaining a variety of species should consider using more than one method. Also, because of differences in habitat preferences and habits of various species, he should attempt to collect all available habitats during different times of the day and even different seasons.

If methods other than those sanctioned for the holder of an ordinary fishing permit are to be used, the collector must first obtain a scientific collector's permit. However, there are few species that cannot be obtained by methods available to any fisherman, if the collector is willing to make the effort. Consult the *Wildlife Code of Missouri* to determine the methods you may use and the qualifications for a scientific collector's permit if one is needed.

Seining is the most practical and widely used method for general collecting of fishes. A surprising variety of species can be collected with a ready-made cotton seine such as can be purchased at any sporting goods store. However, these seines are often not properly constructed nor sufficiently durable, and the serious collector should obtain one or more seines made up to his specifications by one of the companies that supply nets to commercial fishermen. If only one seine can be purchased, it should be of quarter-inch mesh material (preferably woven nylon), about 20 feet in length and at least 4 feet deep. This seine can be used effectively in pools as deep as the collector can wade. A smaller seine, measuring about 6 feet in length and 4 feet in depth, can be used to seine special habitats, such as riffles, weed beds, and small creeks. In riffles, the seine should be set across the current while rocks and other bottom material immediately upstream are moved about by kicking. Many of the fish dislodged by this activity will be carried downstream into the seine. Fish can be frightened into the seine from weed beds or overhanging banks by employing a similar technique. Adults of large, fast-swimming species, such as redhorse suckers, are not readily captured by seining unless very large seines are used. Such seines are unwieldy, and other techniques not ordinarily available to the general collector are often used in studies requiring large numbers of specimens. If only a few specimens are needed, these can often be taken on hook-and-line.

The standard field preservative for fishes consists of one part formalin, an aqueous solution of formaldehyde gas, diluted with nine parts water. Formalin can be purchased at most drug stores. Specimens should be placed in preservative immediately upon capture. Formalin is very toxic to fishes and death comes quickly. Fishes allowed to die before preservation usually have a bleached-out appearance and, if held alive for any length of time, may have frayed fins or lost scales. Specimens more than 6 inches long should have a slit made in the belly soon after death to permit entrance of the preservative into the body cavity. This is particularly important in warm weather to prevent partial decomposition of internal organs. Field containers should be large enough to receive the largest specimen without crowding or serious distortion. Wide-mouth gallon jars, such as those in which cafeterias and other eating establishments purchase pickles and salad dressing, are satisfactory for most specimens. Metal milk cans with stoppered lids make excellent containers for large specimens, but are becoming increasingly difficult to obtain. A metal or plastic garbage can will do as long as it is not filled completely to the top or accidentally tipped on its side. Formalin fumes are very irritating and every effort should be made to avoid spilling preservative, particularly in a poorly ventilated vehicle or work area.

Each field container should have a label placed

inside listing the date, precise locality, field number, and the names of the collectors. Labels should be on good bond paper and should be filled out with waterproof ink or pencil. If large specimens from more than one locality are placed in the same container, a label may be folded and placed under the gill cover of each specimen. The field number on the label will relate the collection to records kept in a field notebook. The nature of these records will depend on the objectives and interests of the collector, but in addition to the same information as is on the label, may include a physical description of the collection site, an indication of the collecting methods and effort expended in collecting, and a list of species with notes on abundance, habitat, habits, life colors, stage of maturity, etc.

After about one week in field preservative specimens should be soaked in water for about three days, with a change of water each day, and transferred to 70% ethyl alcohol or 40% isopropyl alcohol for permanent preservation and study. Ethyl alcohol is the standard preservative used in most large museums. However, isopropyl alcohol is more readily obtained and less expensive to use and is quite satisfactory for permanent storage of a small study collection.

For additional information on collecting and preservation consult Hubbs and Lagler,[8] Lagler,[9] or Cross.[10]

Observing Fishes in Nature

The study of fishes under natural conditions is a pleasant pastime and can provide information on habits obtainable in no other way. Observations can be made either by looking into the water from above, or by diving. Although opportunities for field studies exist wherever there are fishes, the unusually clear streams and reservoirs of the Ozark Region provide especially suitable conditions for this pursuit.

Observing from above the water is the only practical method in situations where underwater observation is hampered by turbidity. In such situations, fishes can be observed from above only when they are in rather shallow water. However, some of the most interesting activities of fishes, including feeding and spawning, may occur in water a foot or less in depth. Many species are easily frightened when in shallow water and must be approached cautiously or viewed from a distance with binoculars. The observer should avoid creating vibrations that would be transferred to the water and should maintain a low profile to avoid being silhouetted against the sky. Surface reflections are a major factor hampering observations from above, so the observer should wear polarized sunglasses to reduce such reflections. Conditions are more favorable for observation on days when there is no wind to break up the water surface.

Diving is the preferred method for observing fishes if conditions will permit it. Depth is less limiting than when observing from above, and a different perspective is obtained by actually being in the medium occupied by the subject under observation. Many fishes exhibit little fear of a diver and are easily approached. Sunfishes seem curious and will swim towards a diver instead of fleeing. Minnows and darters will follow a diver about, much as they would a turtle, to feed on invertebrates and other food items stirred up by his activities. If the observer remains quiet the fishes around him soon lose interest and go about their activities as if he were not present.

Face mask, snorkel, and swimfins are the only special gear required for underwater observation in most situations. Scuba gear can be useful when diving in large rivers and reservoirs, but is more of a hindrance than a help in small streams where conditions for observation are often best. A diver's wet suit is needed to prevent chilling when diving in cool water, particularly if the observer will be inactive or plans to be in the water for extended periods. Watertight flashlights are available for use in making night dives.

Certain seasons of the year or times of the day are best for observing particular activities of fishes. Spring and early summer is an ideal time because many species are spawning then. When spawning, fishes are often concentrated in shallow water for easy observation. Species that exhibit breeding colors will be at their brightest when spawning. Territorial defense, nest construction, courtship, spawning, and parental care are interesting activities that can be observed at that time. Certain species that remain beneath cover or in deep water in the daytime are most readily observed near dusk when they venture into shallow water to feed. Nocturnal species, such as catfishes, can be observed only at night.

Keeping Native Fishes in Aquaria

It is surprising that native fishes are not more widely kept as aquarium fishes, considering the many colorful and attractive species. Most are hardy and require no special care over that given to commonly kept exotic species. An advantage of native species over exotics is the added satisfaction that comes from keeping specimens that you have collected yourself. Nongame fishes may be collected for aquarium purposes by the holder of a fishing permit, using techniques and in numbers specified for bait collecting in the *Wildlife Code of Missouri*.

Virtually any native fish could be kept in an aquarium. I will discuss only a few that I have kept and found suitable. Young gars make desirable pets because of their unusual appearance and interesting feeding habits. However, they soon outgrow a small aquarium. They prefer a diet of small fish which they capture by stalking. I have not kept small bowfin, but they would probably be equally as interesting. The minnow family contains many good aquarium fishes. Probably none are better suited for the home aquarium than the southern redbelly dace. Considering its exacting habitat requirements, this minnow is surprisingly hardy. It has a gentle disposition, and in breeding color is perhaps the most beautiful of our native minnows. Other minnows I have found especially satisfactory are: speckled chub, redfin shiner, ironcolor shiner, bigmouth shiner, red shiner, and bluntnose minnow. All of the catfishes make good aquarium fishes, at least when small. The madtoms are especially desirable, but tend to remain hidden. They can usually be coaxed out with food, particularly under low illumination at night when they are normally active. The brook silverside is not hardy, but is very attractive in an aquarium. The killifish family has always been popular with aquarium enthusiasts, and most of our species are good aquarium fishes. The starhead topminnow and plains topminnow are especially to be recommended, although males of the latter species tend to be aggressive towards other fishes. The orangespotted sunfish is perhaps the most beautiful of our native sunfishes, but tend to be shy in an aquarium. The flier and the banded pygmy sunfish are also to be recommended. Because of their small size, bright colors, and interesting habits, the darters are excellent aquarium fishes. Their main disadvantage is that they prefer live food, although they can be conditioned to eat frozen brine shrimp. Sculpins make interesting aquarium pets because of their bizarre appearance and ability to change color to match their background. Like darters, they require live food. They prefer low temperatures but can be acclimated to tolerate a temperature of about 70° F.

Selected General References on Fishes

Breder, C. M., Jr. and D. E. Rosen. 1966. Modes of reproduction in fishes. The Natural History Press, New York.

Brown, M. E. (Ed.). 1957. The physiology of fishes (two volumes). Academic Press, New York.

Curtis, B. 1949. The life story of the fish, his morals and manners. Harcourt, Brace and Company, New York.

Jordan, D. S. 1905. A guide to the study of fishes (two volumes). Henry Holt and Company, New York.

Lagler, K. F., J. E. Bardach, and R. R. Miller. 1962. Ichthyology. John Wiley and Sons, Inc., New York.

Norman, J. R. 1931. A history of fishes. Ernest Benn, London. Reprint edition, 1951, A. A. Wyn, New York.

Ommanney, F. D. 1969. The fishes. Time-Life Books, New York.

Roule, L. 1935. Fishes and their ways of life. W. W. Nortan and Company, New York.

Schultz, L. P. *et. al.* 1965. Wondrous world of fishes. National Geographic Society, Washington, D. C.

Usinger, R. L. 1967. The life of rivers and streams. McGraw-Hill Book Company, New York.

Key to the Families of Missouri Fishes

1a. Pectoral and pelvic fins absent; 7 gill openings on each side of head; nostril single; jaws absent.
Lampreys
Petromyzontidae ...... **Page 51**

1b. Pectoral fins present; pelvic fins usually present; one gill opening on each side of head; nostrils paired; jaws present.
Go to **2**

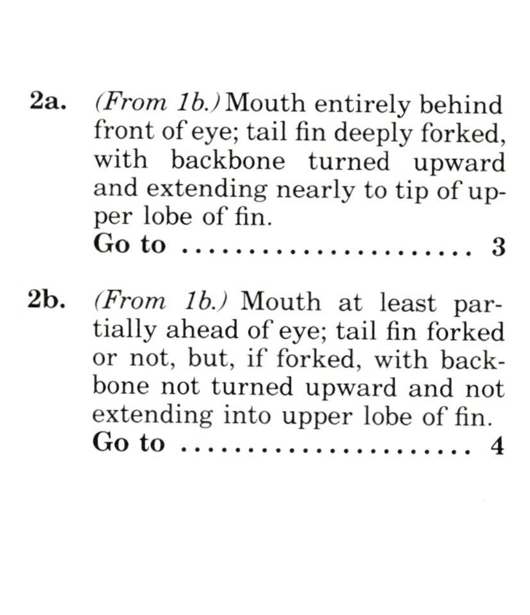

2a. *(From 1b.)* Mouth entirely behind front of eye; tail fin deeply forked, with backbone turned upward and extending nearly to tip of upper lobe of fin.
Go to **3**

2b. *(From 1b.)* Mouth at least partially ahead of eye; tail fin forked or not, but, if forked, with backbone not turned upward and not extending into upper lobe of fin.
Go to **4**

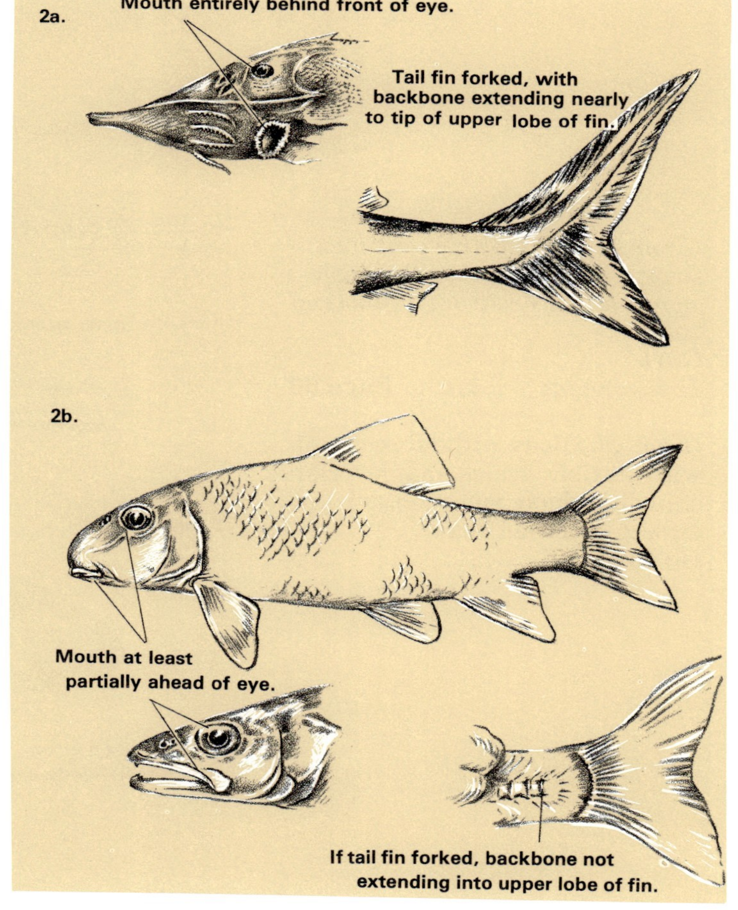

3a. *(From 2a.)* Snout long and paddle-shaped, with 2 small barbels on lower surface; body without bony plates.
Paddlefishes
Polyodontidae .... **Page 63**

3b. *(From 2a.)* Snout shovel-shaped or conical, with 4 large barbels on lower surface; body with several rows of bony plates.
Sturgeon
Acipenseridae .... **Page 59**

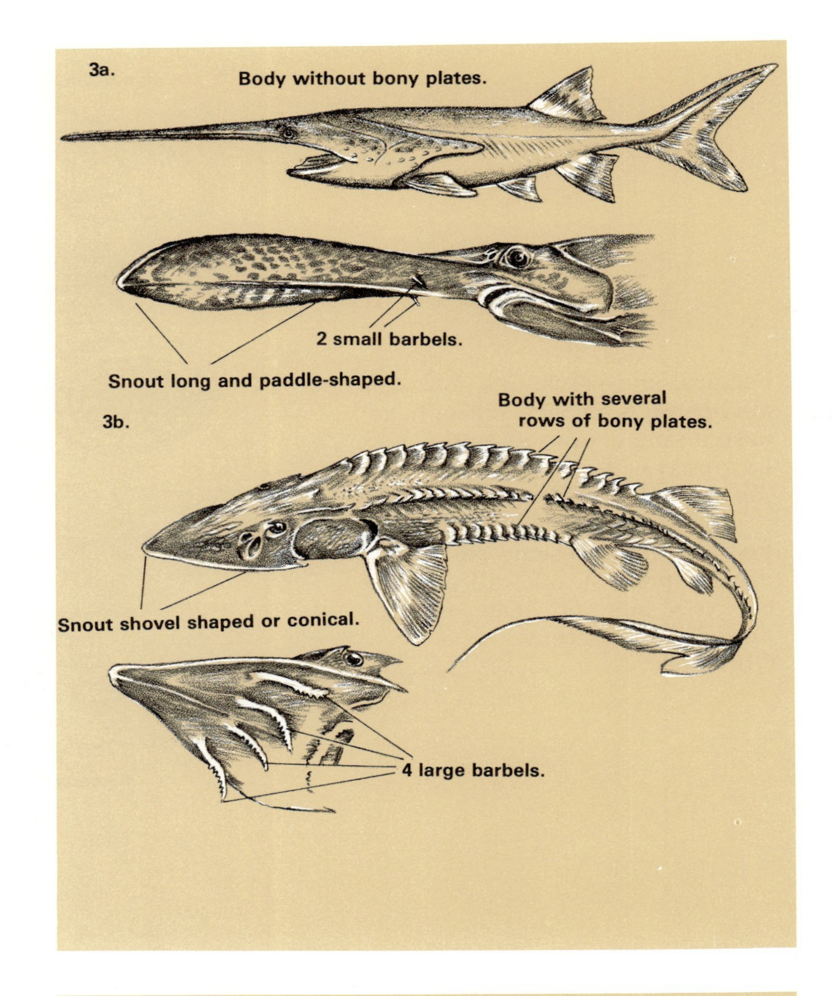

4a. *(From 2b.)* Body with a continuous sheath of hard, plate-like scales; snout a bony, strongly toothed beak.
Gars
Lepisosteidae .... **Page 66**

4b. *(From 2b.)* Body without scales or with flexible scales that overlap shingle-fashion; snout not a bony, strongly toothed beak.
Go to **5**

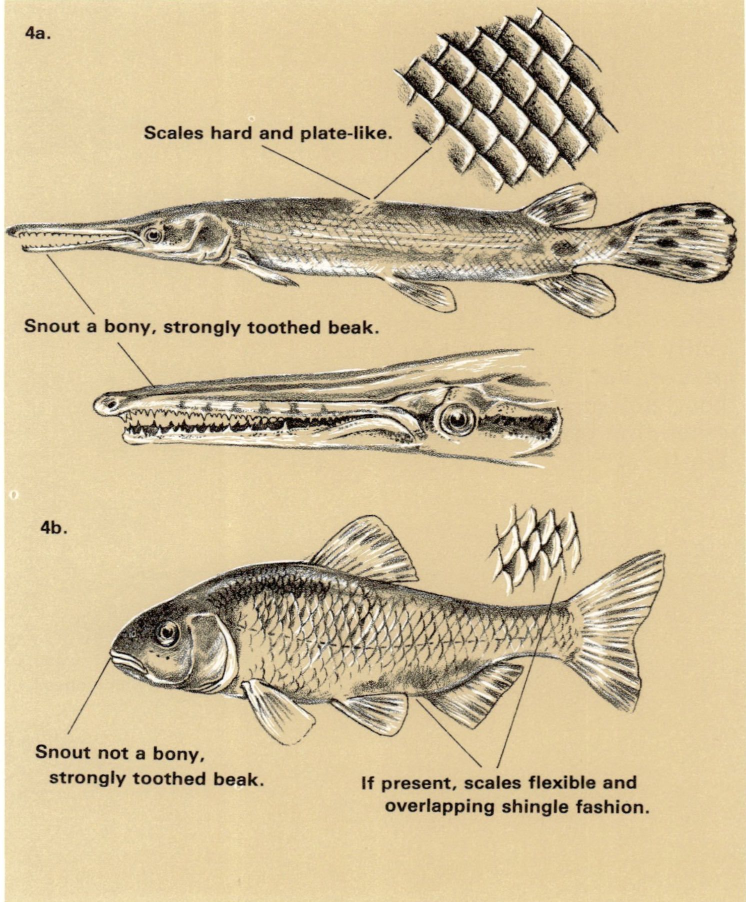

5a. *(From 4b.)* Adipose fin present.
Go to **6**

5b. *(From 4b.)* Adipose fin absent.
Go to **8**

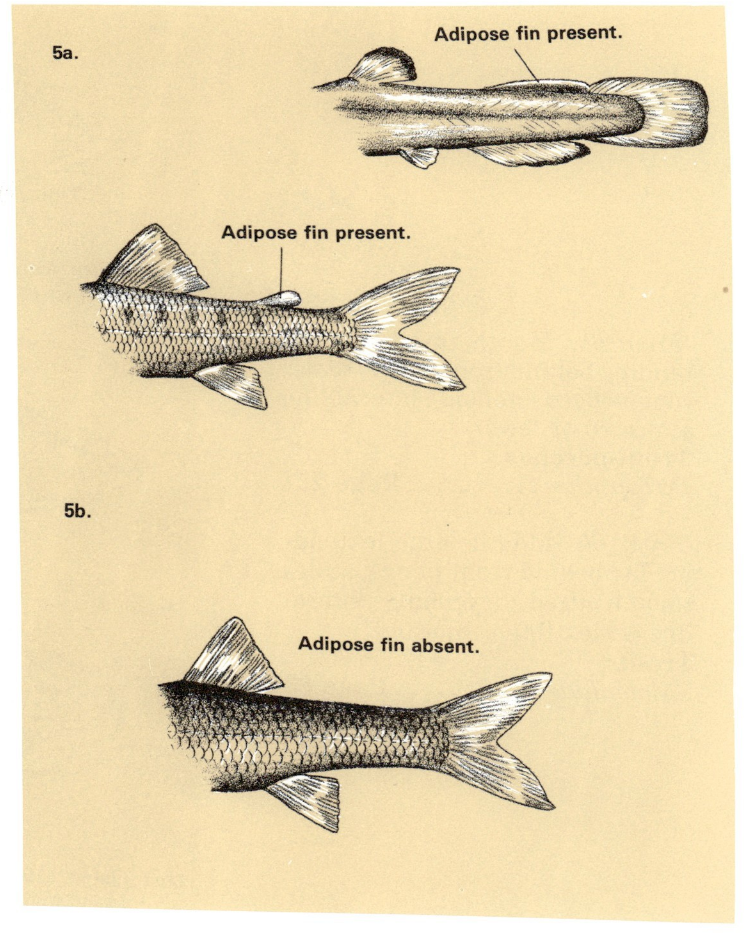

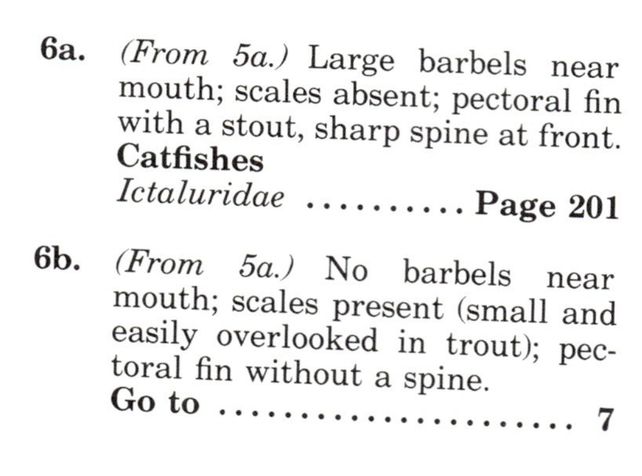

6a. *(From 5a.)* Large barbels near mouth; scales absent; pectoral fin with a stout, sharp spine at front.
Catfishes
Ictaluridae .... **Page 201**

6b. *(From 5a.)* No barbels near mouth; scales present (small and easily overlooked in trout); pectoral fin without a spine.
Go to **7**

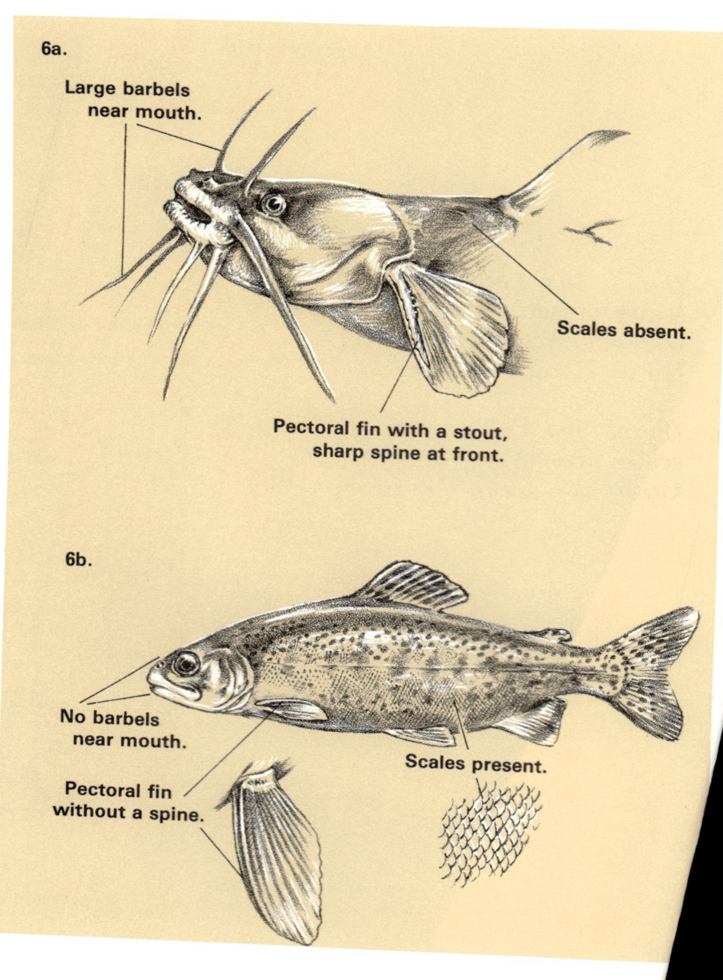

7a. *(From 6b.)* Mouth small, not extending behind front of eye; scales rough-edged (ctenoid); lateral line scales 70 or fewer.
Trout-perches
Percopsidae .... **Page 221**

7b. *(From 6b.)* Mouth large, extending far behind front of eye; scales smooth-edged (cycloid); lateral line scales 100 or more.
Trouts
Salmonidae .... **Page 83**

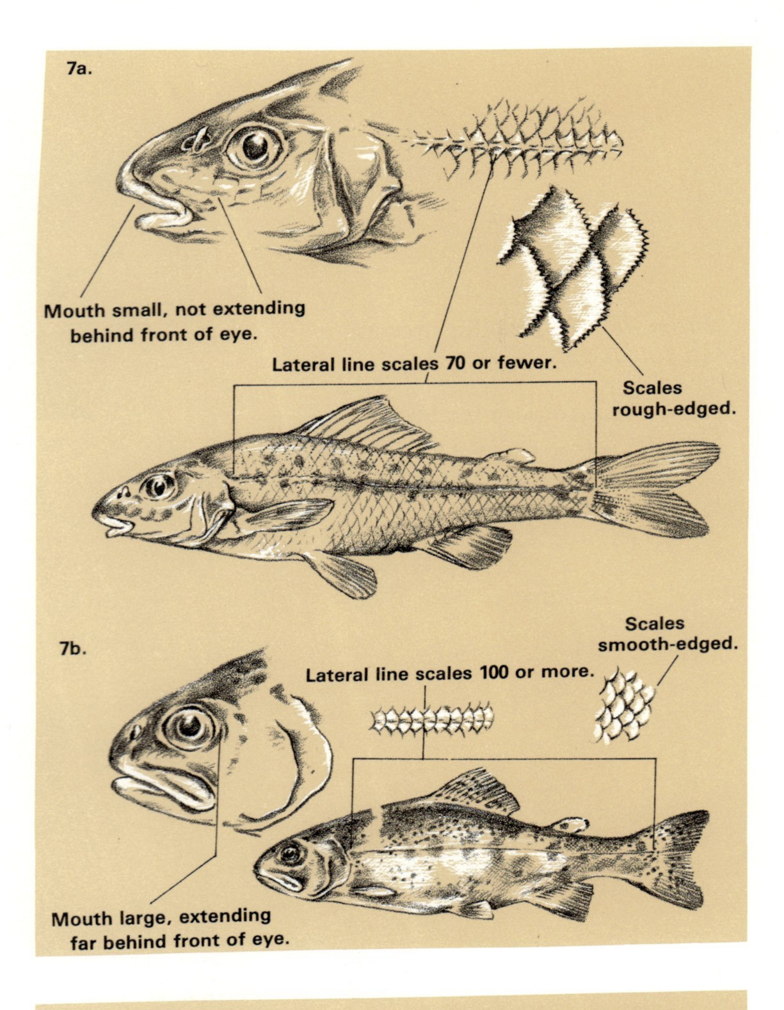

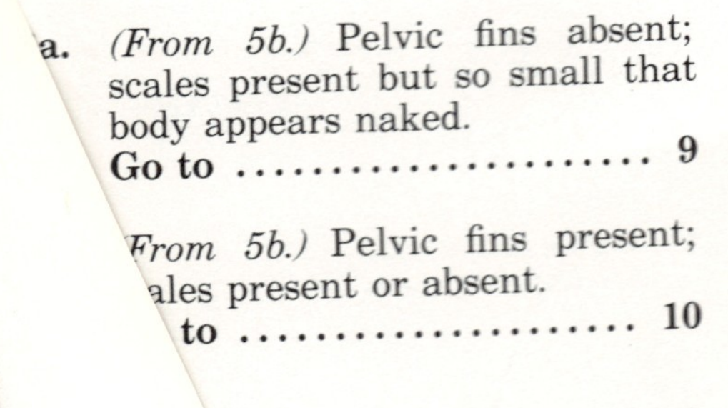

a. *(From 5b.)* Pelvic fins absent; scales present but so small that body appears naked.
Go to 9

From 5b.) Pelvic fins present; ales present or absent.
to 10

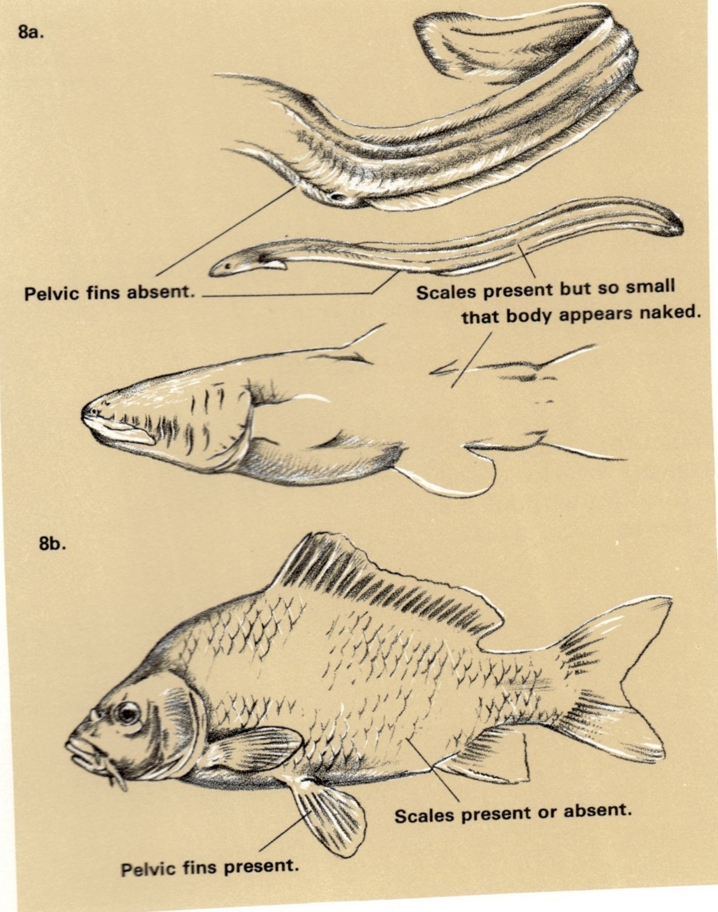

9a. *(From 8a.)* Body snake-shaped; dorsal, tail, and anal fins continuous; eyes present; body yellowish-brown or brown.
Freshwater eels
Anguillidae .... **Page 73**

9b. *(From 8a.)* Body not snake-shaped; dorsal, tail, and anal fins separate; eyes absent; body pale and nearly colorless.
Cavefishes
Amblyopsidae .... **Page 224**

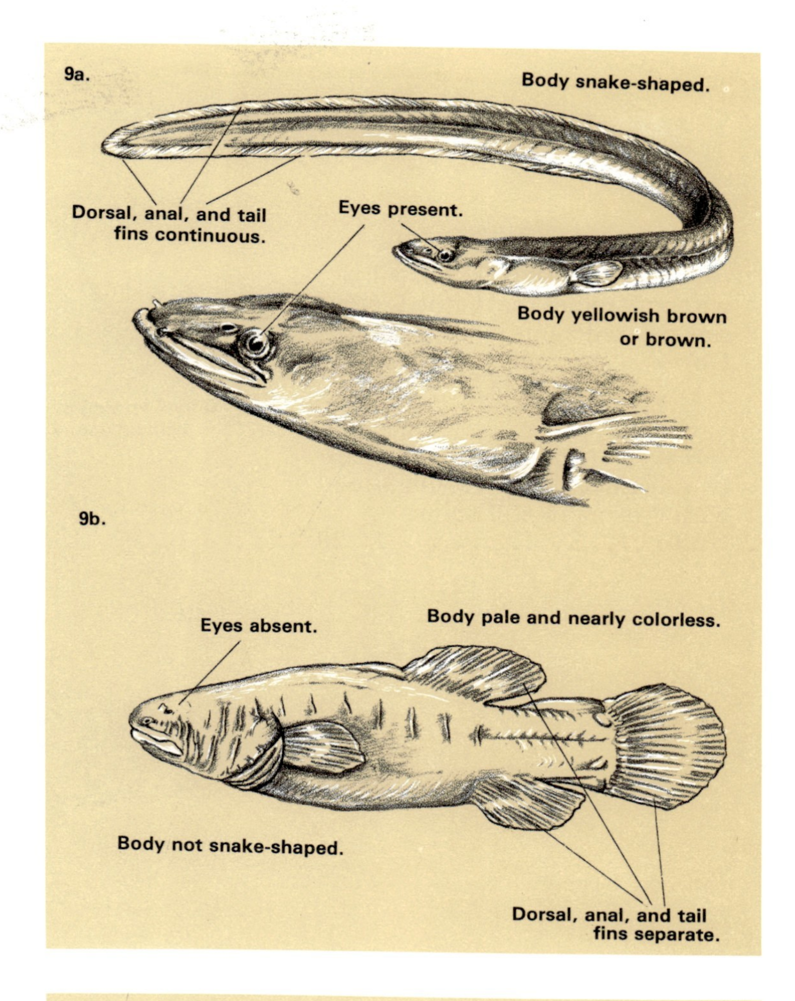

10a. *(From 8b.)* Anus far in front of anal fin, ahead of pelvic fins except in young.
Pirate perches
Aphredoderidae ...... **Page 223**

10b. *(From 8b.)* Anus just in front of anal fin.
Go to **11**

11a. *(From 10b.)* Dorsal fin single, without spines or with 1 stout saw-toothed spine.
Go to 12

11b. *(From 10b.)* Dorsal fin divided into two distinct parts, or single and with 4 or more stiff spines.
Go to 20

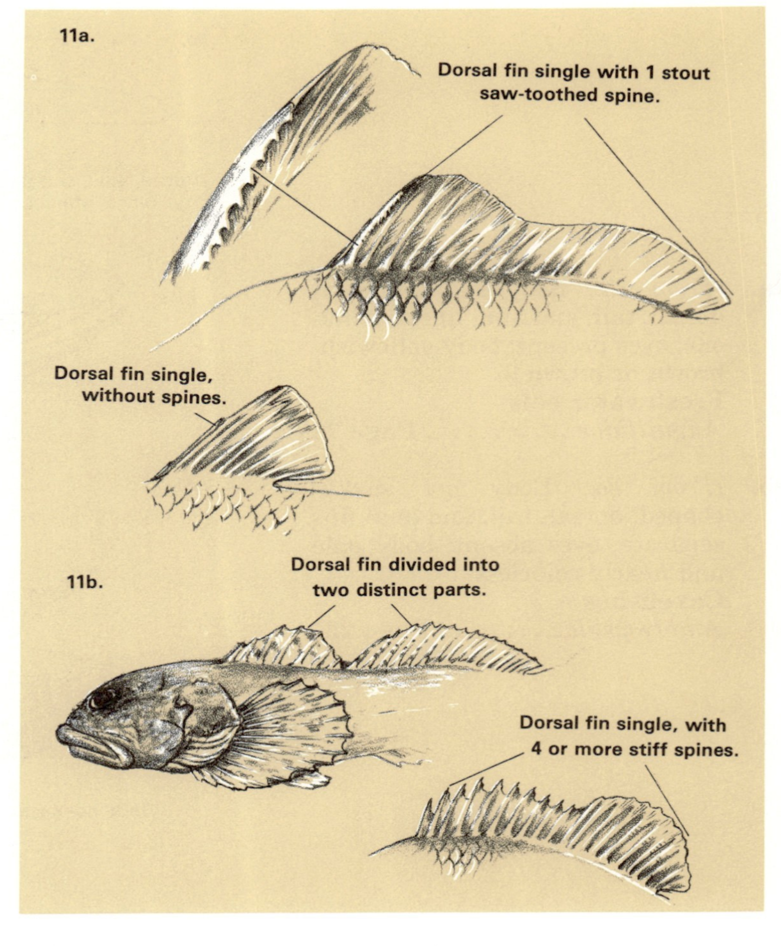

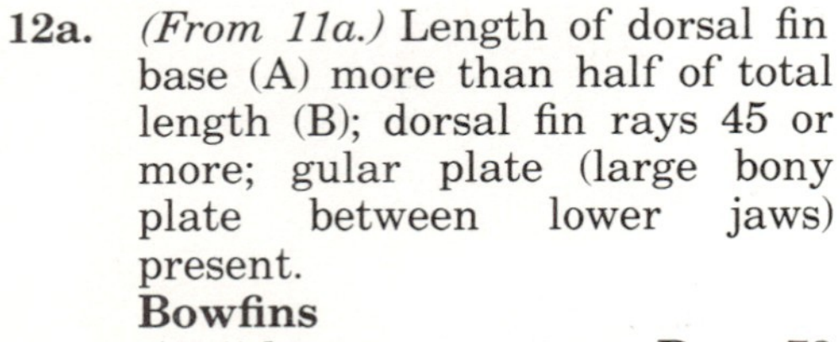

12a. *(From 11a.)* Length of dorsal fin base (A) more than half of total length (B); dorsal fin rays 45 or more; gular plate (large bony plate between lower jaws) present.
Bowfins
Amiidae .... **Page 72**

12b. *(From 11a.)* Length of dorsal fin base (A) less than half of total length (B); dorsal fin rays 40 or fewer; gular plate absent.
Go to 13

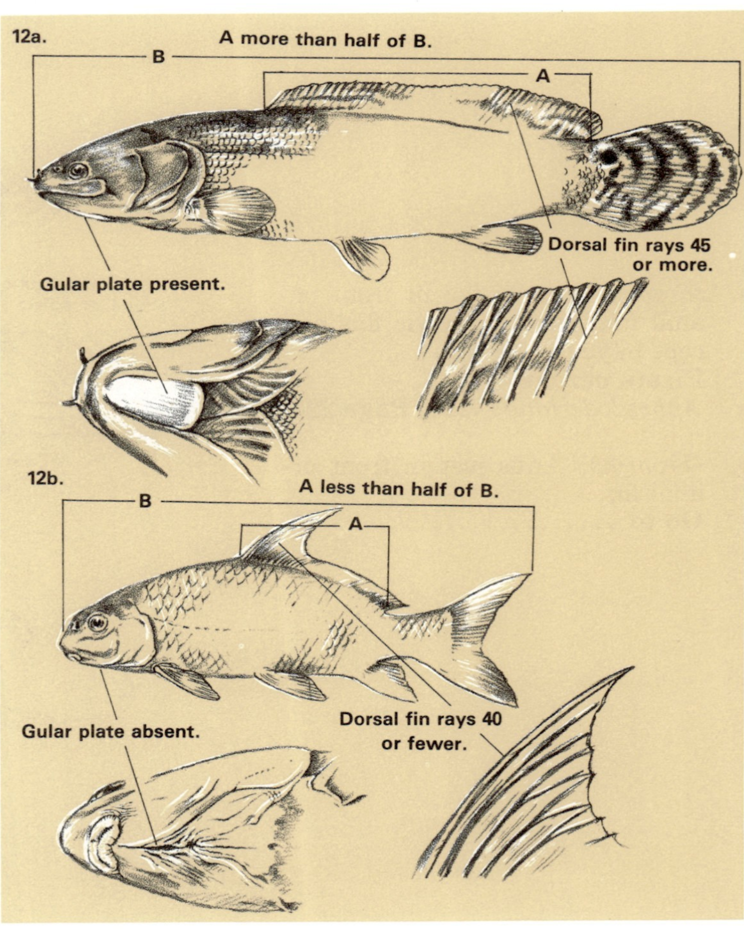

13a. *(From 12b.)* Tail fin forked; scales absent from top of head; lateral line present or absent.
Go to 14

13b. *(From 12b.)* Tail fin rounded; scales present on top of head; lateral line absent.
Go to 19

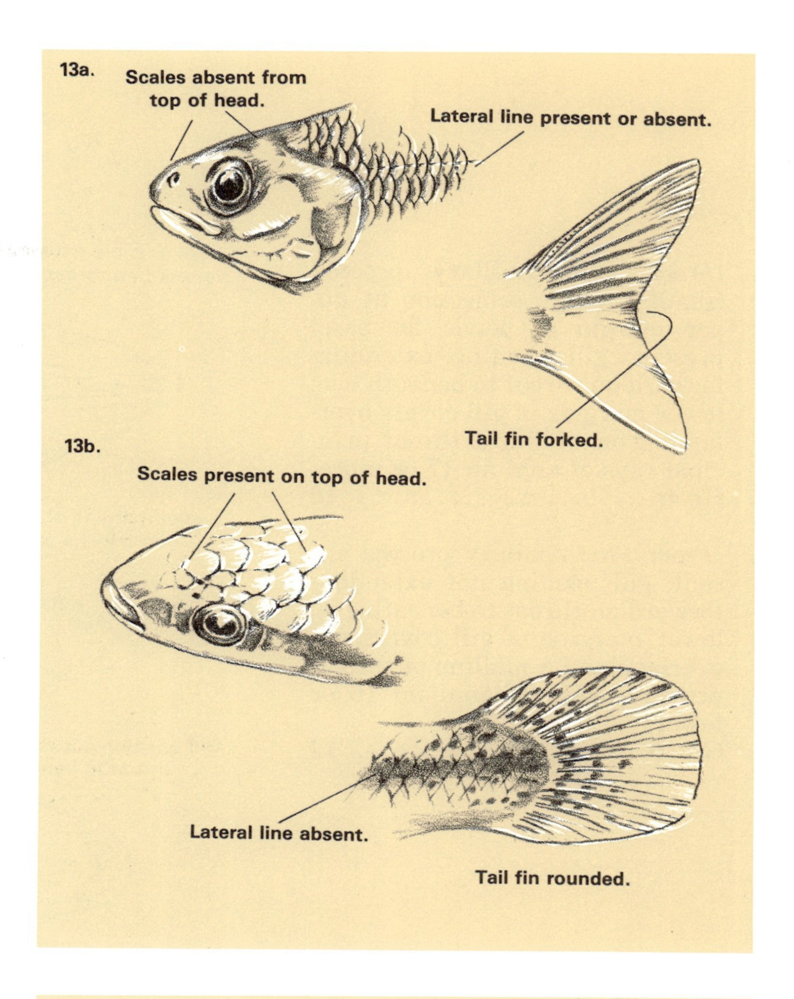

14a. *(From 13a.)* Snout shaped like a duck's bill; scales present on side of head; scales small, more than 95 in lateral series.
Pikes
Esocidae .... **Page 86**

14b. *(From 13a.)* Snout not shaped like a duck's bill; scales absent from side of head; scales large, fewer than 95 in lateral series.
Go to 15

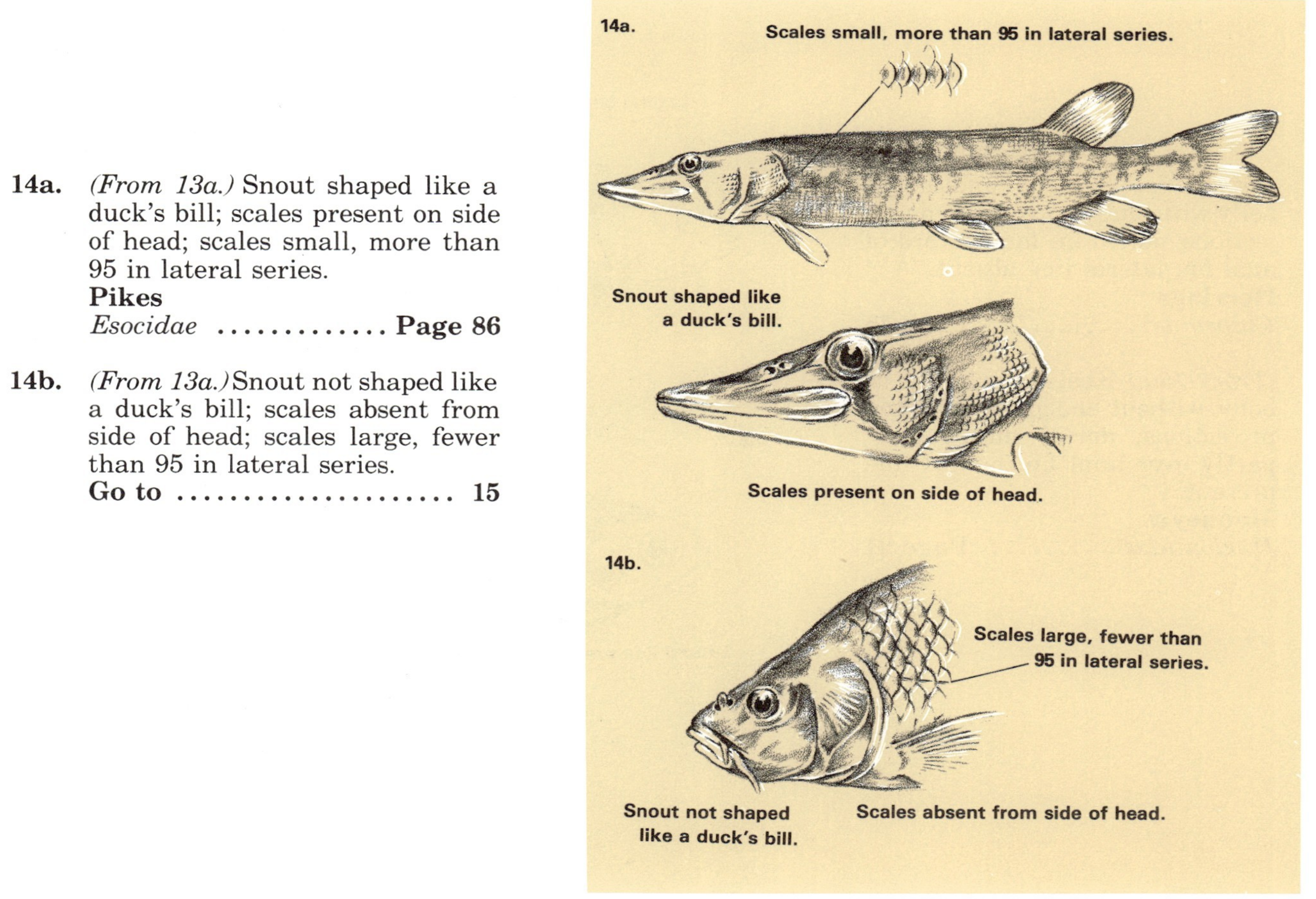

15a. *(From 14b.)* Axillary process (small flap-like projection at upper margin of pelvic fin base) present; gill opening extending forward on throat to beneath eye; lower margins of gill covers overlapping on midline of throat; principal rays of anal fin 17 or more.
Go to 16

15b. *(From 14b.)* Axillary process absent; gill opening not extending forward on throat to beneath eye; lower margins of gill covers not overlapping on midline of throat; principal rays of anal fin 16 or fewer.
Go to 17

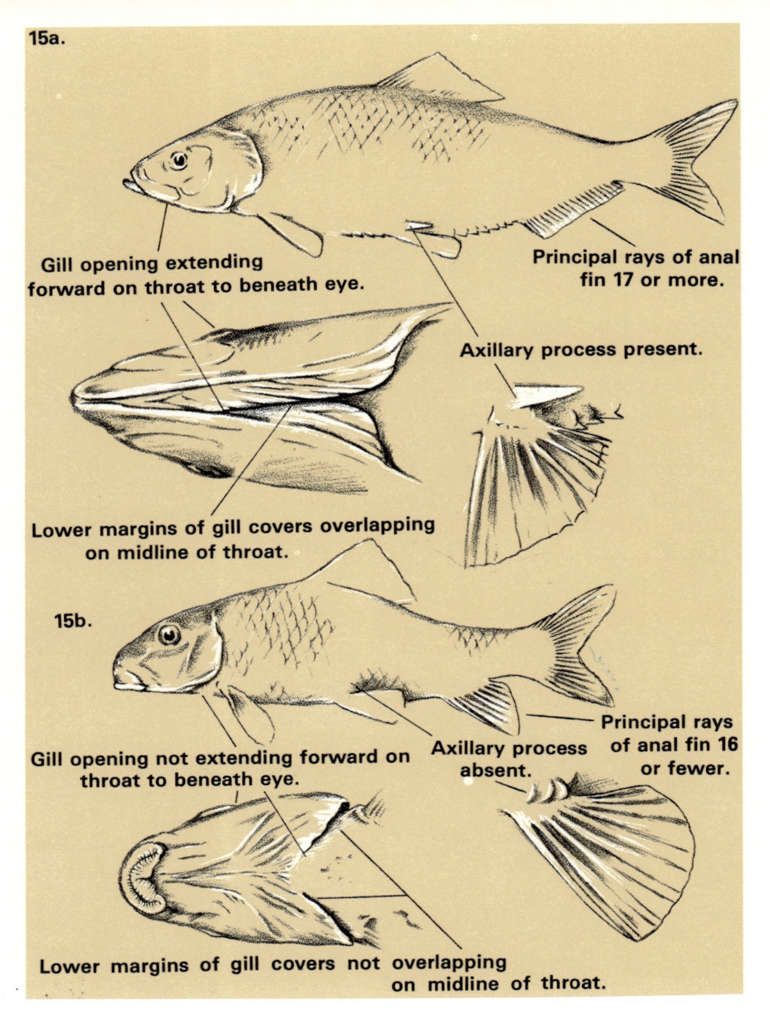

16a. *(From 15a.)* Keel on midline of belly with sharp, saw-toothed projections; dorsal fin far forward of anal fin; lateral line absent.
Herrings
Clupeidae .... **Page 75**

16b. *(From 15a.)* Keel on midline of belly without sharp, saw-toothed projections; dorsal fin at least partly over anal fin; lateral line present.
Mooneyes
Hiodontidae .... **Page 81**

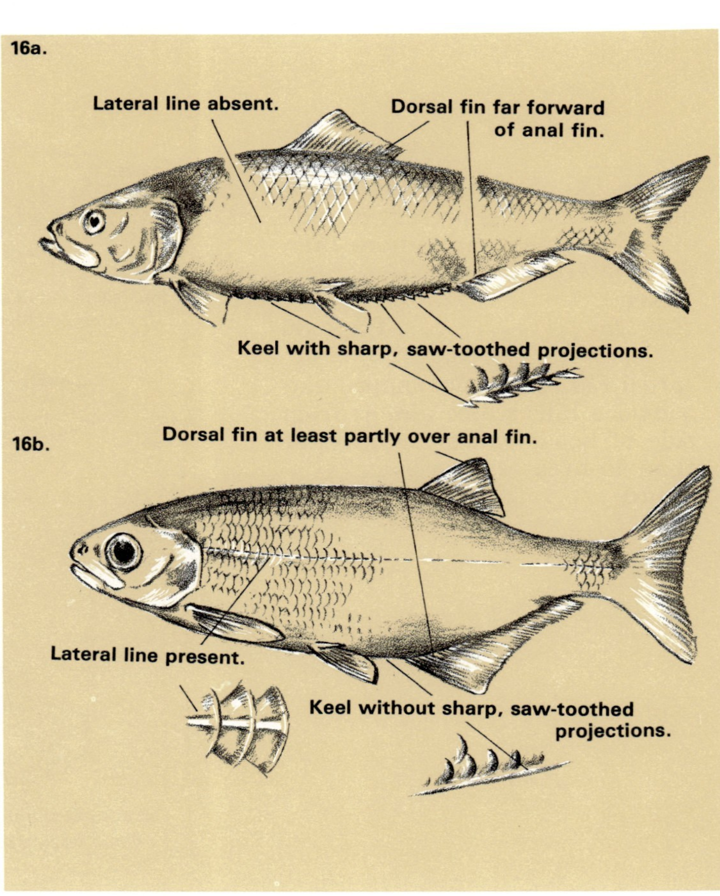

17a. *(From 15b.)* Dorsal and anal fins each with a stout, saw-toothed spine at front.
Carp & Goldfish
Cyprinidae, in part .... **Page 93**

17b. *(From 15b.)* Dorsal and anal fins without stout, saw-toothed spines.
Go to **18**

17a.
Dorsal fin with a stout, saw-toothed spine.
Anal fin with a stout, saw-toothed spine.
17b.
Dorsal fin without a stout, saw-toothed spine.
Anal fin without a stout, saw-toothed spine.

18a. *(From 17b.)* Dorsal fin with 8 (in one species 9) principal rays; throat teeth in 1 or 2 rows, with 6 or fewer teeth in primary row.
Minnows
Cyprinidae, in part .... **Page 93**

18b. *(From 17b.)* Dorsal fin with 10 or more (rarely 9) principal rays; throat teeth in 1 row of 20 or more teeth.
Suckers
Catostomidae .... **Page 178**

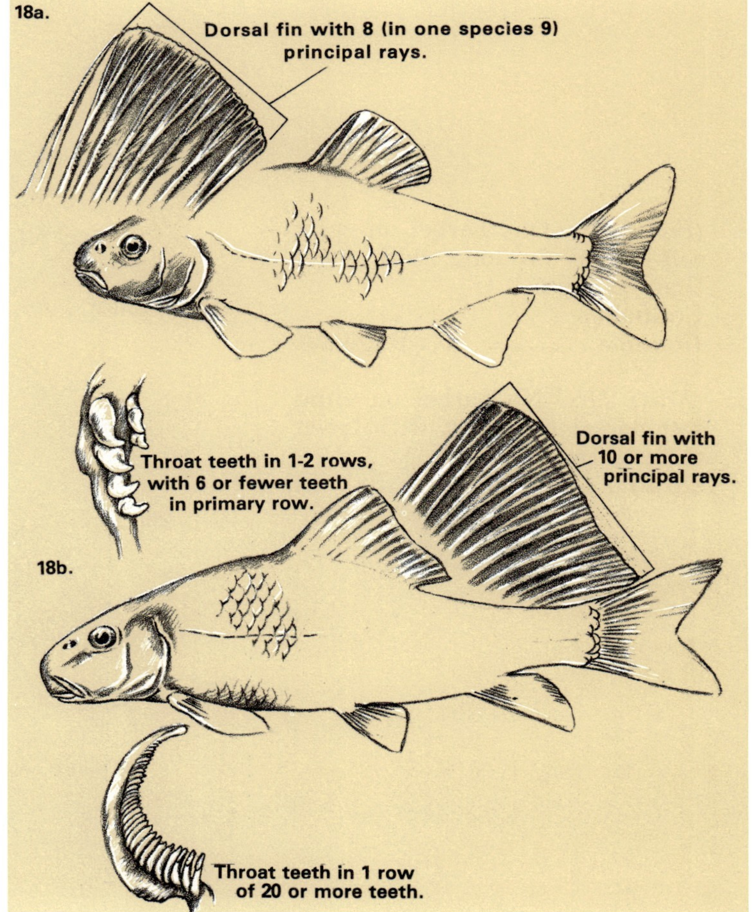

19a. *(From 13b.)* Dorsal fin base almost entirely over anal fin base; scales in lateral series usually more than 30; sensory canal on side of head an enclosed tube, with several pore-like openings; anal fin of male not slender and rod-like; third ray of anal fin branched.
Killifishes
Cyprinodontidae ..... **Page 228**

19b. *(From 13b.)* Dorsal fin base almost entirely (females and immatures) or entirely (males) behind anal fin base; scales in lateral series usually 30 or fewer; sensory canal on side of head an open groove, without pore-like openings; anal fin of male slender and rod-like; third ray of anal fin unbranched.
Livebearers
Poeciliidae .... **Page 237**

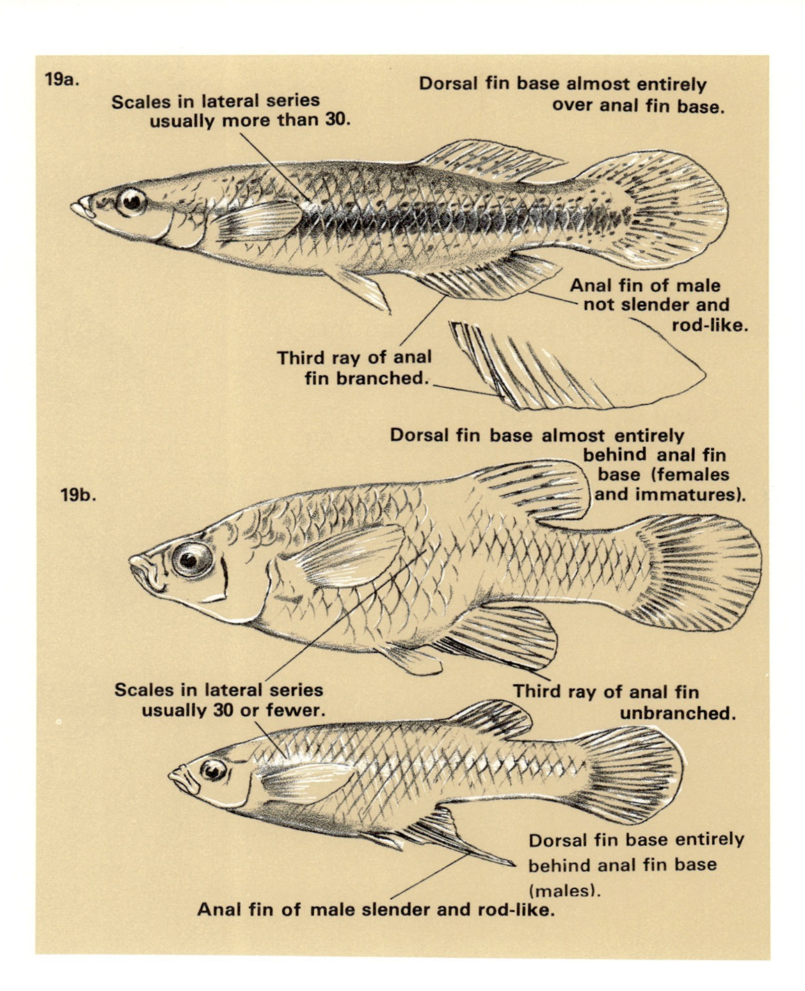

20a. *(From 11b.)* One barbel on chin; soft dorsal fin long, with more than 65 rays.
Codfishes
Gadidae .... **Page 226**

20b. *(From 11b.)* No barbel on chin; soft dorsal fin short, with fewer than 40 rays.
Go to **21**

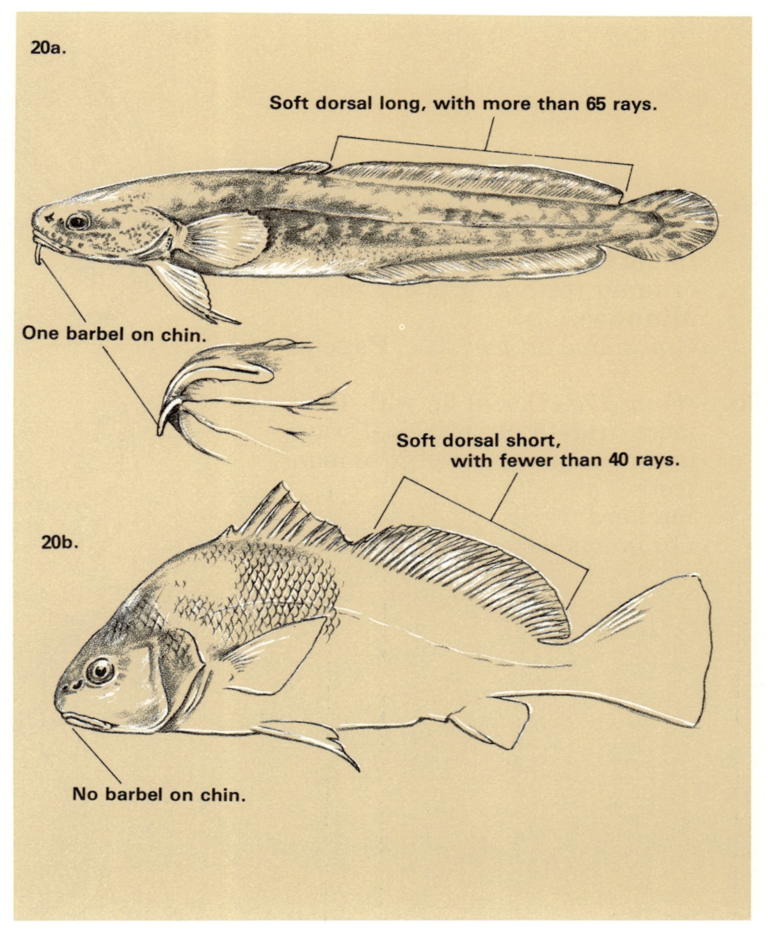

21a. *(From 20b.)* Distance from rear margin of gill cover to base of pelvic fin (A) much greater than distance from base of pelvic fin to front of anal fin (B); base of pectoral fin near upper end of gill opening; spinous dorsal separate from soft dorsal and with 3 to 5 thin spines.
Silversides
Atherinidae .... **Page 239**

21b. *(From 20b.)* Distance from rear margin of gill cover to base of pelvic fin (A) much less than distance from base of pelvic fin to front of anal fin (B); base of pectoral fin far below upper end of gill opening; spinous dorsal separate or not from soft dorsal, but if separate, with 6 or more stout spines.
Go to **22**

21a.
3-5 thin spines.
Base of pectoral fin near upper end of gill opening.
Spinous dorsal separate from soft dorsal.
A
B
A much greater than B.

21b.
Base of pectoral fin far below upper end of gill opening.
Spinous dorsal, if separate from soft dorsal, with 6 or more stout spines.
A
B
A much less than B.

22a. *(From 21b.)* Body without scales; spines of dorsal fin flexible, superficially resembling soft rays; pelvic fin with one thin spine and 3 or 4 soft rays.
Sculpins
Cottidae .... **Page 241**

22b. *(From 21b.)* Body at least partly scaled; spines of dorsal fin stiff; pelvic fin with 1 thin spine and 5 soft rays.
Go to **23**

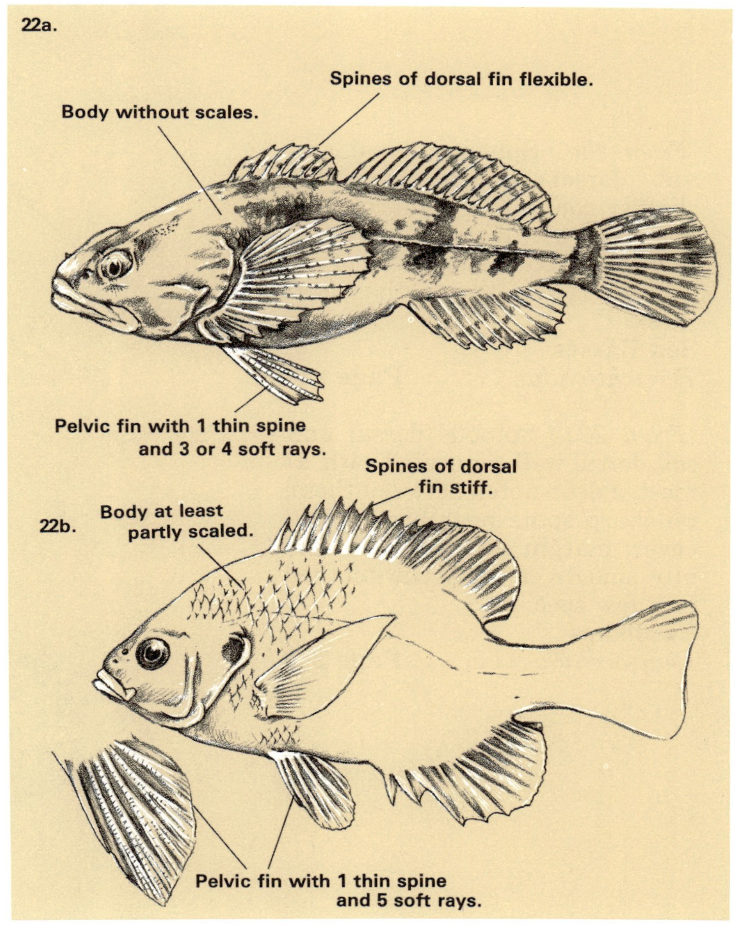

23a. *(From 22b.)* Anal fin spines 3 or more.
Go to 24

23b. *(From 22b.)* Anal fin spines 1 or 2.
Go to 25

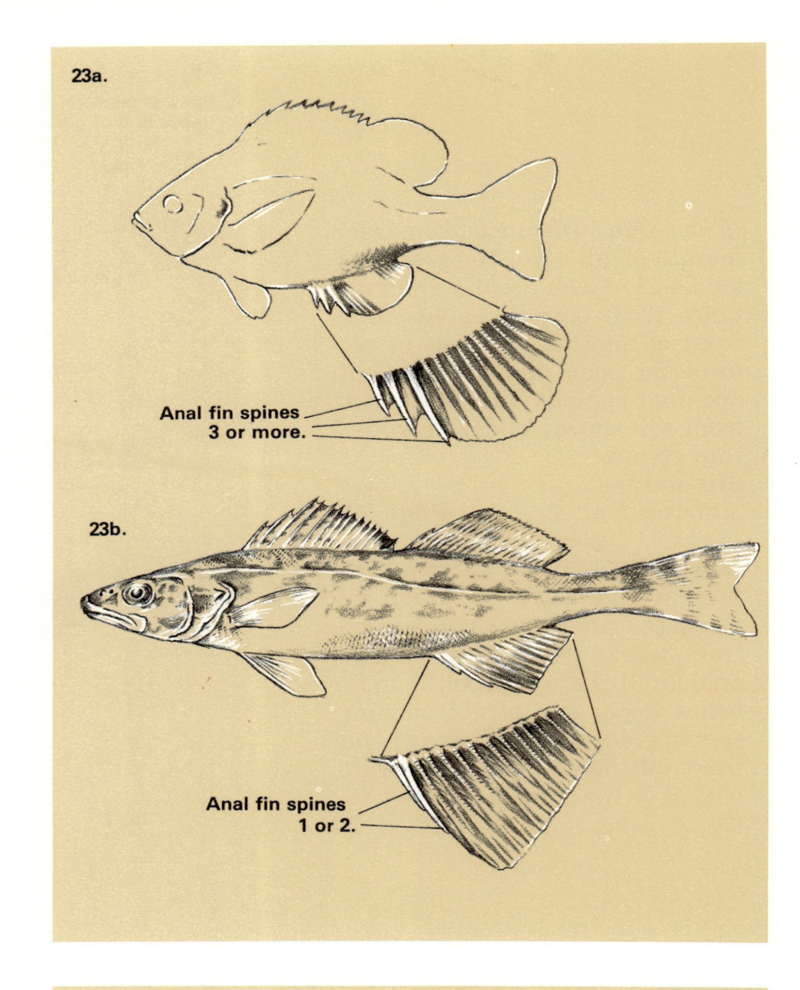

24a. *(From 23a.)* Spinous dorsal and soft dorsal separate or only slightly connected; a sharp spine near back of gill cover; margin of preopercle (bone just ahead of gill cover) strongly saw-toothed (serrate).
Sea Basses
Percichthyidae .... **Page 244**

24b. *(From 23a.)* Spinous dorsal and soft dorsal well connected with, at most, a deep notch between them; no sharp spine near back of gill cover; margin of preopercle usually smooth, weakly saw-toothed in a few species.
Sunfishes
Centrarchidae .... **Page 249**

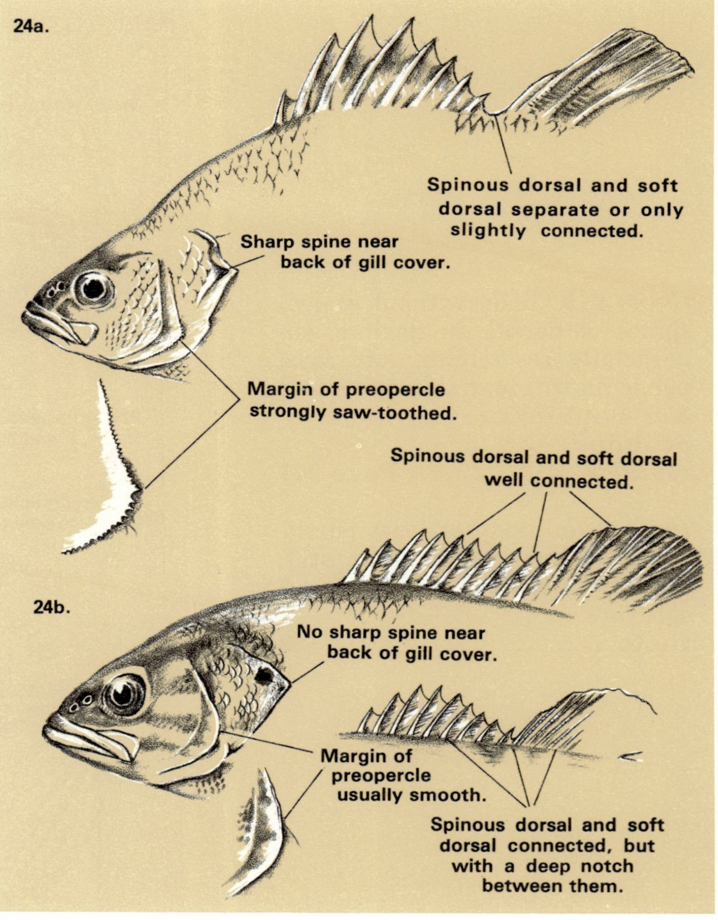

25a. *(From 23b.)* Soft dorsal not longer than spinous dorsal, and with fewer than 23 rays; if present, second spine of anal fin slender and not much longer than first.
Perches
Percidae .... **Page 276**

25b. *(From 23b.)* Soft dorsal much longer than spinous dorsal, and with more than 23 rays; second spine of anal fin stout and much longer than the first.
Drums
Sciaenidae .... **Page 324**

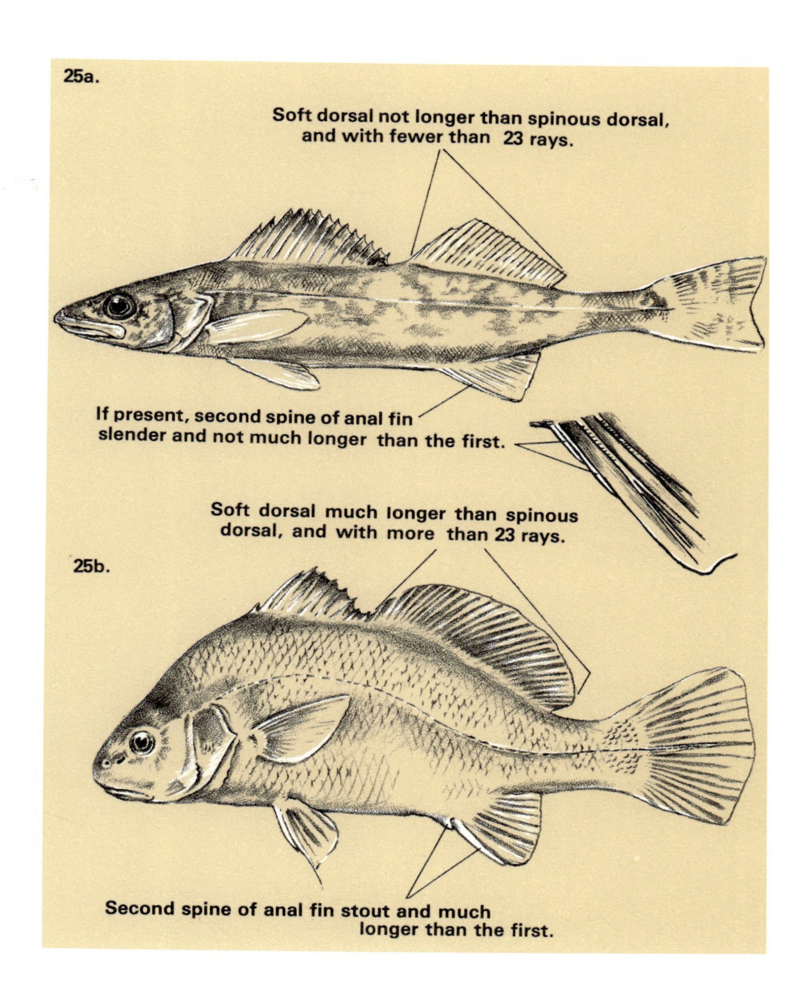

Chestnut lampreys, *Ichthyomyzon castaneus,* **in spawning pit.**

Paddlefish, *Polyodon spathula.*

Bowfin, *Amia calva.*

Wooldridge

Shovelnose sturgeon, *Scaphirhynchus platorynchus.*

Wooldridge

Longnose gar, *Lepisosteus osseus,* **in juvenile colors.**

Rainbow trout, *Salmo gairdneri.*

Grass pickerel, *Esox americanus.*

Hornyhead chub, *Nocomis biguttatus,* **male in spawning colors.**

Male of the black-finned subspecies of redfin shiner, *Notropis umbratilis,* **in spawning colors.**

Spawning aggregation of bleeding shiners, *Notropis zonatus*.

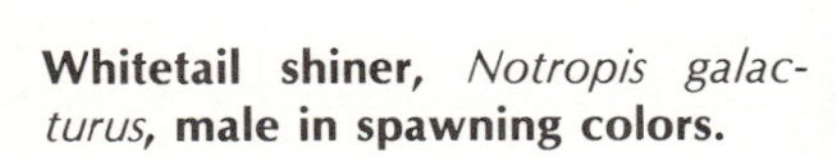

Whitetail shiner, *Notropis galacturus*, **male in spawning colors.**

Central stoneroller, *Campostoma anomalum*, **male in spawning colors.**

Quillback, *Carpiodes cyprinus.*

Northern hog sucker, *Hypentelium nigricans.*

Golden redhorse, *Moxostoma erythrurum,* **spawning or "shoaling".**

Blue catfish, *Ictalurus furcatus.*

Wooldridge

Channel catfish, *Ictalurus punctatus.*

Yellow bullhead, *Ictalurus natalis.*

Brown bullhead, *Ictalurus nebulosus.*

Checkered madtom, *Noturus flavater.*

Plains topminnow, *Fundulus sciadicus.*

Pirate perch, *Aphredoderus sayanus.*

42 **Male smallmouth bass,** *Micropterus dolomieui,* **guarding his nest.**

otted bass, *Micropterus punctulatus.*

Spawning pair of green sunfish, *Lepomis cyanellus.*

Orangespotted sunfish, *Lepomis humilis*, **male in spawning colors.**

Spotted sunfish, *Lepomis punctatus.*

Longear sunfish, *Lepomis megalotis,* **male fans out his nest with violent sweeping motions of his tail fin.**

Bluegill, *Lepomis macrochirus.*

Rock bass, *Ambloplites rupestris.*

White crappie, *Pomoxis annularis.*

Flier, *Centrarchus macropterus.*

Crystal darter, *Ammocrypta asprella*.

Whitley

The male greenside darter, *Etheostoma blennioides*, **is the larger and more colorful of this spawning pair.**

Missouri saddled darter, *Etheostoma tetrazonum,* **male in spawning colors. This fish is found only in the Ozark Region of Missouri.**

Purkett

Niangua darter, *Etheostoma nianguae,* **male in spawning colors. This fish is found only in the Osage River system of Missouri.**

Purkett

Orangethroat darter, *Etheostoma spectabile,* **male of the Spring River subspecies in spawning colors.**

Rainbow darter, *Etheostoma caeruleum,*
male in spawning colors.

Mottled sculpin, *Cottus bairdi.*

Purkett

Freshwater drum, *Aplodinotus grunniens.*

LAMPREYS

Petromyzontidae

Lampreys are primitive survivors from very ancient times. Along with their marine relatives, the hagfishes, they are the remnants of a group of jawless fishes that lived more than 350 million years ago. Actually, the lampreys are no more closely related to other present-day fishes than the fishes are to amphibians and other higher vertebrates.

With their slender, snake-like body and smooth, slippery skin, lampreys somewhat resemble the eel. But here the resemblance ends. They do not have jaws and in adults the mouth is a sucking disc. Paired fins (pectoral and pelvic) are absent. Seven pore-like gill openings are visible along each side of the head, and a single nostril is present in the middle of the head just forward from the eyes. The lamprey's skeleton is composed entirely of cartilage rather than bone.

Lampreys are unique in habit as well as in appearance. Because the life cycle is basically alike for all, it is convenient to describe it here in some detail. The life cycle consists of two distinct stages, a larval stage and an adult stage. The larvae (*ammocoetes*) resemble the adults in body form but do not have eyes, and the mouth is a horseshoe-shaped hood rather than a sucking disc. Lamprey larvae burrow into the soft-bottomed areas of streams where they feed on microscopic life and organic particles strained from the water and from the bottom sediments. Currents created by contraction of the gill region bring in water, and a sieve apparatus consisting of many complexly branched fleshy structures strains food from the water as it enters through the mouth. The larval stage lasts one or more years, the actual time depending on the species, after which the larvae transform to the adult stage. Transformation occurs over a period of several months in late summer and fall. During this period the larvae do not feed and actually become reduced in size.

After transformation the life cycle may follow one of two courses. Some lampreys, including two of the six Missouri species, are parasitic. These migrate into lakes and large rivers after reaching adulthood. Here they attach themselves to other fishes, sucking blood through a hole rasped in the host by a hard, tongue-like structure in the middle of the mouth disc. Several days are required for the lamprey to complete its blood meal, after which it drops off. The host fish usually does not die as a direct result of the attack, but may die of secondary infections that develop in the wound left where the lamprey was attached. The parasitic stage lasts 1 or 2 years, after which the adults return to the smaller streams to spawn.

Spawning occurs in shallow pits excavated near the upper ends of gravelly riffles. The suction-disc mouth is used to carry stones from the pit, and fine material is fanned out by violent vibrations of the body. Pit construction and spawning are communal activities, with 20 or more lampreys sometimes present in a single pit. Adults do not feed once they start to spawn, and death follows shortly after spawning is completed.

The contrasting life cycle is found in the so-called "brook" lampreys in which the parasitic stage is left out. After transforming to the adult stage in late summer and fall, brook lampreys remain in the smaller streams without feeding until the following spring. Then they spawn in a manner similar to that of the parasitic species.

In some areas lampreys are of considerable importance. Destruction of an important lake trout fishery has been attributed to invasion of the upper Great Lakes by the sea lamprey, a species not found in Missouri. In some coastal streams marine lampreys are captured in large numbers for human consumption as they migrate upstream to spawn. Where abundant, larval lampreys are commonly used as bait for bass and other game fishes. Parasitic lampreys are not common enough in Missouri to present much of a problem, and the larvae are not sufficiently abundant to make collecting them for bait worthwhile.

Identification of the species of lampreys depends to a considerable extent on characters that are not developed in larvae. Therefore, only adults can be identified with any degree of confidence in most species. The number of muscle bands (myomeres) remains constant throughout life and, to the extent that the species differ in this character, it can be used to provide an identification.

LAMPREYS

Key to the Lampreys

1a. Mouth a horseshoe-shaped hood without teeth; eyes poorly developed and covered by skin; gill openings connected by a continuous horizontal groove.
Larvae
(Immature stage of lampreys.)

1b. Mouth a circular sucking disc lined with horny teeth (teeth poorly developed in some species); eyes well developed, not covered by skin; gill openings not connected by a horizontal groove.
Go to 2

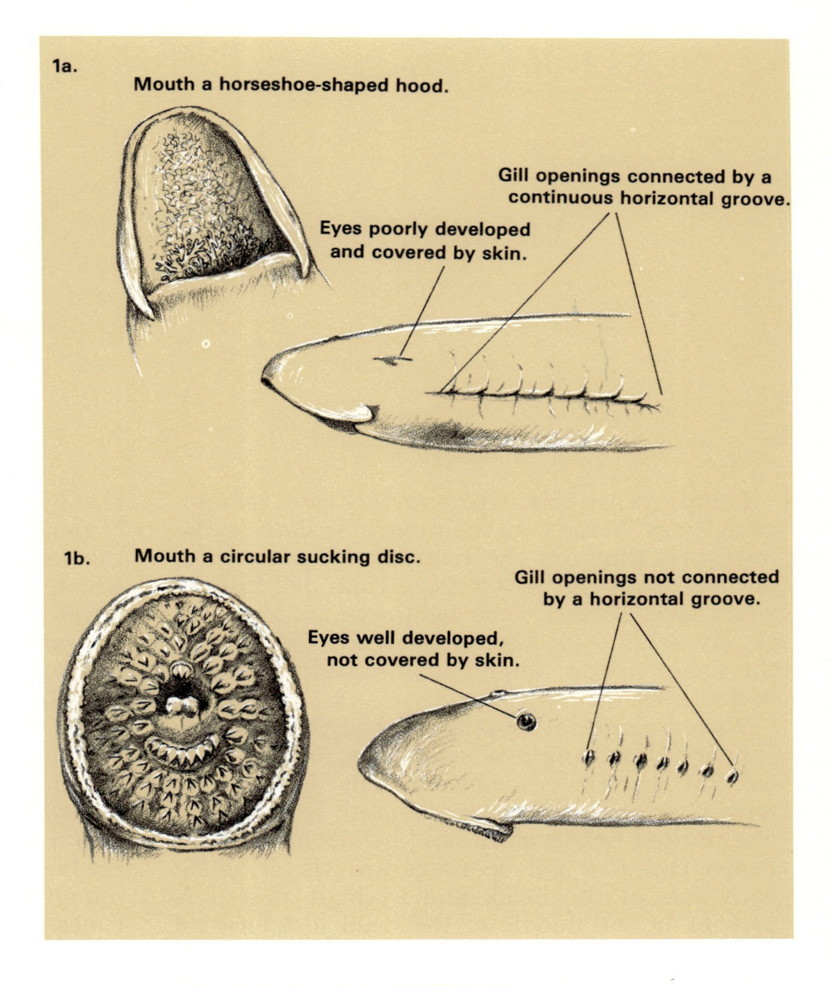

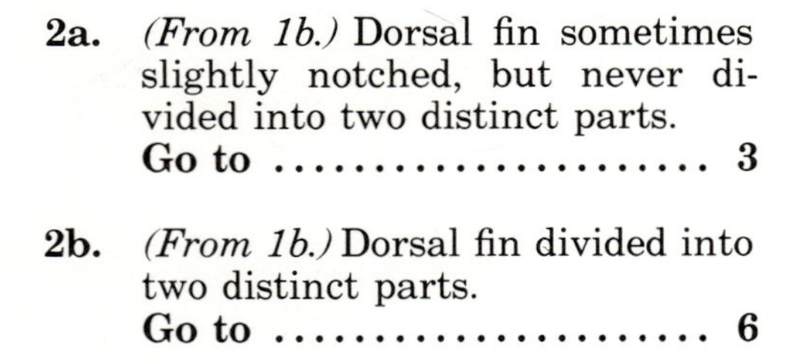

2a. *(From 1b.)* Dorsal fin sometimes slightly notched, but never divided into two distinct parts.
Go to 3

2b. *(From 1b.)* Dorsal fin divided into two distinct parts.
Go to 6

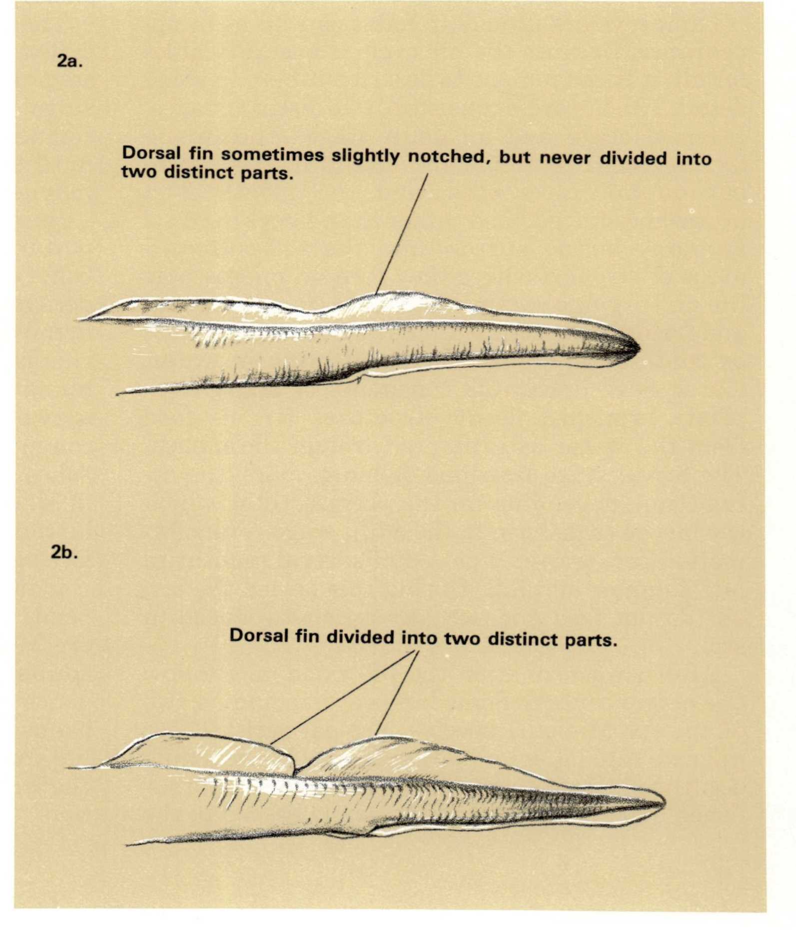

3a. *(From 2a.)* All disc teeth well developed; disc, when expanded, wider than head; total length often more than 7 inches.
Parasitic lampreys
Go to **4**

3b. *(From 2a.)* Most disc teeth poorly developed, especially near outer margins of disc; disc, when expanded, narrower than head; total length never more than 7 inches.
Brook lampreys
Go to **5**

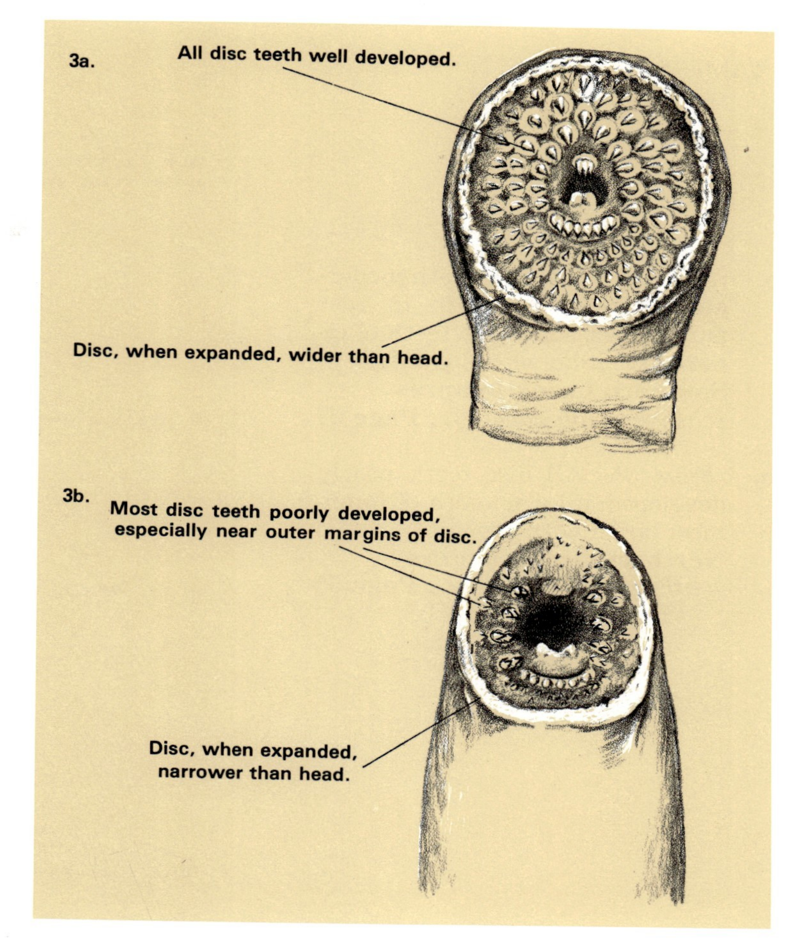

4a. *(From 3a.)* Some disc teeth of innermost circle with 2 points; muscle bands between last gill opening and vent usually 52 to 56.
Chestnut lamprey
Ichthyomyzon castaneus **Page 56**

4b. *(From 3a.)* All disc teeth of innermost circle with 1 point; muscle bands between last gill opening and vent usually 49 to 52.
Silver lamprey
Ichthyomyzon unicuspis **Page 55**

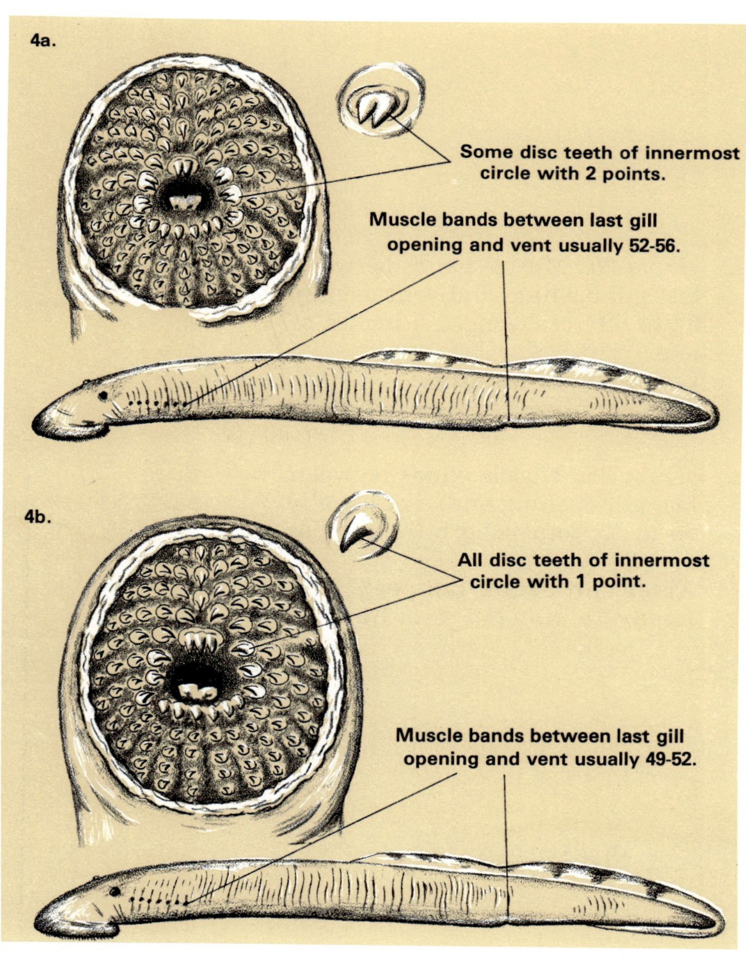

5a. *(From 3b.)* Most disc teeth moderately developed except in rear part of disc; some disc teeth of innermost circle with 2 points.
Southern brook lamprey
Ichthyomyzon gagei ... **Page 57**

5b. *(From 3b.)* All disc teeth poorly developed; all disc teeth of innermost circle with 1 point.
Northern brook lamprey
Ichthyomyzon fossor ... **Page 55**

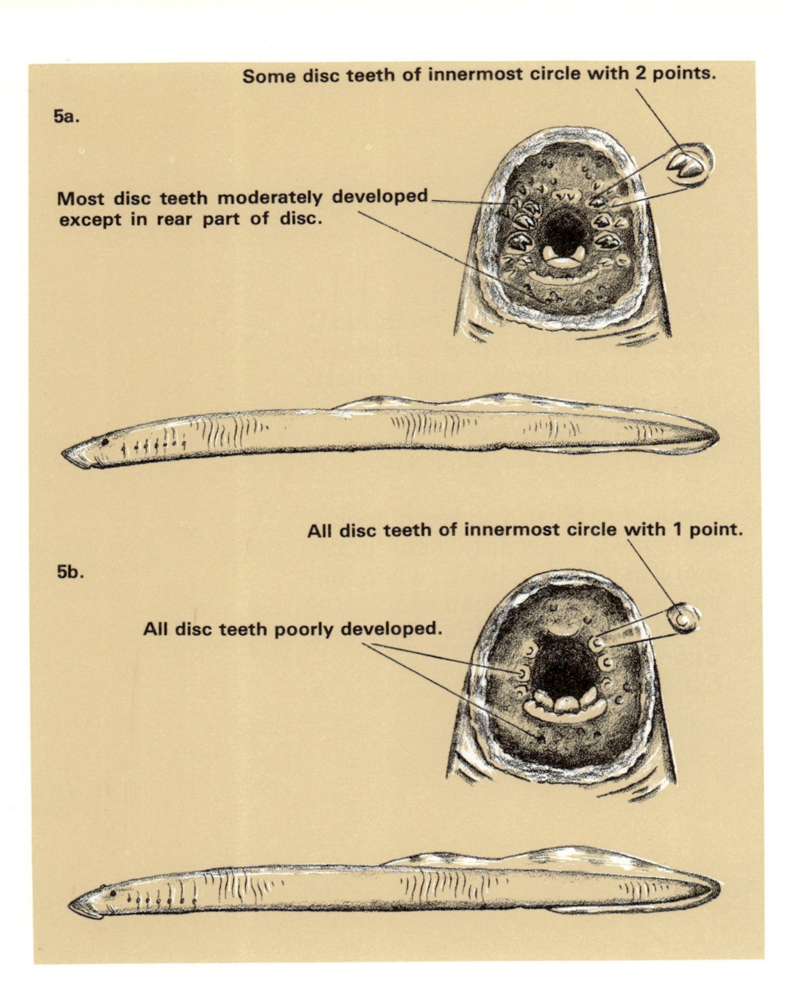

6a. *(From 2b.)* Muscle bands between last gill opening and vent usually 54 to 60; total length 5 inches or less.
Least brook lamprey
Lampetra aepyptera ... **Page 57**

6b. *(From 2b.)* Muscle bands between last gill opening and vent usually 66 to 75; total length 6 inches or more.
American brook lamprey
Lampetra lamottei .... **Page 58**

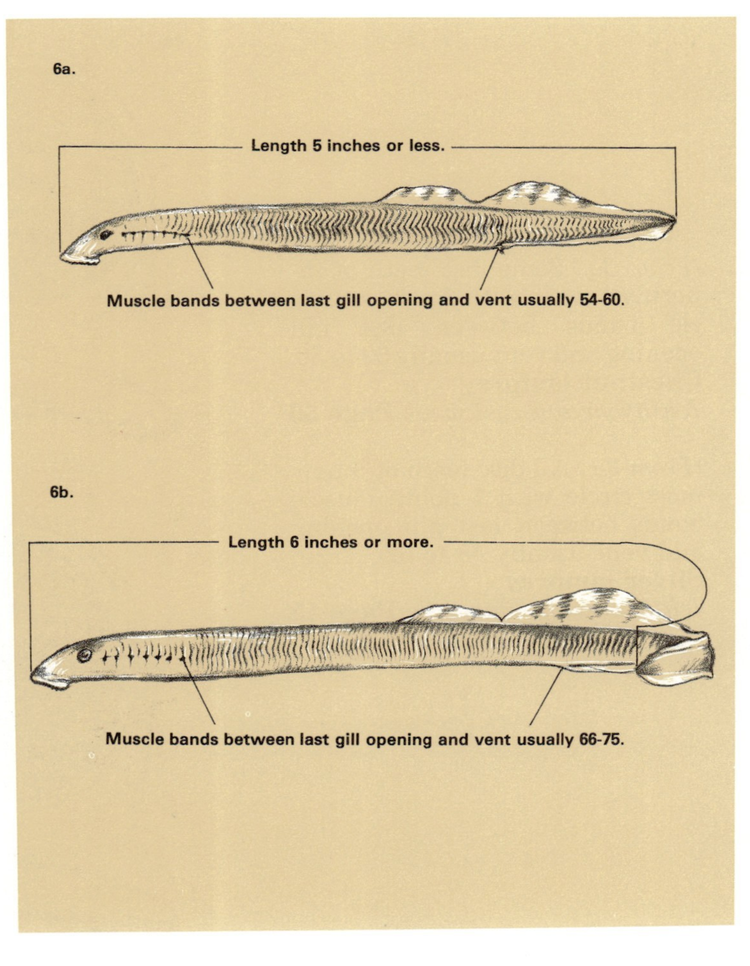

Silver Lamprey

Ichthyomyzon unicuspis Hubbs and Trautman

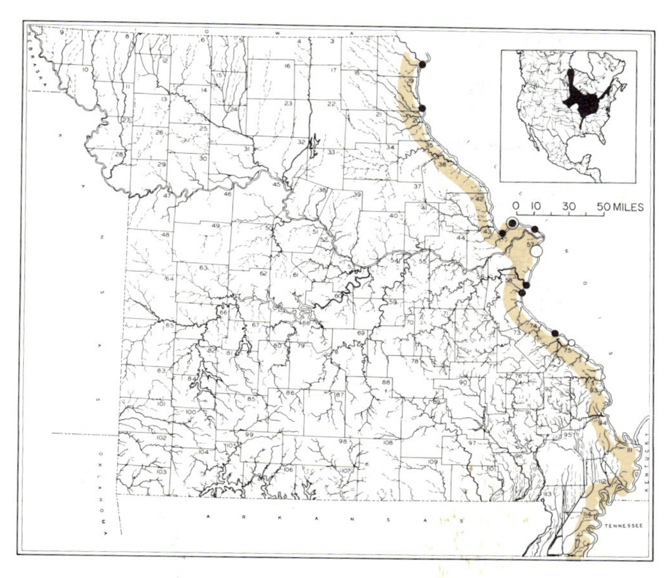

DESCRIPTION

Illustration: Page 53, 4b.

Adult characters: A parasitic lamprey with the dorsal fin shallowly notched, but not divided into two distinct parts. The mouth disc, when expanded, is wider than the head. Disc teeth all well developed; those in innermost circle each with a single point. Muscle bands between last gill opening and vent usually 49 to 52.

Life colors: Larvae and immature adults are yellowish-tan on the back and sides, yellowish on belly and fins. Adults ready to spawn darken to blue or blue-gray, becoming nearly black by the time spawning is completed.

Size: Adults are reported to measure about 6 inches in length when newly transformed, reaching a length of 14 or 15 inches at maturity. Larvae achieve a maximum length of about 7 inches.

Scientific name: *Ichthyomyzon,* Greek, "fish to suck"; *unicuspis,* Latin, "one point," in reference to the number of points on the innermost disc teeth.

DISTRIBUTION AND HABITAT

This northern species has been recorded in Missouri only from the Mississippi River where it is much less common than the chestnut lamprey. The silver lamprey has been reported from the Missouri River in South Dakota and Nebraska but is not known to range downstream into Missouri.

It spends most of its adult life in large rivers and lakes. Spawning and larval development occur in streams of medium size. Larvae have not been found in Missouri.

HABITS AND LIFE HISTORY

General aspects of the life cycle of this and other parasitic lampreys are discussed in the family account, page 51. The number of years required for larval development is not known. The parasitic phase lasts 12 or 13 months. Spawning has not been observed in Missouri, but has been reported elsewhere at this latitude in April or May.

Northern Brook Lamprey

Ichthyomyzon fossor Reighard and Cummins

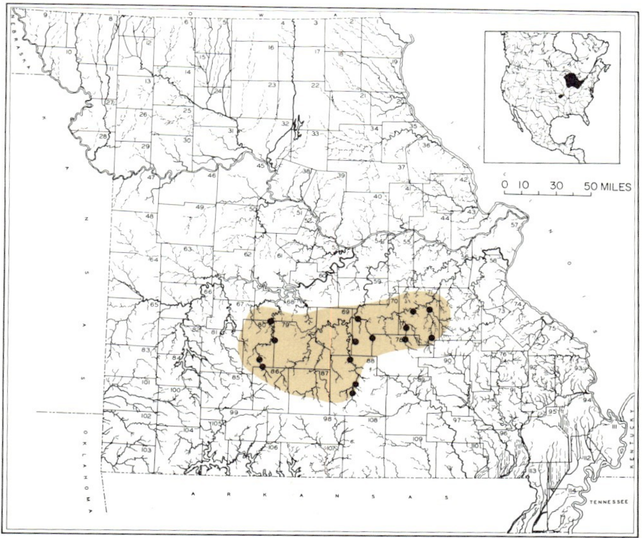

DESCRIPTION

Illustration: Page 54, 5b.

Adult characters: A nonparasitic lamprey with the dorsal fin shallowly notched, but not divided into two distinct parts. The mouth disc, when expanded, is narrower than the head. Disc teeth all poorly developed; those in innermost circle each with a single point. Muscle bands between last gill opening and vent usually 49 to 55.

Life colors: Larvae and recently transformed adults are grayish brown on the back and sides, yellow on the belly and fins. Adults ready to spawn are darker brown, becoming nearly black by the time spawning is completed.

Size: Adults usually measure 4.2 to 4.9 inches in length. Larvae achieve a length of nearly 6 inches just before transforming.

Scientific name: *Ichthyomyzon,* Greek, "fish to suck"; *fossor,* Latin, "a digger," in reference to the nest-building habits of lampreys.

DISTRIBUTION AND HABITAT

The northern brook lamprey is the most common and widely distributed brook lamprey in streams of the northern Ozarks. Ozark populations are far removed from the main body of the range of this northern species and are thought to be relicts of the Pleistocene ice age.

Both larvae and adults of the northern brook lamprey are found in streams of medium size, avoiding both small headwater creeks and large rivers. As with other brook lampreys, this species requires clear, permanent-flowing streams having clean, gravelly riffles for spawning and stable beds of silt, sand, and organic debris for larval development.

HABITS AND LIFE HISTORY

General aspects of the life cycle of this and other species of brook lampreys are discussed in the family account, page 51. Larvae require about six years to complete their development.[11] Transformation to the adult stage begins in late August or September and is not completed until about December. During this period the transforming individuals decrease in length by about 10%.

Spawning of the northern brook lamprey is not preceded by extensive upstream migrations, but adults may move for short distances to compensate for the downstream drift of the larvae during development. The spawning habits of this lamprey are not known in detail. Spawning occurs in Missouri during early May. I have observed adults in pits they had excavated on gravelly riffles. I have also observed adults in the same pits as the chestnut lamprey, suggesting that pits excavated by the large parasitic species are sometimes utilized for spawning by this brook lamprey.

Chestnut Lamprey

Ichthyomyzon castaneus Girard

Other local names: Lamprey eel, Lamper, Bloodsucker, Hitchhiker, Seven-eyed cat

DESCRIPTION

Illustration: Page 53, 4a; **35.**

Adult characters: A parasitic lamprey with the dorsal fin shallowly notched, but not divided into two distinct parts. The mouth disc, when expanded, is wider than the head. Disc teeth all well developed; those in innermost circle mostly with 2 points. Muscle bands between last gill opening and vent usually 52 to 56.

Life colors: The back and upper sides are yellowish-tan, grading to light olive-yellow on the belly and fins.

Size: Adults are 4 to 6 inches in length when newly transformed, reaching a length of 10 to 12 inches at maturity. Larvae achieve a length of 6 inches or more.

Scientific name: *Ichthyomyzon,* Greek, "fish to suck"; *castaneus,* Greek, "of chestnut color."

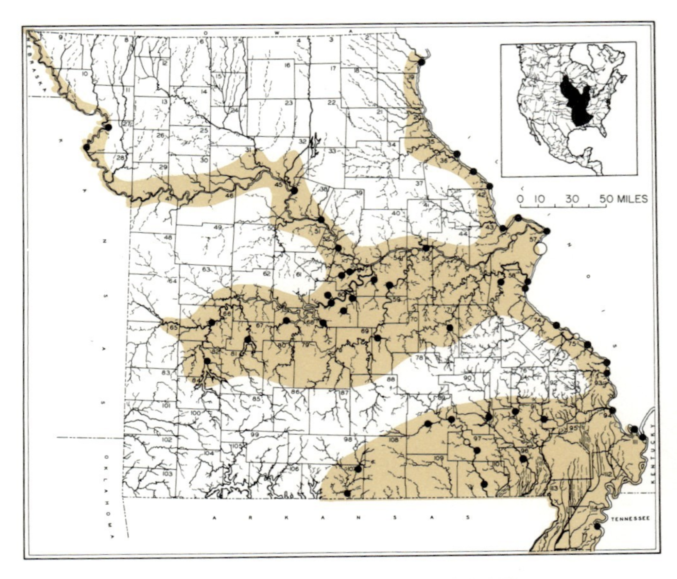

DISTRIBUTION AND HABITAT

The chestnut lamprey is the most abundant and widely distributed lamprey in Missouri. Any lamprey found attached to a fish anywhere except the Mississippi River will almost surely be this species. According to reports of commercial fishermen, parasitic lampreys are common in the lower Missouri River but undergo a marked decrease in abundance upstream. Above St. Joseph they are rarely encountered. The chestnut lamprey is common in the lower Mississippi River but is uncommon northward. Adults are rather common in the larger streams and reservoirs of the Ozarks. Larvae tentatively identified as this species are known from many localities in the Ozarks, but these records have not been plotted on the accompanying map because of the possibility of misidentification.

During the parasitic stage of its life cycle the chestnut lamprey is most often encountered in large rivers and reservoirs. Spawning adults and larvae are found in medium-sized creeks to moderately large rivers. The larvae require clear, permanent-flowing streams having stable bars of silt, sand, and organic debris in which to complete their development. In Missouri, such streams are found only in the Ozarks, which accounts for the progressive decline in abundance of the chestnut lamprey in the large rivers of Missouri outside of that region.

HABITS AND LIFE HISTORY

General aspects of the life history of parasitic lampreys are discussed in the family account, page 51. The chestnut lamprey probably requires at least 2 or 3 years to complete its larval development. Transformation to the adult stage is completed by the middle of November, but the newly transformed individuals do not take up a parasitic existence until the following spring.[12] Adults live about 18 months, but feed actively only for about 5 months near the middle of the adult life span with the peak of the feeding season in June and July. Commercial fishermen in Missouri report finding many lampreys attached to other fish in late winter and early spring.

Adult chestnut lampreys begin moving into tributary streams in late winter and spring. Spawning has been observed in the Ozarks on many occasions, always in the first half of May. An interesting account of the spawning of about 50 individuals of this species in a single nest has been written.[13] Nest construction differed from that reported for other lamprey species in that the nest was continually excavated at the upper end and filled at the lower end. On two separate occasions I have observed chestnut lampreys filling a nest previously excavated, but filling and excavating did not occur simultaneously. In an Oklahoma study, a large female chestnut lamprey was found to contain 42,000 eggs.[14]

Southern Brook Lamprey

Ichthyomyzon gagei Hubbs and Trautman

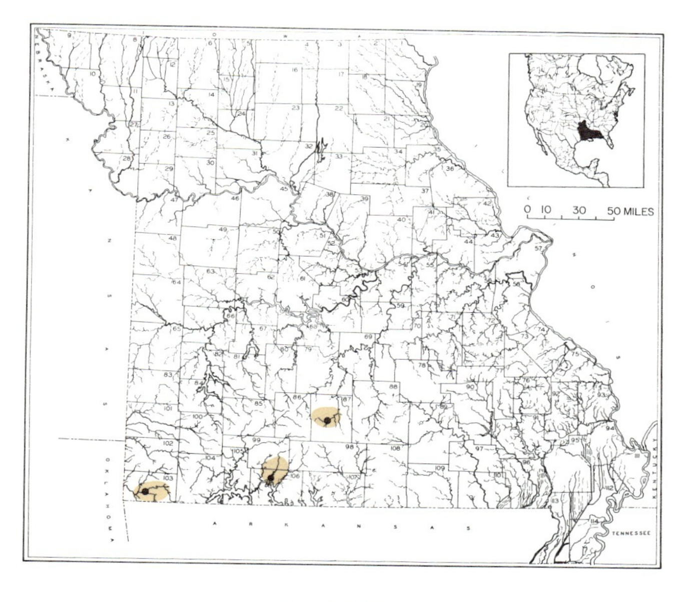

DESCRIPTION

Illustration: Page 54, 5a.
Adult characters: A nonparasitic lamprey with the dorsal fin shallowly notched, but not divided into two distinct parts. The mouth disc, when expanded, is narrower than the head. Disc teeth moderately developed except in hind part of disc; those in innermost circle mostly with 2 points. Muscle bands between last gill opening and vent usually 52 to 56.
Life colors: The back and upper sides are olive-brown, grading to olive-yellow on the belly and fins.
Size: Adults are about 4.5 to 7 inches in length. Larvae reach a length of 7 inches or more.
Scientific name: *Ichthyomyzon,* Greek, "fish to suck"; *gagei,* named for S.H. Gage, one of the foremost students of lampreys.

DISTRIBUTION AND HABITAT

The southern brook lamprey is known from only three widely separate localities in the southwestern Ozarks, but is probably more widespread in that part of the state. It remains in medium-sized, clear, permanent-flowing streams throughout life. The larvae are reported to occur in accumulations of leaves and other debris in slack, marginal water, usually at the downstream ends of sand bars or below obstructions in the stream.[15]

HABITS AND LIFE HISTORY

The life history of the southern brook lamprey conforms closely to the account given for brook lampreys in the family discussion, page 51. In Alabama, at least 3 years are required for larvae to complete their development.[15] Spawning occurs at the same latitude as Missouri in April or May,[14] but is about a month earlier in Alabama. Nests consist of roundish depressions 6 to 8 inches wide and about 2 inches deep. Ten females from Alabama each contained from 1,000 to 3,264 eggs[15]

Least Brook Lamprey

Lampetra aepyptera Abbott

DESCRIPTION

Illustration: Page 54, 6a.
Adult characters: A nonparasitic lamprey with the dorsal fin deeply notched, separating it into two distinct parts. Mouth disc, when expanded, narrower than head. Similar to American brook lamprey but with disc teeth poorly developed and covered by skin, and with about 54 to 60 muscle bands between last gill opening and vent.
Life colors: The back and upper sides are light tan mottled with dark brown; the belly and fins are yellowish.
Size: The smallest Missouri lamprey, with most adults 3.5 to 5 inches long. Larvae reach a length of at least 5.9 inches.

LAMPREYS

Scientific name: *Lampetra,* Greek, "to suck a stone"; *aepyptera,* Greek, "high fin."

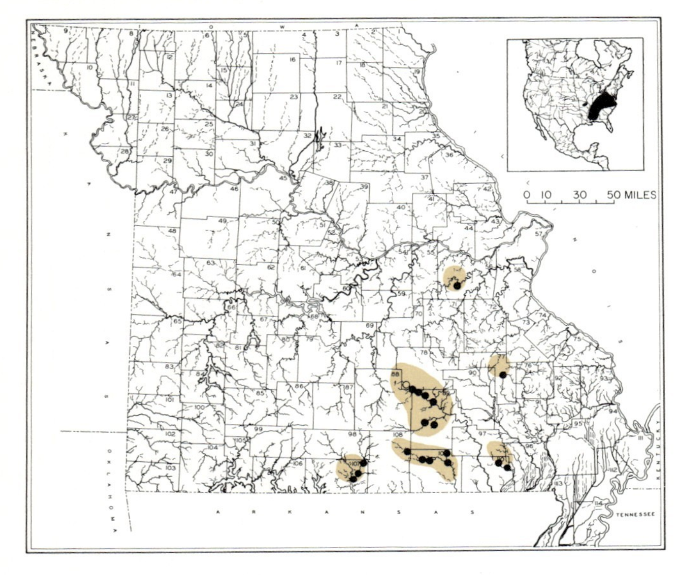

DISTRIBUTION AND HABITAT

The least brook lamprey is widely distributed in the southern Ozarks from the North Fork eastward to the upper St. Francis River, and is known from a single locality (Kratz Spring, Franklin County) in the Meramec drainage. Additional collecting would probably reveal a more widespread distribution in the eastern Ozarks, especially in the Black and St. Francis drainages.

This lamprey is decidedly a creek fish, occurring most abundantly both as adults and larvae in headwater streams and spring branches. Clear water, permanent flow, stable beds of silt and organic debris, and clean gravelly riffles are basic requirements for a stream if it is to support a population of the least brook lamprey.

HABITS AND LIFE HISTORY

General aspects of the life history of brook lampreys are discussed in the family account, page 51. A Maryland study reveals that larval development of the least brook lamprey requires 3 years.[16] Three or more length groups have been noted among larvae collected at a single time and place in Missouri, indicating that here the larval period is also at least 3 years. The smallest larvae are found in deposits of fine sand and silt. As they increase in size, the larvae occupy coarser bottom materials and drift farther downstream. The size attained by the least brook lamprey varies considerably from one locality to another, perhaps depending on the availability of food.

Spawning of the least brook lamprey has been observed in southern Missouri in mid-March and adults that had not finished spawning have been collected as late as mid-April. This small species is reported by other observers[16, 59] to make little effort to carry pebbles, preparing its shallow nest by attaching itself to a stone and fanning away fine gravel and sand by rapid vibrations of the body. However, we have seen least brook lampreys carrying pebbles during nest construction, both in the field and in the aquarium. Occasionally two or more lampreys cooperated in carrying a large pebble. A single female may deposit over 1,100 eggs.[16] These hatch in about four days at a temperature of 65 to 72° F. Newly hatched larvae are about 0.2 inches total length and reach a length of about 1.4 inches by October of their first year.

American Brook Lamprey

Lampetra lamottei (Lesueur)

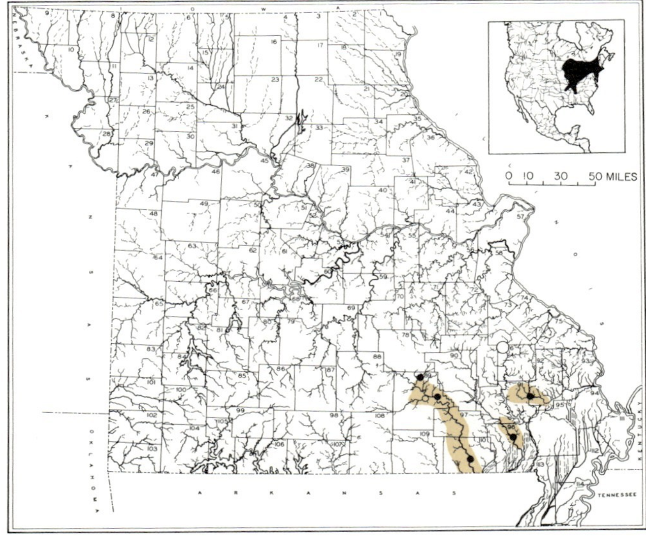

DESCRIPTION

Illustration: Page 54, 6b.

Adult characters: A nonparasitic lamprey with the dorsal fin deeply notched, separating it into two distinct parts. The mouth disc, when expanded, is narrower than the head. Disc teeth arranged in clusters rather than in radiating series. Similar to least brook lamprey but with teeth better developed, and with about 66 to 75 muscle bands between last gill opening and vent.

Life colors: Adults are slate-blue on the back and sides, silvery-white on the belly. Larvae are dark brown on the back and sides, yellowish-olive on the belly and fins.

Size: Adults are usually 6 to 8 inches long. Larvae may achieve a length of nearly 8.5 inches.

Scientific name: *Lampetra,* Greek, "to suck a stone"; *lamottei,* named for Lamotte, one of the discoverer's of the first lead mine in Missouri.

DISTRIBUTION AND HABITAT

The American brook lamprey was first discovered by the French naturalist Charles Lesueur during an excursion through eastern Missouri in 1820. He collected his specimens at a place he called Wilkinson's Cave, presumably in the St. Francis drainage near the present town of Mine La Motte, Madison County. This lamprey has not subsequently been collected in the St. Francis drainage but is known from four localities in the Current River drainage and from one locality each in the Castor and Black river drainages.

The American brook lamprey inhabits clear streams ranging in size from large creeks to medium sized rivers. It avoids small headwater creeks and large, silty rivers. The American brook lamprey and the least brook lamprey have not been collected at the same localities, though both occur in the Current River drainage.

HABITS AND LIFE HISTORY

General aspects of the life history of brook lampreys are given in the family account, page 51. Larvae of the American brook lamprey require about 5 years to complete their development.[17] Transformation to the adult stage is completed in Missouri by late November and spawning occurs at this latitude in April.

STURGEONS

Acipenseridae

The sturgeons are a small group of primitive fishes with a wide distribution in the Northern Hemisphere. Some sturgeons are marine, ascending freshwater streams only to spawn. Others remain in freshwater throughout life. About 25 species are known, of which seven occur in North America. Three of these are found in Missouri.

Sturgeons are quite distinctive in appearance, resembling sharks in some respects. Like sharks, the sturgeon's upper tail fin lobe is larger than the lower one, with the backbone extending for a considerable distance into the upper lobe. Instead of the body being covered by typical fish scales there are several lengthwise rows of bony plates. The sturgeon's snout is long and prominent with the mouth far back on its under side. Four large barbels dangle from the snout in front of the mouth, and the lips consist of fleshy lobes. Some sturgeons rank among the largest freshwater fishes. The white sturgeon of Pacific coastal rivers reaches a length of about 20 feet and a weight of nearly a ton.

These unusual fish were formerly of considerable commercial importance in the Mississippi Valley, but this fishery underwent a sharp decline after 1900. Overfishing, pollution, and construction of dams that block migrations and destroy habitat have all contributed to this decline. Slow growth and late maturity make the sturgeons especially vulnerable to overharvest. The flesh of sturgeons has an excellent flavor, especially when smoked, and the eggs are used for caviar.

STURGEONS

Key to the Sturgeons

1a. Snout rounded and conical; lower lip with 2 lobes; barbels not fringed; caudal peduncle not completely covered with bony plates; upper lobe of tail fin without a filament.
Lake sturgeon
Acipenser fulvescens ... **Page 61**

1b. Snout flattened and shovel-shaped; lower lip with 4 lobes; barbels fringed; caudal peduncle completely covered with bony plates; upper lobe of tail fin with a long filament (sometimes broken off).
Go to 2

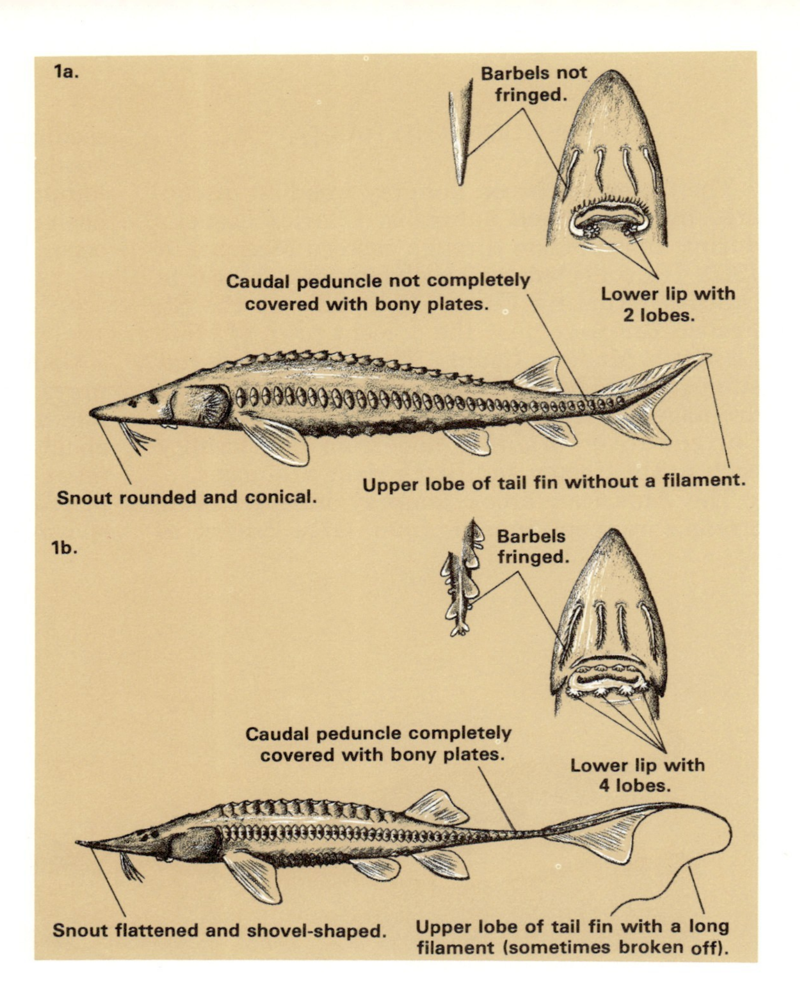

2a. *(From 1b.)* Belly covered with small plates, except in juveniles; bases of outer barbels in line with or ahead of bases of inner barbels; length of inner barbel (A) going less than 6 times into head length (B); anal fin rays 23 or fewer; dorsal fin rays 36 or fewer.
Shovelnose sturgeon
Scaphirhynchus platorynchus
.... **Page 62**

2b. *(From 1b.)* Belly without plates; bases of outer barbels usually behind bases of inner barbels; length of inner barbel (A) going more than 6 times into head length (B); anal fin rays 24 or more; dorsal fin rays 37 or more.
Pallid sturgeon
Scaphirhynchus albus
.... **Page 63**

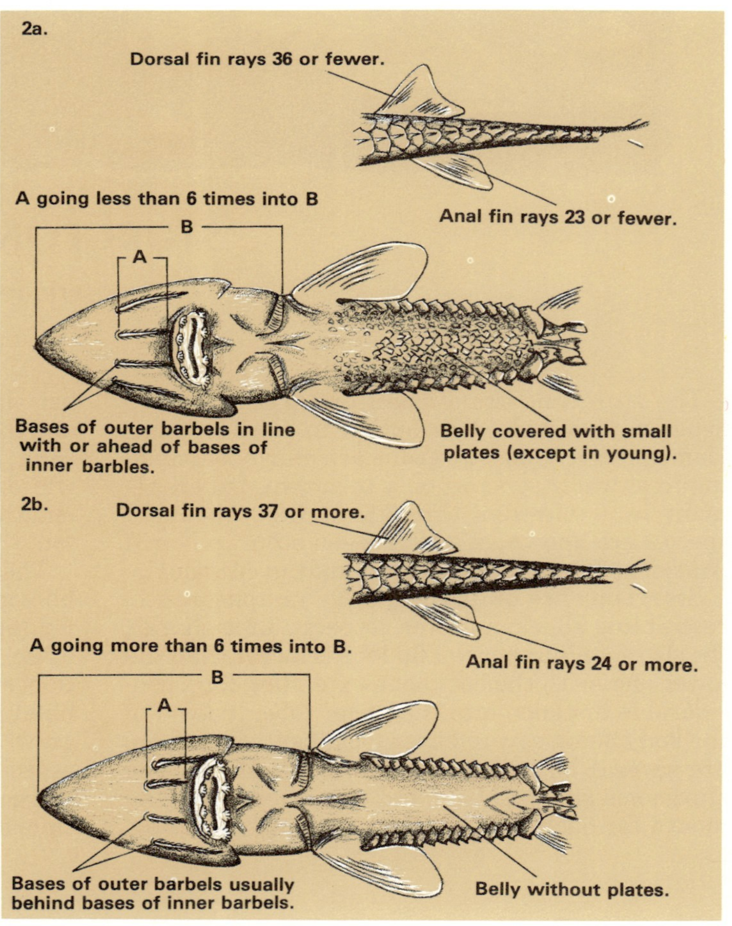

Lake Sturgeon

Acipenser fulvescens Rafinesque

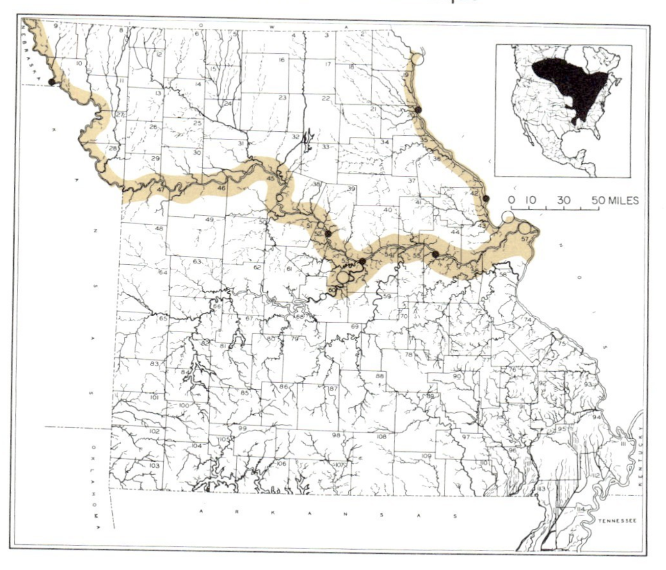

Other local names: Rubbernose sturgeon, Dogface sturgeon

DESCRIPTION

Illustration: Page 60, 1a.

Characters: A sturgeon with a cone-shaped snout and the caudal peduncle relatively short, rounded in cross section, and only partly covered by plates. Upper lobe of tail fin without a filament, except in smallest young. A small opening above and slightly behind eye (spiracle) present. Nostril opening closest to eye smaller than eye. Barbels not fringed. Lower lip with 2 lobes.

Life colors: Back and sides variable, ranging from dark slate to light brown or yellowish-olive; belly white. Fins similar in color to adjacent parts of body.

Size: One of the largest Mississippi Valley fishes, the lake sturgeon is reported to reach a length of 8 feet and a weight of 310 pounds. No specimens approaching this size have been reported from Missouri. The largest specimen to come to my attention weighed 97 pounds. It was caught in the Missouri River near Lupus, Moniteau County, in 1938.

Scientific name: *Acipenser,* Latin for sturgeon; *fulvescens,* Latin, "reddish-yellow," in reference to the body color.

DISTRIBUTION AND HABITAT

Before 1900 the lake sturgeon was a common and economically important fish in Missouri waters. Statistics compiled by the U. S. Fish Commission show that Missouri fishermen harvested 50,000 pounds of lake sturgeon from the Missouri and Mississippi rivers in 1894. After 1900 this fish underwent a dramatic decline in abundance and today is rare in Missouri waters, apparently existing primarily as stray individuals that enter Missouri from the north along the larger rivers. A farmer on the lower Osage River told me that large sturgeons were often caught in that stream until Bagnell Dam was built. If these were lake sturgeons, a reproducing population may have persisted in the Osage River until at least 1930. Overfishing was undoubtedly the cause for decline of this species before 1900. More recently, siltation and other forms of pollution, along with the construction of dams that block movements and destroy habitat, have been unfavorable to the lake sturgeon.

This species is primarily an inhabitant of large, moderately clear rivers and lakes. In Missouri it is known only from the largest rivers. The lake sturgeon is most often found over firm sandy, gravelly, or rocky bottoms.

HABITS AND LIFE HISTORY

No information is available on the life history of the lake sturgeon in Missouri. The following description is based on reviews of studies made in northern states and Canada.[18, 19]

It is a bottom feeder, using the highly protrusible mouth to suck up bottom materials from which the snails, small clams, insect larvae, and crayfish, are selectively removed. In searching for food, it swims close to the bottom with the ends of its sensitive barbels dragging.

Spawning occurs in late spring, at which time the lake sturgeon often ascends rather small streams. The large, adhesive eggs are deposited on the shallow, gravelly riffles of streams or the rocky shoals of lakes. They frequently break the surface or leap clear of the water when spawning, creating splashing sounds that can be heard for considerable distances. A single female may lay more than 500,000 eggs, but females do not spawn every year.

Growth of the lake sturgeon is very slow. Four or 5 years are required to reach a length of 20 inches and a weight of one pound. They do not reproduce before they are 20 years old. At that time they will be nearly 4 feet long and will weigh 20 or 30 pounds. Individuals 40 years of age are not uncommon and the maximum age reported is 152 years. Females live longer than males and attain a larger size.

IMPORTANCE

The catch of lake sturgeon in Missouri before 1900 exceeded the catch of shovelnose sturgeons in some years. Today the lake sturgeon is of no economic importance because of its extreme rarity.

The flesh, like that of all sturgeons, is highly valued as food. The eggs make excellent caviar.

Shovelnose Sturgeon

Scaphirhynchus platorynchus (Rafinesque)

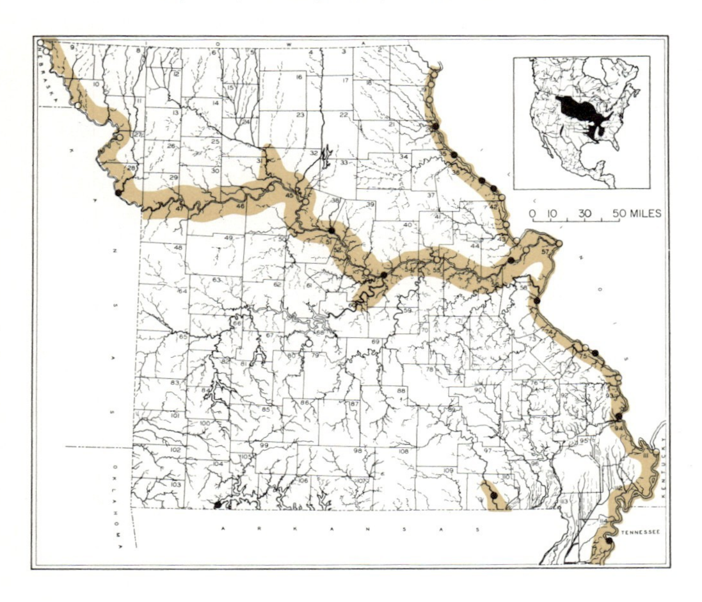

Other local names: Hackleback, Switchtail, Sand sturgeon

DESCRIPTION

Illustration: Page 60, 2a; **36.**

Characters: A sturgeon with the snout flattened and shovel-shaped and the caudal peduncle long, flattened in cross section, and completely covered with plates. Upper lobe of tail fin with a long, slender filament (often broken off in adults). Small opening above and slightly behind eye (spiracle) absent. Nostril opening closest to eye larger than eye. Barbels fringed. Lower lip with 4 lobes.

Very similar to pallid sturgeon, but with the following differences: belly covered with scale-like plates, except in very small individuals; bases of outer barbels in line with or ahead of bases of inner barbels; length of inner barbel going 3.6 to 5.8 times into length of head; dorsal fin with 30 to 36 rays; anal fin with 18 to 23 rays.

Life colors: Back and sides light brown or buff, belly white.

Size: A small sturgeon, seldom exceeding a length of 30 inches or a weight of 5 pounds. The average length and weight of adults from the Mississippi River is about 21 inches and 1.5 pounds.

Scientific name: *Scaphirhynchus,* Greek, "spade snout"; *platorynchus,* Greek for "broad snout".

DISTRIBUTION AND HABITAT

The shovelnose is the most abundant sturgeon in the Missouri and Mississippi rivers, but has declined greatly since 1900. In recent years the catch of sturgeon, consisting almost entirely of this species, has amounted to only about 5,000 pounds annually. This is only a fraction of the 150,530 pounds of "shovelnose sturgeon" reported for Missouri in statistics compiled by the U. S. Fish Commission for 1899. This fish was evidently present in the Osage River before construction of Bagnell Dam. They are occasionally caught by fishermen in the Current River near Doniphan. I have also examined one specimen caught in Table Rock Reservoir in 1970. This occurrence is surprising since there are no other reports for shovelnose sturgeon in the upper White River system. There is an early published report of a young shovelnose from a small tributary of the lower Meramec River, but the accuracy of this report is doubted.

The shovelnose sturgeon inhabits the open channels of large rivers. It lives on the bottom, often in areas with a swift current and a sand or gravel bottom. It is very tolerant of high turbidity, as indicated by its abundance in the Missouri River.

HABITS AND LIFE HISTORY

The shovelnose sturgeon feeds entirely from the bottom, using its highly protrusible mouth to suck up its food. Larvae of aquatic insects, consisting principally of true flies (Diptera) and caddisflies, make up the bulk of the diet of this species in the Missouri and Mississippi rivers.[20, 21]

Little is known about the spawning habits of this fish. Evidently spawning occurs in the open channels of large rivers in a strong current over rocky or gravelly bottoms. The height of the spawning season in the Mississippi River is about May 10.[22] I have taken young that were an inch long from the Missouri River in late June. Shovelnose sturgeon mature and spawn at an age of 5 to 7 years.[23]

IMPORTANCE

The shovelnose is the only sturgeon that is still of commercial importance in Missouri. Most are taken in trammel nets drifted in the current. Many are also taken on trot lines baited with worms or minnows and set in drop-off areas near the lower ends of sand bars.

The demand for shovelnose sturgeon often exceeds the supply and market values are among the highest of all commercial species.

Pallid Sturgeon

Scaphirhynchus albus (Forbes and Richardson)

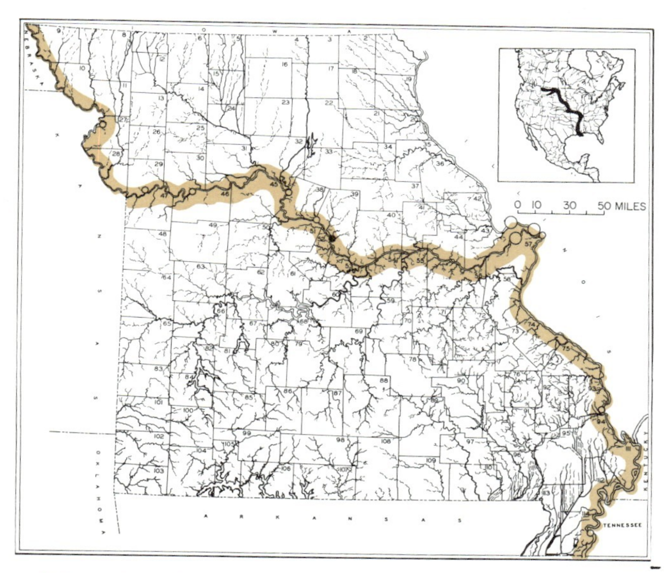

Other local names: White sturgeon, White shovelnose, White hackleback

DESCRIPTION

Illustration: Page 60, 2b.
Characters: Very similar to shovelnose sturgeon but with these differences: belly without plates at all ages; bases of outer barbels slightly farther back than bases of inner barbels; length of inner barbel going 6.3 to 8 times into length of head; dorsal fin with 37 to 42 rays; anal fin with 24 to 28 rays.

Life colors: Averaging lighter than shovelnose sturgeon, the back and sides greyish-white rather than buff.

Size: Larger than shovelnose sturgeon. Early reports indicate that specimens weighing as much as 65 pounds were formerly taken in the Missouri River. However, individuals weighing more than 10 pounds were uncommon.

Scientific name: *Scaphirhynchus,* Greek, "spade snout"; *albus,* Latin, meaning "white," in reference to the color.

DISTRIBUTION AND HABITAT

The pallid sturgeon was not recognized as a species until 1905, so little is known concerning its early abundance and distribution. At present it is exceedingly rare in Missouri waters. It is confined principally to the Missouri and lower Mississippi rivers, penetrating only a few miles into the Mississippi upstream from the mouth of the Missouri.

It is a bottom-dwelling fish of large, turbid rivers where it lives in a strong current over a firm, sandy or gravelly bottom.

HABITS AND LIFE HISTORY

Little is known about the biology of this fish. It feeds on aquatic insects and small fishes[22] and spawns between June 1 and August 1.[24]

PADDLEFISHES

Polyodontidae

The paddlefish was a source of amazement to the first white explorers to reach the Mississippi Valley and this curious fish has been of interest to layman and scientist alike ever since. In appearance and habits it ranks among the most unusual fishes found in Missouri waters. A distinctive feature which immediately sets the paddlefish apart from all other Missouri fishes is the long, paddle-shaped snout whose function is still not known. Although it is one of the larger freshwater fishes of North America, it feeds throughout life on microscopic plants and animals that serve as food for many smaller fishes only during the earliest life history stages. In spite of extensive efforts by fisheries scientists to work out the early life history of the paddlefish, its young were not found until 1932 and it was not until 1960 that fertilized eggs of this species were found in the Osage River above Lake of the Ozarks.

The paddlefish is a hold-over from an ancient family of freshwater fishes represented by only two living species. It is confined to the Mississippi Valley, but its only living relative is *Psephurus gladius* of the Yangtze Valley in China, half a world away.

Paddlefish

Polyodon spathula (Walbaum)

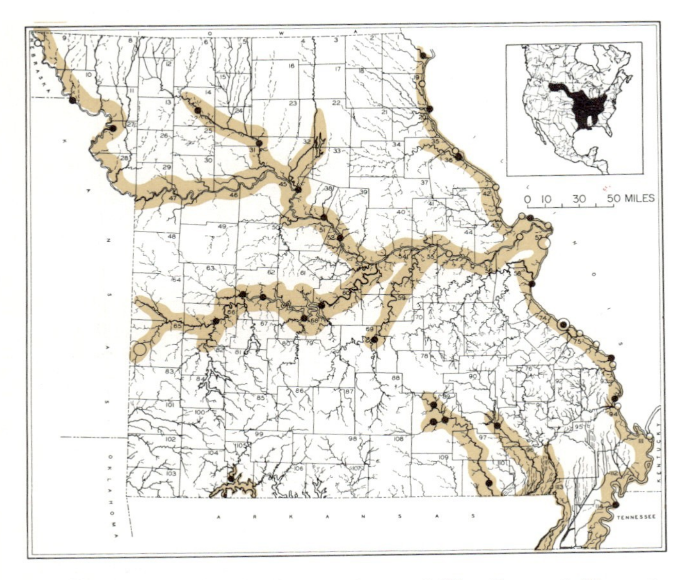

Other local names: Spoonbill, Spoonbill cat, Shovelnose cat, Boneless cat

DESCRIPTION

Illustration: Page 22, 3a; **36.**

Characters: A shark-like fish with a greatly elongated, paddle-shaped snout. The snout in small individuals is more than one-third of the fish's total length. Mouth large, without teeth (except in young), and located far back on underside of head. Eyes very small, placed just above front edge of mouth and directed down and forward rather than directly out to the side. Rear margin of gill cover prolonged into a fleshy, pointed flap. Tail fin deeply forked, the upper lobe longer than lower lobe. Skin without scales except for a patch on upper lobe of tail fin. Gill rakers numerous and usually long and slender. Skeleton composed of cartilage rather than bone.

Life colors: Ranging from bluish-gray to nearly black on the upper parts, grading to white on belly.

Size: One of the largest North American freshwater fishes, reported to attain a weight of 160 pounds or more and a length of about seven feet. Paddlefish caught in Missouri commonly exceed 60 pounds and the largest reported from the Osage River weighed 110 pounds.

Scientific name: *Polyodon,* Greek, meaning "many tooth," probably in reference to the numerous long gill rakers; *spathula,* Latin, a "spatula" or "blade."

DISTRIBUTION AND HABITAT

The paddlefish was formerly abundant over much of the Mississippi Valley but has undergone a drastic decline since 1900. Overharvest and destruction of habitat have contributed to this decline. In Missouri, only the Mississippi, Missouri, and Osage rivers presently support substantial populations. Most other records are based on seasonal migrants of this highly mobile species. They are present in Table Rock Lake as a result of stocking. One of the largest remaining populations of paddlefish in the Mississippi Valley is in Lake of the Ozarks and the upper Osage River. Truman Dam, now under construction on the Osage River near Warsaw, will inundate the only known spawning grounds for this population. Unless means can be found to maintain it artificially, a drastic decline of the population in Lake of the Ozarks can be expected.

The habitat requirements of the paddlefish are very exacting. During most of its life it inhabits quiet or slow-flowing waters rich in the microscopic life (zooplankton) on which it feeds. However, when spawning, it must have access to a large, free-flowing river with gravel bars subject to sustained inundation during spring floods.

Under natural conditions large free-flowing rivers of the Mississippi Valley, with their innumerable oxbows and backwaters for feeding and extensive gravel bars for spawning, provided ideal habitat. But stream channelization and drainage of bottomland lakes has eliminated much of the feeding habitat. Now the largest populations are in man-made impoundments that likewise provide favorable feeding habitat. However, to support a population such an impoundment must be fed by a river that meets the fish's exacting spawning requirements. These conditions are met by Lake of the Ozarks and the upper Osage River, accounting for the large population that exists there.

HABITS AND LIFE HISTORY

The paddlefish is primarily a fish of open water rather than of the bottom, swimming about continuously, apparently aimlessly, near the surface or in shallow areas. It frequently leaps clear of the water and the sudden eruption of a large paddlefish through the surface of a placid stream or lake is a spectacular and startling sight. They are very mobile and probably do not have a definite home range. Movements of as much as 260 miles in 6 weeks have been recorded.[25]

Food of the paddlefish consists primarily of microcrustaceans and insect larvae filtered from the water.[26, 27] It feeds by swimming slowly through areas where food is concentrated, mouth agape, passing water through the elaborate filtering device of its long, closely set gill rakers. Mayfly larvae that burrow in the bottom are also eaten occasionally, but the way in which these are captured is not known. Apparently the paddle-shaped snout is not used to stir up the bottom, as might be supposed. The snout is covered by an elaborate system of sense organs and perhaps functions primarily as a device for locating concentrations of food organisms. Instances of paddlefish eating other fishes have been reported.[28]

Present knowledge concerning reproduction and early development is based largely on studies made in the Osage River, Missouri, since 1960.[29, 30] Spawning occurs in April or May and is preceded by a migration of adults out of Lake of the Ozarks. They move upstream at least as far as Osceola, 55 miles above the lake. Upstream migration occurs during high water after the stream has warmed up to 50° F. The silt-free gravel bars where the eggs are deposited are exposed to the air or covered only by very shallow water at normal water levels. Floods of several days' duration are required for the adults to finish spawning and the eggs to hatch. Since such floods do not come at the proper time every year, spawning is not successful some years.

The complete spawning act has not been observed, but it is believed that a single female accompanied by several males makes a spawning "rush" for a considerable distance over the spawning area, at which time the eggs and sperm are released. The adhesive eggs sink to the bottom and stick to the first object they touch. Eggs hatch in 9 days at a temperature of about 57° F. The larvae begin a persistent swimming action immediately upon hatching and are swept from the gravel bar by currents. The snout does not begin to grow until 2 or 3 weeks after hatching, but grows rapidly thereafter and soon attains its typical proportions.

Early growth is rapid. Young nearly 6 inches in length have been collected from overflow pools of the Missouri River in early July. Two specimens kept in a fertilized pond reached a length of about 3 feet and a weight of 6 pounds when they were 17 months old.[31] Paddlefish in Lake of the Ozarks attain a length of 10 to 14 inches their first year and about 21 inches their second year. Seventeen-year-old fish average nearly 60 inches and 37 pounds.[5] The largest individuals are invariably females. Paddlefish are very long-lived. Individuals 20 years old are common and some live 30 years or more.

IMPORTANCE

For a time near the turn of the century the paddlefish ranked as the most important commercial fish in the Mississippi Valley. Full utilization of this fish did not begin until about 1895 after a decline of the sturgeon fishery. In 1899 the total harvest was nearly 2,500,000 pounds. It was valued not only for its flesh, but also as a source of caviar. The fishery peaked about 1900. Overharvest was responsible for this decline, as it had been for sturgeon prior to 1895. The commercial catch in Missouri was about 190,000 pounds in 1899, but in recent years has generally amounted to less than 5,000 pounds annually.

The principal value of the paddlefish in Missouri is as a sport fish. The largest sport fishery in the United States is in the Osage River above Lake of the Ozarks. The total harvest during the two-month spring snagging season amounts to about 100 tons annually.[5] In some years many are caught in the Osage River below Bagnell Dam and lesser numbers are taken by sport fishermen from the Missouri and Mississippi rivers. Because it is one of the most primitive rayed fishes, the paddlefish is of considerable significance in biological research. The Osage River population has been an important source of research material.

FISHING METHODS

Because the paddlefish will not take a bait, few are caught by conventional fishing methods. Virtually all of those taken by sport fishermen are caught by blind snagging. The gear used consists of a strong rod threaded with heavy monofilament line to which a heavy sinker and one or two treble hooks are attached. This gear is fished either by casting from shore or by trolling from a boat. In either case, a jerking motion is given to the hooks so they will penetrate the tough skin of any paddlefish contacted. This method is effective only where large concentrations are present. The return would not be worth the effort when the paddlefish are dispersed throughout a lake or other large body of water. Thus, the principal fishery is in the spring, when the fish are concentrated on the spawning grounds.

Barriers to further upstream movement by spawning migrants provide especially favorable areas for snagging. A low dam at Osceola on the Osage River is a barrier at most river stages, accounting for the good fishing immediately downstream. Seining was the principal method for commercial harvest along the Mississippi River at the turn of the century. Nets nearly two miles long were used and catches of 150 barrels or more in a single haul were reported.[26] Most paddlefish taken by Missouri commercial fishermen today are caught in trammel nets.

GARS

Lepisosteidae

The gars are a small group of primitive bony fishes that are a characteristic element in the fish fauna of the Mississippi Valley. They range from southern Canada south to Cuba and Central America in fresh and brackish waters.

They are easily recognized. All are slender, cylindrical fishes with the jaws developed into a long beak armed with many prominent teeth. The body is covered with hard, diamond-shaped, nonoverlapping scales arranged in oblique rows. The head and beak are without scales but are very hard and bony. Gars are thus provided with a continuous, nearly inflexible sheath of armor making them immune to the attacks of most would-be predators. The dorsal and anal fins are placed nearly opposite each other, far back near the tail. The tail fin is rounded, with the backbone curved upward and extending part way into the upper part of the fin. Five species occur in the United States, of which four are found in Missouri.

Gars are characteristic of the warm, sluggish backwaters of lowland rivers and lakes. In areas of favorable habitat, large numbers are often observed basking quietly in the sun just beneath the water's surface. They have the curious habit of rising to the surface of the water at frequent intervals, opening and closing the jaws with a loud snap, and then sinking once again from sight. This behavior has been termed "breaking" and its purpose is to renew the supply of air in the swim bladder. In gars the swim bladder is connected to the throat and is richly supplied with blood vessels. Thus it can function much as do the lungs of air-breathing animals. This auxiliary oxygen supply permits them to survive in waters so low in oxygen as to be unsuitable for most other fishes.

They feed to a large extent on other fishes. Prey is captured by stalking rather than by active pursuit. The gar propels itself toward its prey by rapid vibrating motions of its fins, appearing for all the world like a stick or log drifting slowly with the current. When within striking distance it makes a quick lunge and grasps its prey sideways in its jaws. The many sharp teeth make escape impossible. When the prey has ceased to struggle it is turned in the jaws and taken down head first.

Because they feed upon or compete for food with more desirable fishes, gars are often considered to be a worthless nuisance. On the other side of the ledger, they may serve as a natural control in preventing overpopulation and unbalanced fish populations. They are seldom taken on hook and line and are rarely used as food. Their eggs are reported to be highly toxic to warm-blooded animals.

The hard, bony jaws of gars do not readily take a hook and special techniques are required to capture them consistently with rod and reel. One technique consists of using a frayed nylon lure in which the fish's teeth become entangled when it strikes. No hook is used and the lure is attached to a wire leader to keep the sharp teeth from severing the line. Another technique is to snare them using a loop of fine wire with a baited hook centered in the loop. The loop is jerked tight when the fish strikes at the bait, which is most often a minnow. Because they often bask near the surface, gars provide a ready target for the bow hunter. They can provide considerable sport when taken by these methods and deserve to be more widely utilized.

Key to the Gars

1a. Snout long and narrow, its least width (A) going more than 10 times into its length (B); width of upper jaw at nostrils (C) less than eye diameter (D).
Longnose gar
Lepisosteus osseus ..... **Page 70**

1b. Snout short and broad, its least width (A) going less than 10 times into its length (B); width of upper jaw at nostrils (C) greater than eye diameter (D).
Go to **2**

2a. *(From 1b.)* Snout very short and broad; distance from tip of snout to corner of mouth (A) shorter than rest of head (B); size large, length and weight commonly exceeding 3 feet and 8 pounds.
Alligator gar
Lepisosteus spatula .... **Page 68**

2b. *(From 1b.)* Snout longer and not as broad; distance from tip of snout to corner of mouth (A) longer than rest of head (B); size small, length and weight not exceeding 3 feet and 8 pounds.
Go to **3**

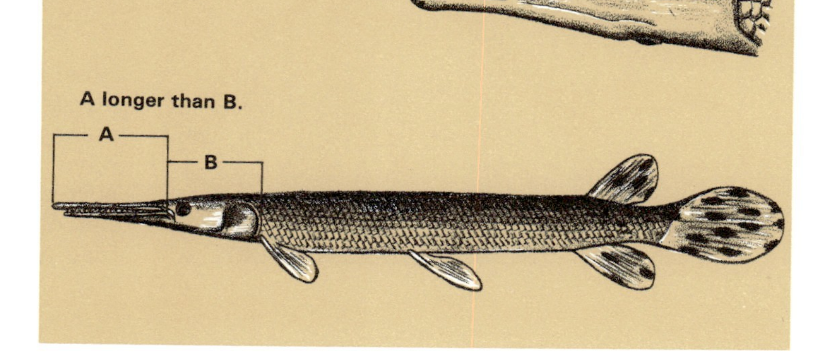

3a. *(From 2b.)* Top of head, pectoral fins and pelvic fins with dark, roundish spots; scales in lateral series (including small scales at base of tail fin) usually 54 to 58.
Spotted gar
Lepisosteus oculatus . . . **Page 70**

3b. *(From 2b.)* Top of head, pectoral fins and pelvic fins without dark, roundish spots; scales in lateral series usually 60 to 64.
Shortnose gar
Lepisosteus platostomus
. . . . **Page 69**

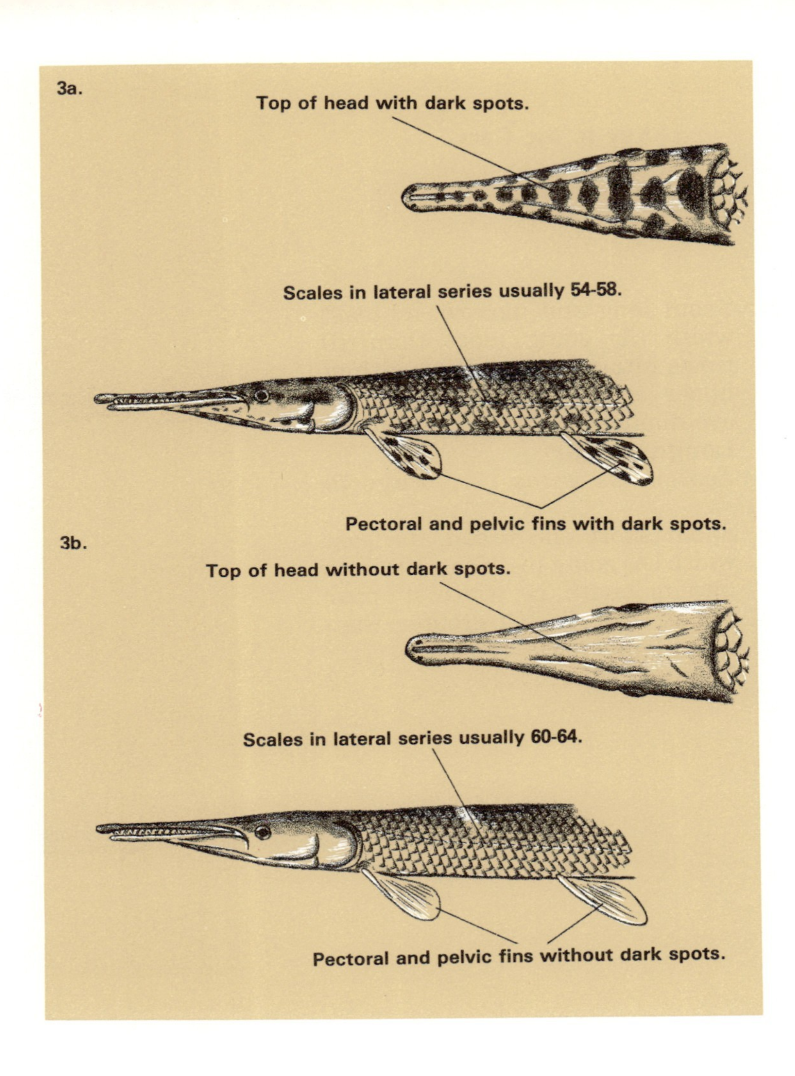

Alligator Gar

Lepisosteus spatula Lacépède

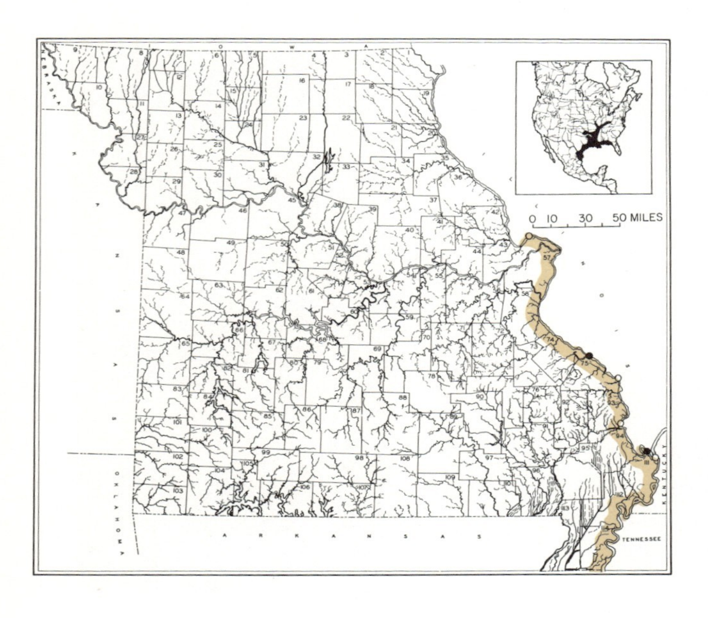

DESCRIPTION

Illustration: Page 67, 2a.

Characters: A gar with a very short and broad snout. Least width of snout going about 3 to 5 times into its length. Distance from tip of snout to corner of mouth shorter than rest of head. Large teeth in upper jaw in two rows on each side. Scales in a diagonal row from scale at front of anal fin to scale on midline of back, both included, usually 23 to 25.

Life colors: Adults brownish or dark olive above, becoming lighter towards belly. Unpaired fins often with numerous roundish black spots. Young with a blackish band along midside and a narrow, white stripe along midline of back.

Size: By far the largest of the gars and one of the largest freshwater fishes in North America. Specimens nearly 10 feet long and weighing 300 pounds have been reported. The largest specimen reported in recent years was from the Missouri section of the Mississippi River. It was 6 feet, 8 inches long and weighed 130 pounds.

Scientific name: *Lepisosteus,* Greek, "bony scale"; *spatula,* Latin for "spoon", in reference to the broad snout.

DISTRIBUTION AND HABITAT

The alligator gar is known in Missouri only from the Mississippi River, where it is rare. Barnickol and Starrett[32] examined 85 specimens from the Missouri section of the Mississippi, of which 80 were taken at Cairo, Illinois. It is not known to ascend the Mississippi River much above the mouth of the Missouri. The only recent records to come to my attention are two large specimens caught by fishermen in 1965. One, weighing 110 pounds, was taken near Chester, Illinois. The other, weighing 130, pounds was taken near Cairo. Photographs of these specimens were furnished by Dr. Philip W. Smith of the Illinois Natural History Survey.

This fish is an inhabitant of the sluggish pools and overflow waters of large rivers. It seems to tolerate slightly higher salinities than the other gars.

HABITS AND LIFE HISTORY

Little is known of the habits and life history of this huge fish. Because of its great size and strength, it often breaks up the nets of fishermen.

In freshwater, its food probably consists mainly of fish, but it is also known to eat ducks and other water birds.[33] In brackish waters of Mississippi alligator gar feed heavily on marine catfish, but also eat dead fish and other refuse discarded around docks and piers.[34] Young alligator gar have been found in Lake Texoma, Oklahoma, in July, and spawning is thought to occur at that locality during the first half of May.[35]

Shortnose Gar

Lepisosteus platostomus Rafinesque

Other local names: Billy gar, Short-bill gar, Stub-nose gar.

DESCRIPTION

Illustration: Page 68, 3b.

Characters: This gar has a moderately short, broad snout. Least width of snout going about 6 to 10 times into its length. Distance from tip of snout to corner of mouth equal to or longer than rest of head. Large teeth in upper jaw in a single row on each side.

Very similar to spotted gar, but with roundish black spots absent or poorly defined on top of head and paired fins. Also, scales in a diagonal row from scale at front of anal fin to scale on midline of back, both included, usually number 20 to 23, and scales in lateral line usually number 60 to 64.

Life colors: Upper parts brownish or olive, grading to white below. Unpaired fins often with definite roundish black spots; spots occasionally somewhat developed on top of head and paired fins in specimens from clear water. Young less than 10 inches long have a broad, black stripe along midside.

Size: One of the smaller gars, reaching a length and weight of about 31 inches and 3.5 pounds.

Scientific name: *Lepisosteus,* Greek, "bony scale"; *platostomus,* Greek, meaning "broad mouth".

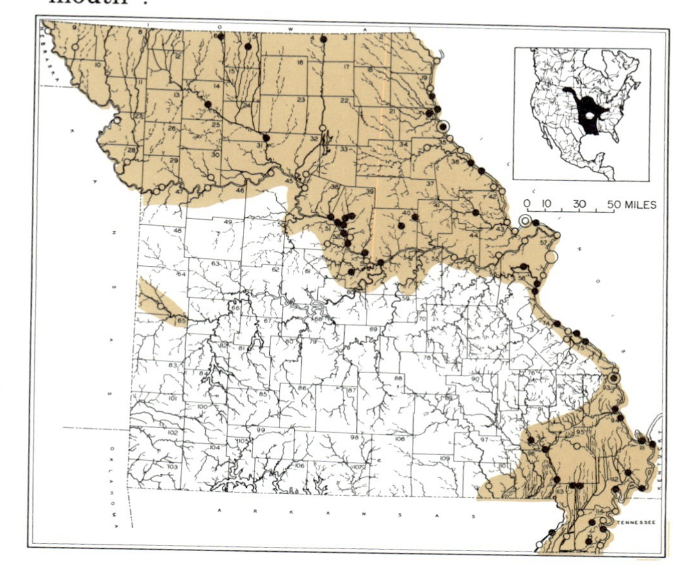

DISTRIBUTION AND HABITAT

The shortnose is the commonest gar over much of Missouri outside of the Ozarks. It is often found along major rivers, in quiet pools, backwaters and oxbow lakes, but also occurs in the large, permanent pools of Prairie creeks. It is more tolerant of high turbidity than other gars.

HABITS AND LIFE HISTORY

The shortnose is somewhat more generalized in its food habits than the spotted and longnose gars, often feeding on insects and crayfish in addition to fish.[36] The first food of the shortnose gar is mostly insect larvae and small crustaceans, but fish appear in the diet by the time the young gar are 1¼ inches in length.

Spawning has been reported at this latitude from mid-May into July, varying from year to year in response to differences in temperature and other climatic factors.[37] The eggs are scattered over vegetation and other submerged objects in quiet, shallow water. The spawning fish are sometimes in pairs, but often a single female is accompanied by two or more males. The yellowish eggs are about the size of large buckshot. These hatch about 8 days after spawning and the young become active about 7 days later when the yolk sac has been absorbed.

The young gars are slender and slate-grey in color, resembling small sticks as they drift about near the water's surface. Early growth is extremely rapid. A large series of young collected in mid-July from an overflow pool of the Missouri River in central Missouri ranged from 3.6 to 7 inches long. The shortnose gar attains sexual maturity when 15 or more inches long and 3 years old.

Spotted Gar

Lepisosteus oculatus (Winchell)

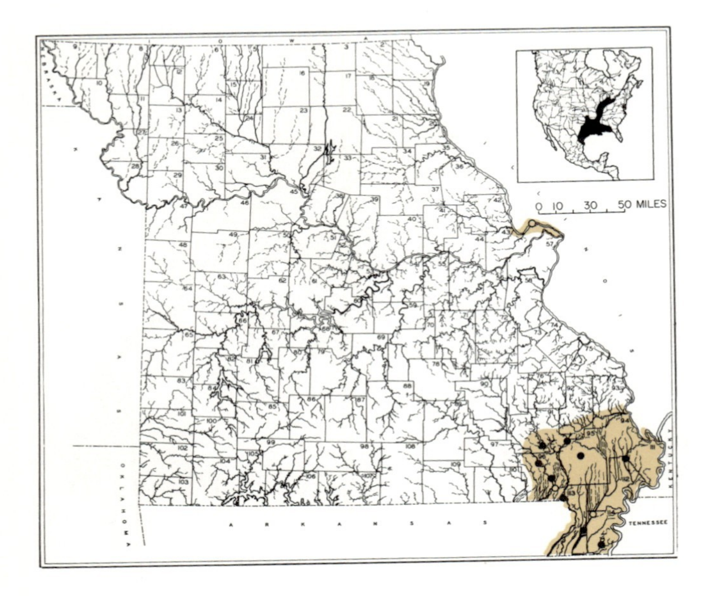

DESCRIPTION

Illustration: Page 68, 3a.
Characters: Very similar to shortnose gar, but with many well defined roundish black spots on top of head and paired fins. Also, scales in a diagonal row from scale at front of anal fin to scale on midline of back, both included, usually number 17 to 20, and scales in lateral line usually number 54 to 58.
Life colors: Upper parts brownish or olive, grading to white below, with well defined roundish black spots on top of head, snout, and all fins.
Size: Reaching a length and weight in Missouri of about 36 inches and 8 pounds.
Scientific name: *Lepisosteus,* Greek, "bony scale"; *oculatus,* Latin, meaning "provided with eyes," in reference to the numerous roundish dark spots on the head and body.

DISTRIBUTION AND HABITAT

The spotted gar is rather common in the Lowlands and occurs rarely along the Mississippi River. It is known from the Neosho River in southeastern Kansas, and therefore is to be expected in extreme southwestern Missouri. It is not abundant anywhere in Missouri and is outnumbered at most localities by the shortnose or longnose gar.

The spotted gar seems less tolerant of continuous turbidity and shows a greater affinity for submerged aquatic vegetation than other Missouri gars. It achieves its greatest abundance in quiet, clear waters having much aquatic vegetation or standing timber.

HABITS AND LIFE HISTORY

The following information is from a study of the spotted gar in Mingo Swamp of southeastern Missouri.[38] The first food of young spotted gar at this locality is mosquito larvae and small crustaceans, but fish appear in the diet at an early age and thereafter are the main food. Mosquitofish and topminnows are the principal species eaten by young gar. Fishes, mostly gizzard shad, make up 90% of the adult spotted gar's diet. Freshwater shrimp, crayfish, and insects represent most of the remaining 10%.

Spotted gar were observed spawning in Mingo Swamp in late April, in rapidly-flowing water coming from a tract of flooded timber. Young 2 to 3 inches in length were present by the latter part of May.

In Mingo Swamp this gar reaches a length of about 10 inches at the end of the first year of life and is about 20 inches long when 3 years old. Males grow faster than females for the first two years, but thereafter females grow more rapidly and attain the largest size. Males mature when 2 or 3 years old, while females do not mature until their third or fourth year. The oldest fish found in the Mingo study, a female, was at least 18 years old.

Longnose Gar

Lepisosteus osseus (Linnaeus)

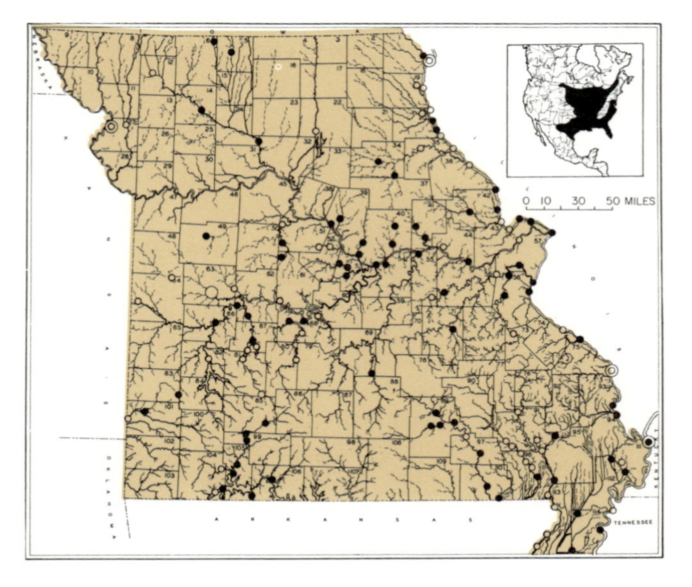

Other local names: Needlenose gar, Billfish, Billy gar

DESCRIPTION

Illustration: Page 67, 1a; **37.**

Characters: A gar with a very long, narrow snout. Least width of snout going about 15 or 20 times into its length. Width of snout at nostrils less than eye diameter. Large teeth in upper jaw in a single row on each side. Scales in a diagonal row from scale at front of anal fin to scale on midline of back, both included, usually 17 to 19. Scales in lateral line usually 60 to 63.

Life colors: Upper parts brown or dark olive, grading to white on belly. Unpaired fins with numerous roundish black spots; body often spotted in specimens from clear water. Young with a conspicuous black stripe along midside.

Size: A large gar, commonly reaching a length of 3 feet or more. The largest specimen reported from Missouri was 53.5 inches long and weighed 21 pounds.

Scientific name: *Lepisosteus,* Greek, "bony scale"; *osseus,* Latin, meaning "of bone".

DISTRIBUTION AND HABITAT

The longnose is the most widely distributed gar in Missouri, probably occurring in nearly every major stream of the state. It is the only species found in the clear, high-gradient streams of the central Ozarks and is most abundant in the large reservoirs of that region. Elsewhere in the state it is less abundant at most localities than the shortnose gar.

The longnose gar typically inhabits the sluggish pools, backwaters, and oxbows along large, moderately clear streams. It thrives in man-made impoundments. The adults are usually found in the larger, deeper pools. The young occur in shallow backwaters, often around thick growths of aquatic vegetation. Spawning is preceded by upstream movements into smaller and higher gradient streams than those occupied at other times, and young remain in these streams during the first summer of life.

HABITS AND LIFE HISTORY

Except for a brief period after hatching, the longnose gar feeds almost entirely on fish. A central Missouri study revealed that young-of-the-year feed mostly on minnows, while gizzard shad are the most common item in the diet of older gar.[39]

Adults appear in the spawning streams by late April and spawning has been observed from early May to mid-June. When spawning, adults gather in large numbers over the gravelly stretches of shallow riffles. No nest is prepared, but the gravel is cleaned by the spawning activities. Males far outnumber females on the spawning areas.

The females are invariably much larger than the males, and each female is accompanied by from one to several males as she lies quietly on the riffle or cruises slowly about a nearby pool. The female does not deposit all of her eggs at one time, and the spawning act is repeated at widely spaced and irregular intervals. Spawning by one female and her retinue of males stimulates similar activity by others and frequently all the individuals in the vicinity gather in a compact group and vibrate rapidly. Often they break the surface, creating splashing sounds that can be heard for a considerable distance. The large, adhesive eggs are mixed in the gravel as a result of these activities. They hatch in 6 to 8 days. The newly hatched young have an adhesive disc on the snout by which they attach themselves to submerged objects until the yolk sac is absorbed.

Early growth of the longnose gar is rapid. In central Missouri a length of about 20 inches is reached the first year.[40] Males mature when they are 3 or 4 years old and about 28 inches in length. Females do not mature until they are 6 years old and about 33 inches in length. Males rarely live more than 11 years and do not exceed 3 feet in length, but females sometimes live 20 years or more and attain a length of at least 4½ feet.

BOWFINS

Amiidae

This family contains only one living species, the bowfin of the eastern United States. However, fossil bowfins that lived 180 million years ago have been found in Europe. The bowfin and the gars are surviving remnants of an ancient group that was ancestral to most kinds of fishes living today.

Bowfin

Amia calva Linnaeus

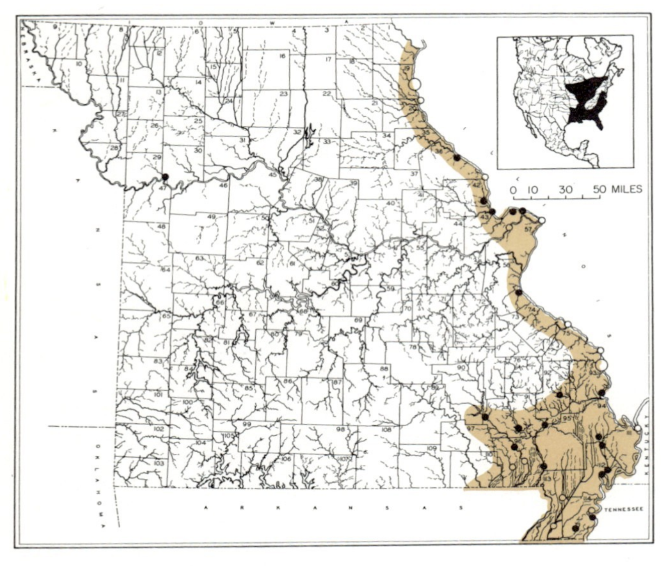

Other local names: Dogfish, Grindle, Grinnel, Cypress trout, Mud fish

DESCRIPTION

Illustration: Page 26, 12a; **36.**

Characters: A stout-bodied, nearly cylindrical fish. Dorsal fin extending more than half the length of the back and containing more than 45 rays. Tail fin rounded, with rear part of backbone flexed upward and extending partway into upper part of fin. Mouth large, and equipped with many sharp teeth. Body covered with smooth-edged (cycloid) scales; head without scales. Gular plate (thin, bony plate between lower jaws) present. Each nostril with a prominent barbel-like flap. Fins without spines.
Life colors: Back and upper sides mottled olive-green, shading to pale green on belly. Dorsal and tail fins dark green with darker bands or bars; lower fins bright green. Young with a prominent black spot, margined by yellow or orange, near base of upper rays of tail fin. Spot persisting in adults, but less distinct in females.
Size: Most adults are 15 to 27 inches in length and weigh 1 to 5 pounds. The largest authenticated specimen known from Missouri weighed 19 pounds.
Scientific name: *Amia,* an ancient Greek name for some fish, probably the bonito; *calva,* Latin, meaning "smooth".

DISTRIBUTION AND HABITAT

In Missouri the bowfin is most abundant in the Lowlands. It occurs along the entire length of the Mississippi River, but is more abundant above the mouth of the Missouri River than below.[32] The only authenticated records in the Missouri River drainage of Missouri are one from the Missouri River near St. Charles[41] and another from the Fishing River, Clay County. Others have been reported from the Missouri River drainage of Kansas.[42] Except for the specimen taken near St. Charles, not far from the Mississippi River, all records for the Missouri drainage may be attributable to escape of bowfins stocked in private lakes.

The bowfin occurs in a variety of habitats, but tends to avoid those with swift current or excessively turbid waters. In the Lowlands they are found in a variety of habitats, including swamps, sloughs, borrow pits, ditches, abandoned stream channels, and the pools of sluggish streams. Along the Mississippi River they are more often found in backwaters and oxbows than in the main channel.

HABITS AND LIFE HISTORY

Adult bowfins remain in deeper water or under cover during daylight hours, venturing into shallow water to feed at night. Like gars, the bowfin surfaces periodically to renew the supply of air in the swim bladder which functions as a lung to supplement oxygen supplied by the gills. The habit of surfacing is ordinarily discontinued in cold weather, except under conditions of low oxygen. Under these conditions, they may surface so frequently that they maintain an area of open water in a lake that is otherwise completely frozen over.

In a study of the bowfin in southeastern Missouri,[43] fish represented about 65% of the diet of adults, with crayfish making up most of the remainder. Gizzard shad were eaten more frequently than any other fish, followed by the golden shiner, bullheads, and sunfish. Crayfish were important only in the months of March through June. The first food of young bowfin consisted mostly of water fleas and other microscopic animals, but these were largely replaced by fish by the time the young were 4 inches long.

The bowfin spawns in southeast Missouri from early April into May or early June. The following information on reproductive behavior is from an early study.[44] The eggs are laid in nests constructed by the males in shallow, weedy sites. Vegetation is removed from the nest by biting and rubbing, and the silt is fanned away. This leaves a clean bed of rootlets, sand, or gravel, to which the adhesive eggs become attached. Care of the eggs and young is left entirely to the male.

Eggs hatch 8 to 10 days after spawning and the fry remain in the nest for about nine more days. The newly hatched young have an adhesive organ on their snout by which they attach to objects in the nest. The fry are feeding by the time they leave the nest. They leave in a compact swarm, still guarded by the male. Schooling continues until the young are about 4 inches long, when they take up the solitary existence of the adults.

In southeast Missouri the bowfin is 7 to 9 inches long by the end of its first year and reaches a length of about 20 inches when 5 or 6 years old.[43] Sexual maturity is reached at an age of 2 or 3 years. Ten years is about the maximum longevity under natural conditions, but individuals kept in captivity have lived as long as 30 years.

IMPORTANCE

Many fishermen hold the bowfin in contempt, but this attitude is not entirely justified. Some fish fight more spectacularly, but few have the bowfin's strength or endurance. In southeast Missouri it makes up about 4.5% of the sport fishing creel.[45] The bowfin is generally classed as a poor food fish. The commercial catch in Missouri is negligible.

ANGLING

Most bowfin are caught by fishermen who are seeking other species. They are taken on a variety of live baits, including minnows, crayfish, worms, and frogs. Artificial lures that are effective for largemouth bass will also take the bowfin.

EELS

Anguillidae

Many kinds of eels are found in the sea, but only one species occurs in the fresh waters of eastern North America. The marine eels all belong to different families than our species, whose closest relatives are found in Europe and Asia.

American Eel

Anguilla rostrata (Lesueur)

DESCRIPTION

Illustration: Page 25, 9a.

Characters: A brownish-colored fish with a slender, snake-like body and a small, pointed head. Scales present, but so small that body appears naked. Dorsal fin long, extending more than half length of body, and continuous with tail and anal fins. Pectoral fins present; pelvic fins absent. Gill slit single and small, located just in front of pectoral fin. Jaws present and equipped with numerous small teeth. Lower jaw projecting well beyond upper jaw.

Life colors: Back and sides yellow or olive-brown. Belly pale yellow or white. Fins similar in color to adjacent parts of body.

Size: Most eels caught in Missouri weigh from ¼ to 3¾ pounds and are 16 to 33 inches long. The largest specimen to come to my attention weighed 4½ pounds and was 37 inches long.

Scientific name: *Anguilla,* Latin name for eel; *rostrata,* Latin, meaning "beaked", in reference to the snout.

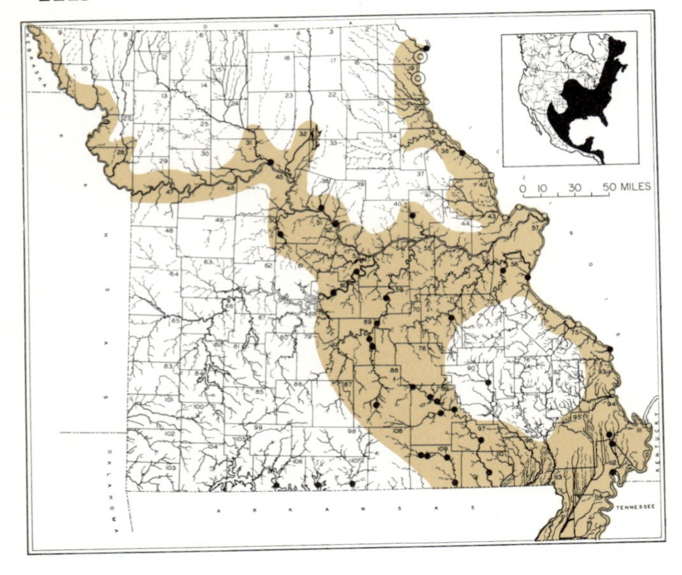

DISTRIBUTION AND HABITAT

The eel probably occurs occasionally in every large stream in the state where its movements are not impeded by dams. The exact distribution and abundance are difficult to determine because it is not readily captured by the kind of equipment ordinarily used in fish surveys. It seems to be more abundant in the southern Ozarks and in the Lowlands than elsewhere. High dams on the Osage and White rivers have eliminated the eel from large areas in the Ozarks. It is present in navigation pools of the upper Mississippi River, but is less abundant there than before the river was impounded.

The eel occurs in a variety of stream types but is most abundant in streams of moderate or large size having continuous flow and moderately clear water. During daylight hours it is invariably found in deep pools about logs, boulders, or other cover.

HABITS AND LIFE HISTORY

The reproductive habits and life history of the eel were a mystery until they were painstakingly worked out during the late 19th and early 20th centuries. Most of the pioneering studies were made by European scientists led by the Danish biologist, Johannes Schmidt, and were summarized in a publication titled, *The Breeding Places of the Eel.*[46] These workers were primarily interested in the European eel, but their findings apply also to our American species.

Although it spends most of its adult life in fresh or brackish waters, the eel breeds in the Sargasso Sea area of the Atlantic Ocean, northeast of Cuba. One of the unsolved mysteries is what happens to the adults after they leave our shores on their spawning migration. No adult eel has ever been taken in the open ocean.[47] The place of spawning has been determined solely through the collection of newly hatched eels.

Spawning occurs in deep water, but nothing is known of the mating activity. Presumably the adults spawn once and die. The eggs have not been identified. Newly hatched eels are transparent, leaf-shaped fish, quite different in appearance from the adults. They are so different, in fact, that when first discovered the small eels were thought to be an entirely new kind of fish and were given the scientific name *Leptocephalus.*

These "leptocephalus larvae," as they are now called, grow and gradually assume a more eel-like shape as they swim and drift with the ocean currents towards the American and European shores. By the time they are ready to enter rivers their resemblance to adult eels is unmistakable and they are called "glass eels" or "elvers". Development is appropriately timed to correspond with the time required for the journey from the spawning grounds to the river mouths. The American eel requires about a year to develop to the elver stage while its European relative, with a longer journey to make, requires nearly 3 years to reach this stage.

Male eels do not move far inland, remaining in brackish or fresh water near the river mouths. The females, on the other hand, penetrate the rivers almost to their sources or until further upstream movement is blocked by dams or other obstructions. It is certain, therefore, that any eel caught in Missouri is a female.

Eels are secretive, hiding by day beneath rocks, submerged logs, or other cover, moving actively about only at night. Their food consists entirely of animal material, either living or dead. Fish and crayfish, supplemented by worms and other animals that wash or fall into the water, make up the bulk of their diet. Males do not grow as large as females, seldom exceeding a length of 18 inches. Females are reported to reach a length of 52 inches and a weight of 7 pounds or more. Females are thought to spend anywhere from 5 to 20 years in fresh water, after which they undertake the long migration to the Sargasso Sea to spawn and die.

IMPORTANCE

Eels are seldom caught in Missouri by either sport or commercial fishermen, and most are taken while fishing for other species. There is a popular prejudice against the eel in this country because of its snake-like appearance, but in Europe it is a popular and important food fish. The flesh is reported to be excellent when fried, smoked, or pickled. The eel puts up a strong fight when taken on hook and line.

HERRINGS

Clupeidae

The herring family is primarily marine and includes some of the most valuable food fishes in the sea. Many are anadromous, spending most of their adult life in salt water but ascending fresh water streams to spawn. Others, including three of the four species found in Missouri, can complete their life cycle in fresh water.

Herrings are silvery, flat-sided fish, easily recognized by the row of sharp-edged, spiny scales or scutes along the midline of the belly. These scutes are readily apparent when the fingers are rubbed forward along the fish's belly. The herrings most nearly resemble the mooneyes but differ in having the dorsal fin far forward of the anal fin. The head is without scales, but the body is covered with thin, smooth-edged (cycloid) scales that are easily dislodged. The lateral line is absent. A small, triangular projection called an axillary process is present just above the base of the pelvic fin, and the eyes are partly covered by transparent membranes called adipose eye lids.

Of the four members of the herring family found in Missouri, none are commonly used as food and only the skipjack herring is taken on hook and line.

Key to the Herrings

1a. Last ray of dorsal fin elongated into a long, slender filament; principal rays of dorsal fin usually 14 or fewer; a dark spot behind upper end of gill opening (spot sometimes absent in large adults).
Go to 2

1b. Last ray of dorsal fin not elongated into a long, slender filament; principal rays of dorsal fin usually 16 or more; no dark spot behind upper end of gill opening.
Go to 3

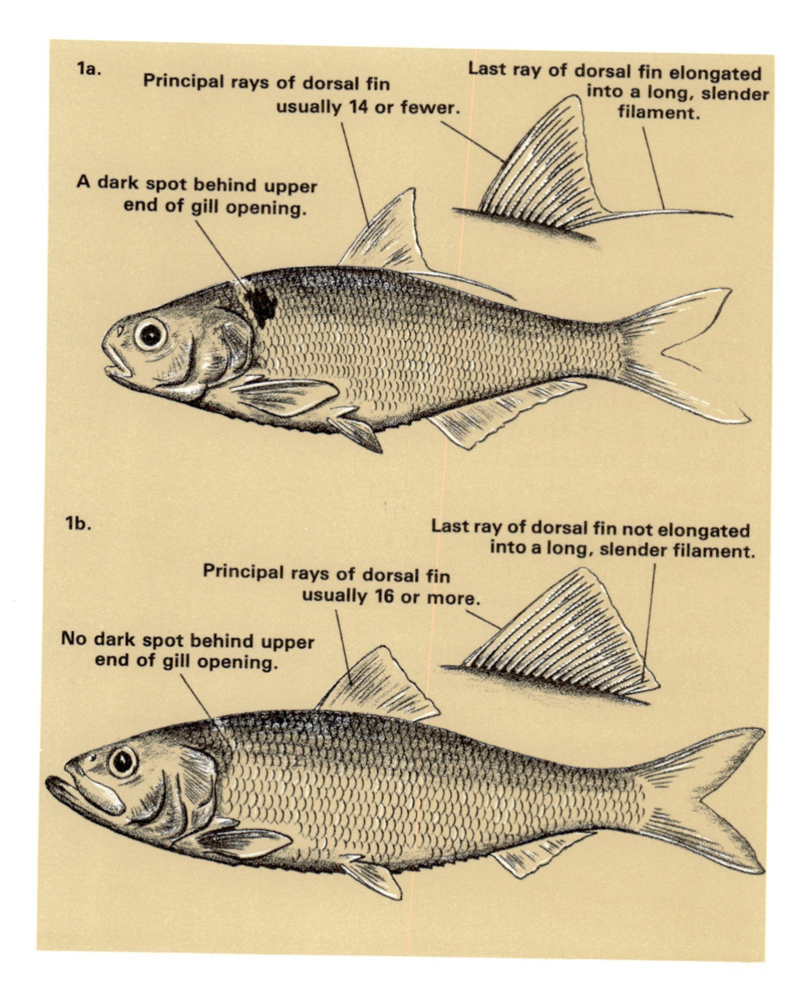

2a. *(From 1a.)* Lower jaw projecting beyond tip of snout; rays of anal fin usually 20 to 25; scales in lateral series usually 50 or fewer; tail fin bright yellow in life.
Threadfin shad
Dorosoma petenense . . . **Page 79**

2b. *(From 1a.)* Lower jaw not projecting beyond tip of snout; rays of anal fin usually 29 to 35; scales in lateral series usually 55 or more; tail fin not yellow in life.
Gizzard shad
Dorosoma cepedianum . **Page 78**

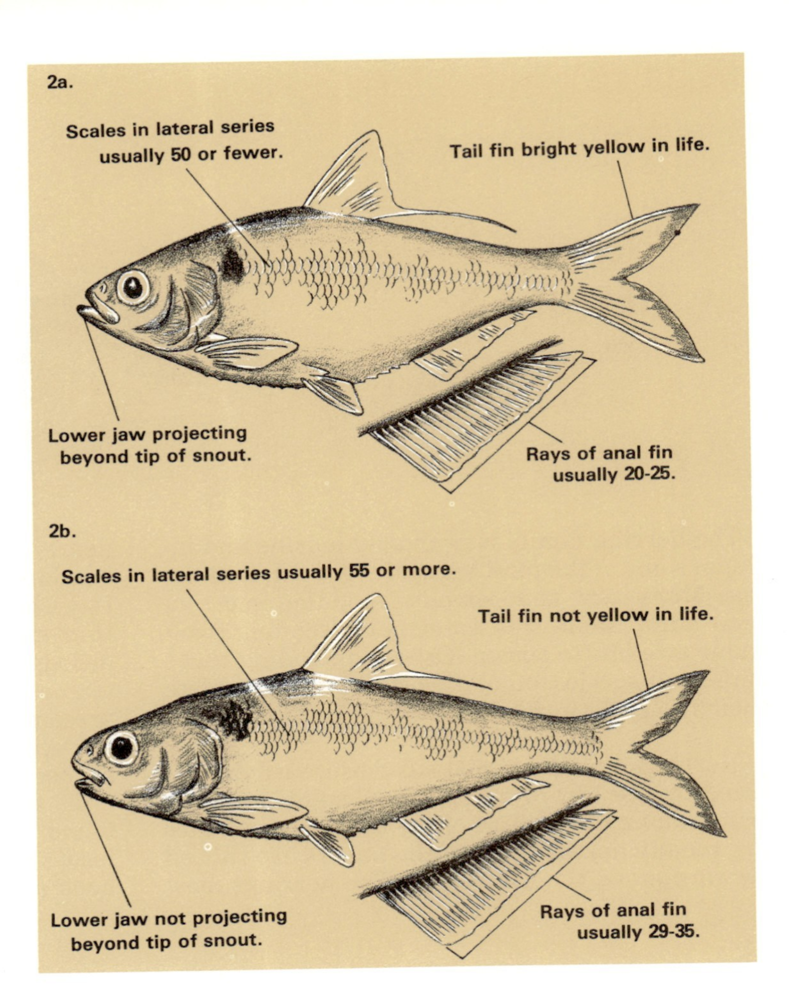

3a. *(From 1b.)* Lower jaw projecting far beyond tip of snout; lower jaw with dark speckles only near tip; teeth on tongue in 2 to 4 rows; gill rakers on lower half of first arch usually fewer than 30.
Skipjack herring
Alosa chrysochloris . . . . **Page 77**

3b. *(From 1b.)* Lower jaw equal to or projecting only slightly beyond tip of snout; lower jaw with dark speckles along much of length; teeth on tongue in single median row; gill rakers on lower half of first arch usually more than 30.
Alabama shad
Alosa alabamae . . . . **Page 77**

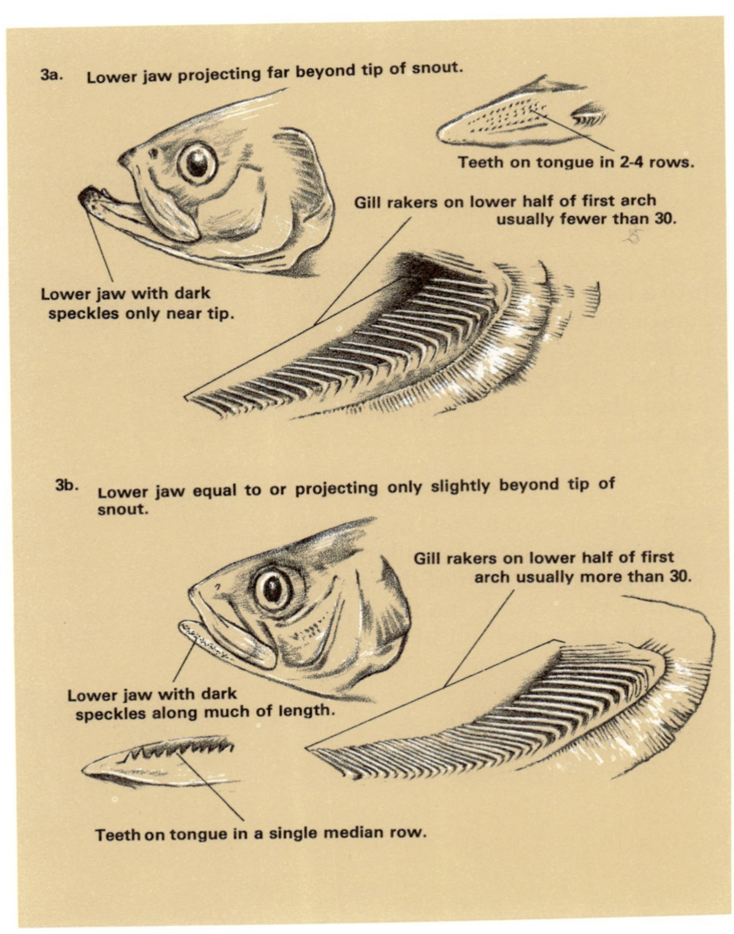

Skipjack Herring

Alosa chrysochloris (Rafinesque)

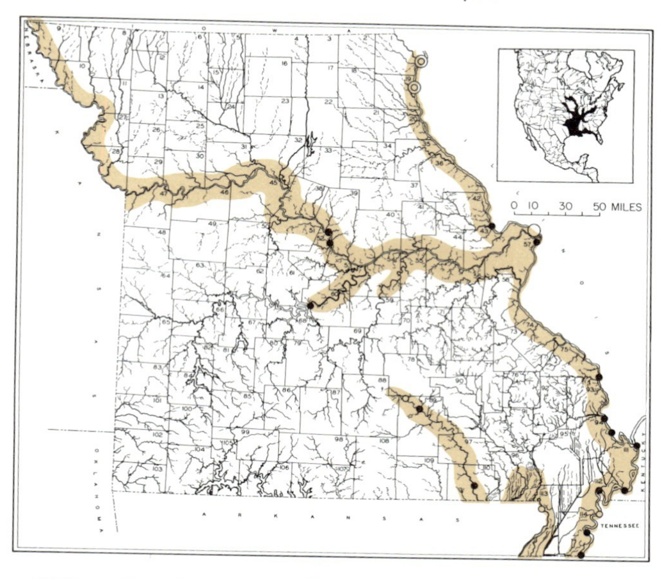

Other local names: Skipjack, River herring

DESCRIPTION

Illustration: Page 76, 3a.

Characters: A slender, streamlined fish with a large, terminal mouth, and a projecting lower jaw. Last ray of dorsal fin not prolonged into a slender filament. Body depth going about 3.6 to 4.3 times into standard length. Dorsal fin with 16 to 18 (usually 17) rays.

Similar to Alabama shad, but differing in the following respects: lower jaw projecting far beyond upper jaw; lower jaw with black pigment confined to its tip; fewer than 30 gill rakers present along lower half of first gill arch; jaw teeth present at all ages; small teeth on tongue in 2 to 4 rows.

Life colors: Upper parts bluish or greenish with silvery reflections, shading to silvery-white on sides and belly.

Size: Adults are commonly 12 to 16 inches in length; the maximum length and weight reported is 21 inches and 3.5 pounds.

Scientific name: *Alosa,* Latin name for shad; *chrysochloris,* Greek for "golden green," in reference to the color of the back.

DISTRIBUTION AND HABITAT

The highly migratory skipjack herring probably occurs at least occasionally in most of the large rivers of the state where its movements are not blocked by dams. At present, the skipjack is most abundant in the Mississippi River downstream from the mouth of the Ohio River. Elsewhere in the state it is taken only occasionally. Early reports indicate that the skipjack herring was more abundant in the upper Mississippi River before that stream was impounded for navigation.[22]

This fish inhabits the open waters of large rivers, often congregating in large numbers in the swift currents below dams. It seems to be intolerant of continuous high turbidity. There are no early records for the skipjack herring in the Missouri River, but I have examined several taken in recent years from the river near Easley in Boone County. This suggests that the skipjack is now more common in the river than formerly. It has probably been favored by the construction of large up-stream impoundments that have reduced turbidity of the Missouri River.

HABITS AND LIFE HISTORY

The skipjack herring is an active fish, moving about continuously in large schools. It often leaps from the water when hooked or when pursuing the minnows and other small fishes that make up the bulk of its diet.

The time and place where the skipjack spawns are not definitely known. Coker thought that it had an extended spawning season, possibly beginning early in May and ending soon after the first of July.[22] In the Mississippi River the young reach a length of about 3 to 5 inches by the end of their first summer of life.

IMPORTANCE

The skipjack is bony, lacking in flavor, and is seldom used as food. But it fights spectacularly when hooked and can provide considerable sport on light tackle. The oil present in its flesh is said by fishermen to be very attractive to catfishes and many skipjacks are caught specifically for use as jug or trotline bait.

ANGLING

Skipjacks may be caught on minnows or on a variety of small spinners and other artificial lures that imitate a minnow. White bucktails are a favorite with Mississippi River fishermen. Two or more lures are often fished simultaneously on the same line and multiple catches on a single cast are not uncommon. The swift water below dams and around the ends of wing dikes are good places to fish for skipjacks.

Alabama Shad

Alosa alabamae Jordan and Evermann

DESCRIPTION

Illustration: Page 76, 3b.

Characters: Similar to skipjack herring, but with the following differences: lower jaw not projecting appreciably beyond upper jaw and with black pigment along most of its length; first gill arch with more than 30 gill rakers along lower half; jaw teeth present only in the young; tongue with small teeth present in a single median row.

Life colors: Upper parts bluish or greenish with silvery reflections, shading to silvery-white on sides and belly.

Size: Reported to reach a length of 18 inches and a weight of 3 pounds.

Scientific name: *Alosa,* Latin name for shad; *alabamae,* "from Alabama".

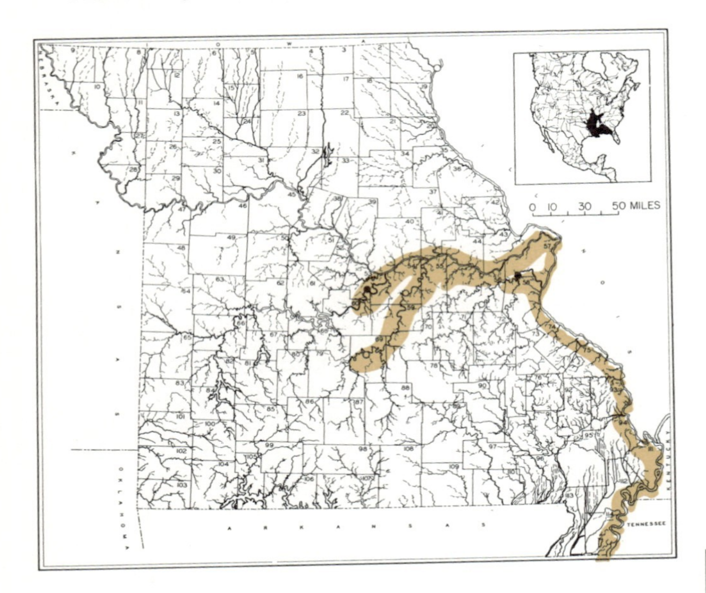

DISTRIBUTION AND HABITAT

Over the past 25 years the Alabama shad has been taken in Missouri on at least eight occasions from the Meramec, Gasconade, and Osage rivers. Previously it had been reported in the Mississippi River system (as the Ohio shad, *Alosa ohiensis* Evermann) only from the Ohio River at Louisville,[48] from the Mississippi River near Keokuk,[22] and from Oklahoma.[49] Evidently it has undergone a marked decline in abundance in the Mississippi River system, because it was said to be common enough in the early 1900's to support a limited commercial fishery.[22, 48]

The Alabama shad is anadromous, spending most of its adult life in the sea and entering fresh water streams only to spawn. In the Osage River the young were captured in swift water about rock wing dikes.

HABITS AND LIFE HISTORY

That the Alabama shad is anadromous in the Mississippi River system, as elsewhere in its range, was suggested by Coker,[22] who noted that it was present in the Mississippi River near Keokuk only from early May to the middle or latter part of July, and that all specimens were in a spawning condition. From this he concluded that its appearance at Keokuk coincided with a spawning migration. Data from Missouri collections support this conclusion. The only adult specimen was collected in July. All of the remaining 90-plus specimens are young-of-the-year collected between late July and early October. The scarcity of adults suggests that they are present only briefly, and the collection of young only in late summer and early fall suggests that the Alabama shad migrates elsewhere after its first summer of life.

Adults do not feed while in fresh water, but the young feed on small fishes and aquatic insects.[50] Young in a collection from the Osage River had attained a length of 3.1 to 4.6 inches by late August.

IMPORTANCE

The flesh of this fish is reported to be comparable in flavor to that of the Atlantic shad, a highly regarded food fish that enters streams along the Atlantic coast. The Alabama shad does not support a commercial fishery, even in the Apalachicola River, Florida, where large spawning runs occur. However, some are taken there by sport fishermen while fishing for other species.

Gizzard Shad

Dorosoma cepedianum (Lesueur)

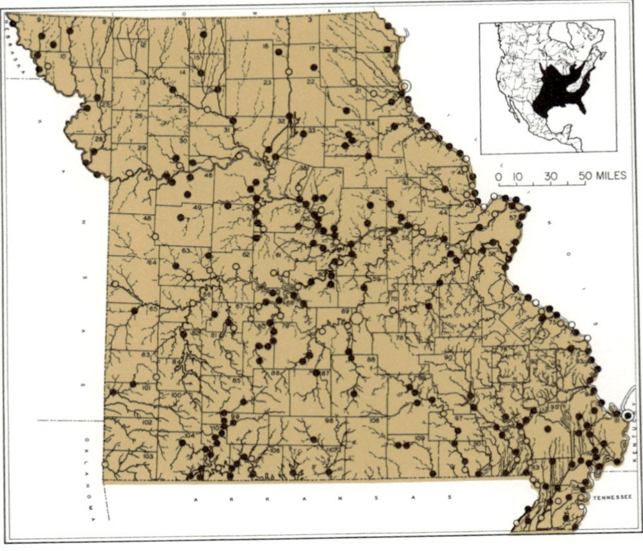

Other local names: Shad, Hickory shad, Herring, Skipjack.

DESCRIPTION

Illustration: Page 76, 2b.

Characters: A moderately deep-bodied herring

with a small, subterminal mouth, and with the last ray of the dorsal fin prolonged into a long, slender filament. Body depth going about 2.3 to 3.1 times into standard length. Dorsal fin with 10 to 13 (most often 12) rays.

Very similar to threadfin shad, but differing in these respects: upper jaw projecting well beyond lower jaw and with a deep notch at its center; chin and floor of mouth not speckled with black pigment; scales in lateral series about 59 to 67; and rays in anal fin usually 29 to 35.

Life colors: Upper parts silvery-blue, grading to silvery-white on lower sides and belly. Upper sides with several horizontal dark streaks. A large, lustrous purple spot, sometimes faint in large adults, just behind upper end of gill opening. Fins dusky, without prominent yellow colors.

Size: Adults are commonly 9 to 14 inches long and weigh a pound or less. Maximum length and weight reported is 20.5 inches and 3 pounds, 7 ounces.

Scientific name: *Dorosoma,* Greek, meaning "lance body," in reference to the body shape of the young; *cepedianum,* named for Citoyen Lacépède, author of *Histoire Naturelle des Poissons.*

DISTRIBUTION AND HABITAT

The gizzard shad is one of the most common and widely distributed of the larger Missouri fishes, occurring at least occasionally in every principal stream system of the state. It is most abundant in reservoirs and large rivers.

This fish inhabits a variety of quiet-water habitats, including natural lowland lakes and ponds, man-made impoundments, and the pools and backwaters of streams. It occurs in both extremely clear and extremely turbid waters, but prefers those where fertility and productivity are high. It avoids streams with very high gradients and those that lack large, permanent pools.

HABITS AND LIFE HISTORY

The gizzard shad travels in large, more or less constantly moving schools, often at or very near the water's surface. It frequently leaps clear of the water or skips along the surface on its side, earning it the common name of "skipjack."

The first food of the gizzard shad consists mostly of microscopic animal life, including protozoa and zooplankton, but soon this diet is supplemented by free-floating algae and small aquatic insect larvae.[51] The adults are primarily "filter-feeders," removing particulate matter from the water by passing it through the net formed by the long, closely-set gill rakers. They also graze over logs and other objects on the bottom.

Spawning occurs at this latitude from early April through May, most often in the shallow water of protected bays and inlets. The eggs and milt are released by a mixed school of males and females as they swim along near the water's surface. The adhesive eggs sink to the bottom, attaching to the first object they touch. Eggs hatch in about 4 days and the young begin to feed about 5 days later. Young gizzard shad are slender fish with terminal mouths, appearing quite different than the adults. By the time the young are 1¼ inches long they have acquired the typical adult shape.

Growth of the gizzard shad is variable, depending on fertility of the water and other factors. In Missouri streams it averages 5.1 inches long by the end of its first year and is about 11 inches long when 3 years old.[52] Comparable growth has been found in Missouri reservoirs. A few gizzard shad live 10 or more years, but 4 to 6 years is the usual life span. Maturity is reached the second or third year.

IMPORTANCE

Fishery workers have long debated the true role of the gizzard shad. It is very prolific, producing numerous young that are extensively used as food by game fishes. But growth is rapid and soon the adults are so large that they are relatively immune to predation. At times adults are so numerous that they are thought to compete for food and space with more desirable species. In Missouri's large reservoirs the importance of the gizzard shad as forage seems to outweigh its nuisance qualities. It forms a short, efficient link in the food chain of the white bass, crappies and largemouth bass, and the well-being of these species seems to depend to a considerable extent on fluctuations in abundance of the gizzard shad.

Because of its specialized food habits it is taken on hook and line only by accident; and its soft, tasteless flesh is of little value as food. It is sometimes used as cut bait for jug or set-line fishing along the Mississippi River.

Threadfin Shad

Dorosoma petenense (Gunther)

DESCRIPTION

Illustration: Page 76, 2a.

Characters: Similar to gizzard shad, but differing in the following respects: upper jaw not projecting beyond lower jaw and only slightly notched at center; chin and floor of mouth speckled with black pigment; scales in lateral series about 42 to 48; and rays in anal fin usually 20 to 25.

Life colors: Similar to gizzard shad, but with much yellow in all fins except dorsal.

Size: Adults in Missouri are usually 4 to 5 inches in length and rarely exceed 6 inches. The maximum length reported is about 8.5 inches.

Scientific name: *Dorosoma,* Greek, meaning "lance body," in reference to the body shape of the young; *petenense,* for Lake Peten, Yucatan, the type locality.

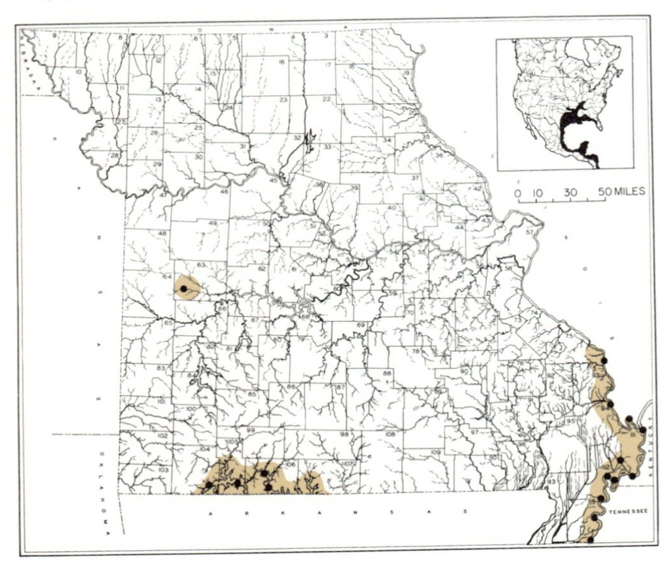

DISTRIBUTION AND HABITAT

Possibly the threadfin shad has only recently extended its range into Missouri, since it was not collected here until 1962. More likely it occurred naturally in the Mississippi River but was overlooked by early collectors. In a series of collections made in 1963, the threadfin was more abundant than the gizzard shad in the Mississippi River downstream from the mouth of the Ohio River. The threadfin is well established as a result of introduction into large reservoirs of the White River system, and in Montrose Lake, Henry County. It is being widely stocked in other lakes managed by the Missouri Department of Conservation, but the status of these populations is still undetermined.

The habitat of this fish is much like that of the gizzard shad, except that the threadfin is more often found in waters with a noticeable current. The threadfin is very sensitive to low temperatures and extensive die-offs have been reported at temperatures below 45°F. Survival in Montrose Lake is thought to depend on a continuous discharge of warm water by a steam-generating power plant. That this assumption may be correct is indicated by apparent failure of the threadfin to become established in Lake of the Ozarks, to which it has had access from Montrose Lake.

HABITS AND LIFE HISTORY

The threadfin is similar in habit to the gizzard shad. In lakes the threadfin occurs in the upper 5 feet of water, and large numbers congregate below dams in spring and fall. An Arkansas study revealed that the threadfin shad is quite unselective in its food habits and does not change its diet as it increases in size.[53] Microscopic plants and animals that live suspended in the water are eaten in about equal quantities and make up the bulk of the diet. Like the gizzard shad, the threadfin is primarily a filter feeder.

Spawning begins in the spring when the water warms up to 70°F. and may continue at intervals throughout the warmer months of the year. It has been observed in Missouri reservoirs from mid-April into June. Spawning activity is confined to the period from dawn to shortly after sunrise. Schools of spawning shad run the shoreline, often actually beaching themselves. One or more females, accompanied by several smaller males, swim erratically near the surface and then suddenly rush towards a log or other submerged object, releasing eggs and sperm as they go. The adhesive eggs stick to submerged objects and hatch in about 3 days.

Individuals hatched early in the year commonly mature and spawn late in their first summer of life. Few individuals live more than 2 or 3 years. In Bull Shoals Reservoir the threadfin grows more slowly but has a longer life span than populations at more southern localities.[54] Females live longer and attain a larger size than males. In Bull Shoals Reservoir, the threadfin shad averages 2.1 inches in length at the end of one growing season and averages 4.9 (males) or 5.3 (females) inches at the end of three growing seasons. The maximum life span in the reservoir is about 3 years for males and 4 years for females.

MOONEYES

Hiodontidae

This family includes only two living species, the mooneye and goldeye. They are restricted to North America and both occur in Missouri. Neither is very common in our waters and many experienced fishermen have never caught one. The bony flesh of these fish is generally little valued as food, but smoked goldeye is considered a delicacy in Manitoba and Ontario. In these Canadian Provinces and adjacent parts of the United States a commercial fishery exists based on the market for smoked goldeye.

Mooneyes are silvery, flat-sided fishes with unusually large eyes and with prominent teeth on the jaws, roof of the mouth, and tongue. The presence of teeth and the superficial resemblance to herrings has earned for mooneyes the common name "toothed herring." In addition to the prominent teeth, several other characters are useful in distinguishing mooneyes from herrings. The midline of the belly in mooneyes is keeled but lacks the row of spiny scutes found in herrings. Also, the dorsal fin in mooneyes is immediately above the base of the anal fin rather than far forward as in herrings, and the lateral line is present. The mooneyes resemble the herrings in having a small triangular-shaped projection, the axillary process, above the base of the pelvic fin, and in having smooth-edged (cycloid) scales over the body, but not the head.

Key to the Mooneyes

1a. Front of dorsal fin slightly behind front of anal fin; dorsal fin with 9 or 10 principal rays; keel on midline of belly extending forward from vent nearly to pectoral fin bases.
Goldeye
Hiodon alosoides ...... **Page 82**

1b. Front of dorsal fin distinctly forward of front of anal fin; dorsal fin with 11 or 12 principal rays; keel on midline of belly extending forward from vent only as far as pelvic fin bases.
Mooneye
Hiodon tergisus .... **Page 82**

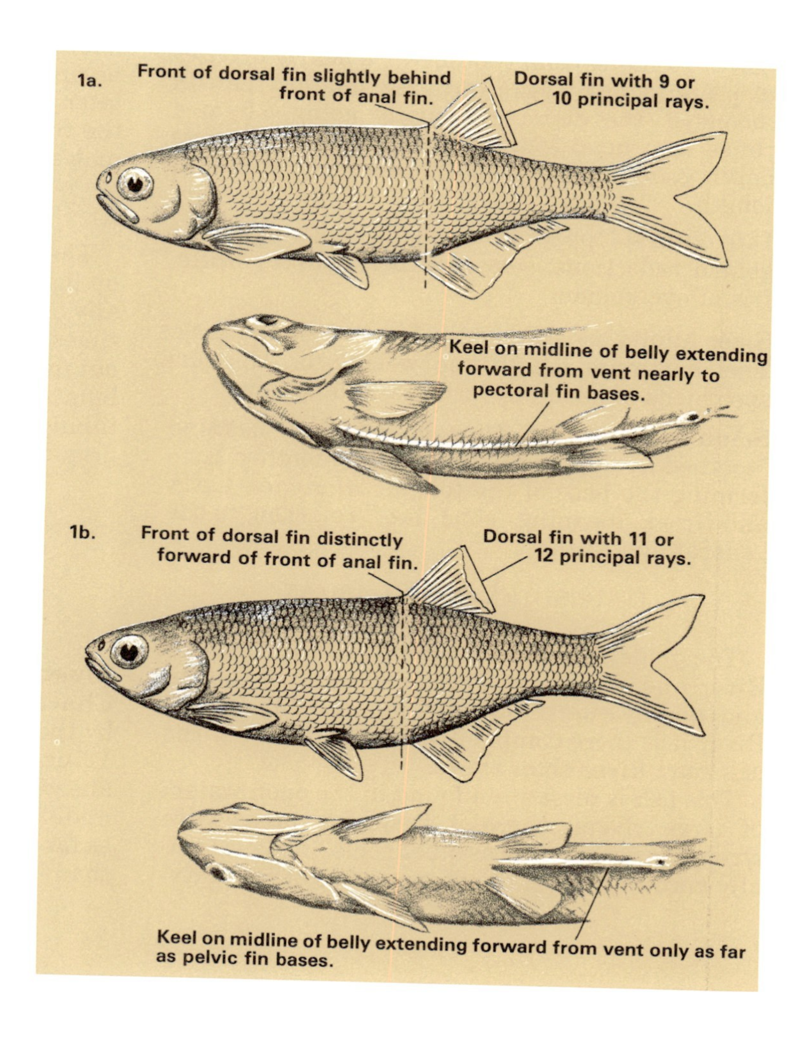

Goldeye

Hiodon alosoides (Rafinesque)

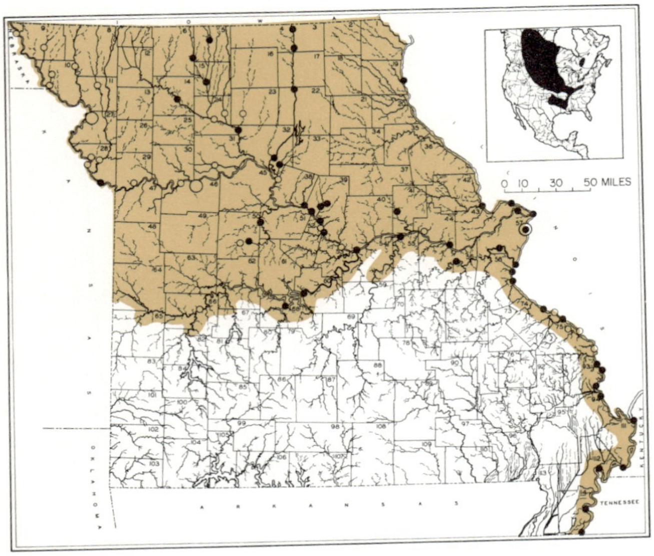

DESCRIPTION

Illustration: Page 81, 1a.

Characters: Can be separated from the mooneye by the following characters: dorsal fin containing 9 or 10 rays, with front of its base slightly behind front of anal fin base; fleshy keel along midline of belly extending from vent forward nearly to bases of pectoral fins; eyes averaging smaller than in mooneye, the diameter usually going 3.6 to 4 times into head length; body more slender, its depth going about 3.4 to 3.7 times into standard length.

Life colors: Upper parts greenish with silvery or golden reflections; sides and belly silvery-white. Iris of eye golden.

Size: Adults are commonly 14 to 16 inches long. The maximum length and weight for Missouri specimens is about 18 inches and 3 pounds.

Scientific name: *Hiodon,* Greek, meaning "toothed hyoid," in reference to the toothed bone forming the base of the tongue; *alosoides,* Latin and Greek, meaning "shad-like," referring to the general appearance.

DISTRIBUTION AND HABITAT

The goldeye is rather common in the Missouri River and the larger Prairie streams of central and northwestern Missouri. In the Mississippi River it is more common below the mouth of the Missouri River than above.

This fish is most often found in the open waters of large rivers where it frequents areas with strong current as well as quiet pools. It is occasionally encountered in the deeper pools of small rivers and creeks where these are tributaries of large rivers. The goldeye is more tolerant of continuous high turbidity than the mooneye.

HABITS AND LIFE HISTORY

The goldeye is an active, fast-moving fish, taking much of its food at or near the surface of the water. Much of its feeding is done in late evening or at night. The diet includes a wide variety of animal life, but aquatic and terrestrial insects are most important. Small fishes are also commonly taken.

In Canadian waters the goldeye begins spawning in late May when the ice goes out and continues until about the first week of July.[55] No information is available on spawning in Missouri, but young an inch in length have been taken from the Missouri River in late May. This suggests that spawning is earlier at this latitude than in Canada. Spawning of the goldeye has not been observed, but is thought to take place in mid-water. The eggs float free in the water and the newly hatched larvae float for a time at the water's surface with the body vertical and the head uppermost.

An Oklahoma study indicates that in a new impoundment the goldeye may reach a length of nearly 7 inches its first year and lengths of about 9, 12, and 14 inches in succeeding years.[56] Growth is most rapid the first three years, declining thereafter. Growth of the sexes is similar at first, but females grow faster than males in later years. The sexes are readily distinguished by the front rays of the anal fin which are longer in males, giving the fin a distinctive shape.

ANGLING

The goldeye can provide some sport when taken on light tackle, although it lacks stamina. It usually makes a short, swift run, or jumps a few times, and then permits itself to be reeled in without further struggle. Flies or fly and spinner combinations are the most effective artificial lures for taking the goldeye. They can also be caught on grasshoppers, crickets, or small minnows.

Mooneye

Hiodon tergisus Lesueur

DESCRIPTION

Illustration: Page 81, 1b.

Characters: Can be separated from the goldeye by the following characters: dorsal fin containing 11 or 12 principal rays, with front of its base ahead of front of anal fin base; fleshy keel along midline of belly extending from vent forward only as far as bases of pelvic fins; eyes averaging larger than in goldeye, the diameter usually going 2.8 to

3.6 times into head length; body usually deeper, its depth going about 3.1 to 3.4 times into standard length.

Life colors: Similar to goldeye but iris of eye silvery with only a trace of gold.

Size: Adults are commonly 9 to 11 inches long. The maximum length and weight for Missouri specimens is about 13 inches and ¾ of a pound.

Scientific name: *Hiodon,* Greek, meaning "toothed hyoid," in reference to the toothed bone forming the base of the tongue; *tergisus,* Greek for "polished," probably in reference to the silvery coloration.

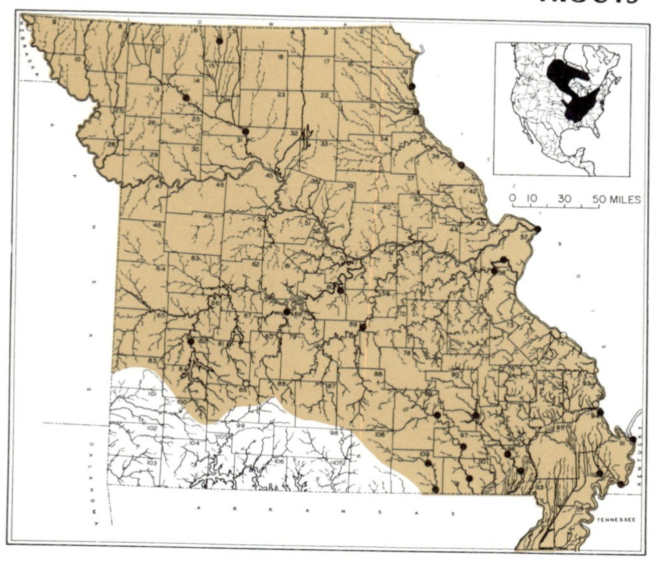

DISTRIBUTION AND HABITAT

The mooneye is less common than the goldeye over much of Missouri, but occurs to the exclusion of the latter species in large streams and reservoirs of the central and southern Ozarks. The mooneye is also common in the Mississippi River.

This species inhabits the larger pools of streams and the open waters of reservoirs. It usually occurs in clearer, quieter water than the goldeye.

HABITS AND LIFE HISTORY

Little has been written concerning the habits and life history of this fish. Like the goldeye, it often feeds at or near the water's surface and its diet consists mostly of insects and small fishes. The unusually large eye is probably an adaptation for sight feeding under conditions of low light intensity, at night or near dusk.

Adult mooneyes in spawning condition have been taken in Current River in March, indicating an early spring spawning season. In Lake Erie the mooneye attains a length of about 8 inches during its first year of life but requires 6 or 7 years to reach 13 inches.[57] It matures the third or fourth year at a length of 9 to 11 inches.

TROUTS

Salmonidae

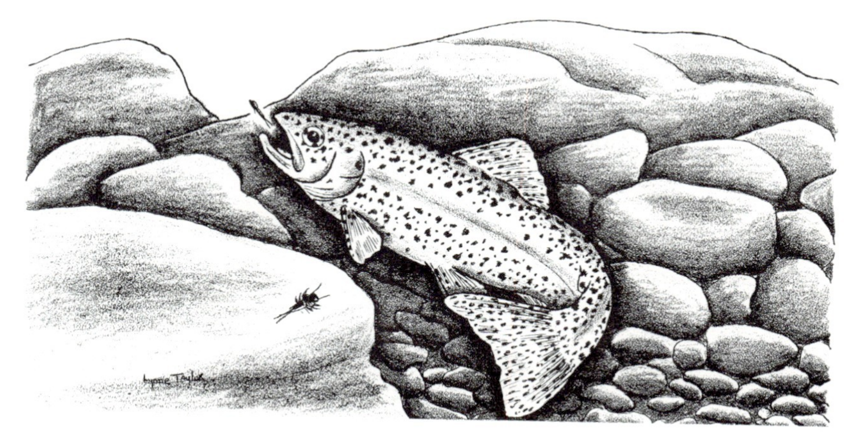

The trout family is not large but includes species of great economic importance. The family Salmonidae formerly included only the trouts and salmons, but recently was enlarged to include the graylings and whitefishes. Virtually all salmonids are cold-water fishes and were originally confined to Arctic and North Temperate regions. Some of the more popular members of this family have been introduced into suitable waters throughout the world. No salmonids are native to Missouri, and efforts to establish them here have met with only very limited success. However, important fisheries for rainbow trout and brown trout are maintained by stocking in suitable waters of the Ozarks.

Members of the trout family can be recognized by their small scales, more than 100 in the lateral line in our species, and by the presence of a small, fleshy adipose fin on the midline of the back behind the dorsal fin. The scales are smooth-edged (cycloid). There are no spines in the fins. In common with the herrings and mooneyes, the trouts have a small, triangular projection, the axillary process, at the upper end of the pelvic fin base.

TROUTS

Key to the Trouts

1a. Dark spots on tail faint or absent; side (in life) usually with orange or reddish spots, but without a pink or reddish longitudinal stripe; tail fin not forked; anal fin rays usually 9.
Brown trout
Salmo trutta .... **Page 85**

1b. Dark spots on tail prominent; side (in life) without orange or reddish spots, but with a pink or reddish longitudinal stripe; tail fin definitely forked; anal fin rays usually 10 to 12.
Rainbow trout
Salmo gairdneri .... **Page 84**

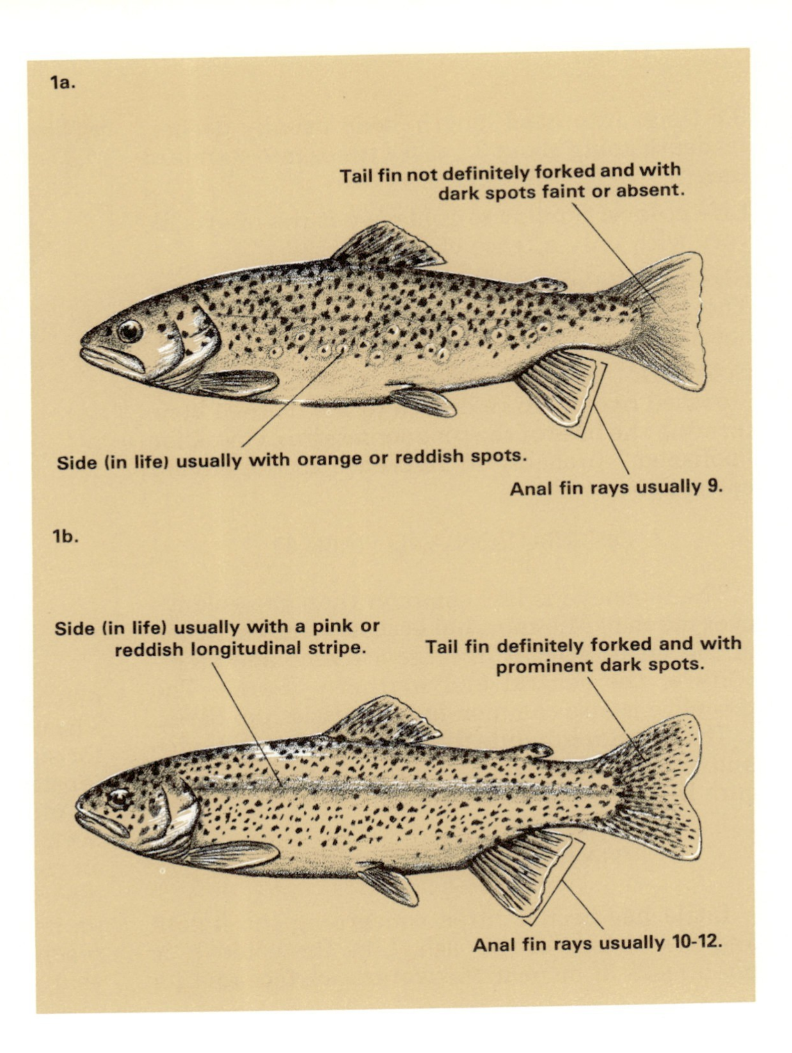

Rainbow Trout

Salmo gairdneri Richardson

DESCRIPTION

Illustration: Page 84, 1b; **37.**
Characters: Similar to brown trout but with the following differences: tail fin with numerous small, blackish spots; side (in life) with a broad, pink or reddish longitudinal stripe, but without orange or reddish spots; tail fin slightly forked; anal fin usually with 10 or 11 rays.
Life colors: Upper parts dark olive, thickly speckled with black spots. Side with a broad pinkish or red stripe. Belly silvery white. Young are less spotted and have a series of vertically elongate dusky blotches (parr marks) along side.
Size: Most rainbow trout caught in Missouri are 10 to 15 inches in length and weigh ½ to 1½ pounds. The present state record, 15 pounds, 6 ounces, was caught in Lake Taneycomo.
Scientific name: *Salmo,* Latin name for the Atlantic salmon, derived from *salio,* "to leap"; *gairdneri,* named for Dr. Gairdner, its discoverer.

DISTRIBUTION AND HABITAT

The rainbow trout is native to the Pacific Coast from Alaska to northern Mexico. The first reported introduction into Missouri was in June, 1882, when 1,500 fry were stocked in Spring

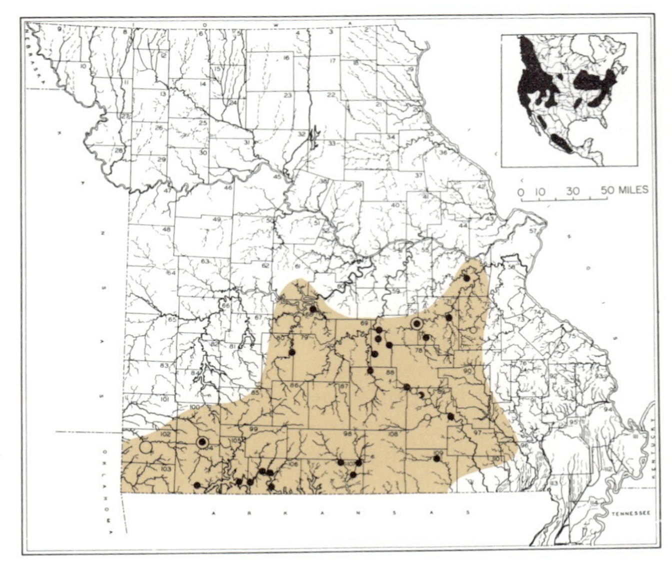

River, Lawrence County.[58] Since that time untold thousands have been liberated by state and federal agencies and by private individuals into streams and spring branches throughout the Ozarks. Small, self-sustaining populations have been established in some streams, but most populations are maintained by continuous stocking.

The rainbow trout inhabits a variety of habitats within its range, including streams, lakes, and reservoirs. It tolerates slightly higher temperatures than some other trouts, but does best in waters that remain more or less continuously below 70°F. In Missouri the rainbow trout occurs in streams kept cool by discharge from springs. Lake Taneycomo on White River is suitable for trout because of cold water discharged from the lower levels of Table Rock Reservoir just upstream.

HABITS AND LIFE HISTORY

The rainbow trout feeds on a variety of animal life, but aquatic insects, terrestrial insects, snails and small fishes often make up the bulk of its diet. In upper Lake Taneycomo amphipod crustaceans are nearly 90% of the diet.

The rainbow spawns from early winter to late spring, depending on the genetic strain and local conditions. In Ozark streams evidence of spawning has been found in December and January. In hatcheries the adults are ready to spawn in November. Under natural conditions the eggs are laid in a shallow pit dug by the female on clean, gravelly riffles. The incubation time varies considerably with temperatures. About 21 days are required for the eggs to hatch at a temperature of 55°F. Hatchery-reared trout reach a length of about 10 inches when a year old, at which time they are considered large enough to stock.

In Lake Taneycomo, where conditions for rapid growth are favorable, stocked rainbows grow about three-fourths of an inch per month. In a study by biologist Spencer Turner, rainbow trout stocked at a length of 4 inches were 15 inches long and weighed a little over one pound after 14 months.

IMPORTANCE

Trout are considered by many fishermen to be the king of sport fish, and the demand for trout fishing has resulted in the establishment of an important "put and take" trout fishery in suitable waters of the Ozark Region. The rainbow trout was selected for stocking because of its game qualities and because it is well suited for propagation in hatcheries. At present, trout are being reared by the Department of Conservation in four full-sized hatcheries and one with limited production. These trout are stocked in four parks and nine less intensively managed areas. Over the years the demand for trout fishing has increased dramatically. During the period from 1955 to 1965, the number of trips made by fishermen annually to the four trout parks maintained by the Department rose from 73,000 to 238,000, an increase of 326%.[251]

ANGLING

The rainbow trout may be taken on a variety of live and prepared baits including worms, grasshoppers, crickets, salmon eggs, and cheese. Wet and dry flies, spinners, fly and spinner combinations, and small spoons are also effective.

Brown Trout

Salmo trutta Linnaeus

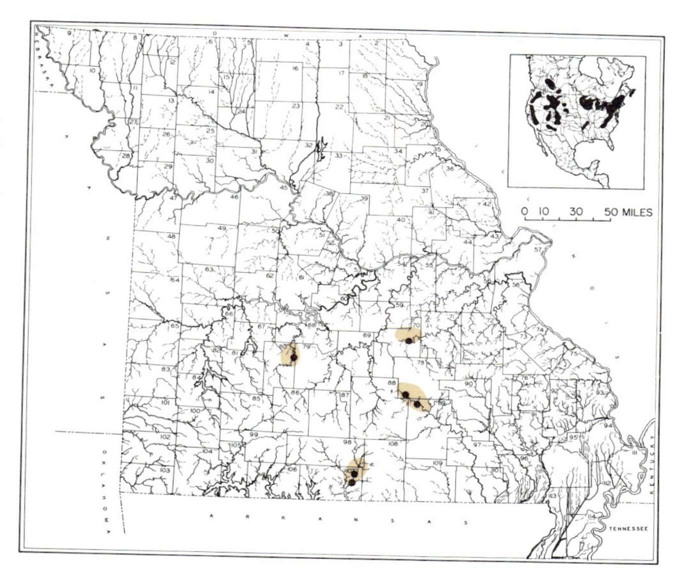

DESCRIPTION

Illustration: Page 84, 1a.

Characters: Similar to rainbow trout, but with the following differences: tail fin without blackish spots, or with faint spots that are mostly restricted to upper margin of fin; sides (in life) with orange or rusty spots but without a pink or red longitudinal stripe; tail fin not forked; anal fin usually with 9 rays.

Life colors: Upper parts dark olive-brown with scattered dark spots, these larger and more regular in outline than in rainbow trout, interspersed with orange or rusty-red spots. Lower sides and belly yellowish or white. Fins similar in color to adjacent parts of body.

Size: About the same as rainbow trout. The largest specimen reported from Missouri waters was 28 inches long and weighed 15 pounds.

Scientific name: *Salmo,* Latin name for the Atlantic salmon, derived from *salio,* "to leap"; *trutta,* Latin for trout.

DISTRIBUTION AND HABITAT

A native of Europe and the British Isles, the brown trout was introduced into the United States as early as 1883. Reports of the Missouri Fish Commission indicate that approximately 260,000 brown trout were introduced in Missouri waters between 1927 and 1933. After that, interest in this fish lagged until 1966 when the Department of Conservation began stocking them on an experimental basis in Current and North Fork rivers. Growth and survival from these stockings has been excellent and the program has been expanded to include the Niangua River downstream from Bennett Spring and the Meramec River downstream from Maramec Spring.

The brown trout thrives in both streams and lakes. In streams the brown trout is most often found around dense cover such as submerged logs or undercut banks, or in deep water below riffles.

HABITS AND LIFE HISTORY

The brown trout is more secretive than the rainbow, remaining beneath cover or in deeper water during daylight hours. It feeds most actively from near dusk to early morning. Most studies suggest that the brown trout is something of an opportunist, varying its diet with what is available. In streams smaller trout feed largely on insects, including both aquatic and terrestrial kinds, and other aquatic invertebrates, including snails and amphipods. Larger trout feed to a considerable extent on crayfish and fish. The brown trout tends to consume larger quantities of fish than does the rainbow. In Current River, sculpins are a major item in the diet of adult brown trout.

The brown trout spawns in fall and early winter. Spawning occurs in a shallow pit dug by the female in a gravelly riffle. The number of eggs deposited in the nest may be as many as 3,000, varying with the size of the female. After spawning the eggs are covered with gravel and receive no further attention from the parent fish. Hatching occurs in 48 to 52 days at a temperature of 51°F.[60]

Growth of the browns in Ozark streams is comparable to that of the rainbow trout, according to studies by biologist Spencer Turner. At the end of 3 years these trout may be 19 inches long and weigh 5 pounds.

IMPORTANCE

The principal advantage of brown trout over rainbows is that they are less vulnerable to fishing pressure. Thus, brown trout remain in the stream longer, achieving a larger size and increasing the opportunities for catching a trophy-size fish. Also, because they are more difficult to catch, brown trout can provide an additional challenge to the angler.

ANGLING

Brown trout can be caught using the same methods as for rainbow trout. Fly fishing can provide the ultimate challenge to the skill and perseverance of the trout fisherman. Live baits, particularly minnows and crayfish, are most effective for trophy-size fish.

PIKES

Esocidae

The pike family is represented by four species in North America. Three, grass pickerel, chain pickerel and northern pike, are native to Missouri. The fourth, muskellunge, was recently introduced. The northern pike and muskellunge reach a large size and are highly regarded game fishes. Both are being stocked at present in large Missouri reservoirs and show promise of providing added sport for anglers. It is hoped that these large predators will help convert the populations of shad and other non-game fishes in these reservoirs to usable fish. The chain pickerel provides some fishing opportunities in the few streams where it occurs, but the grass pickerel seldom reaches a catchable size.

Members of the pike family can be recognized by the duck-bill shaped snout, large mouth with many sharp teeth, and single dorsal fin. The dorsal fin is similar in size and shape to the anal fin, and placed far back near the distinctly forked tail fin. The moderately slender body is covered with smooth-edged (cycloid) scales that are deeply scalloped on their frong margins. Scales are also present on the side of the head, but not on its upper surface. The upper jaw is joined to the snout at the middle by a bridge of skin (frenum). The lateral line is present but weakly developed.

1a. Gill cover with scales only on upper half; 5 or more sensory pores on lower jaw; branchiostegal rays (slender bones in membrane along lower margin of gill cover) usually 14 to 19.
Go to 2

1b. Gill cover completely scaled; 4 sensory pores on lower jaw; branchiostegal rays usually 11 to 14.
Go to 3

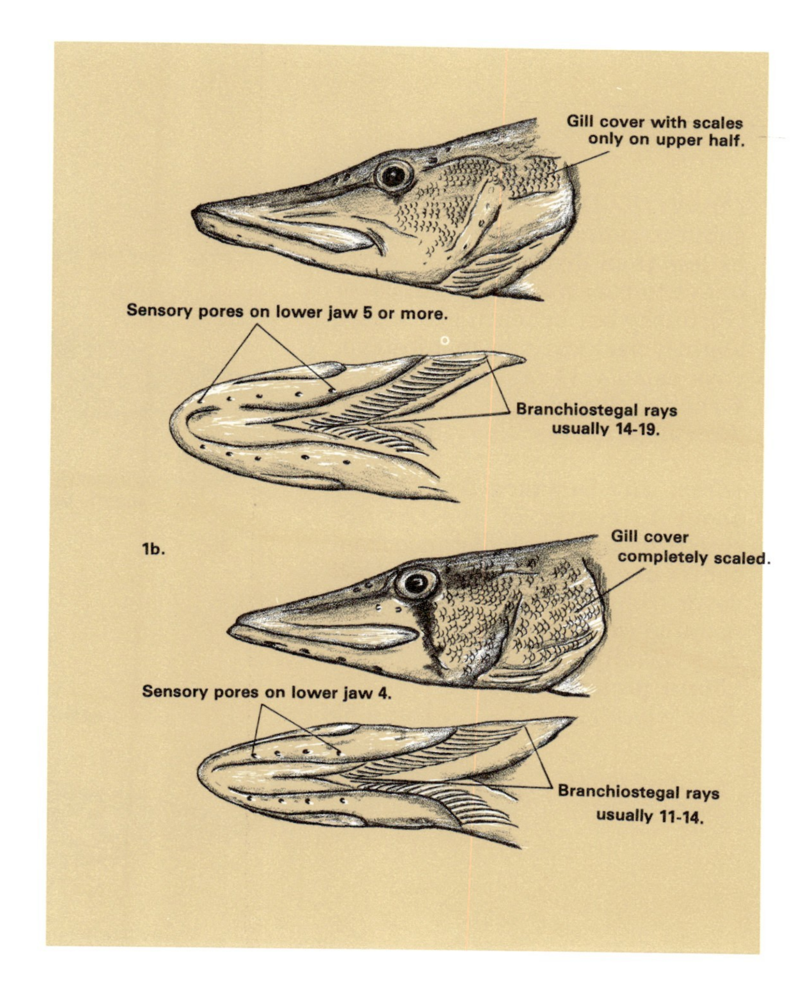

2a. *(From 1a.)* Cheek fully scaled; usually 5 sensory pores on lower jaw; body with whitish spots in large young and adults; branchiostegal rays usually 14 to 16.
Northern pike
Esox lucius .... **Page 90**

2b. *(From 1a.)* Cheek scaled only on upper half; 6 or more sensory pores on lower jaw; body with dark spots in large young and adults; branchiostegal rays usually 17 to 19.
Muskellunge
Esox masquinongy .... **Page 91**

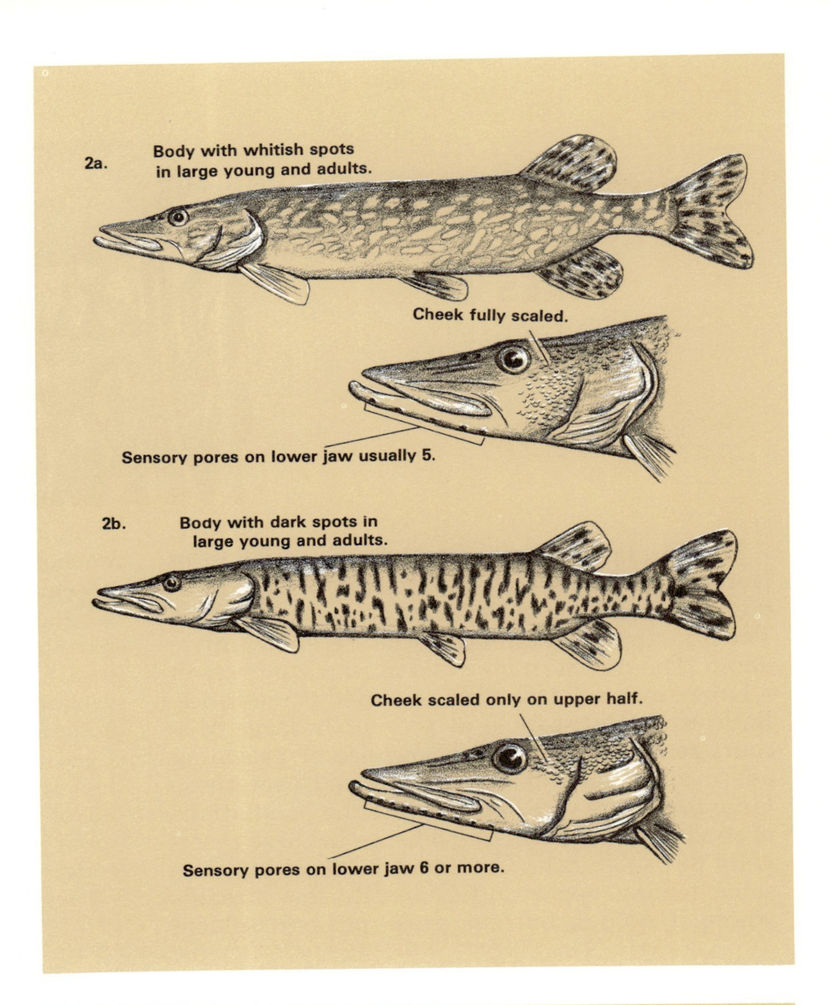

(From 1b.) Distance from tip of snout to center of eye (A) equal to or less than distance from center of eye to rear margin of gill cover (B); dusky bar beneath eye angled slightly backward; branchiostegal rays usually 11 or 12.
Grass pickerel
Esox americanus ...... **Page 88**

3b. *(From 1b.)* Distance from tip of snout to center of eye (A) distinctly greater than distance from center of eye to rear margin of gill cover (B); dusky bar beneath eye usually vertical; branchiostegal rays usually 13 or 14.
Chain pickerel
Esox niger .... **Page 89**

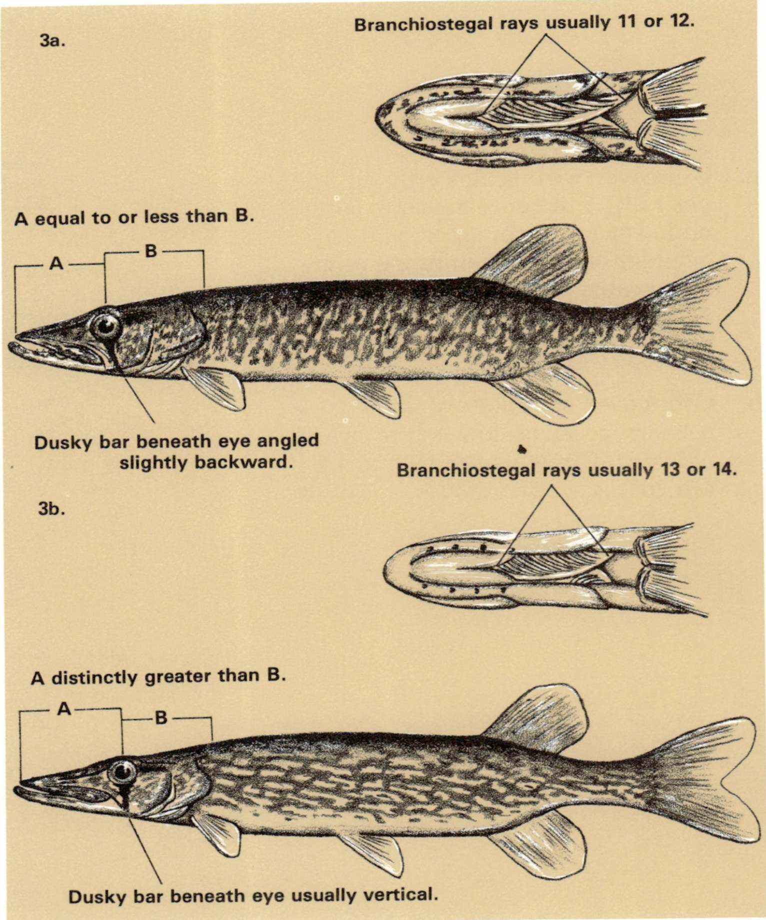

Grass Pickerel

Esox americanus Gmelin

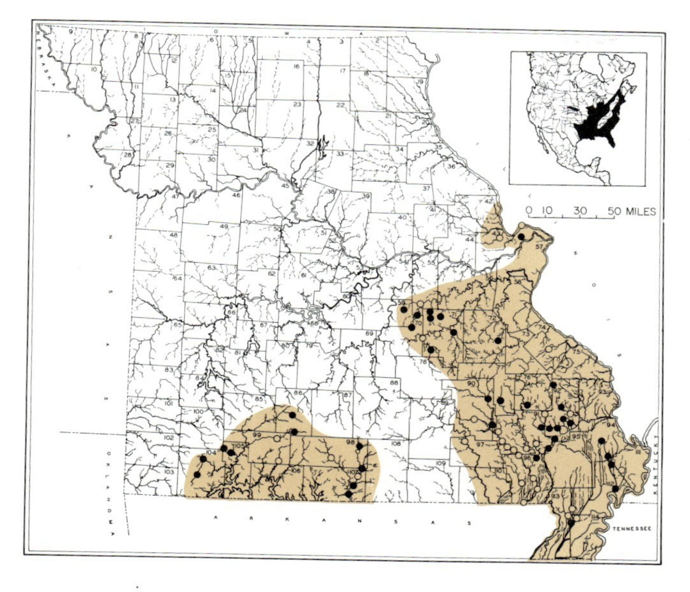

DESCRIPTION

Illustration: Page 88, 3a; **37.**

Characters: Similar to chain pickerel in having both gill cover and cheek fully scaled and a row of 4 sensory pores along undersurface of lower jaw. Snout shorter than chain pickerel, the distance from tip of snout to center of eye equal to or less than distance from center of eye to rear margin of gill cover. Usually there are 11 or 12 slender bones (branchiostegal rays) in membrane along lower edge of gill cover, and 92 to 117 scales in lateral line.

Life colors: Back and sides olive or yellowish-brown, sometimes uniformly colored, but often barred or mottled with darker color. A dusky vertical bar angles downward and slightly backward from eye.

Size: The smallest of the pikes, adults seldom exceed 10 or 12 inches in length. Maximum length and weight is about 14 inches and ¾ of a pound.

Scientific name: *Esox,* Latin for pike; *americanus,* "from America".

DISTRIBUTION AND HABITAT

The grass pickerel is the most common and widely distributed pike in Missouri. It is common in the Lowlands of southeastern Missouri, as well as in some streams of the southern and eastern Ozarks. In the southeastern Ozarks the distribution of the grass pickerel largely complements that of the chain pickerel, with one or the other predominating at any one locality. Although the grass pickerel has been reported from the Missouri River system in Nebraska, it does not occur in Missouri River tributaries in Missouri, even where conditions appear suitable.

In Lowland areas the grass pickerel frequents natural lakes, sloughs, borrow pits, and the sluggish sections of ditches and streams. In the Ozarks it is typically found in small headwater creeks having large, permanent pools but little flow during much of the year, and in the spring pools, protected inlets, and overflow waters along major streams. All of these habitats are characterized by clear water, little current, and thick growths of aquatic vegetation.

HABITS AND LIFE HISTORY

The grass pickerel is carnivorous and hunts by ambush, darting out to seize its prey from a place of concealment. Small fishes make up the bulk of its diet, but aquatic insects and crayfish are also eaten in significant quantities.

The following information on the life history of the grass pickerel is from an Oklahoma study.[61] Spawning at this latitude is in late February and early March, but there is some evidence of an additional spawning in late fall or early winter. The eggs are broadcast over submerged vegetation without preparation of a nest. There is no parental care of the eggs or young. In Oklahoma, the grass pickerel averages 4.6 inches long at the end of the first year of life and 7.8, 9.9, and 10.2 inches in succeeding years. Females grow more rapidly and live longer than males. Few live more than 3 years and 4 years seems to be about the maximum life span.

Chain Pickerel

Esox niger Lesueur

DESCRIPTION

Illustration: Page 88, 3b.

Characters: Like the grass pickerel, its cheek and gill cover are fully scaled and it has a row of 4 sensory pores along undersurface of lower jaw. Snout longer than in grass pickerel, the distance from tip of snout to center of eye distinctly greater than distance from center of eye to rear margin of gill cover. Usually there are 13 or 14 slender bones (branchiostegal rays) in membrane along lower edge of gill cover, and 110 to 138 scales in lateral line.

Life colors: Back and sides olive or yellowish-brown with a chain-like network of dark lines. Dusky bar beneath eye usually more nearly vertical than in grass pickerel.

Size: A somewhat larger fish than grass pickerel, adults commonly reach a length of 18 inches or more. The largest recorded from Missouri weighed 4 pounds, 5 ounces. There are unconfirmed reports of individuals weighing up to 7 pounds. Even larger chain pickerel have been reported from elsewhere in its range.

Scientific name: *Esox,* Latin for pike; *niger,* Latin, meaning "dark" or "black".

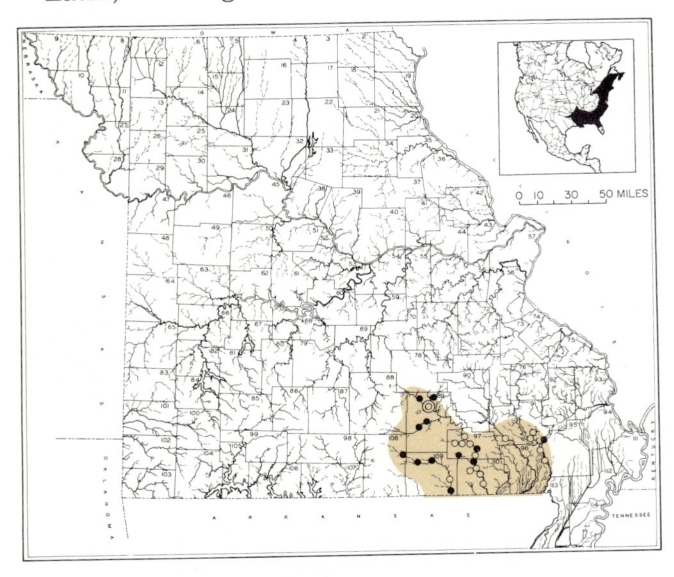

DISTRIBUTION AND HABITAT

The chain pickerel occurs in streams in the southeastern Ozarks from Eleven Point River east to the St. Francis. In the Eleven Point and Current rivers it occurs to the virtual exclusion of the grass pickerel.

Like other pikes, this species inhabits clear, quiet waters where aquatic vegetation is abundant. In the Ozarks it occurs along major streams in marginal waters having no perceptible current. Unlike the grass pickerel, it avoids warm, Lowland rivers and ditches and does not penetrate into small headwater creeks. The chain and grass pickerel may compete intensively, accounting for the rarity with which they are found together.

HABITS AND LIFE HISTORY

The following account of the habits of the chain pickerel in streams of the southern Ozarks was given by one early observer.[62] "This species, which is locally called 'mountain-trout', and occasionally 'pike', is abundant in all of the larger streams in the mountains of Missouri. It delights to quietly loiter in the shelter of the pads of the pond lily and in the shadows of the dense masses of *Potomogeton,* a few inches below the surface of the water. Motionless, in such situations, it awaits the coming of the unwary minnow, when, quicker than thought, it darts upon its prey, and, while you look, slowly sinks from sight. There is no apparent motion of fin or tail but, ere you realize it, the 'ravenous beauty' is gone." As this account implies, the chain pickerel is carnivorous, feeding primarily on other fishes.

It is a spring spawner, probably spawning in Missouri at about the same time and in the same manner as the grass pickerel. Growth varies considerably between habitats and even between individuals exposed to similar conditions. In Massachusetts the chain pickerel averages 6.7 inches in length at the end of its first year, and 9.4, 11.4, 13.9, 15.5, and 17.6 inches at the end of succeeding years.[63]

Northern Pike

Esox lucius Linnaeus

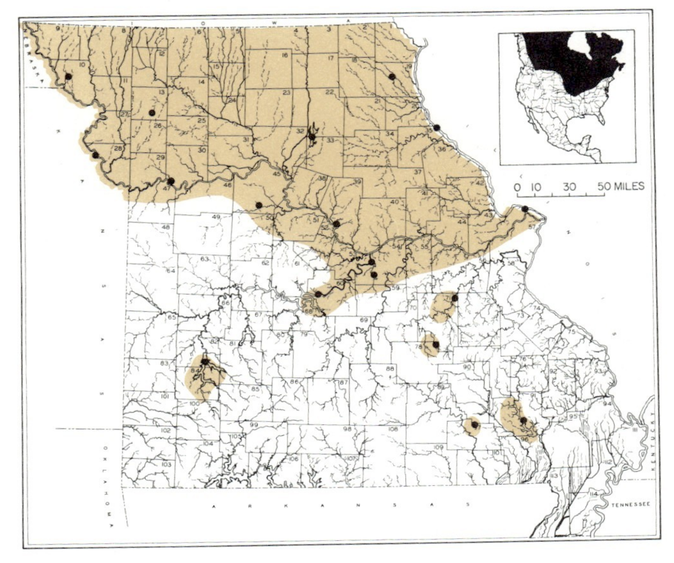

DESCRIPTION

Illustration: Page 87, 2a.

Characters: Differs from other pikes in having cheek fully scaled but the gill cover scaled only on upper half, and in having a row of 5 sensory pores along each side of lower jaw. Color pattern of body consisting of light spots against a darker background. Usually there are 14 to 16 slender bones (branchiostegal rays) in the membrane along lower edge of gill cover, and 119 to 128 scales in lateral line.

Life colors: Upper parts green or blue-gray with numerous roundish yellow spots on sides. No dusky bar beneath eye. Fins, except pectorals, often marked by roundish black spots.

Size: The largest pike native to Missouri, reaching a length of over 4 feet and a weight of 40 pounds or more. The largest specimen thus far reported from Missouri was 39½ inches long and weighed 18 pounds.

Scientific name: *Esox,* Latin for pike; *lucius,* Latin name for this species.

DISTRIBUTION AND HABITAT

Missouri is on the southern edge of the range for this northern species and, until the Department of Conservation began stocking it in 1966, the northern pike was rare in Missouri waters. Before 1966 occasional pike were reported by fishermen from widely scattered localities in northern and central Missouri. Most reports were from the lower Osage River where a small self-sustaining population may have been present. Other records probably were based on individuals that strayed into Missouri from the north along the Missouri and Mississippi rivers. The first stockings of northern pike were of adults into Deer Ridge Lake, Lewis County, and Miller Lake, Carter County, in March, 1966. Adults were also placed in ponds at Indian Trail Hatchery, Dent County. The latter fish spawned successfully and some of the resulting fry may have escaped into the Meramec River. Northern pike were subsequently stocked into Thomas Hill Reservoir in 1967 and Stockton Reservoir in 1970. Growth and survival from these stockings has been excellent and many are now being caught.

The northern pike inhabits a variety of habitats, including lakes, reservoirs, and large streams. Like the other pikes, it avoids strong currents and is partial to waters with dense growths of aquatic vegetation.

HABITS AND LIFE HISTORY

In habit as well as appearance, the northern pike is in most respects a larger counterpart of the grass and chain pickerels. Like its smaller relatives, the northern is a carnivore, and feeds principally on other fishes. Where abundant it plays an important role in regulating the numbers and maintaining the population balance of prey species.[64] One reason for stocking northern pike in Missouri reservoirs was to introduce a predator that was large enough to utilize the larger prey species, such as gizzard shad, that were not being fully utilized by largemouth bass and other predators already present.

The northern pike spawns in early spring, with spawning preceded by movements into marshes or other shallow, marginal waters. The eggs are broadcast over submerged vegetation and receive no further attention from the adults. A single large female may produce as many as 150,000 eggs.[64] Reproduction in Missouri reservoirs has been quite limited because of a lack of adequate spawning habitat or for other reasons not yet determined. Growth of the northern pike is extremely rapid. At Indian Trail Hatchery young pike attained a length of 17 inches by the time they were 8 months old. Northerns stocked in Thomas Hill and Stockton reservoirs reach a legal catchable length of 30 inches in about 2½ years. Females grow more rapidly and live longer than males. The maximum length for males is reported not to exceed 30 inches.[64] Under natural conditions the northern pike rarely lives more than 13 years, but specimens are reported to have lived as long as 75 years in zoos.

IMPORTANCE

Because of its rarity in Missouri waters, the northern pike was of little importance as a game fish until the Department of Conservation began stocking it in impoundments around the state. Now it is a much sought-after sport fish in Stockton and Thomas Hill reservoirs. The northern has been stocked to provide another trophy-size sport fish and to introduce a predator that can more effectively utilize the large stocks of carp and gizzard shad present in these reservoirs. Northern pike are more readily caught and average smaller in size than the muskellunge, but the sporting qualities of these species are similar.

ANGLING

Northern pike can be taken by the same methods that are effective for muskellunge. Probably more northern pike are caught on large, brightly colored spoons than any other type of artificial lure. Plugs, particularly those that imitate the action of a swimming fish, are also effective. Large fish such as suckers are the most commonly used natural bait.

Muskellunge

Esox masquinongy Mitchell

Other local names: Muskie

DESCRIPTION

Illustration: Page 87, 2b.
Characters: Differs from other pikes in having both the gill cover and cheek scaled only on their upper halves, and in having a row of 6 to 9 pores along each side of lower jaw. Color pattern on body consisting of dark spots or bars on a light background. Usually there are 17 to 19 slender bones (branchiostegal rays) in the membranes along lower edge of gill cover, and 130 to 157 scales in lateral line.

Life colors: Color quite variable. Upper parts are silver gray to yellowish green, with scattered blackish spots or bars. No dusky bar beneath eye.
Size: The largest of the pikes. Authenticated records indicate a maximum length and weight of at least 5 feet and 70 pounds. The current state record, from Pomme de Terre Reservoir, was 44½ inches long and weighed 26 pounds, 12 ounces.
Scientific name: *Esox,* Latin for pike; *masqui-*

nongy, from the Ojibway Indian name for this species.

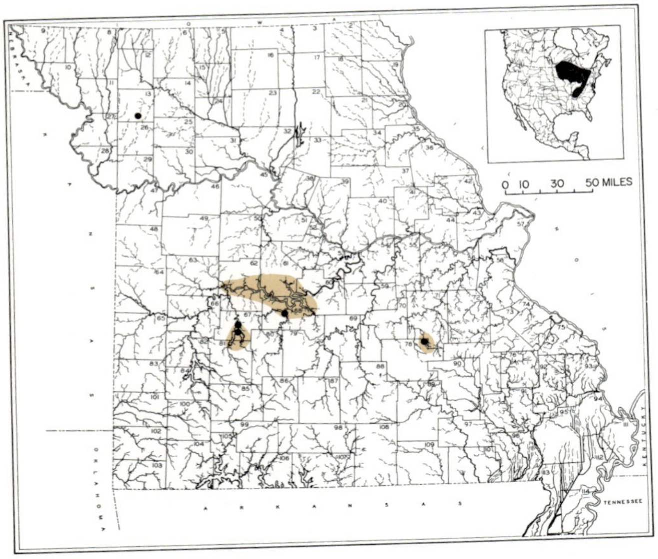

DISTRIBUTION AND HABITAT

The muskellunge is not native to Missouri, but efforts are being made to establish it in Pomme de Terre Reservoir. The first introductions were made in 1966 and additional stockings have been made on an annual basis. Survival from these stockings has been good and muskellunge began appearing in the creel in 1968. A few have been stocked in Lake of the Ozarks, and some of these have been caught. Muskellunge that escaped from hatchery ponds have been caught in the creek below Indian Trail Hatchery. Eighty-seven muskellunge, 62 northern pike, and 85 muskellunge x northern pike hybrids were stocked in Pony Express Lake, De Kalb County, in July, 1973.

In its native range, the muskie is an inhabitant of lakes and of the pools and backwaters of slow-moving streams. Like the other pikes, it exhibits a definite affinity for clear water and dense growths of aquatic vegetation. It frequently thrives after introduction into reservoirs, but often fails to reproduce in such situations.

HABITS AND LIFE HISTORY

The general habits of the muskellunge differ little from those of the other pikes. It is a solitary fish, lurking about cover from which it darts out to capture its prey. The first food of the muskie is zooplankton, but after the first 4 days of life it begins eating fish, and fish are the principal food throughout the rest of its life.[65] The muskellunge spawns in the spring, slightly later than the northern pike. The eggs are scattered over dead vegetation in shallow water. Reproduction in Missouri waters has not been documented.

Muskellunge held in rearing ponds at Indian Trail Hatchery were about 12 inches in length when 4 months old. In Pomme de Terre Lake, they attain a legal catchable length of 30 inches by the third year. A 30-inch muskellunge will weigh about 12 pounds. Wisconsin studies reveal the growth of this species is quite variable and that males and females grow at different rates.[65] Males grow more slowly and achieve sexual maturity at a smaller size and an earlier age than females.

IMPORTANCE

Fishermen began catching legal-sized muskellunge in Pomme de Terre Reservoir in 1968 and the establishment of a significant fishery through continuous stocking seems assured. The majority of fishermen interviewed would prefer to catch muskies over any other fish species in this reservoir. However, muskies are not expected to achieve the abundance of other game fishes and will remain "trophy" or "bonus" fish.

ANGLING

Muskellunge are caught by a variety of methods, including casting, trolling, and still fishing. Large spoons, plugs, and bucktail spinners, fished on or near the surface, are effective. Fish are the most effective live bait. Suckers up to 12 inches long are a popular bait fish in northern states. Heavy tackle and wire leaders should be used by the fisherman who expects to catch muskies. However, some are caught in Pomme de Terre Reservoir by bass and crappie fishermen using light tackle. Muskie fishing requires a great deal of patience, since the time between strikes is often long, but the large size and sporting qualities make the wait worthwhile.

MINNOWS

Cyprinidae

Although the term "minnow" is sometimes loosely applied to any small fish, it is properly used only in referring to the largest of all fish families, the minnow family. While many are indeed small, some minnows attain considerable size. The Colorado squawfish is the largest North American minnow, reaching a length of 4 or 5 feet and a weight of 80 pounds. No native Missouri minnow exceeds a length of 14 inches or a weight of 12 ounces, but the introduced carp reaches a weight of 40 pounds or more.

About 1,500 species of minnows are known and they occur on every continent except South America and Australia. The family is well represented in Missouri. Nearly one-third of all our fishes, a total of 63 species, are minnows.

Native Missouri minnows share the following combination of characters that are useful in separating them from other small fishes: 1) fins without spines, but with 8 (9 in one species) principal rays in the dorsal fin, and 16 or fewer principal rays in the anal fin; 2) body covered with smooth-edged (cycloid) scales; head without scales; 3) jaws without teeth; 4) adipose fin absent. The introduced carp and goldfish are minnows, but they differ from this description in having 17 or more rays in the dorsal fin and a stout, saw-toothed spine at the front of the dorsal and anal fins. Minnows are most likely to be confused with the killifishes, mosquitofish, silversides, and the young of suckers.

Minnows are found in nearly all natural waters of the state that are not polluted or otherwise unsuited for fish life, but are more characteristic of streams than of lakes or ponds. In streams they are often more numerous than all other fishes combined. Each species has its own particular habitat requirements and few are state-wide in distribution. Those with similar requirements tend to have similar distributions and each section of the state and each habitat has its own characteristic minnows.

They exhibit a diversity of interesting habits and adaptations. Perhaps none are of greater interest than those associated with reproduction. The breeding males of many minnows are brightly colored and have small wart-like structures called breeding tubercles scattered over various parts of the head, body, and fins. The common names of some species—bleeding shiner, redfin shiner, hornyhead chub—refer to these features. The bright colors serve to advertise the presence of the male to other individuals of his own species, and the tubercles are used for driving other males from his territory, in jostling for favored positions over the spawning site, or for clasping the female during the spawning embrace.

The hornyhead chub and creek chub spawn in pits dug by the male, who then laboriously fills the pits again with pebbles he carries in his mouth. Other minnows, such as the Ozark minnow and redfin shiner, spawn over the nests of their more ambitious relatives, or even over the nest of fishes belonging to entirely different families. Still others deposit their eggs over vegetation, logs, or gravel, with little advance preparation of the spawning site.

Few minnows practice parental care, deserting the eggs once spawning is completed. The bluntnose and fathead minnows are exceptions. They attach their eggs to the underside of submerged objects and the male remains with the eggs, cleaning and guarding them until they hatch.

There is a definite correlation between the diet of minnows and the structures associated with feeding. Carnivorous minnows typically have large, terminal mouths and sharp, hooked throat-teeth for capturing and holding their prey, which is often swallowed whole. Herbivorous minnows often have small, subterminal mouths and molar-like throat teeth for grinding up plant material before it is swallowed. The short intestine of carnivorous minnows suffices for the rapid digestion of animal material. Plant material is less readily digested and, as a consequence, most herbivorous minnows have very long intestines. The lining of the body cavity (peritoneum) is usually silvery in carnivorous minnows and uniformly black in herbivorous minnows, but no satisfactory reason for this has as yet been found.

Few Missouri minnows are large enough to provide much in the way of food or fishing opportunities for man. The carp is an obvious exception. The hornyhead chub and creek chub will rise readily to a fly or other small lure and provide some sport when taken on light tackle. Minnows are an effective bait for taking a variety of game fishes.

Perhaps the greatest importance of minnows lies in their role in converting the basic productivity of streams and lakes into food for fish of more direct benefit to man.

Key to the Minnows

1a. Dorsal and anal fins each with a stout, saw-toothed spine at front; dorsal fin long, with more than 15 principal rays.
Go to 2

1b. Dorsal and anal fins without spines; dorsal fin short, with 8 (in one species 9) principal rays.
Go to 3

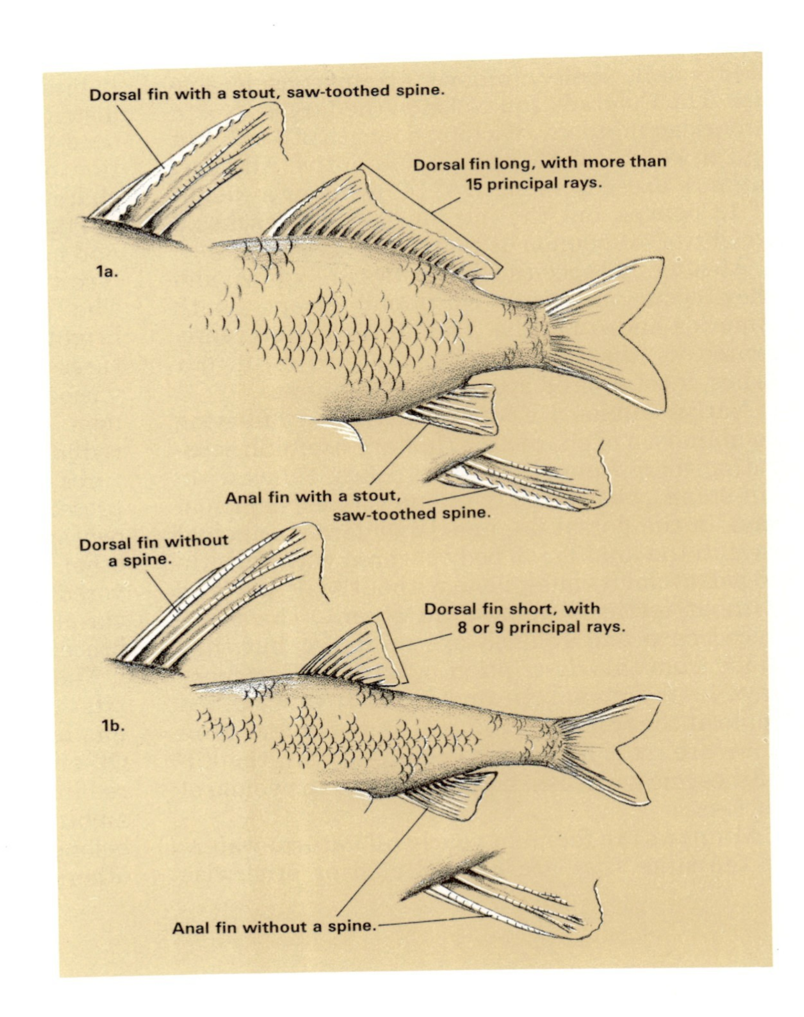

2a. *(From 1a.)* Upper jaw with two fleshy barbels on each side; lateral line scales 35 to 38; throat teeth in 3 rows, those of main row heavy and with flattened grinding surfaces.
Carp
Cyprinus carpio ...... **Page 127**

2b. *(From 1a.)* Upper jaw without barbels; lateral line scales 26 to 29; throat teeth in 1 row, not heavy and without flattened grinding surfaces.
Goldfish
Carassius auratus .... **Page 128**

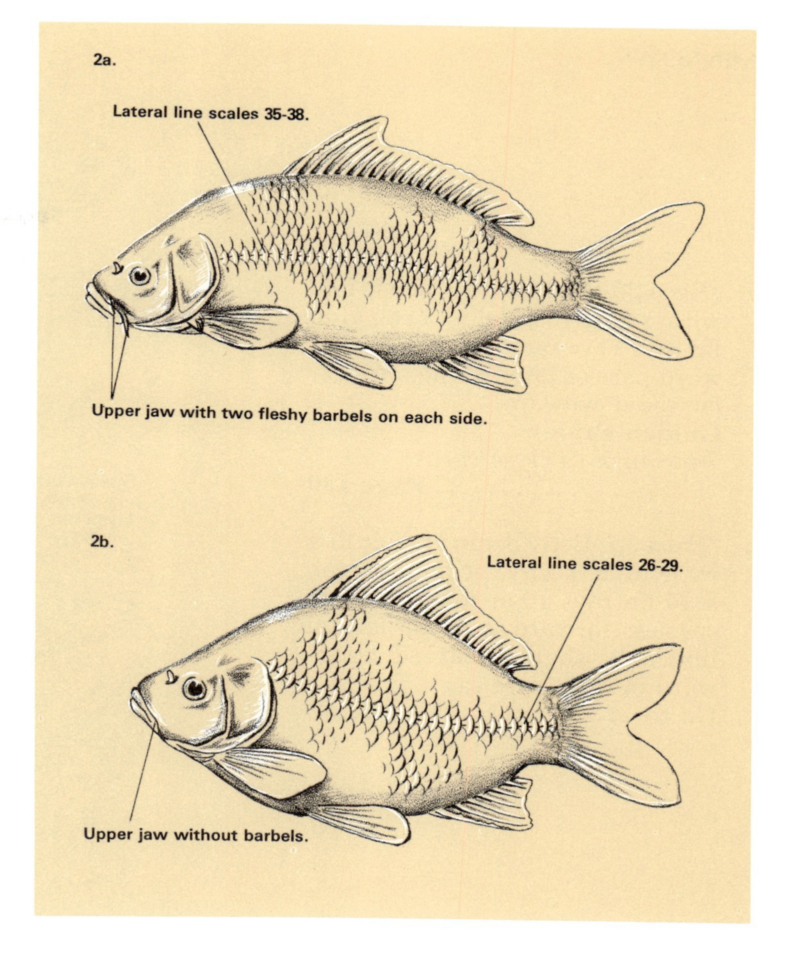

3a. *(From 1b.)* Distance from front of anal fin base to base of tail fin (A) going 3 times or more into distance from front of anal fin base to tip of snout (B); size large, length commonly exceeding 14 inches; throat teeth with prominent parallel grooves.
Grass carp
Ctenopharyngodon idella
.... **Page 129**

3b. *(From 1b.)* Distance from front of anal fin base to base of tail fin (A) going 2½ times or less into distance from front of anal fin base to tip of snout (B); size smaller, length not exceeding 14 inches; throat teeth without prominent parallel grooves.
Go to **4**

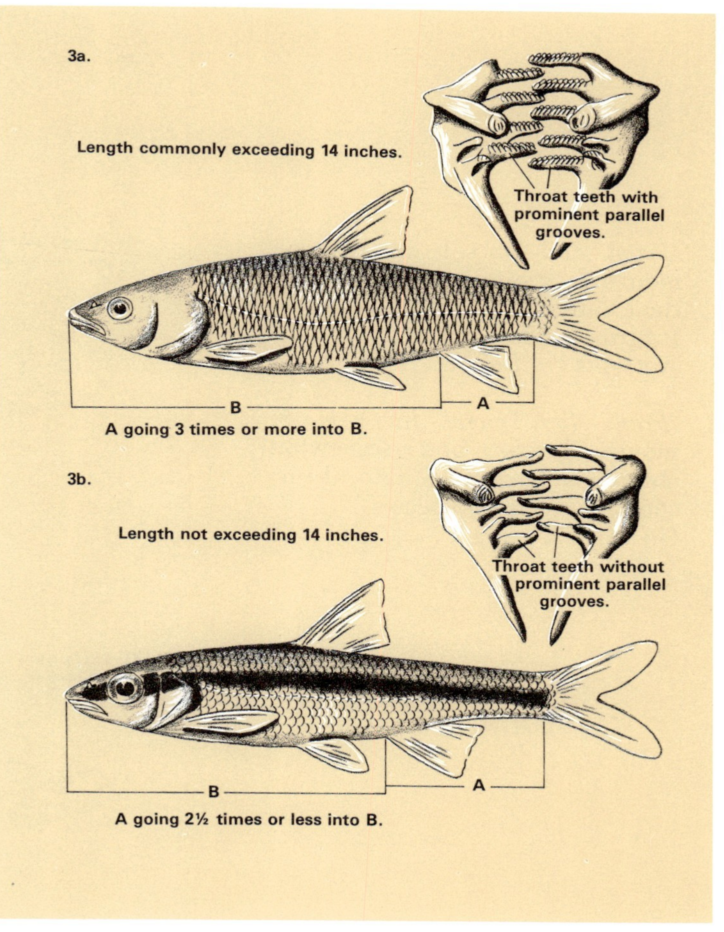

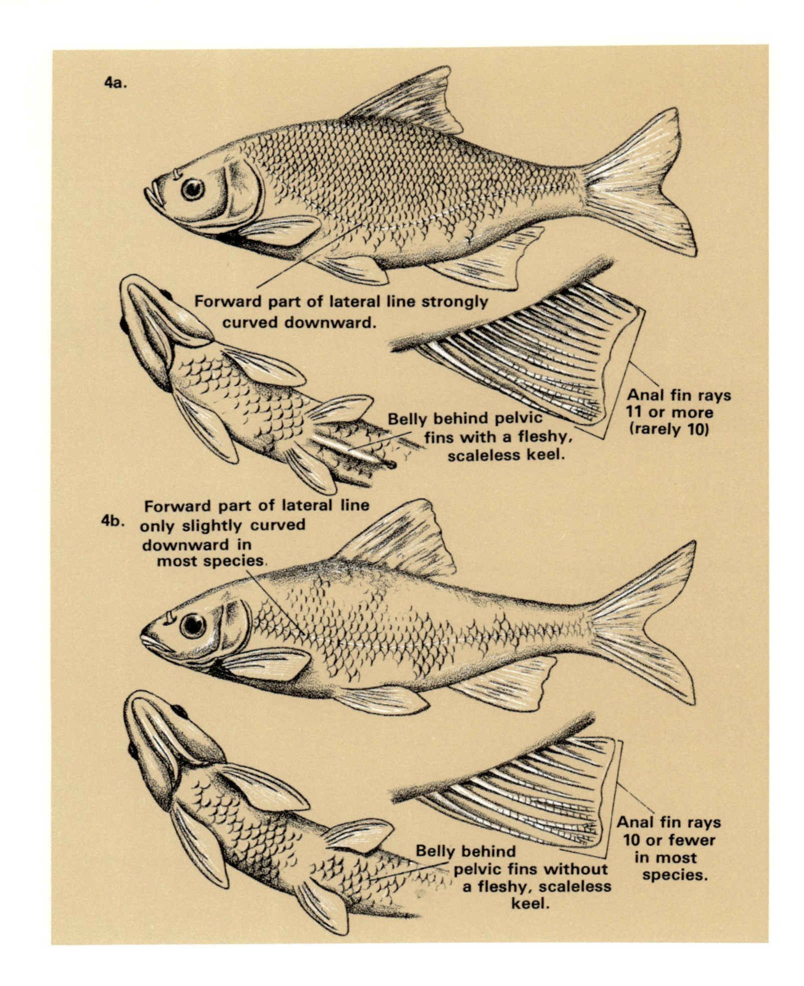

4a. *(From 3b.)* Belly behind pelvic fins with a fleshy, scaleless keel; anal fin rays 11 or more (rarely 10); forward part of lateral line strongly curved downward.
Golden shiner
Notemigonus crysoleucas
.... **Page 130**

4b. *(From 3b.)* Belly behind pelvic fins without a fleshy, scaleless keel; anal fin rays 10 or fewer in most species; forward part of lateral line only slightly curved downward in most species.
Go to 5

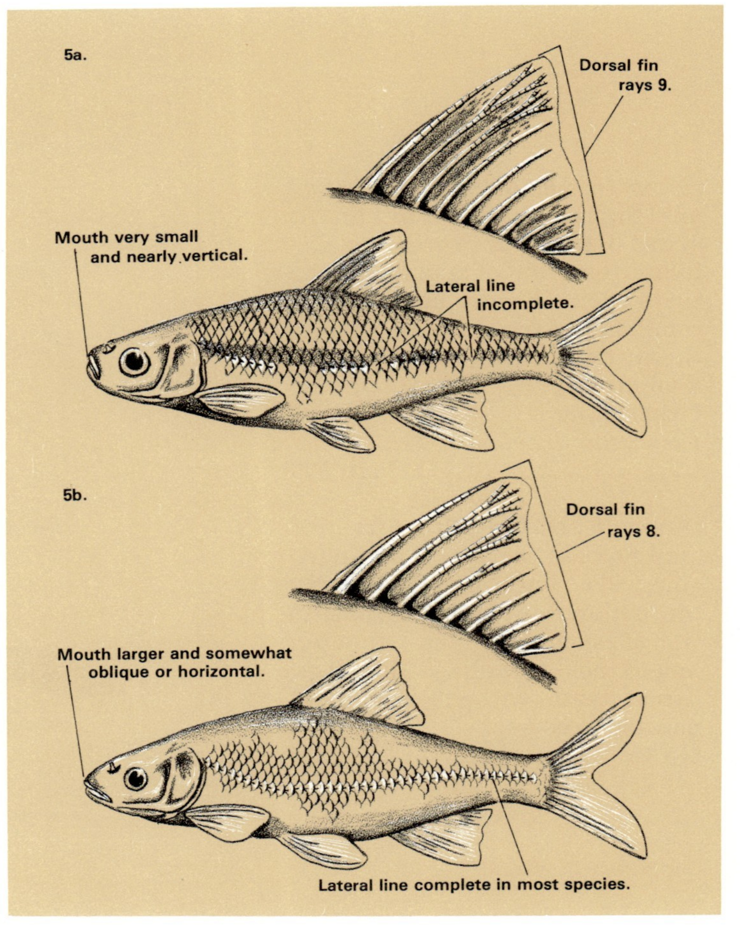

5a. *(From 4b.)* Dorsal fin rays 9; mouth very small and nearly vertical; lateral line incomplete.
Pugnose minnow
Notropis emiliae ..... **Page 141**

5b. *(From 4b.)* Dorsal fin rays 8; mouth larger and somewhat oblique or horizontal; lateral line complete in most species.
Go to 6

6a. *(From 5b.)* Scales very small, scarcely visible without magnification; lateral line scales 70 or more; side with 2 dusky stripes, separated by a broad light or yellowish stripe.
Southern redbelly dace
Phoxinus erythrogaster
.... **Page 132**

6b. *(From 5b.)* Scales larger, plainly visible without magnification; lateral line scales 65 or fewer; side usually with 1 dusky stripe or without a dusky stripe.
Go to **7**

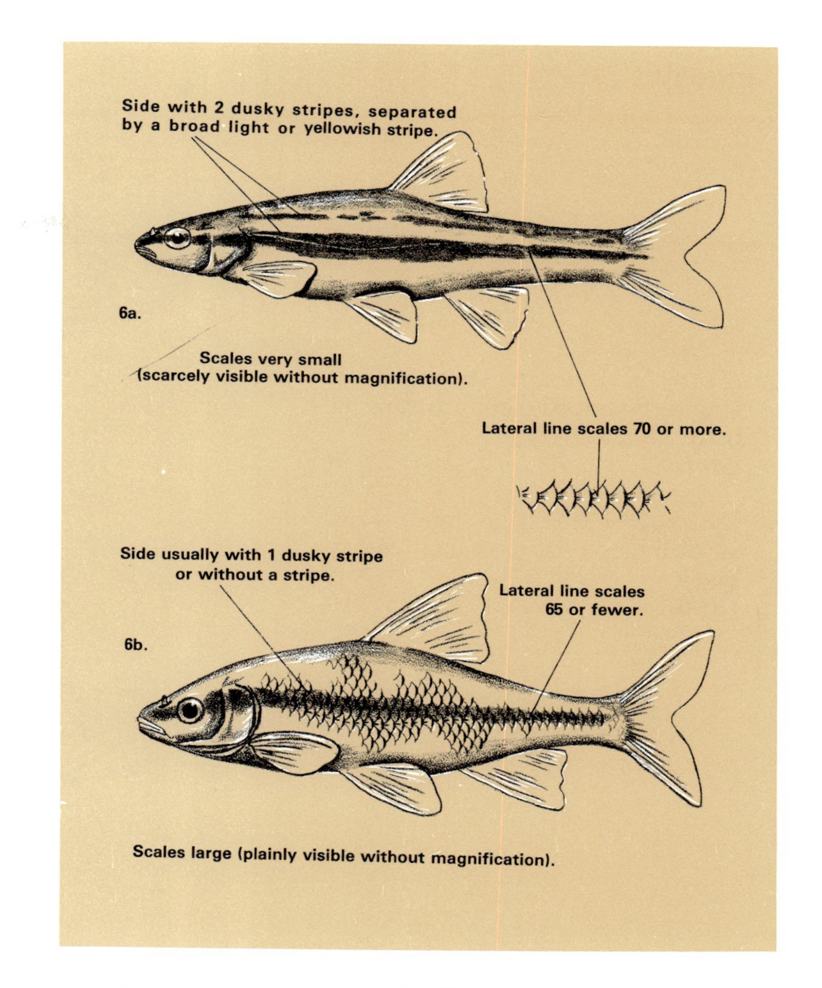

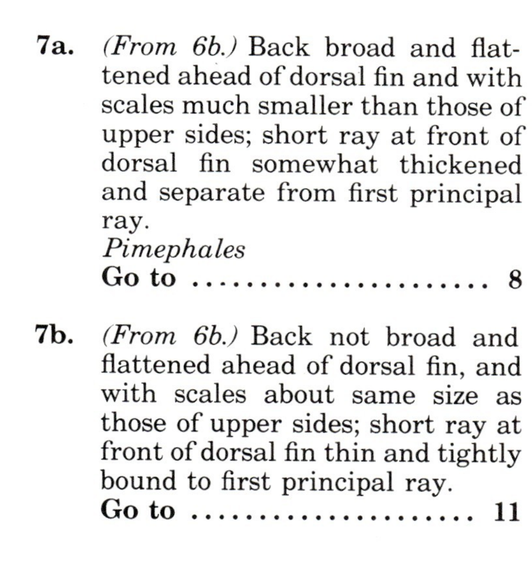

7a. *(From 6b.)* Back broad and flattened ahead of dorsal fin and with scales much smaller than those of upper sides; short ray at front of dorsal fin somewhat thickened and separate from first principal ray.
Pimephales
Go to **8**

7b. *(From 6b.)* Back not broad and flattened ahead of dorsal fin, and with scales about same size as those of upper sides; short ray at front of dorsal fin thin and tightly bound to first principal ray.
Go to **11**

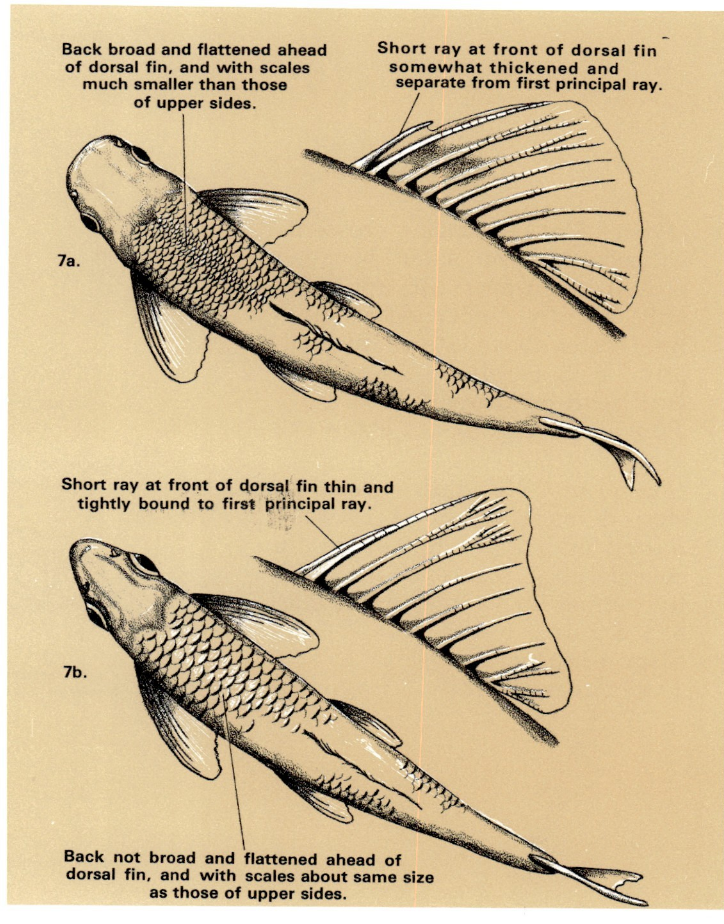

8a. *(From 7a.)* Intestine short, with a single S-shaped loop; lining of body cavity silvery.
Go to **9**

8b. *(From 7a.)* Intestine long, with several loops; lining of body cavity black.
Go to **10**

8a.
Lining of body cavity silvery.
Intestine short, with a single S-shaped loop.

8b.
Lining of body cavity black.
Intestine long, with several loops.

9a. *(From 8a.)* A dark, crescent-shaped mark on snout between nostril and upper lip; upper lip only slightly thickened at midline; scales above lateral line usually 7 or 8, rarely 6.
Bullhead minnow
Pimephales vigilax ... **Page 172**

9b. *(From 8a.)* No dark, crescent-shaped mark on snout between nostril and upper lip; upper lip considerably thickened at midline; scales above lateral line usually 6, rarely 5 or 7.
Slim minnow
Pimephales tenellus .. **Page 173**

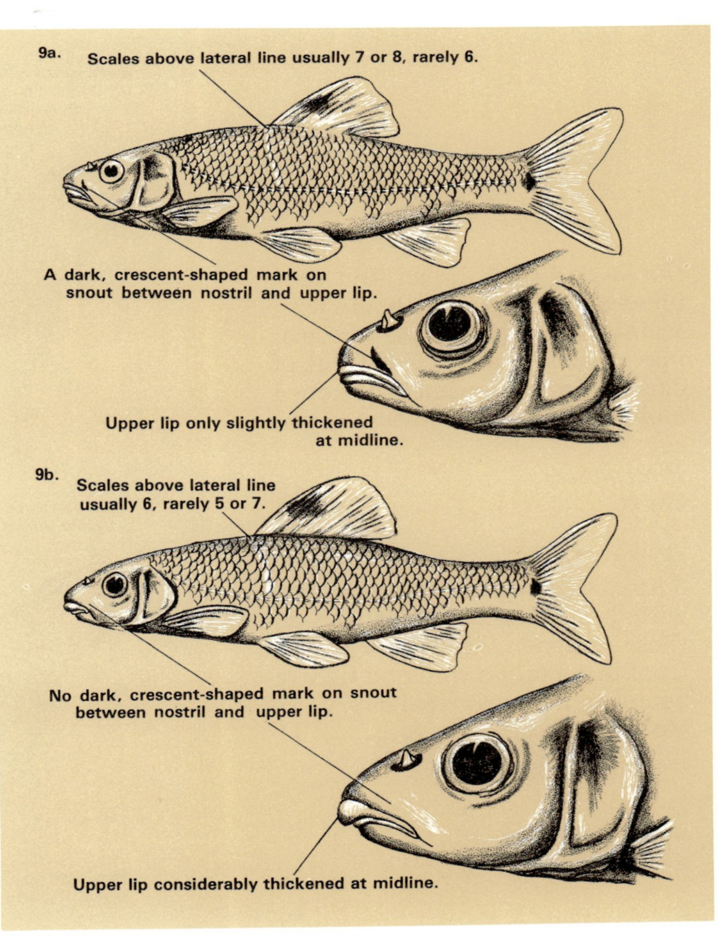

10a. *(From 8b.)* Mouth nearly horizontal and overhung by snout; dusky stripe along midside and spot at base of tail fin usually distinct; lateral line complete, extending to base of tail fin.
Bluntnose minnow
Pimephales notatus . . . **Page 173**

10b. *(From 8b.)* Mouth oblique, and not overhung by snout; dusky stripe along midside and spot at base of tail fin usually indistinct; lateral line incomplete, not extending to base of tail fin.
Fathead minnow
Pimephales promelas . **Page 174**

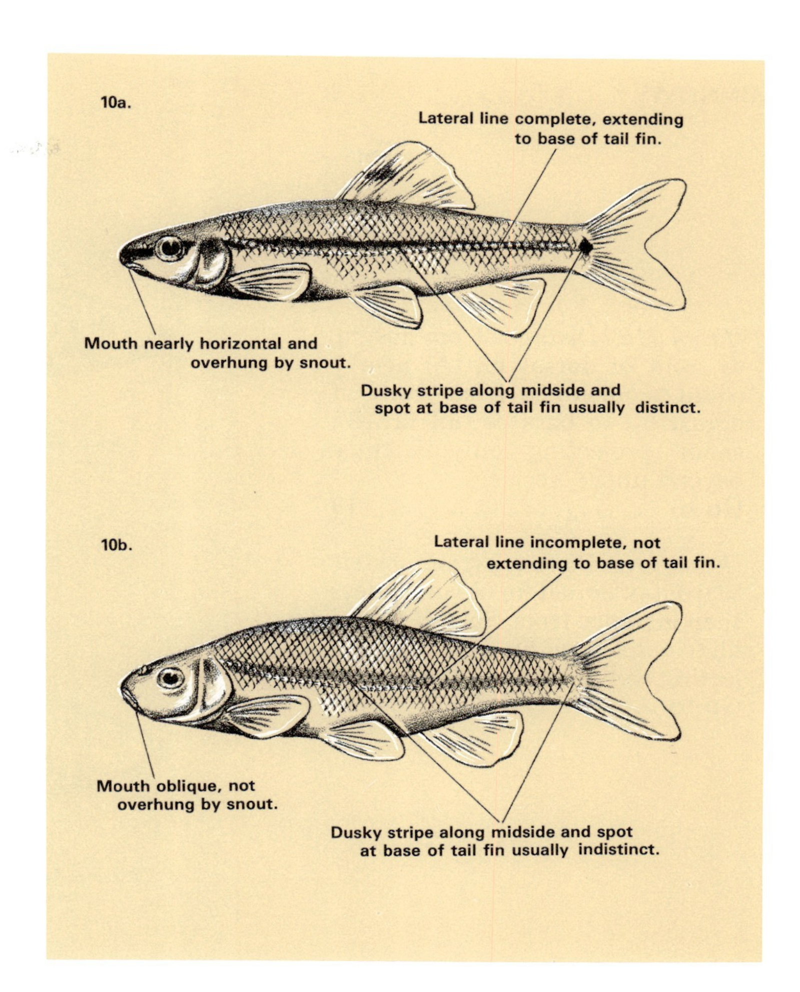

11a. *(From 7b.)* A small conical barbel at corner of mouth.
Go to **12**

11b. *(From 7b.)* No barbel at corner of mouth (a small flap-like barbel in groove above upper lip just forward of corner of mouth in creek chub).
Go to **21**

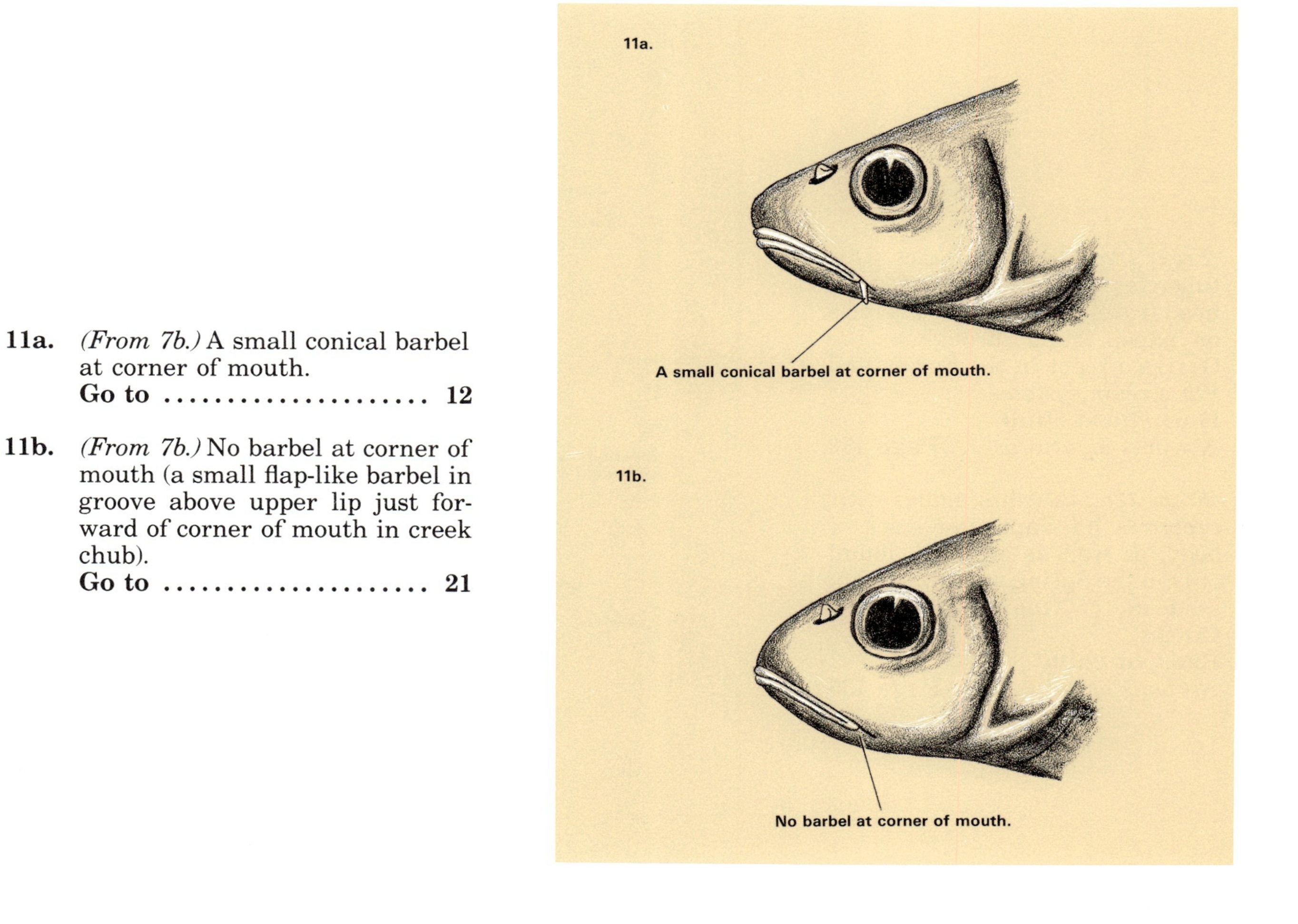

12a. *(From 11a.)* Distance from nostril to front of dorsal fin (A) nearly equal to distance from front of dorsal fin to base of tail fin (B); snout projecting only slightly beyond upper lip.
Go to **13**

12b. *(From 11a.)* Distance from nostril to front of dorsal fin (A) much less than distance from front of dorsal fin to base of tail fin (B); snout projecting well beyond upper lip.
Go to **14**

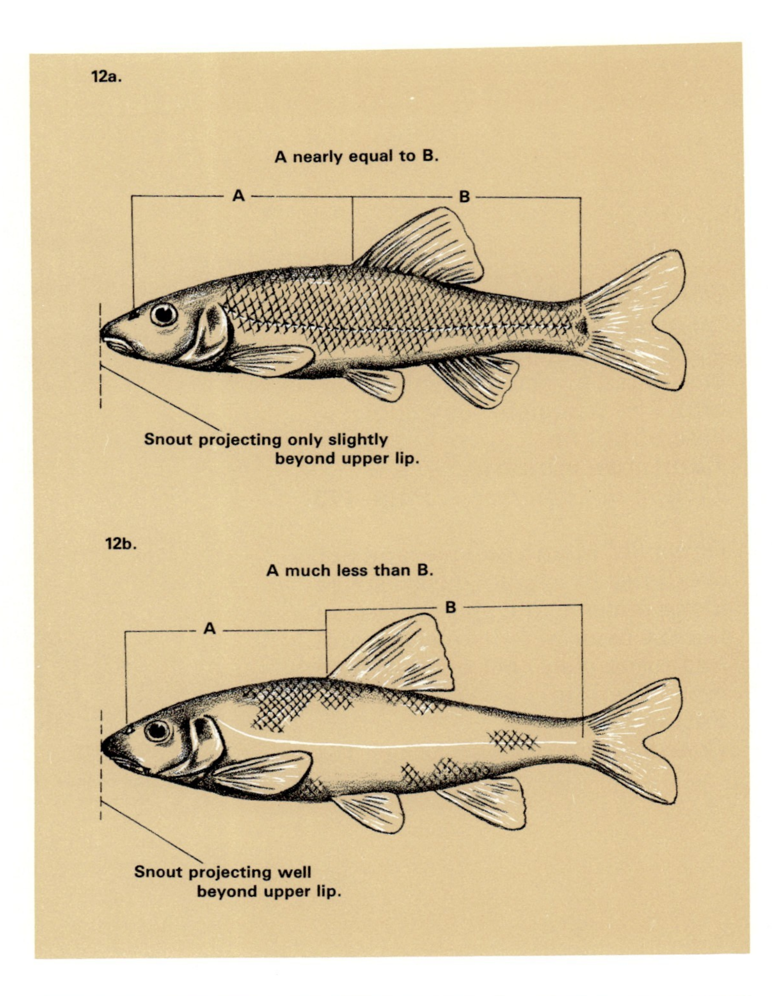

13a. *(From 12a.)* Breeding males with tubercles usually restricted to head (rarely with a few tubercles on nape); found throughout the Ozarks, except in the Spring and Elk stream systems.
Hornyhead chub
Nocomis biguttatus ... **Page 133**

13b. *(From 12a.)* Breeding males with tubercles on nape and sides of body, as well as on head; found only in the Spring and Elk stream systems of the southwestern Ozarks.
Redspot chub
Nocomis asper .... **Page 135**

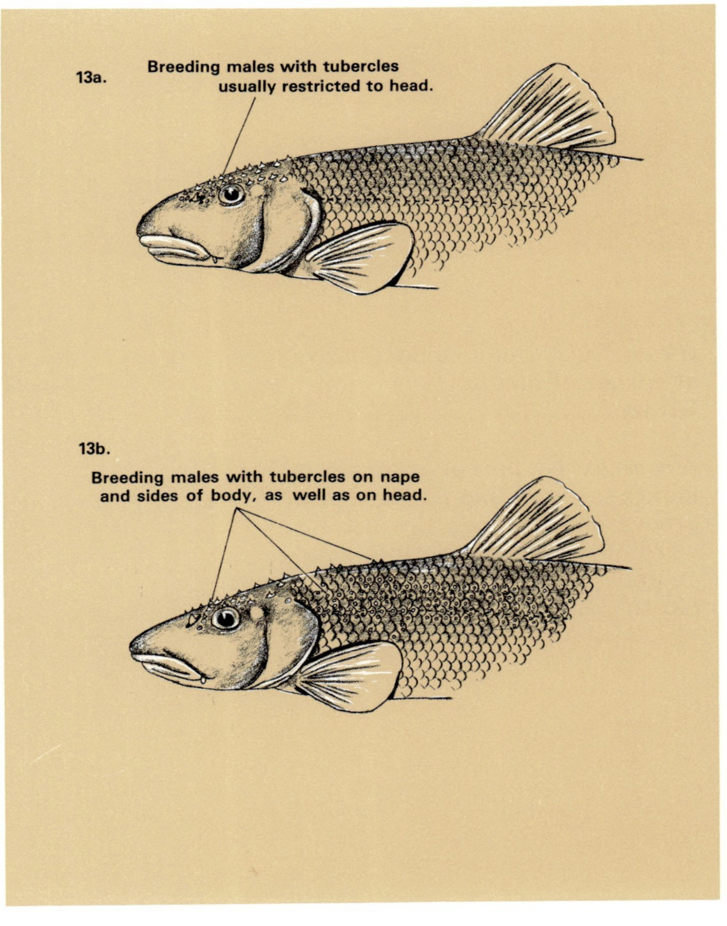

14a. *(From 12b.)* Side with a continuous dark stripe extending forward from base of tail fin to tip of snout, or side uniformly colored.
Go to 15

14b. *(From 12b.)* Side with a row of dark blotches, numerous dark X-shaped markings, or speckles.
Go to 19

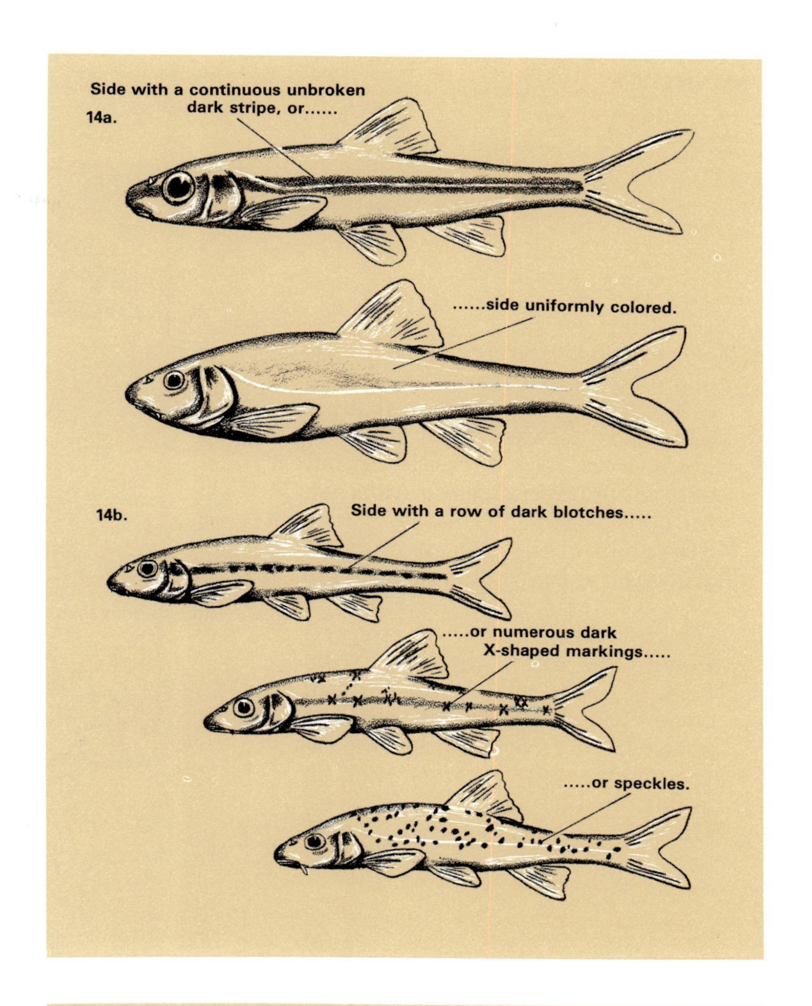

15a. *(From 14a.)* Eye small, its diameter (A) going more than 4.5 times into head length (B); lateral line scales usually more than 40.
Go to 16

15b. *(From 14a.)* Eye large, its diameter (A) going fewer than 4 times into head length (B); lateral line scales usually fewer than 40.
Go to 18

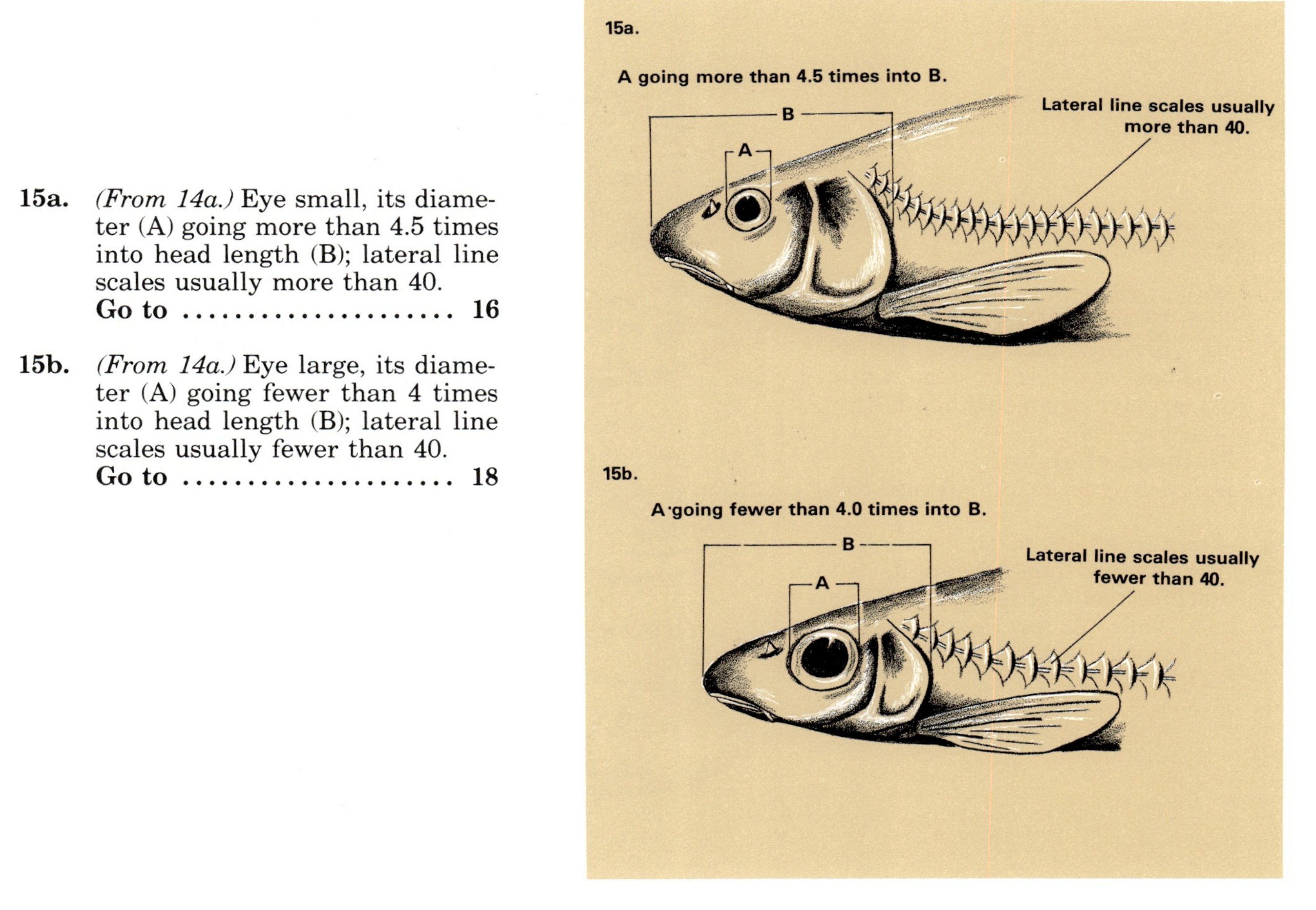

16a. *(From 15a.)* Snout length (A) about equal to distance from back of eye to rear margin of gill cover (B); body scales with distinct keels; front rays of dorsal fin not extending beyond rear rays when fin is flattened.
Sturgeon chub
Hybopsis gelida ...... **Page 139**

16b. *(From 15a.)* Snout length (A) much less than distance from back of eye to rear margin of gill cover (B); body scales without keels; front rays of dorsal fin extending beyond rear rays when fin is flattened.
Go to **17**

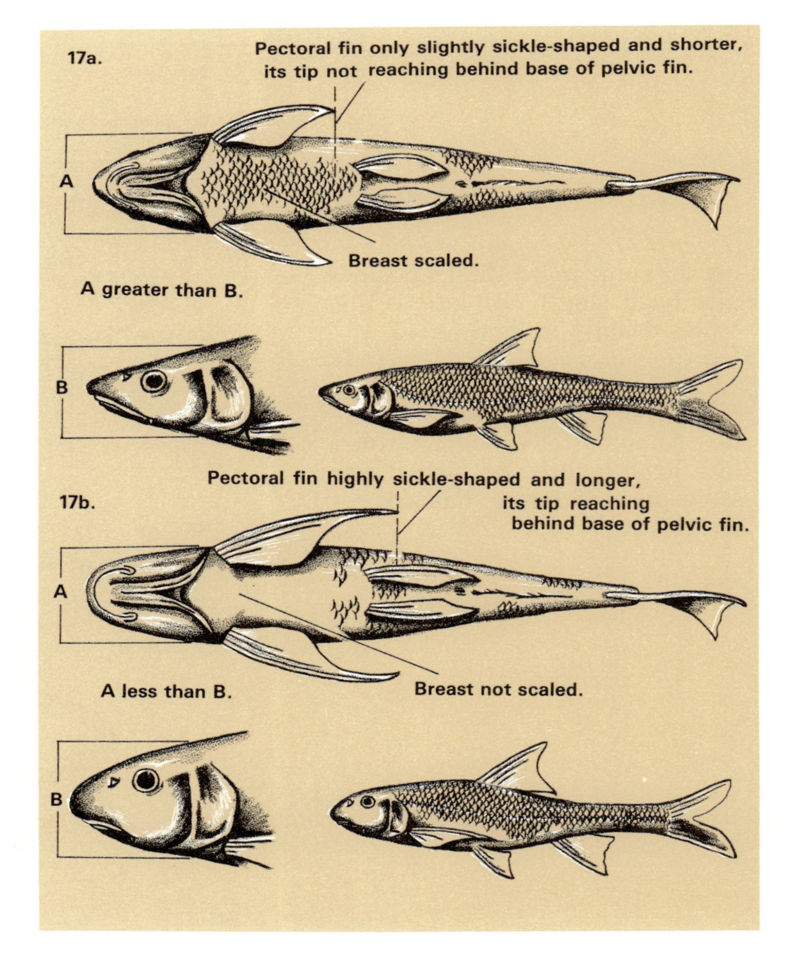

17a. *(From 16b.)* Pectoral fin only slightly sickle-shaped and shorter, its tip not reaching behind base of pelvic fin; head width (A) greater than its depth (B); breast scaled.
Flathead chub
Hybopsis gracilis ..... **Page 138**

17b. *(From 16b.)* Pectoral fin highly sickle-shaped and longer, its tip reaching behind base of pelvic fin; head width (A) less than its depth (B); breast not scaled.
Sicklefin chub
Hybopsis meeki ...... **Page 140**

18a. *(From 15b.)* Distance from tip of snout to front of dorsal fin (A) equal to or greater than distance from front of dorsal fin to base of tail fin (B); stripe along midside dark and well developed.
Bigeye chub
Hybopsis amblops .... **Page 136**

18b. *(From 15b.)* Distance from tip of snout to front of dorsal fin (A) much less than distance from front of dorsal fin to base of tail fin (B); stripe along midside indistinct or absent.
Silver chub
Hybopsis storeriana .. **Page 135**

18a.
A equal to or greater than B.
A
B
Stripe along midside dark and well developed.

18b.
A much less than B.
A
B
Stripe along midside indistinct or absent.

19a. *(From 14b.)* Eye smaller, its diameter (A) less than distance from back of eye to upper end of gill opening (B); upper jaw extending past front of eye; side with numerous small, roundish, dark speckles.
Speckled chub
Hybopsis aestivalis ... **Page 138**

19b. *(From 14b.)* Eye larger, its diameter (A) about equal to distance from back of eye to upper end of gill opening (B); upper jaw not extending past front of eye; side with numerous X-shaped markings or a row of dark blotches.
Go to **20**

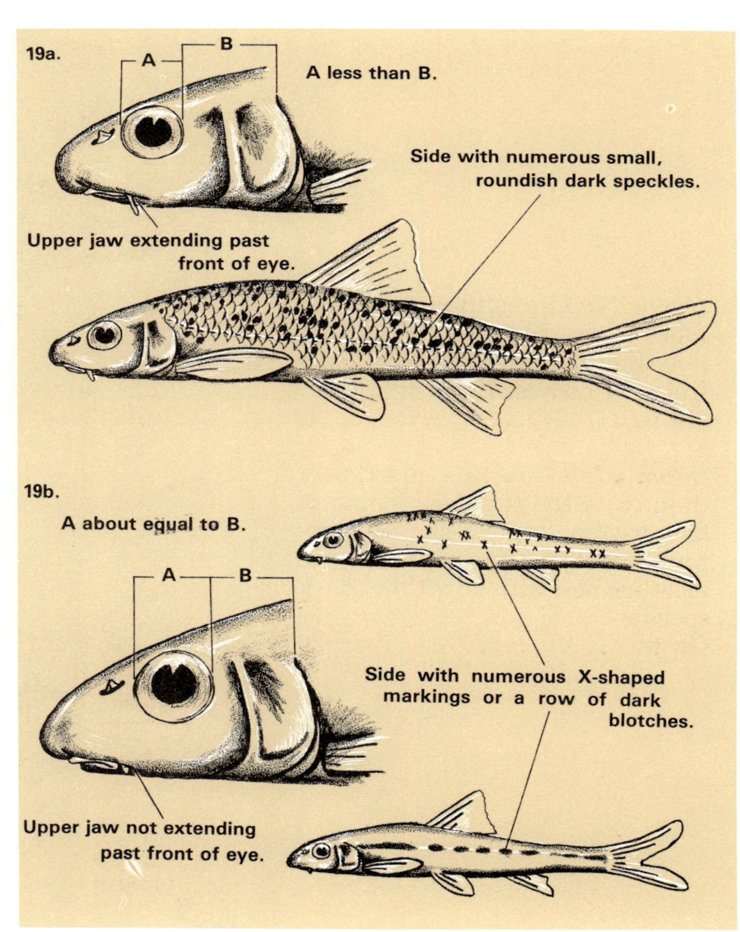
19a.
A
B
A less than B.
Side with numerous small, roundish dark speckles.
Upper jaw extending past front of eye.
19b.
A about equal to B.
A
B
Side with numerous X-shaped markings or a row of dark blotches.
Upper jaw not extending past front of eye.

20a. *(From 19b.)* Stripe along midline of back composed of a series of alternating light and dark areas; midside with a row of dark blotches; body without scattered X-shaped markings; lateral line scales usually 46 to 49.
Streamline chub
Hybopsis dissimilis ... **Page 136**

20b. *(From 19b.)* Stripe along midline of back uniformly colored; midside without a row of dark blotches; body with numerous scattered X-shaped markings; lateral line scales usually 40 to 43.
Gravel chub
Hybopsis x-punctata .. **Page 137**

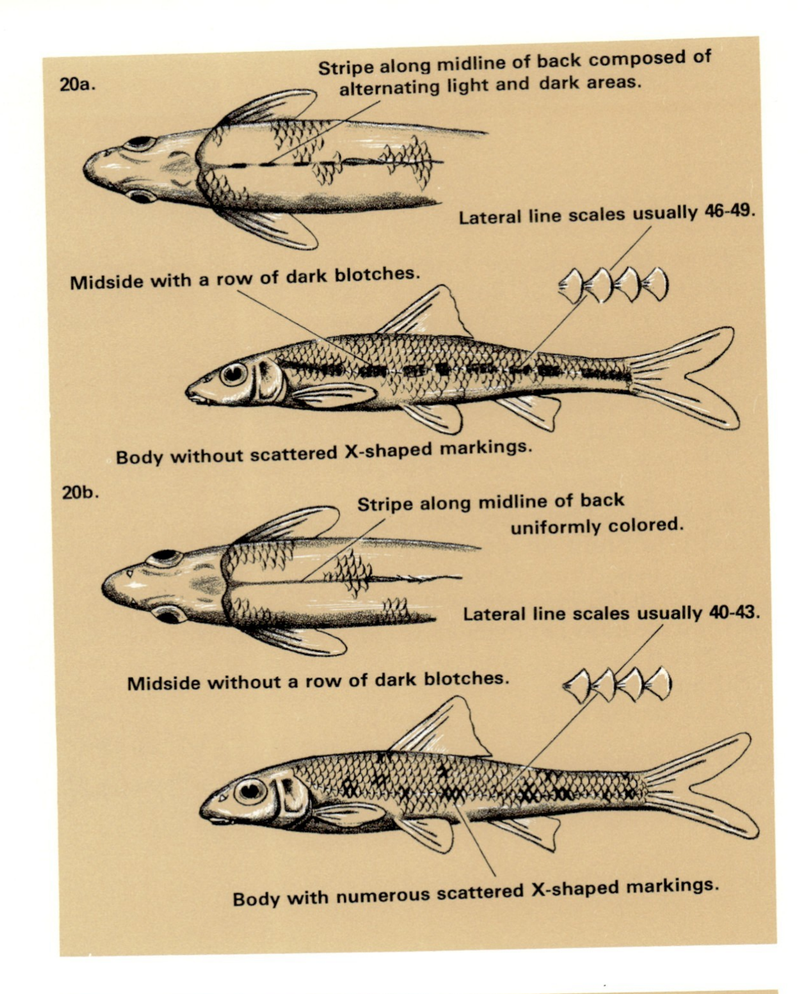

21a. *(From 11b.)* Intestine long, much more than twice the standard length of fish, with several loops; lining of body cavity black.
Go to **22**

21b. *(From 11b.)* Intestine short, less than twice the standard length of fish, with a single S-shaped loop; lining of body cavity silvery in most species, with or without dark speckles.
Go to **29**

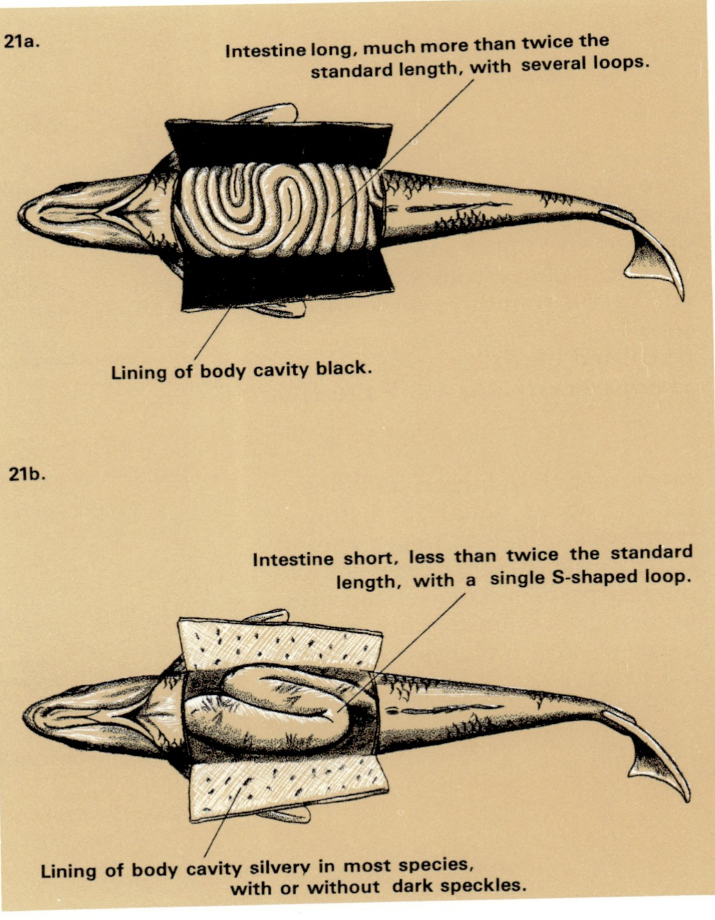

22a. *(From 21a.)* Lower jaw with a hard, shelf-like extension, separated from lower lip by a groove; anal fin rays usually 7.
Go to **23**

22b. *(From 21a.)* Lower jaw without a hard, shelf-like extension; anal fin rays usually 8.
Go to **24**

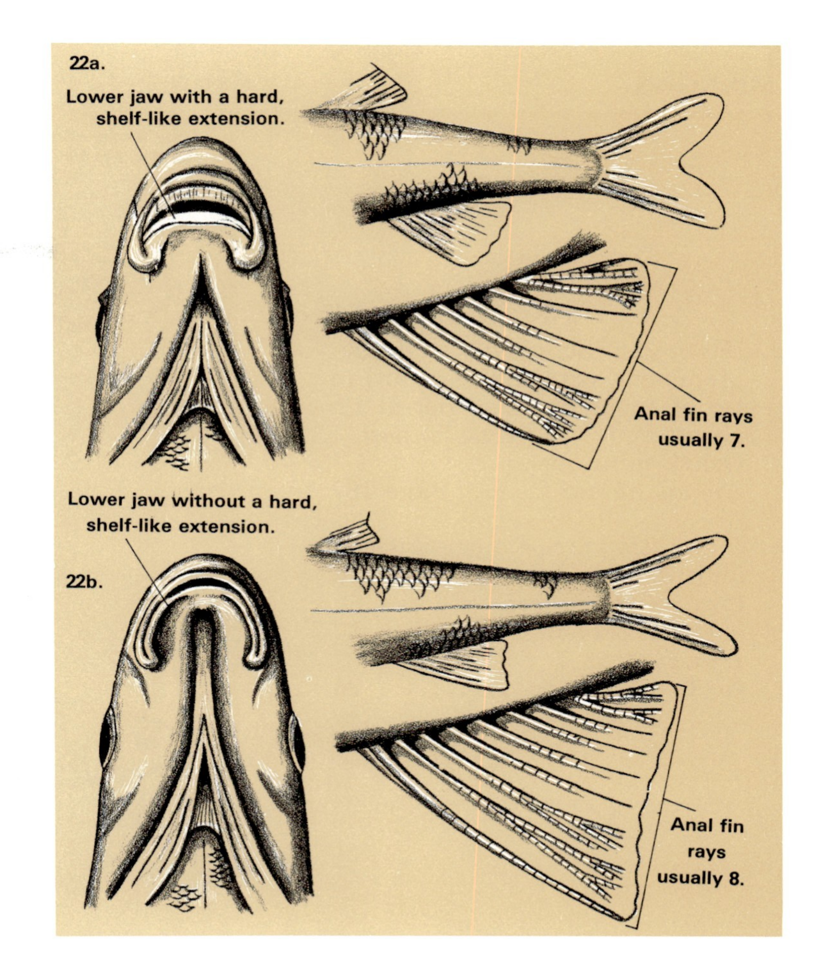

23a. *(From 22a.)* Number of scale rows around body just in front of dorsal fin usually 40 to 55; least width of skull between eyes (A) usually less than distance from back of eye to upper end of gill opening (B); breeding males with black pigment in anal fin and with 1 to 3 tubercles beside each nostril.
Central stoneroller
Campostoma anomalum
.... **Page 175**

23b. *(From 22a.)* Number of scale rows around body just in front of dorsal fin usually 32 to 39; least width of skull between eyes (A) about equal to distance from back of eye to upper end of gill opening (B); breeding males without black pigment in anal fin and without tubercles beside each nostril.
Largescale stoneroller
Campostoma oligolepis
.... **Page 177**

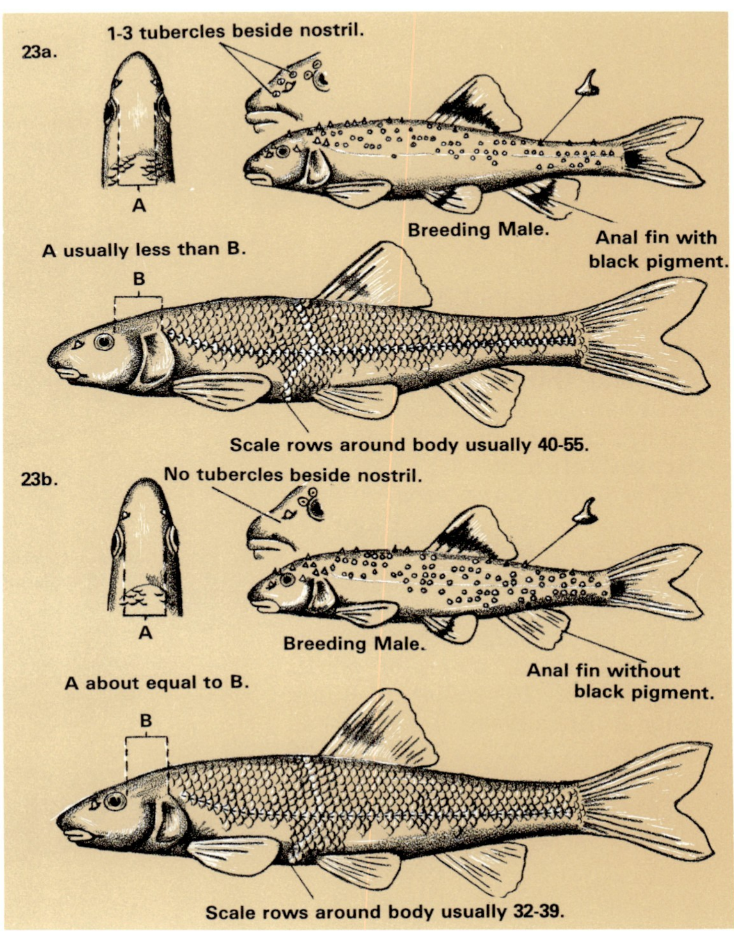

24a. *(From 22b.)* Stripe along midside prominent, extending forward to tip of snout; front of dorsal fin about even with pelvic fin base.
Ozark minnow
Dionda nubila .... **Page 167**

24b. *(From 22b.)* Stripe along midside indistinct, not extending forward to tip of snout; front of dorsal fin ahead of pelvic fin base.
Hybognathus
Go to **25**

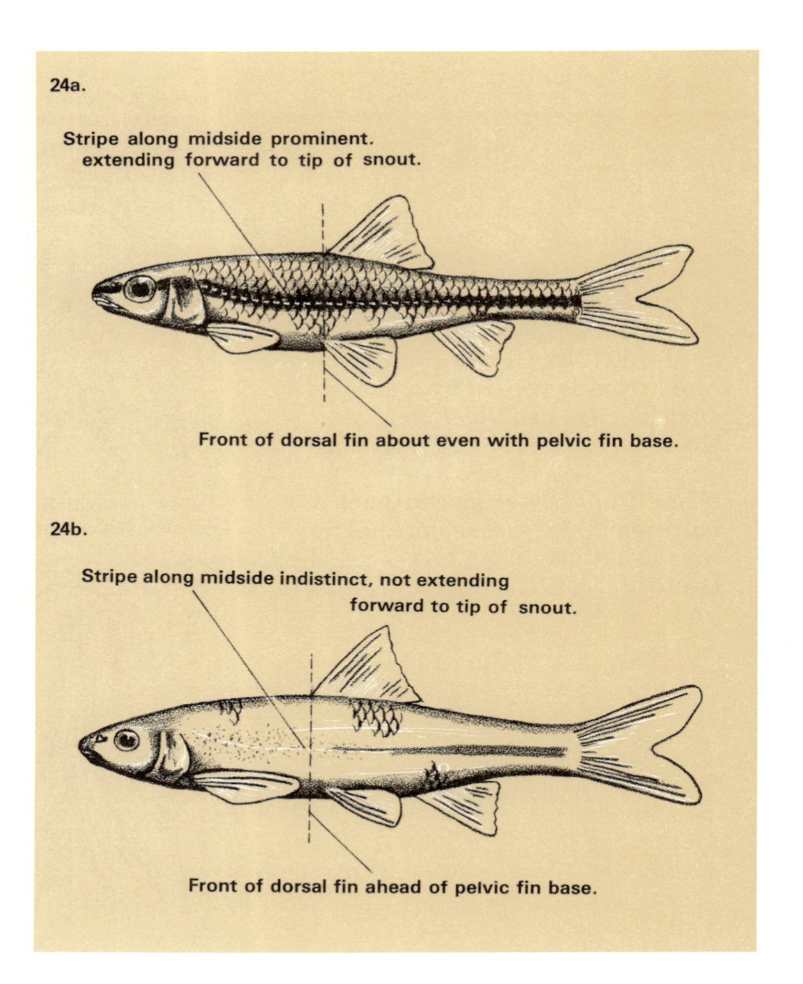

25a. *(From 24b.)* Dorsal fin somewhat rounded at outer margin, its first principal ray shorter than the second and third; scales of adults with about 20 radiating lines (radii); color in life yellowish.
Brassy minnow
Hybognathus hankinsoni
.... **Page 171**

25b. *(From 24b.)* Dorsal fin pointed at outer margin, its first principal ray as long or longer than the second and third; scales of adults with about 10 radiating lines; color in life silvery.
Go to **26**

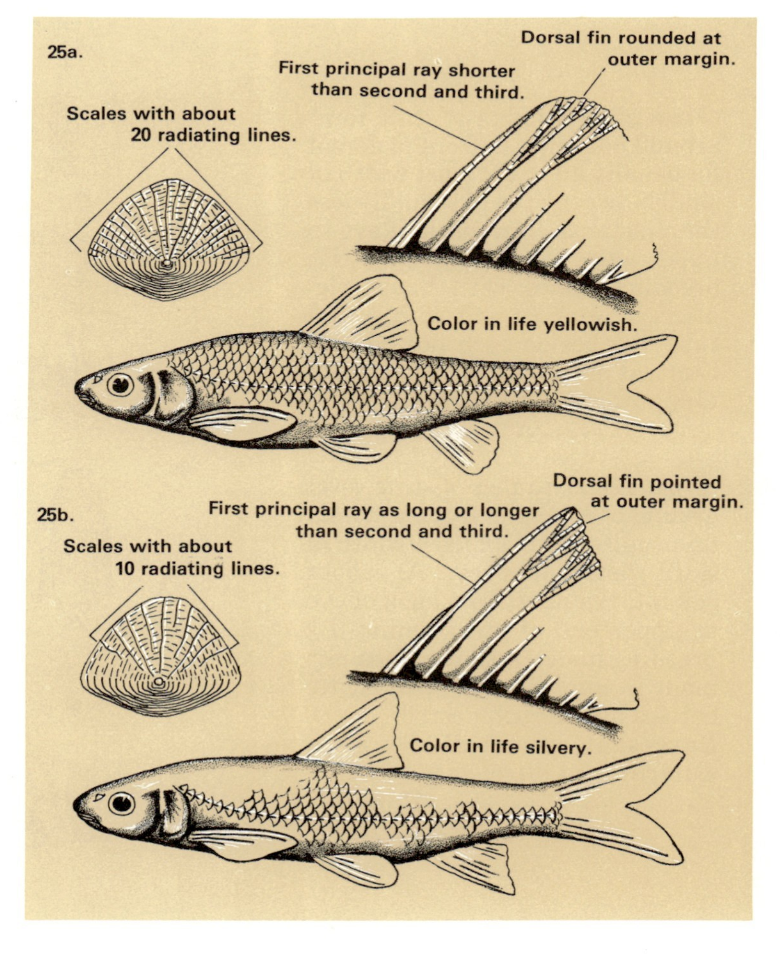

26a. *(From 25b.)* Snout length (A) less than eye diameter (B); front of upper lip about level with middle of eye; scales on forward part of side prominently dark-edged, forming a distinct diamond-shaped pattern.
Cypress minnow
Hybognathus hayi .... **Page 171**

26b. *(From 25b.)* Snout length (A) greater than eye diameter (B); front of upper lip below middle of eye; scales on forward part of side not prominently dark-edged, not forming a distinct diamond-shaped pattern.
Go to **27**

26a.
Scales on forward part of side with prominent dark edges forming a distinct diamond-shaped pattern.
A less than B.
A
B
Front of upper lip about level with middle of eye.

26b.
Scales on forward part of side without prominent dark edges.
A greater than B.
A
B
Front of upper lip below middle of eye.

27a. *(From 26b.)* Basioccipital process (backward extension of bone at lower rear margin of skull) narrow and peg-like; muscles nearly touching at point of attachment to basioccipital process.
Plains minnow
Hybognathus placitus . **Page 170**

27b. *(From 26b.)* Basioccipital process broad and blade-like; muscles well separated at point of attachment to basioccipital process (see illustrations, couplet 28).
Go to **28**

27a.

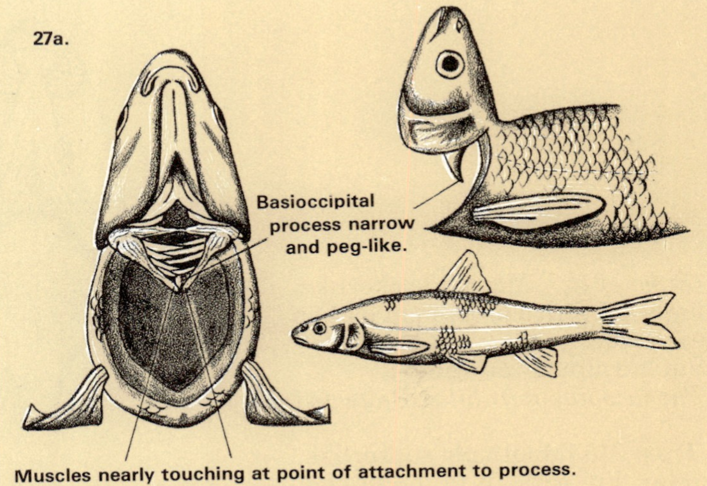
Basioccipital
process narrow
and peg-like.
Muscles nearly touching at point of attachment to process.

27b.

See illustrations, couplet 28.

28a. *(From 27b.)* Diameter of eye (A) less than width of mouth opening (B); rear margin of basioccipital process straight or only slightly concave.
Western silvery minnow
Hybognathus argyritis
.... **Page 169**

28b. *(From 27b.)* Diameter of eye (A) greater than width of mouth opening (B); rear margin of basioccipital process deeply concave.
Central silvery minnow
Hybognathus nuchalis
.... **Page 168**

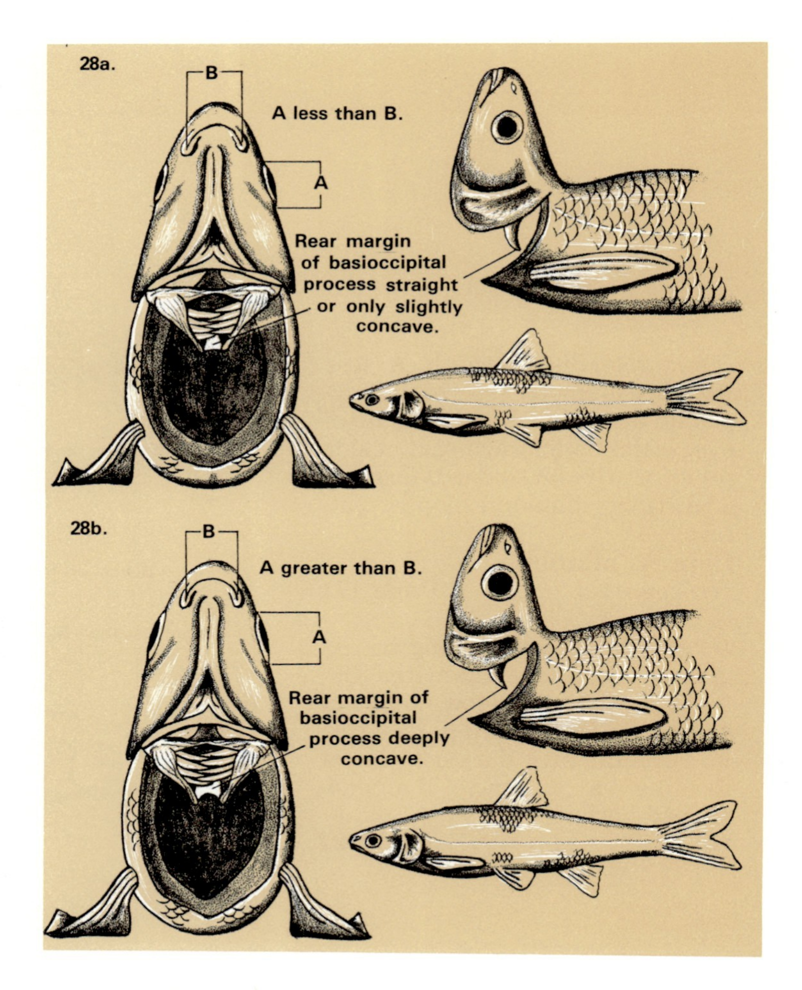

29a. *(From 21b.)* Mouth suckerlike; lower lip with a prominent lobe on each side.
Suckermouth minnow
Phenacobius mirabilis **Page 141**

29b. *(From 21b.)* Mouth not suckerlike; lower lip without a prominent lobe on each side.
Go to **30**

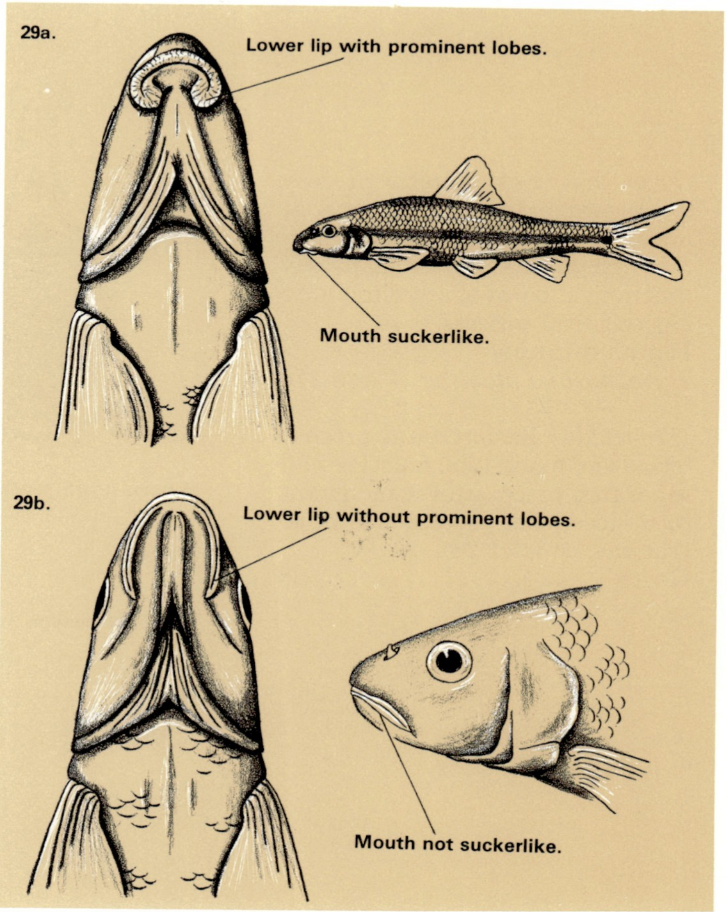

30a. *(From 29b.)* Upper lip much wider at midline than on either side; a small flap-like barbel in groove above upper lip near corner of mouth; lateral line scales usually more than 50.
Creek chub
Semotilus atromaculatus
.... **Page 131**

30b. *(From 29b.)* Upper lip nearly uniform in width; no flap-like barbel in groove above upper lip; lateral line scales usually fewer than 50.
Go to **31**

30a.
Upper lip much wider at midline than on either side.
Lateral line scales usually more than 50.
Small flap-like barbel in groove.

30b.
Lateral line scales usually fewer than 50.
Upper lip nearly uniform in width.
No flap-like barbel in groove.

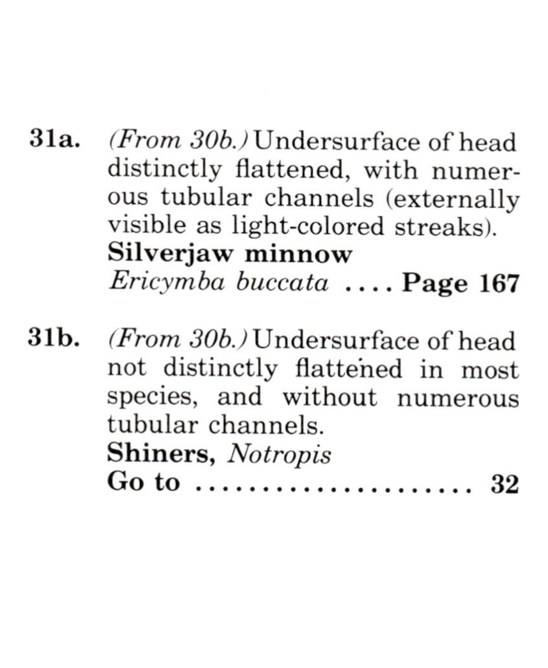

31a. *(From 30b.)* Undersurface of head distinctly flattened, with numerous tubular channels (externally visible as light-colored streaks).
Silverjaw minnow
Ericymba buccata .... **Page 167**

31b. *(From 30b.)* Undersurface of head not distinctly flattened in most species, and without numerous tubular channels.
Shiners, ***Notropis***
Go to **32**

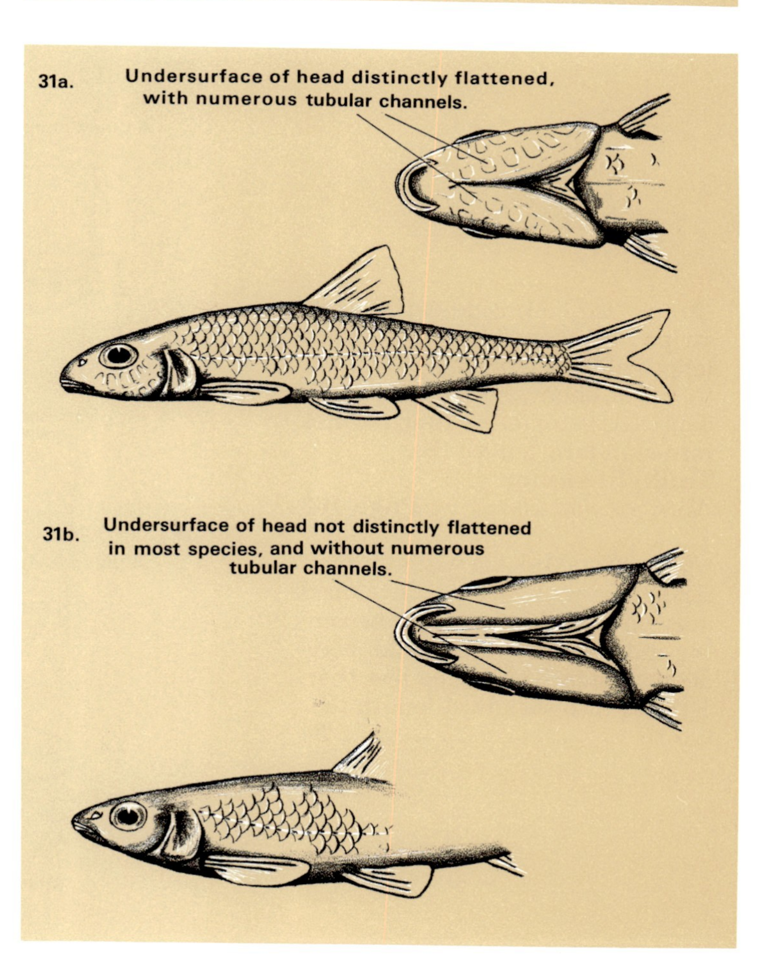
31a.
Undersurface of head distinctly flattened, with numerous tubular channels.
31b.
Undersurface of head not distinctly flattened in most species, and without numerous tubular channels.

32a.

Black spot prominent, as large or larger than pupil of eye, and roundish or squarish in outline.

Black spot much smaller than pupil of eye, and often triangular in outline, or........

32b.

........black spot absent.

32a. *(From 31b.)* Base of tail fin with a prominent black spot, as large or larger than pupil of eye, and roundish or squarish in outline.
Go to 33

32b. *(From 31b.)* Base of tail fin with spot much smaller than pupil of eye and often triangular in outline, or base of tail fin without a prominent black spot.
Go to 35

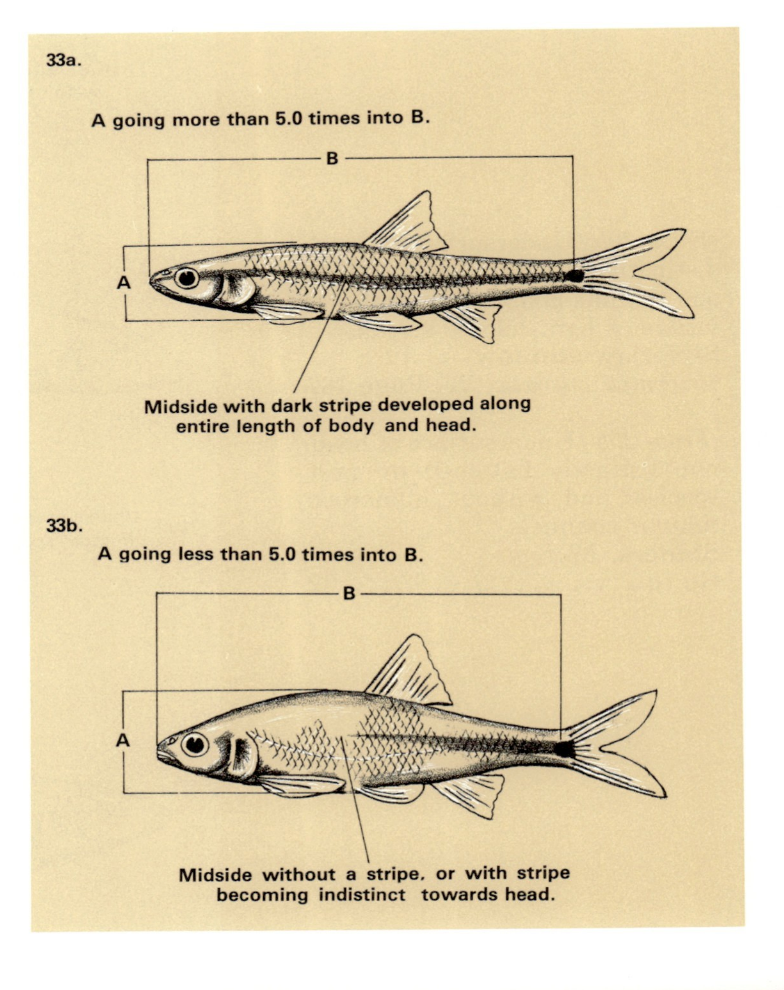
33a.
A going more than 5.0 times into B.
B
A
Midside with dark stripe developed along entire length of body and head.
33b.
A going less than 5.0 times into B.
B
A
Midside without a stripe, or with stripe becoming indistinct towards head.

33a. *(From 32a.)* Midside with dark stripe developed along entire length of body from base of tail fin to tip of snout; body slender, its depth (A) going more than 5 times into standard length (B).
Taillight shiner
Notropis maculatus **.. Page 163**

33b. *(From 32a.)* Midside without dark stripe or with stripe developed only on back half of body, becoming indistinct towards head; body deep, its depth (A) going less than 5 times into standard length (B).
Go to 34

34a. *(From 33b.)* Dorsal fin with dark speckles on some membranes between fin rays, forming a dusky blotch in back part of fin in adults; distance from tip of snout to front of dorsal fin (A) greater than distance from front of dorsal fin to base of tail fin (B).
Blacktail shiner
Notropis venustus .... **Page 158**

34b. *(From 33b.)* Dorsal fin with dark speckles absent or confined to margins of fin rays; distance from tip of snout to front of dorsal fin (A) less than distance from front of dorsal fin to base of tail fin (B).
Spottail shiner
Notropis hudsonius ... **Page 151**

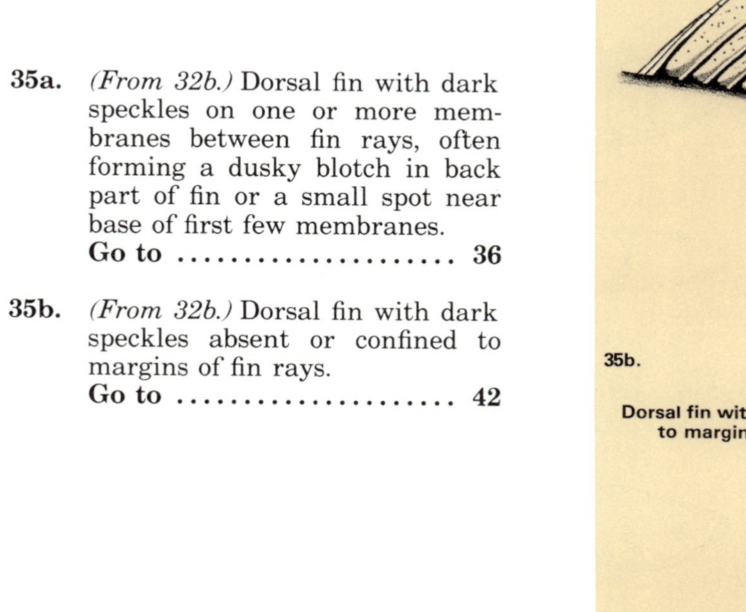

35a. *(From 32b.)* Dorsal fin with dark speckles on one or more membranes between fin rays, often forming a dusky blotch in back part of fin or a small spot near base of first few membranes.
Go to 36

35b. *(From 32b.)* Dorsal fin with dark speckles absent or confined to margins of fin rays.
Go to 42

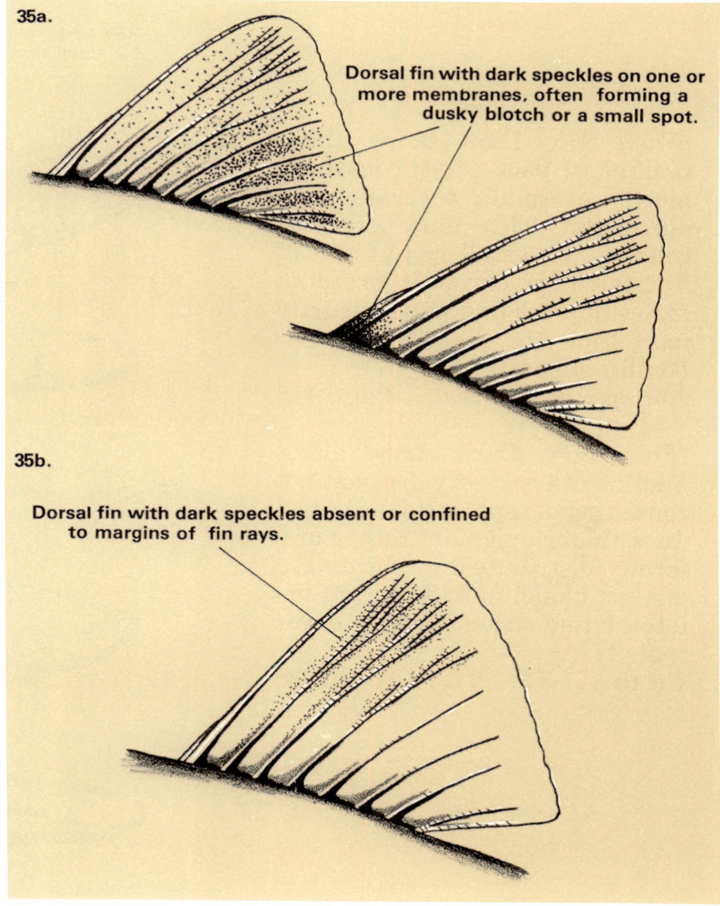
35a.
Dorsal fin with dark speckles on one or more membranes, often forming a dusky blotch or a small spot.
35b.
Dorsal fin with dark speckles absent or confined to margins of fin rays.

36a. *(From 35a.)* Body slender, its depth (A) going more than 5 times into standard length (B); tip of upper lip on a level with or below middle of eye; scales in forward part of lateral line with rear margin slightly scalloped.
Ozark shiner
Notropis ozarcanus ... **Page 164**

36b. *(From 35a.)* Body deeper, its depth (A) going less than 5 times into standard length (B); tip of upper lip on a level with upper part of eye; scales in forward part of lateral line with rear margin rounded.
Go to 37

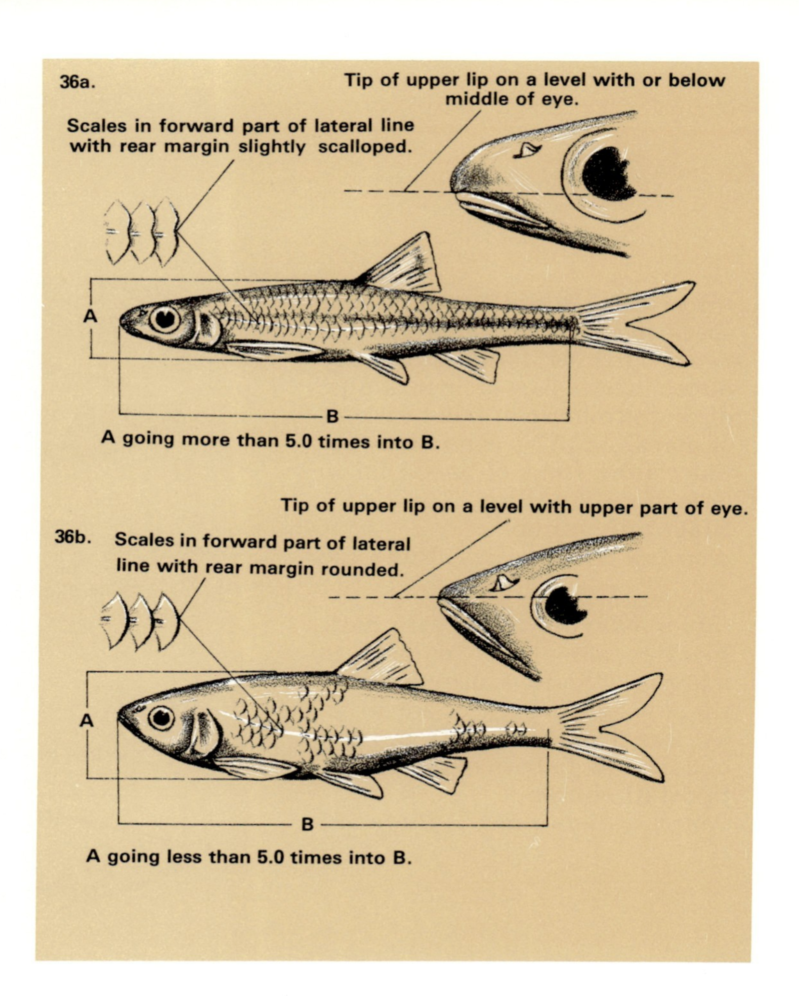
36a.
Tip of upper lip on a level with or below middle of eye.
Scales in forward part of lateral line with rear margin slightly scalloped.
A
B
A going more than 5.0 times into B.
Tip of upper lip on a level with upper part of eye.
36b.
Scales in forward part of lateral line with rear margin rounded.
A
B
A going less than 5.0 times into B.

37a. *(From 36b.)* Dark stripe along midline of back faint, consisting mostly of small, separate dots; dorsal fin with dark pigment confined to a small spot at base of first few rays, except in breeding males; lateral line scales usually more than 41.
Redfin shiner
Notropis umbratilis .. **Page 145**

37b. *(From 36b.)* Dark stripe along midline of back very distinct, not consisting of separate dots; dorsal fin with dark pigment rather uniformly distributed, or forming a distinct blotch in back part of fin; lateral line scales usually fewer than 41.
Go to 38

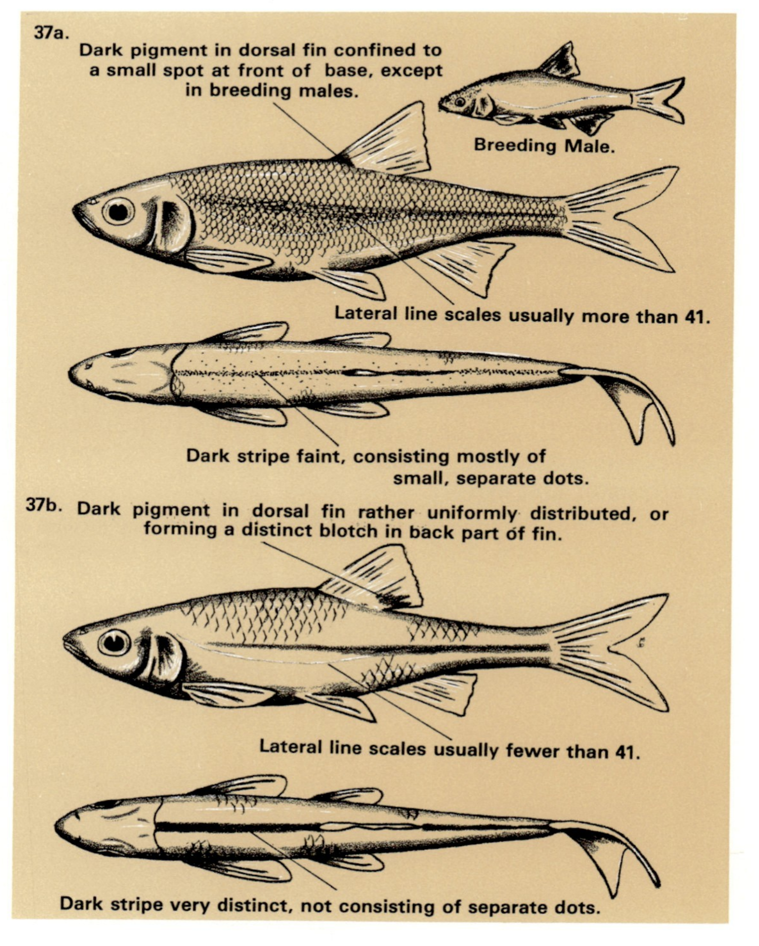
37a.
Dark pigment in dorsal fin confined to a small spot at front of base, except in breeding males.
Breeding Male.
Lateral line scales usually more than 41.
Dark stripe faint, consisting mostly of small, separate dots.
37b. Dark pigment in dorsal fin rather uniformly distributed, or forming a distinct blotch in back part of fin.
Lateral line scales usually fewer than 41.
Dark stripe very distinct, not consisting of separate dots.

38a. *(From 37b.)* Dorsal fin with dark pigment rather uniformly distributed on membranes, not forming a distinct blotch in back part of fin; body depth (A) usually going less than 3.5 times into standard length (B).
Red shiner
Notropis lutrensis .... **Page 160**

38b. *(From 37b.)* Dorsal fin with dark pigment concentrated on membranes in back part of fin, forming a distinct black blotch in adults; body depth (A) usually going more than 3.5 times into standard length (B).
Go to **39**

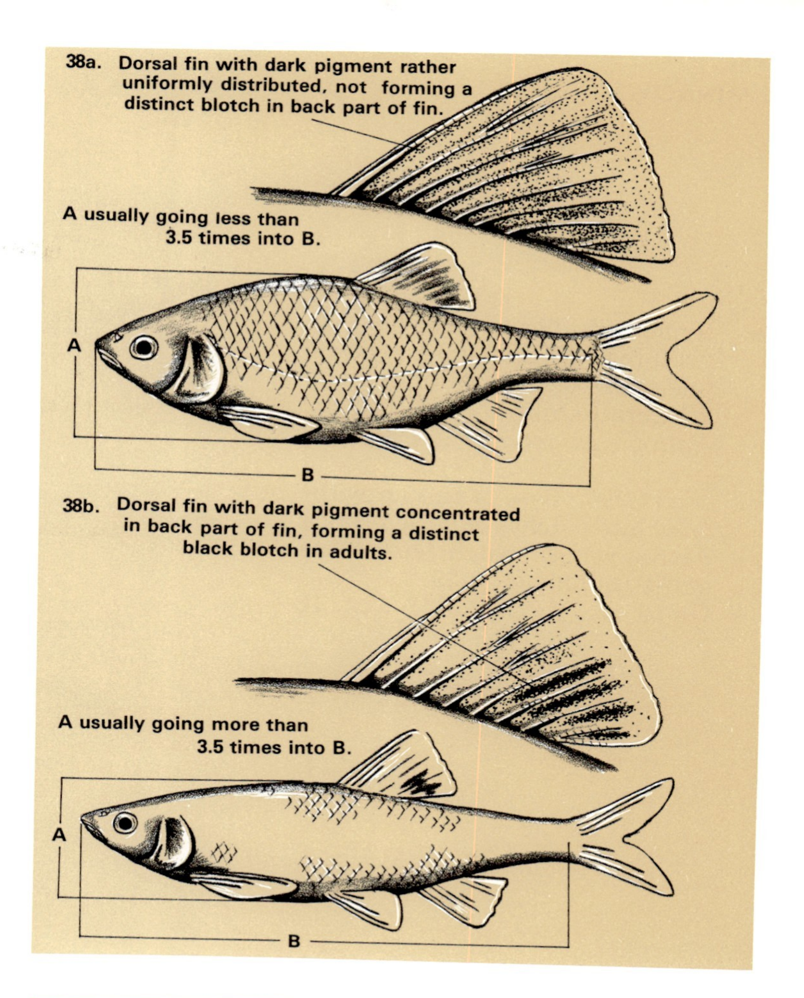
38a. Dorsal fin with dark pigment rather uniformly distributed, not forming a distinct blotch in back part of fin.
A usually going less than 3.5 times into B.
A
B
38b. Dorsal fin with dark pigment concentrated in back part of fin, forming a distinct black blotch in adults.
A usually going more than 3.5 times into B.
A
B

39a. *(From 38b.)* Anal fin rays usually 8; first 2 or 3 membranes of dorsal fin with dark pigment faint or absent except in breeding males; dark stripe on side of caudal peduncle narrow and prominent, sharply defined above, and centered below pores of lateral line.
Spotfin shiner
Notropis spilopterus .. **Page 157**

39b. *(From 38b.)* Anal fin rays usually 9; first 2 or 3 membranes of dorsal fin with dark pigment present except in very small young; dark stripe on side of caudal peduncle broad and faint, poorly defined above, and centered on pores of lateral line.
Go to **40**

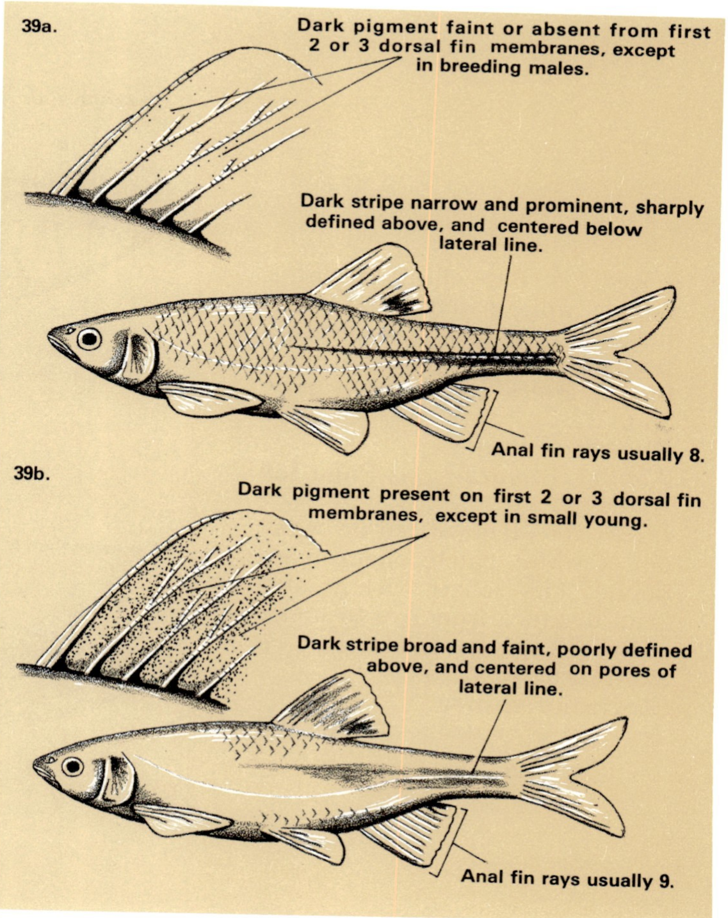
39a.
Dark pigment faint or absent from first 2 or 3 dorsal fin membranes, except in breeding males.
Dark stripe narrow and prominent, sharply defined above, and centered below lateral line.
Anal fin rays usually 8.
39b.
Dark pigment present on first 2 or 3 dorsal fin membranes, except in small young.
Dark stripe broad and faint, poorly defined above, and centered on pores of lateral line.
Anal fin rays usually 9.

40a. *(From 39b.)* Base of tail fin with two broad white patches; lateral line scales usually 39 to 41.
Whitetail shiner
Notropis galacturus .. **Page 158**

40b. *(From 39b.)* Base of tail fin without white patches or with a single narrow vertical patch; lateral line scales usually 35 to 39.
Go to **41**

40a.
Base of tail fin with two broad white patches.
Lateral line scales usually 39-41.

40b.
Base of tail fin without white patches, or.....
.....with a single narrow vertical patch.
Lateral line scales usually 35-39.

41a. *(From 40b.)* Base of tail fin with a narrow white patch; snout blunt, its length (A) less than distance from eye to upper end of gill opening (B); lateral line scales usually 35 to 37.
Bluntface shiner
Notropis camurus .... **Page 159**

41b. *(From 40b.)* Base of tail fin without a white patch; snout more pointed, its length (A) greater than distance from eye to upper end of gill opening (B); lateral line scales usually 37 to 39.
Steelcolor shiner
Notropis whipplei .... **Page 156**

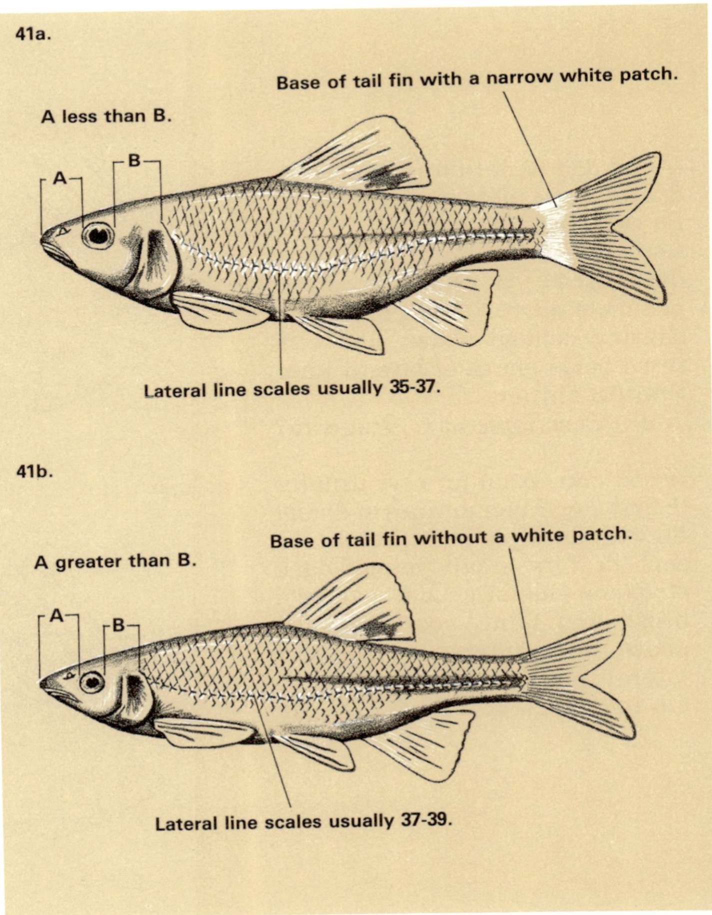
41a.
Base of tail fin with a narrow white patch.
A less than B.
A
B
Lateral line scales usually 35-37.
41b.
Base of tail fin without a white patch.
A greater than B.
A
B
Lateral line scales usually 37-39.

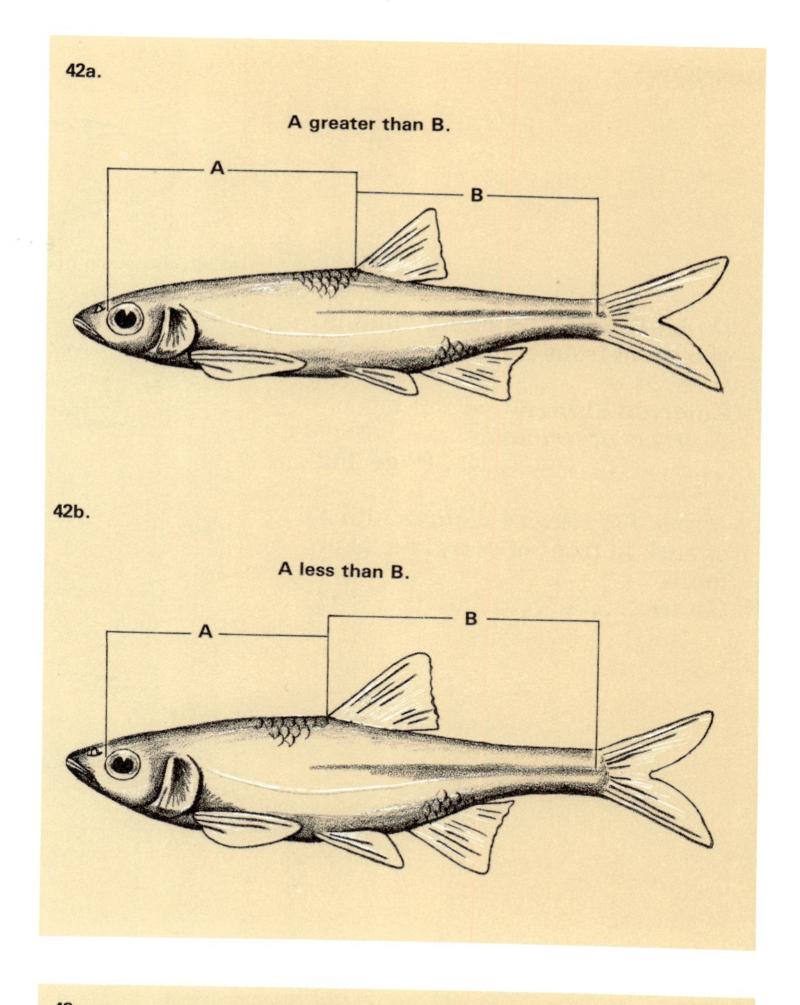

42a. *(From 35b.)* Distance from front of eye to front of dorsal fin (A) greater than distance from front of dorsal fin to base of tail fin (B).
Go to 43

42b. *(From 35b.)* Distance from front of eye to front of dorsal fin (A) less than distance from front of dorsal fin to base of tail fin (B).
Go to 46

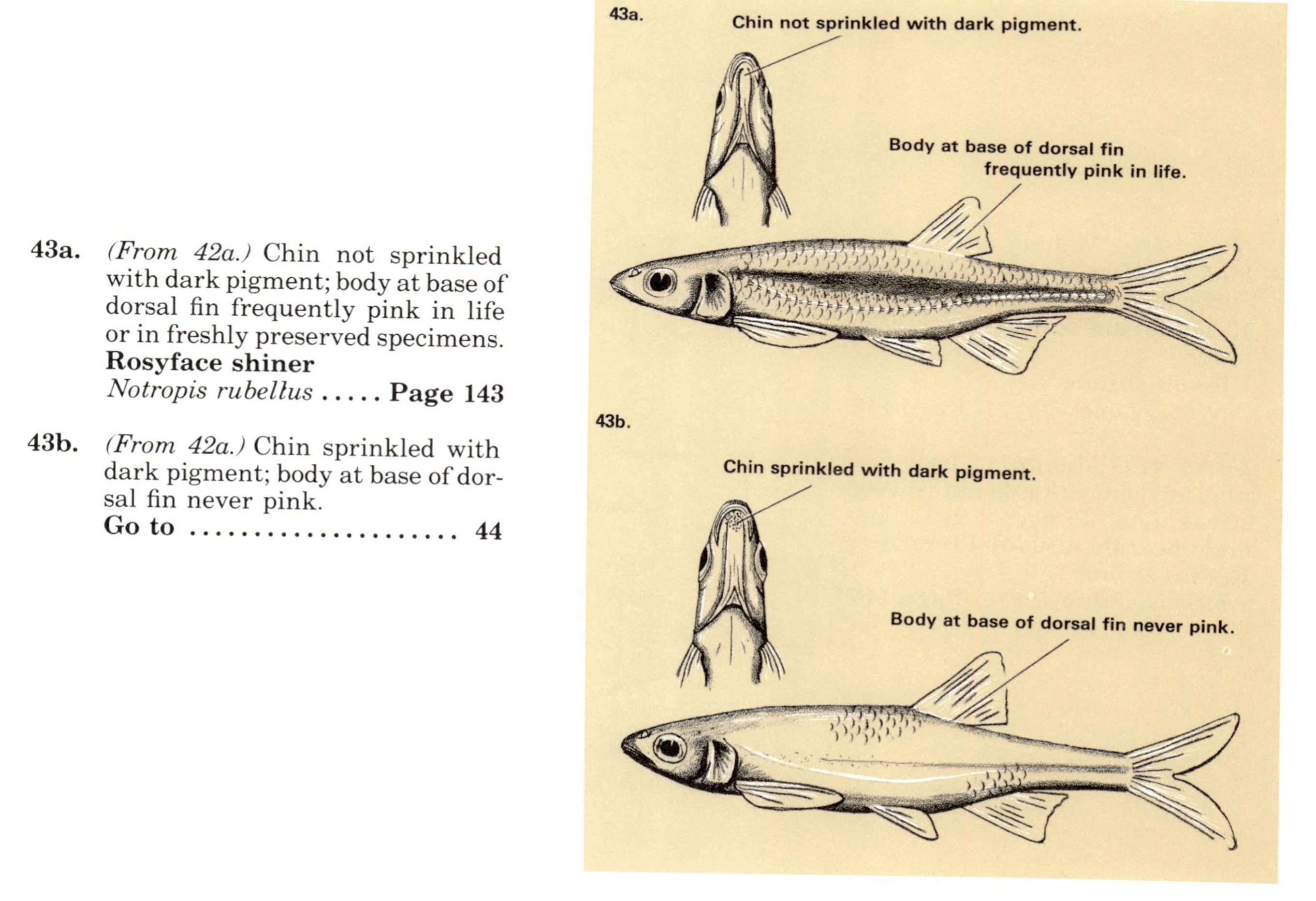

43a. *(From 42a.)* Chin not sprinkled with dark pigment; body at base of dorsal fin frequently pink in life or in freshly preserved specimens.
Rosyface shiner
Notropis rubellus ..... **Page 143**

43b. *(From 42a.)* Chin sprinkled with dark pigment; body at base of dorsal fin never pink.
Go to 44

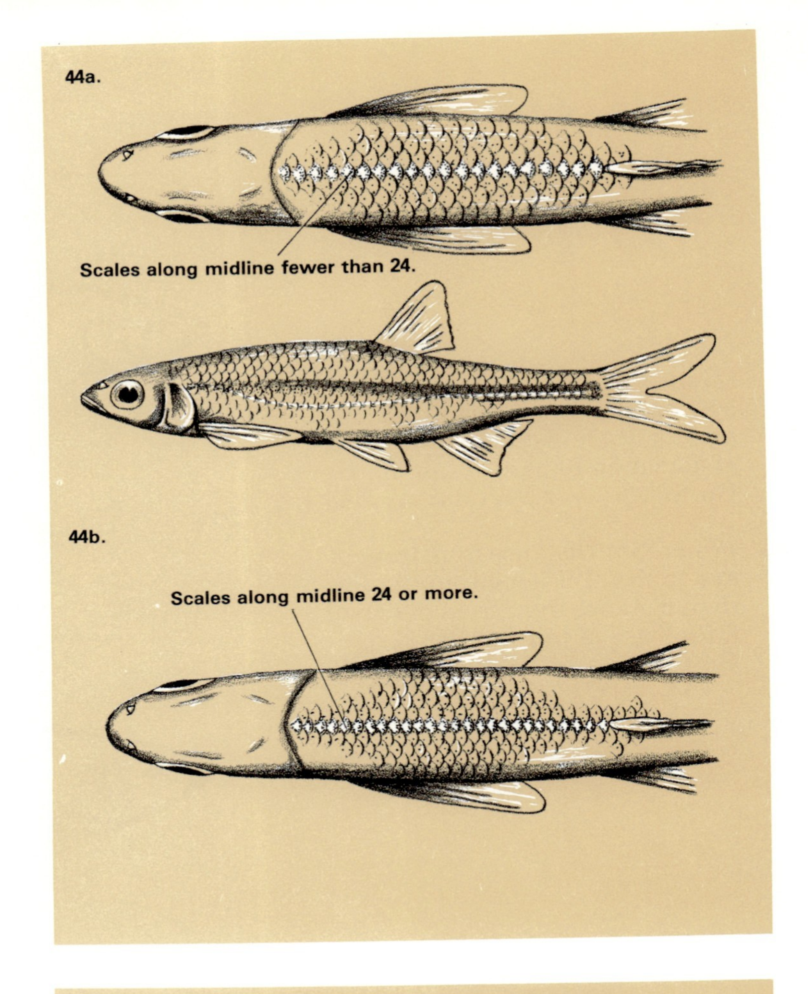
44a.
Scales along midline fewer than 24.
44b.
Scales along midline 24 or more.

44a. *(From 43b.)* Scales along midline of back in front of dorsal fin fewer than 24.
Emerald shiner
Notropis atherinoides
.... **Page 142**

44b. *(From 43b.)* Scales along midline of back in front of dorsal fin 24 or more.
Go to **45**

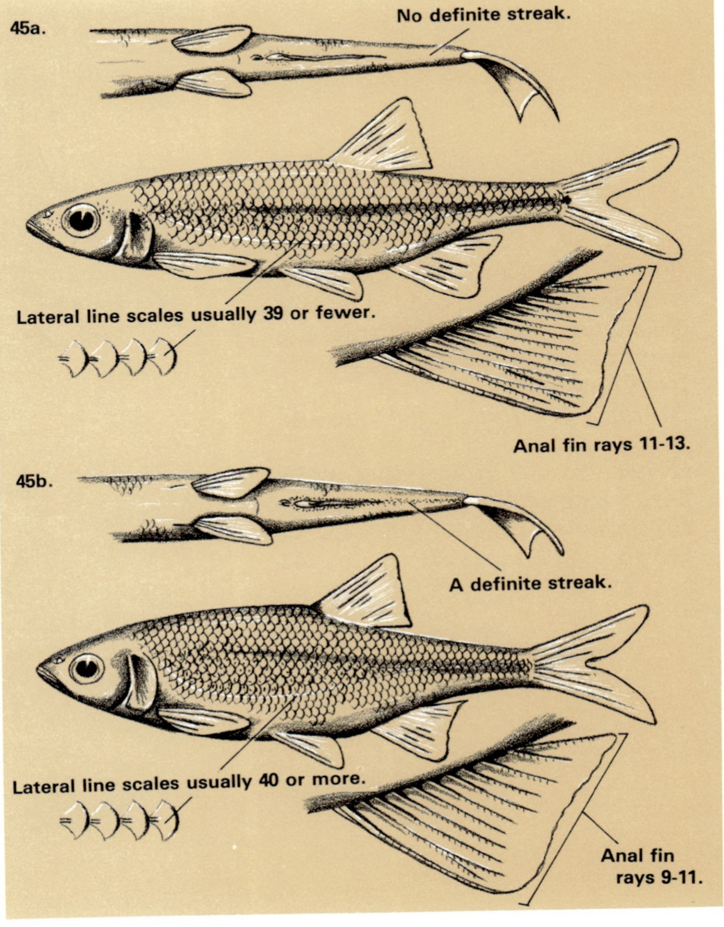
45a.
No definite streak.
Lateral line scales usually 39 or fewer.
Anal fin rays 11-13.
45b.
A definite streak.
Lateral line scales usually 40 or more.
Anal fin
rays 9-11.

45a. *(From 44b.)* Midline of body behind anal fin without a definite dusky streak; anal fin rays 11 to 13; lateral line scales usually 39 or fewer.
Ribbon shiner
Notropis fumeus ..... **Page 146**

45b. *(From 44b.)* Midline of body behind anal fin with a definite dusky streak; anal fin rays 9 to 11; lateral line scales usually 40 or more.
Redfin shiner
Notropis umbratilis .. **Page 145**

46a. *(From 42b.)* Dark stripe on midline of back sharply defined in front of dorsal fin, not consisting of separate black specks, and frequently as wide or wider than dorsal fin base.
Go to 47

46b. *(From 42b.)* Dark stripe on midline of back rather poorly defined in front of dorsal fin, consisting of separate dark specks or reduced to a thin line narrower than dorsal fin base.
Go to 57

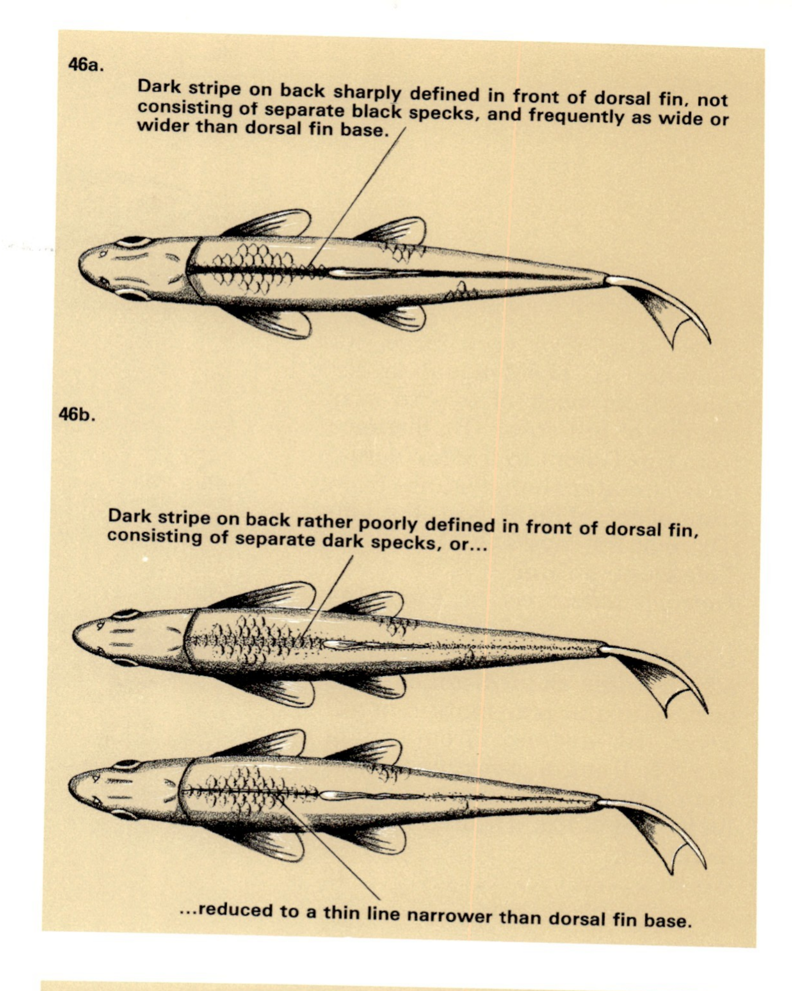

46a.
Dark stripe on back sharply defined in front of dorsal fin, not consisting of separate black specks, and frequently as wide or wider than dorsal fin base.
46b.
Dark stripe on back rather poorly defined in front of dorsal fin, consisting of separate dark specks, or...
...reduced to a thin line narrower than dorsal fin base.

47a. *(From 46a.)* Anal fin rays usually 9 to 11; lining of body cavity uniformly black.
Go to 48

47b. *(From 46a.)* Anal fin rays usually 7 or 8; lining of body cavity silvery, with or without dark speckles.
Go to 52

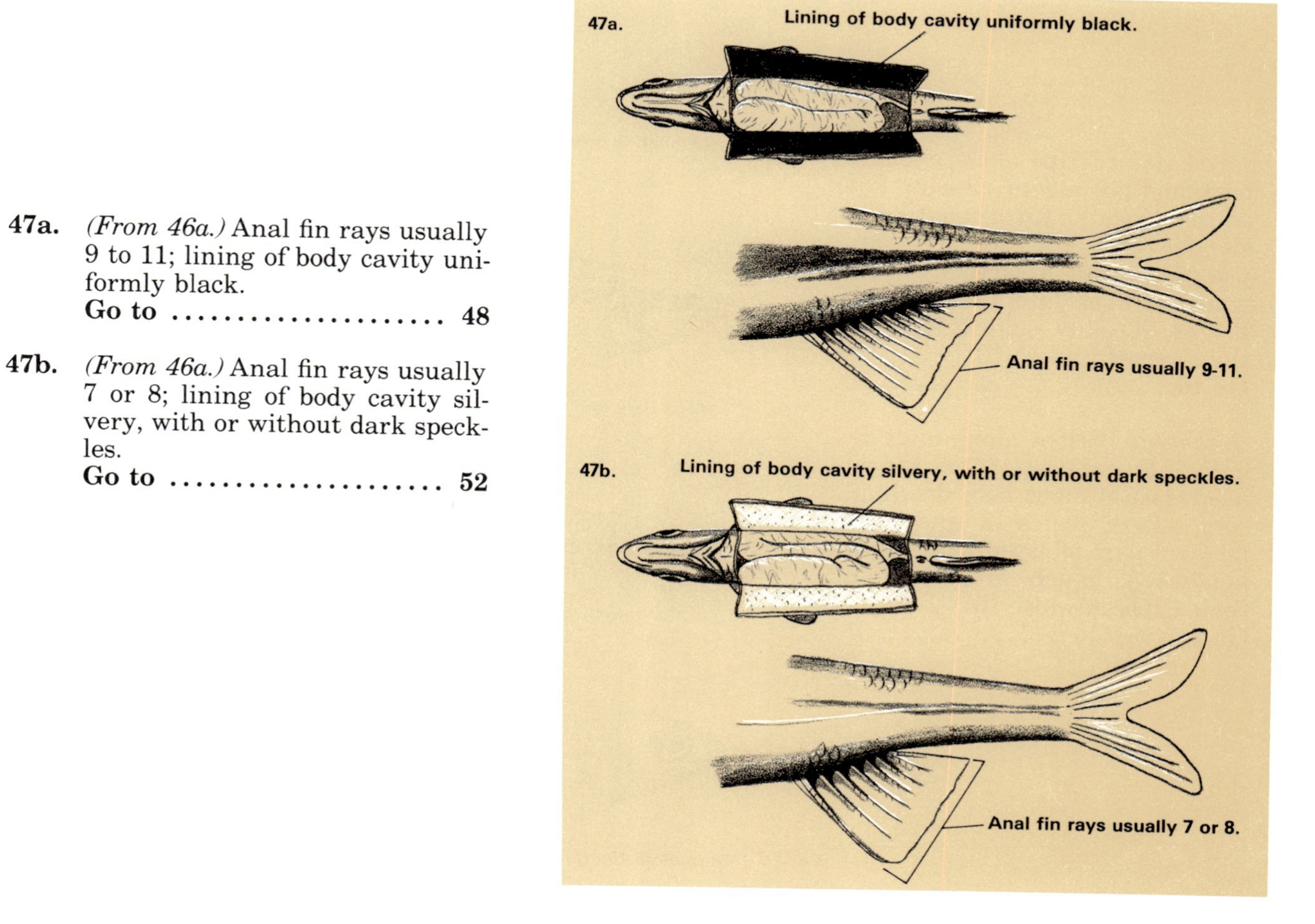

47a.
Lining of body cavity uniformly black.
Anal fin rays usually 9-11.
47b.
Lining of body cavity silvery, with or without dark speckles.
Anal fin rays usually 7 or 8.

48a. *(From 47a.)* Eye very large, its diameter (A) about equal to distance from back of eye to rear margin of gill cover (B); distance from tip of snout to front of dorsal fin (C) greater than distance from front of dorsal fin to base of tail fin (D); anal fin rays 9 to 11.
Telescope shiner
Notropis telescopus **... Page 144**

48b. *(From 47a.)* Eye smaller, its diameter (A) less than distance from back of eye to rear margin of gill cover (B); distance from tip of snout to front of dorsal fin (C) less than distance from front of dorsal fin to base of tail (D); anal fin rays usually 9.
Go to 49

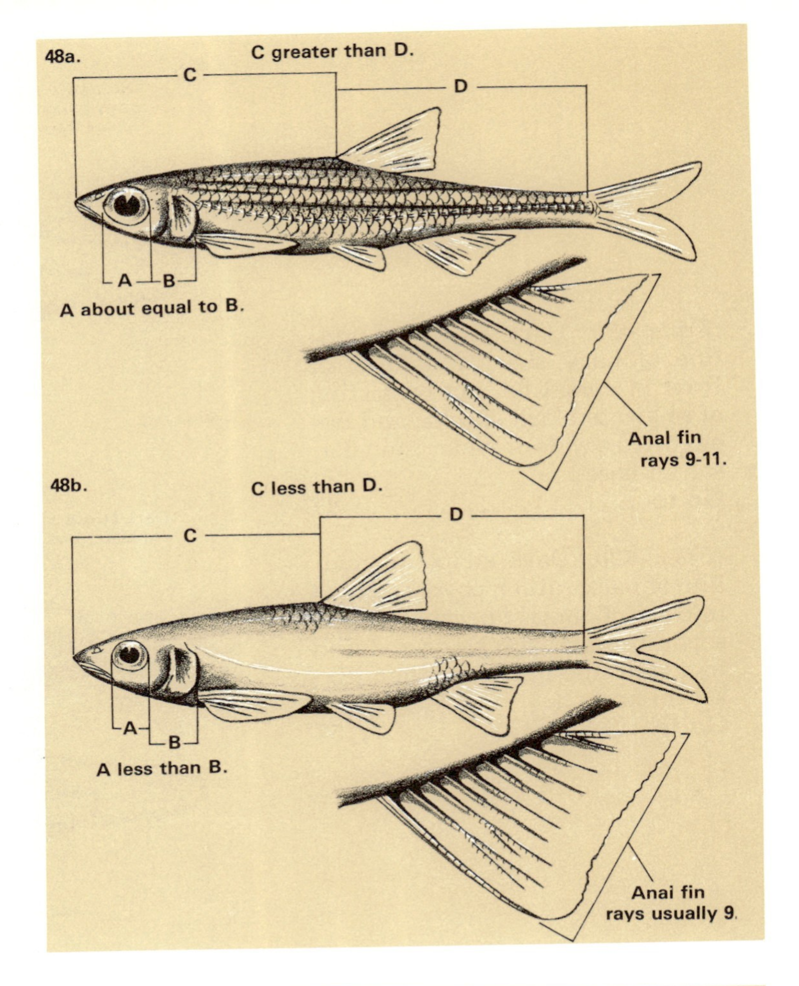

48a.
C greater than D.
C
D
A
B
A about equal to B.
Anal fin rays 9-11.
48b.
C less than D.
C
D
A
B
A less than B.
Anai fin rays usually 9.

49a. *(From 48b.)* Stripe along midside dark and prominent, passing forward on head to tip of snout; body slender and not notably compressed; scales in and near forward part of lateral line with height (A) only slightly greater than exposed width (B).
Go to 50

49b. *(From 48b.)* Stripe along midside indistinct, not passing forward on head to tip of snout; body deep and compressed; scales in and near forward part of lateral line with height (A) much greater than their exposed width (B).
Go to 51

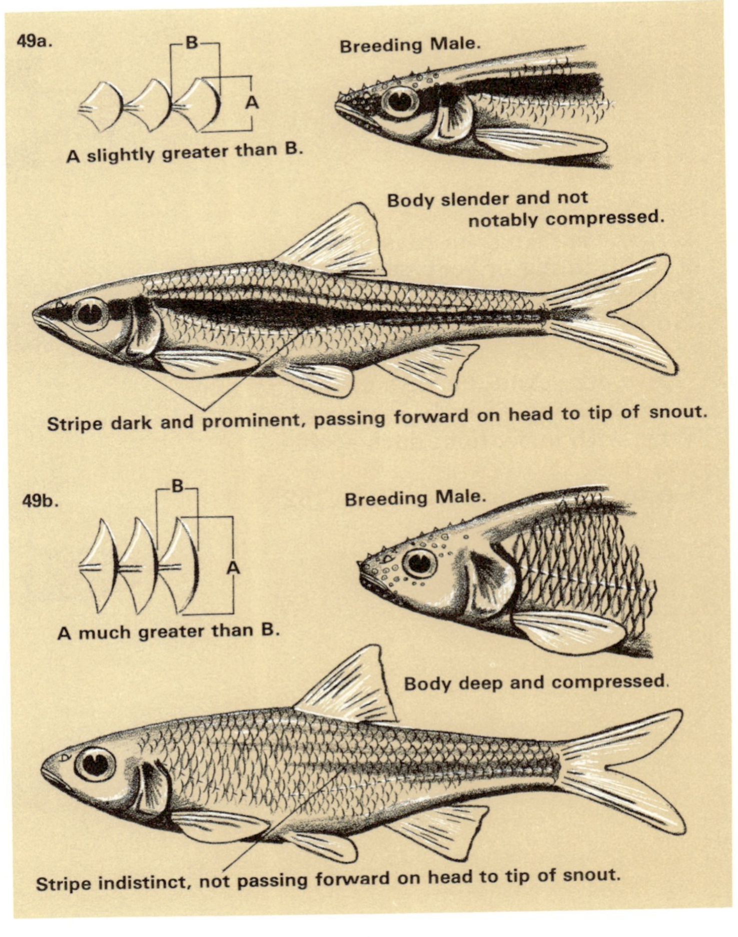

49a.
B
A
A slightly greater than B.
Breeding Male.
Body slender and not notably compressed.
Stripe dark and prominent, passing forward on head to tip of snout.
49b.
B
A
A much greater than B.
Breeding Male.
Body deep and compressed.
Stripe indistinct, not passing forward on head to tip of snout.

50a. *(From 49a.)* Stripe along midside becoming abruptly narrower just behind gill opening and not touching lateral line beneath dorsal fin (except in breeding males); rear margin of gill opening bordered by a dark bar.
Bleeding shiner
Notropis zonatus ..... **Page 147**

50b. *(From 49a.)* Stripe along midside not becoming abruptly narrower just behind gill opening and touching lateral line beneath dorsal fin; rear margin of gill opening not bordered by a dark bar.
Duskystripe shiner
Notropis pilsbryi ..... **Page 148**

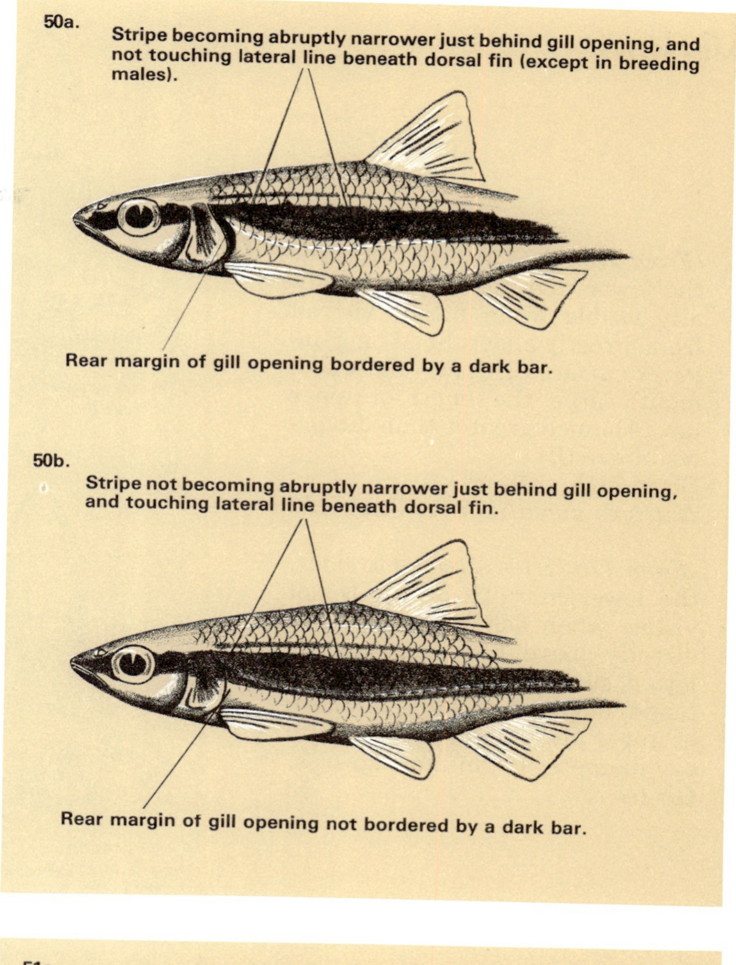
50a.
Stripe becoming abruptly narrower just behind gill opening, and not touching lateral line beneath dorsal fin (except in breeding males).
Rear margin of gill opening bordered by a dark bar.
50b.
Stripe not becoming abruptly narrower just behind gill opening, and touching lateral line beneath dorsal fin.
Rear margin of gill opening not bordered by a dark bar.

51a. *(From 49b.)* Chin sprinkled with dusky pigment; upper surface of body with dark lines, those from opposite sides of body converging behind dorsal fin forming V-shaped markings; scales along midline of back in front of dorsal fin usually 22 or less.
Striped shiner
Notropis chrysocephalus
.... **Page 149**

51b. *(From 49b.)* Chin not sprinkled with dusky pigment; upper surface of body without dark lines except in breeding males; scales along midline of back in front of dorsal fin usually 23 or more.
Common shiner
Notropis cornutus .... **Page 148**

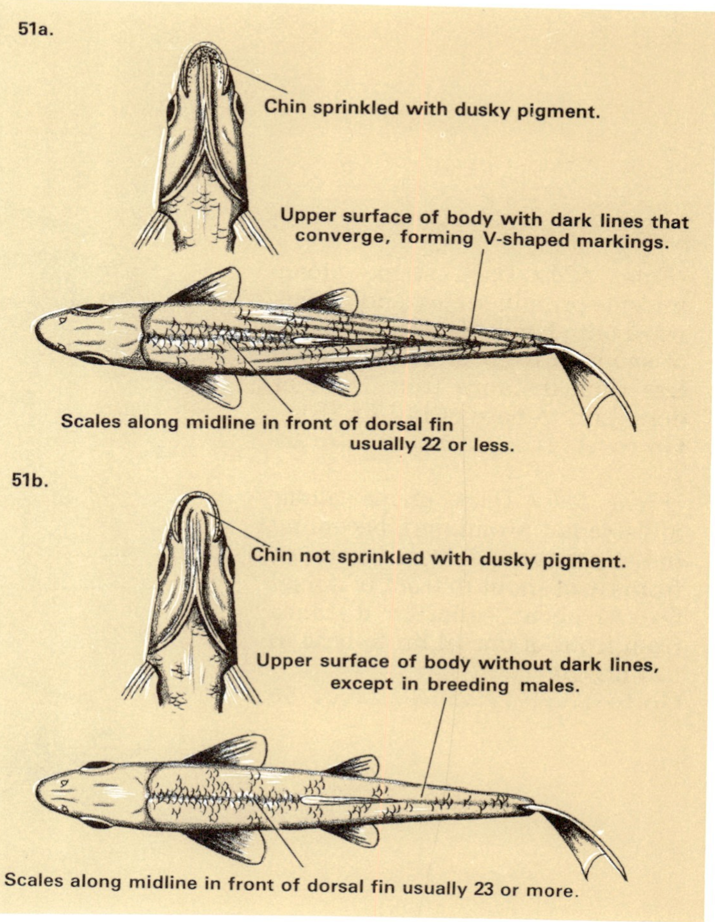
51a.
Chin sprinkled with dusky pigment.
Upper surface of body with dark lines that converge, forming V-shaped markings.
Scales along midline in front of dorsal fin usually 22 or less.
51b.
Chin not sprinkled with dusky pigment.
Upper surface of body without dark lines, except in breeding males.
Scales along midline in front of dorsal fin usually 23 or more.

52a. *(From 47b.)* Eyes directed upward, the lower margins of pupils usually visible when fish is viewed from directly above; head long, its lower surface distinctly flattened; mouth large, the length of upper jaw (A) much greater than diameter of eye (B).
Bigmouth shiner
Notropis dorsalis ..... **Page 153**

52b. *(From 47b.)* Eyes directed to sides, the lower margins of pupils not visible when fish is viewed from directly above; head not long, its lower surface not notably flattened; mouth smaller, the length of upper jaw (A) not greater than eye diameter (B) in most species.
Go to **53**

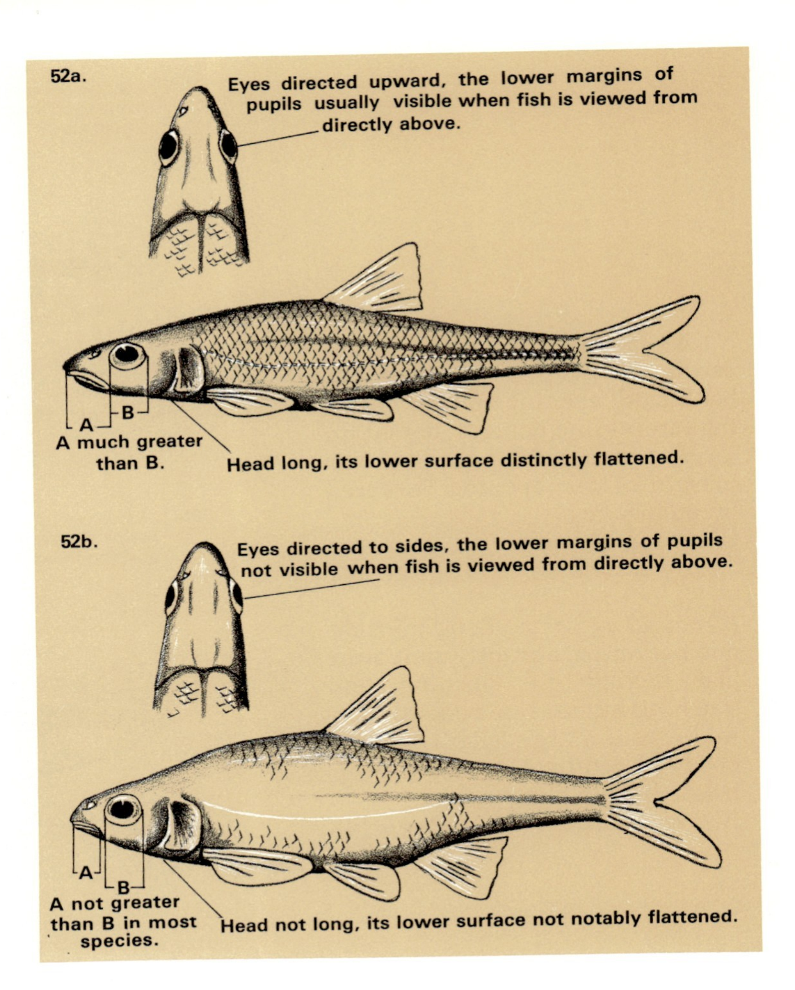
52a.
Eyes directed upward, the lower margins of pupils usually visible when fish is viewed from directly above.
A
B
A much greater than B.
Head long, its lower surface distinctly flattened.
52b.
Eyes directed to sides, the lower margins of pupils not visible when fish is viewed from directly above.
A
B
A not greater than B in most species.
Head not long, its lower surface not notably flattened.

53a. *(From 52b.)* Dark stripe along midside prominent, extending forward onto head; distance from tip of snout to front of dorsal fin (A) less than distance from front of dorsal fin to base of tail fin (B).
Go to **54**

53b. *(From 52b.)* Dark stripe along midside not prominent, becoming indistinct towards head; distance from tip of snout to front of dorsal fin (A) about equal to distance from front of dorsal fin to base of tail fin (B).
Go to **56**

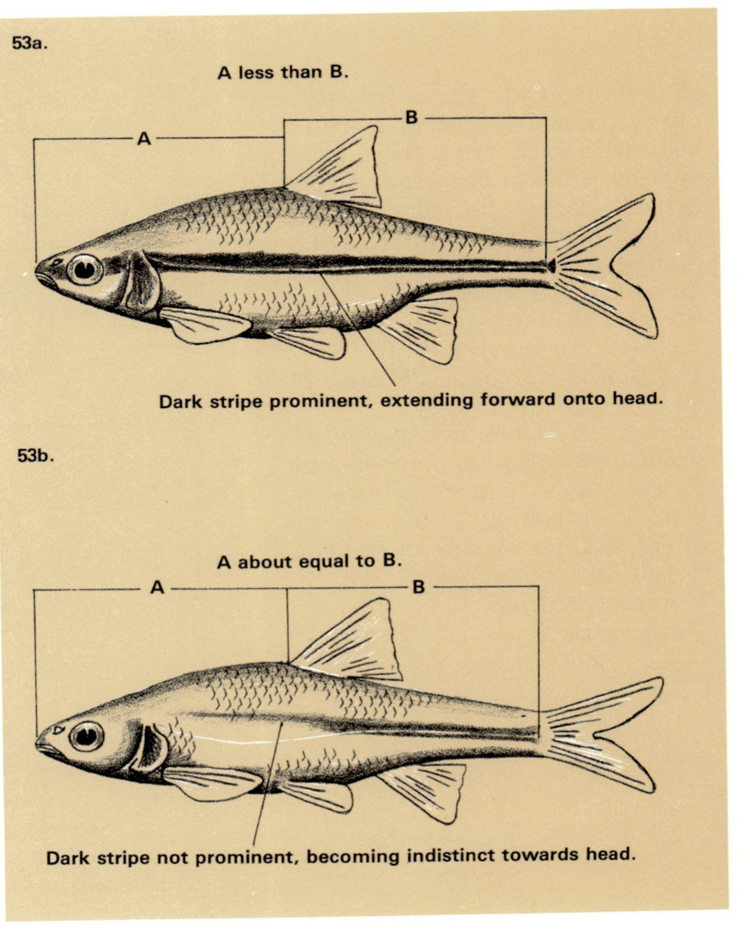
53a.
A less than B.
A
B
Dark stripe prominent, extending forward onto head.
53b.
A about equal to B.
A
B
Dark stripe not prominent, becoming indistinct towards head.

54a. *(From 53a.)* Anal fin rays 8 (rarely 7 or 9); inside of mouth sprinkled with black pigment.
Ironcolor shiner
Notropis chalybaeus .. **Page 150**

54b. *(From 53a.)* Anal fin rays 7 (rarely 6 or 8); inside of mouth not sprinkled with black pigment.
Go to 55

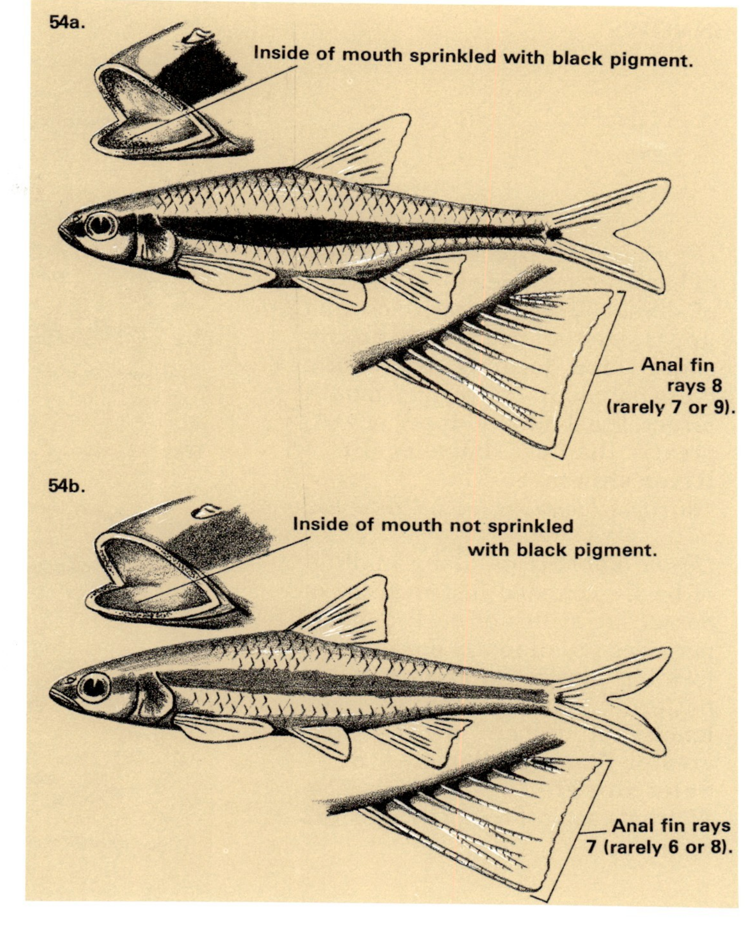

54a.
Inside of mouth sprinkled with black pigment.
Anal fin rays 8 (rarely 7 or 9).
54b.
Inside of mouth not sprinkled with black pigment.
Anal fin rays 7 (rarely 6 or 8).

55a. *(From 54b.)* Dark spot at base of tail fin rounded or irregular in outline; dark stripe along midside bordered above by a broad light-colored zone.
Weed shiner
Notropis texanus ..... **Page 151**

55b. *(From 54b.)* Dark spot at base of tail fin triangular; dark stripe along midside not bordered above by a light-colored zone.
Topeka shiner
Notropis topeka ...... **Page 161**

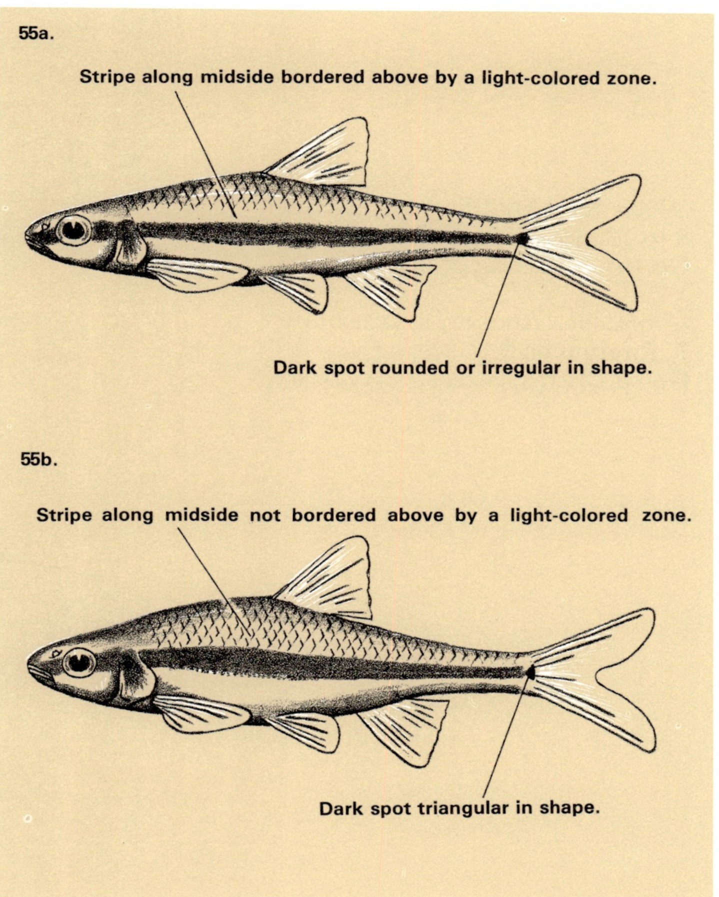

55a.
Stripe along midside bordered above by a light-colored zone.
Dark spot rounded or irregular in shape.
55b.
Stripe along midside not bordered above by a light-colored zone.
Dark spot triangular in shape.

56a. *(From 53b.)* Stripe along midline of back not expanded just in front of dorsal fin; scales of back and upper sides not prominently dark-edged, nor forming a definite cross-hatched pattern; mouth larger, the length of upper jaw (A) greater than eye diameter (B).
River shiner
Notropis blennius .... **Page 152**

56b. *(From 53b.)* Stripe along midline of back expanded just in front of dorsal fin; scales of back and upper sides prominently dark-edged, forming a definite cross-hatched pattern; mouth smaller, the length of upper jaw (A) not greater than eye diameter (B).
Sand shiner
Notropis stramineus .. **Page 162**

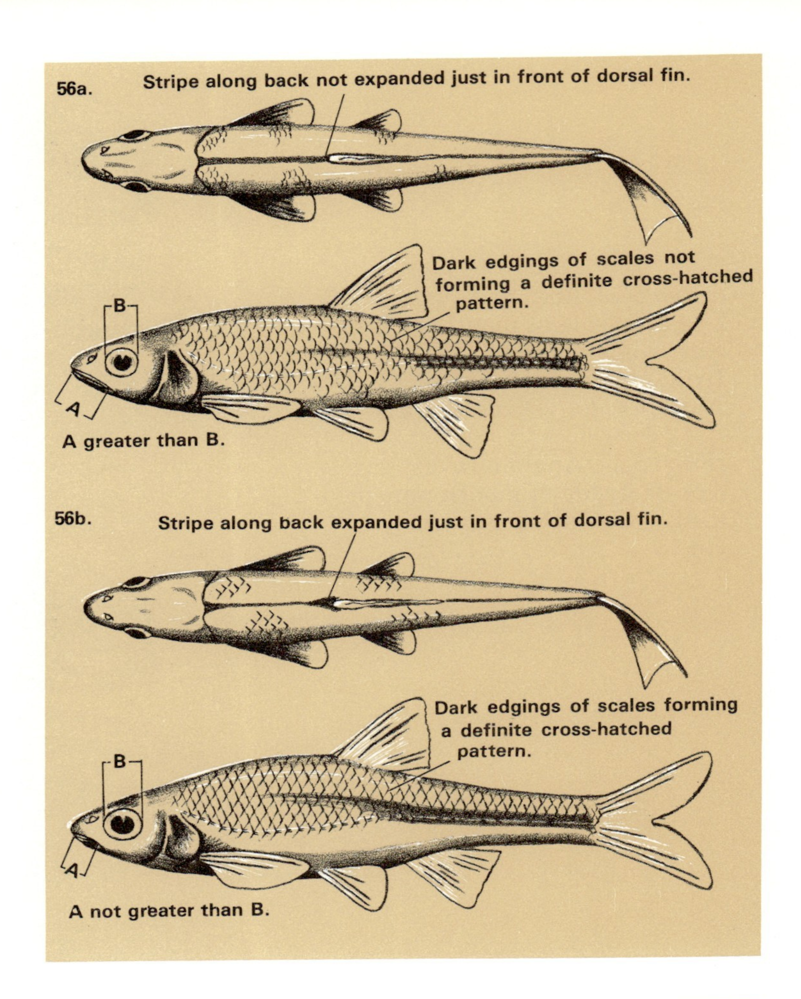
56a.
Stripe along back not expanded just in front of dorsal fin.
Dark edgings of scales not forming a definite cross-hatched pattern.
B
A
A greater than B.
56b.
Stripe along back expanded just in front of dorsal fin.
Dark edgings of scales forming a definite cross-hatched pattern.
B
A
A not greater than B.

57a. *(From 46b.)* Anal fin rays usually 8 to 13, occasionally 7.
Go to **58**

57b. *(From 46b.)* Anal fin rays usually 7, rarely 6 or 8.
Go to **64**

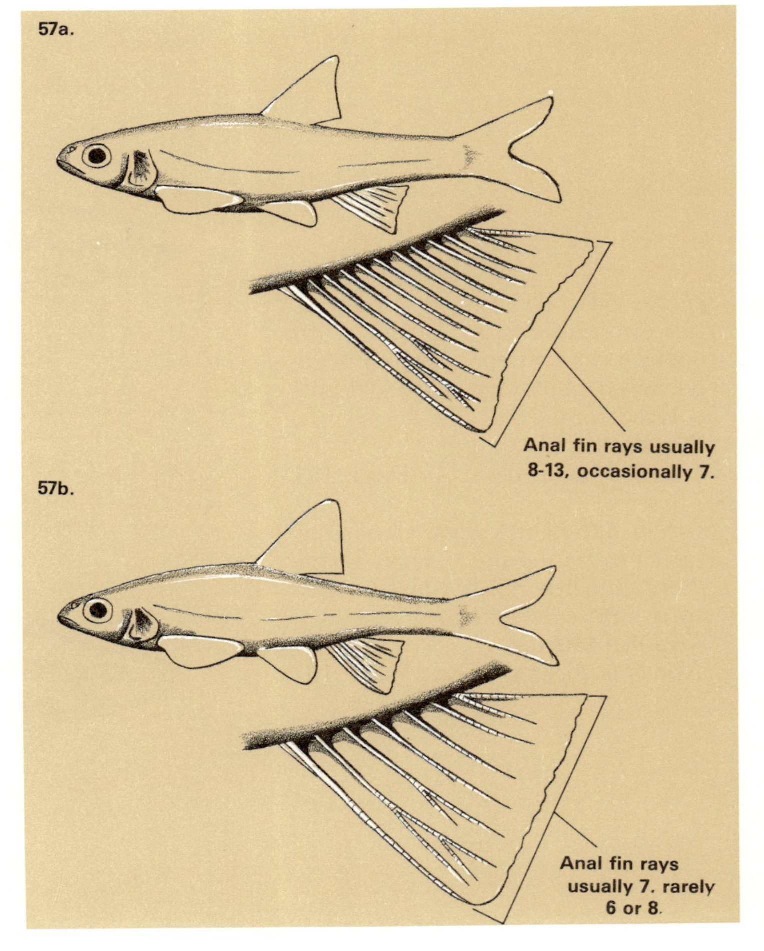
57a.
Anal fin rays usually 8-13, occasionally 7.
57b.
Anal fin rays usually 7. rarely 6 or 8.

58a. *(From 57a.)* Stripe along midside dark and prominent, extending forward on head to tip of snout and bordered above by a broad light-colored zone.
Go to 59

58b. *(From 57a.)* Stripe along midside indistinct or absent, not extending forward on head to tip of snout and not bordered above by a broad light-colored zone.
Go to 60

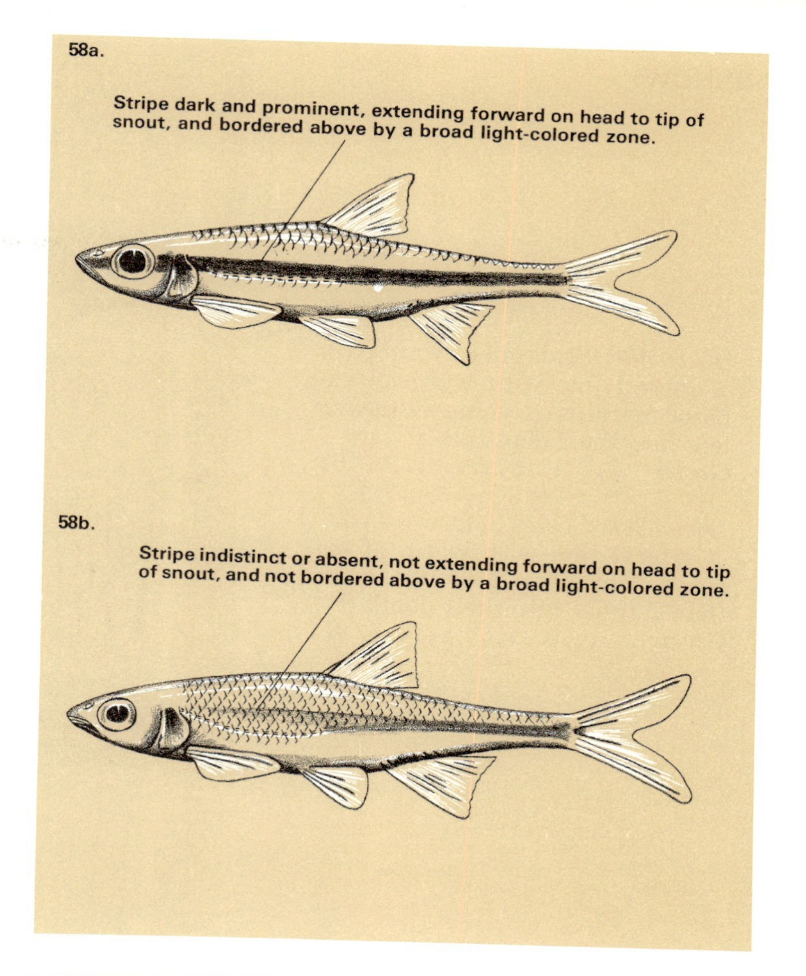

58a.
Stripe dark and prominent, extending forward on head to tip of snout, and bordered above by a broad light-colored zone.
58b.
Stripe indistinct or absent, not extending forward on head to tip of snout, and not bordered above by a broad light-colored zone.

59a. *(From 58a.)* Lips and chin without dark pigment; dark borders of lateral line pores expanded into crescent-shaped vertical bars; a dark stripe on lower surface of caudal peduncle; mouth small, upper jaw not extending to front of eye.
Blacknose shiner
Notropis heterolepis **.. Page 163**

59b. *(From 58a.)* Lips and chin with dark pigment; dark borders of lateral line pores not expanded into crescent-shaped bars; no dark stripe on lower surface of caudal peduncle; mouth large, upper jaw extending to front of eye.
Bigeye shiner
Notropis boops **....... Page 154**

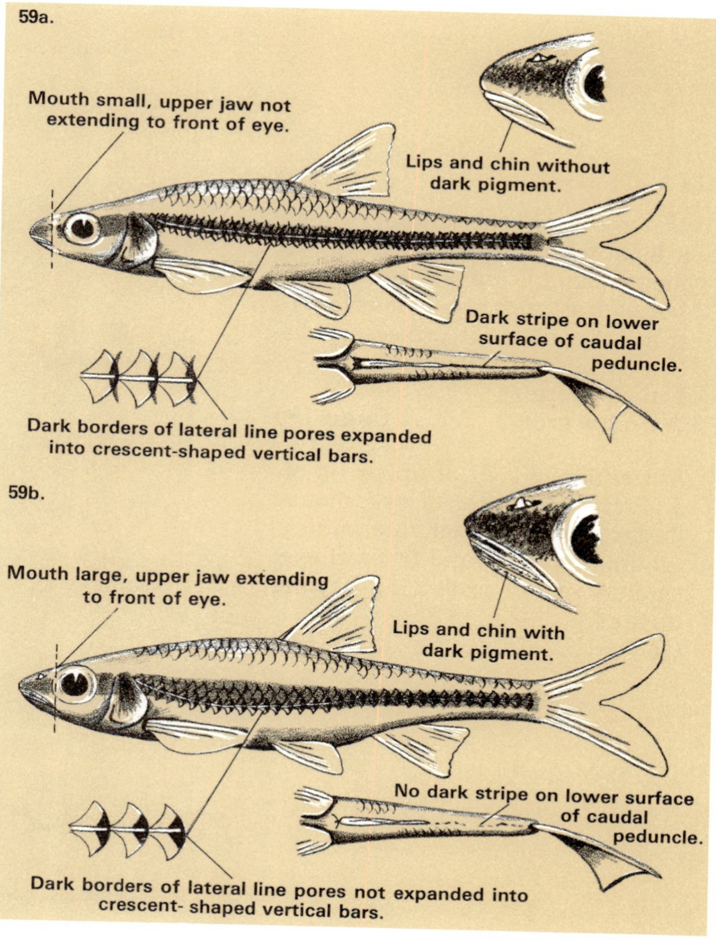

59a.
Mouth small, upper jaw not extending to front of eye.
Lips and chin without dark pigment.
Dark stripe on lower surface of caudal peduncle.
Dark borders of lateral line pores expanded into crescent-shaped vertical bars.
59b.
Mouth large, upper jaw extending to front of eye.
Lips and chin with dark pigment.
No dark stripe on lower surface of caudal peduncle.
Dark borders of lateral line pores not expanded into crescent- shaped vertical bars.

60a. *(From 58b.)* Scales in forward part of lateral line with width of exposed margins (A) going 2 times or less into their depth (B).
Go to 61

60b. *(From 58b.)* Scales in forward part of lateral line with width of exposed margins (A) going more than 2 times into their depth (B).
Go to 63

60a.
A
B
A going 2 times or less into B.

60b.
A
B
A going more than 2 times into B.

61a. *(From 60a.)* Front of upper lip on a level with lower margin of eye; mouth small, upper jaw nearly horizontal and not extending to front of eye; snout projecting distinctly beyond upper lip.
Pallid shiner
Notropis amnis ...... **Page 155**

61b. *(From 60a.)* Front of upper lip on a level with center of eye; mouth larger, upper jaw oblique and extending to or beyond front of eye; snout scarcely projecting beyond upper lip.
Go to 62

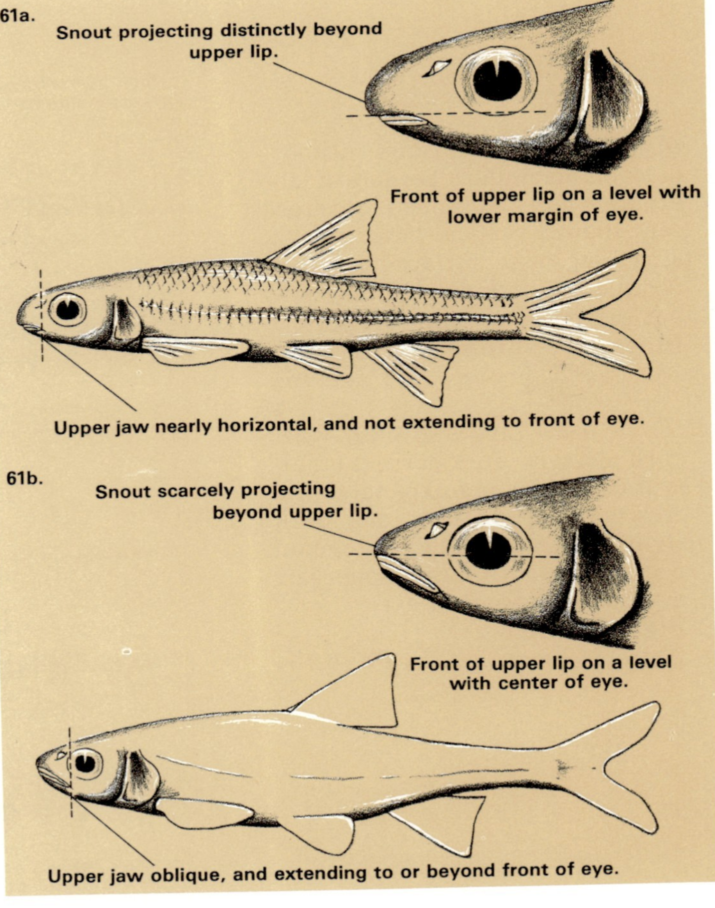
61a.
Snout projecting distinctly beyond upper lip.
Front of upper lip on a level with lower margin of eye.
Upper jaw nearly horizontal, and not extending to front of eye.
61b.
Snout scarcely projecting beyond upper lip.
Front of upper lip on a level with center of eye.
Upper jaw oblique, and extending to or beyond front of eye.

62a. *(From 61b.)* Dorsal fin very high and pointed, front rays projecting far beyond rear rays when fin is depressed; base of tail fin without a spot; lining of body cavity with dark speckles scarcely developed or absent.
Silverband shiner
Notropis shumardi ... **Page 144**

62b. *(From 61b.)* Dorsal fin not high and pointed, front rays scarcely projecting beyond rear rays when fin is depressed; base of tail fin with a small, dark triangular spot (occasionally absent); lining of body cavity with dark speckles well developed.
Wedgespot shiner
Notropis greenei ...... **Page 153**

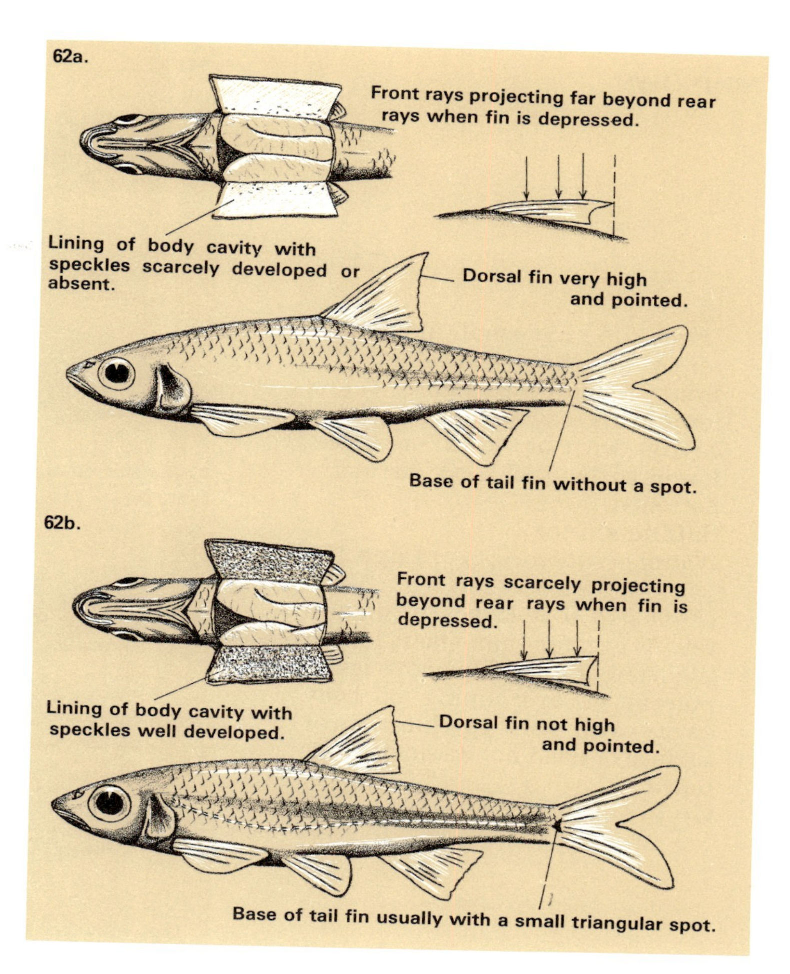

62a.
Front rays projecting far beyond rear rays when fin is depressed.
Lining of body cavity with speckles scarcely developed or absent.
Dorsal fin very high and pointed.
Base of tail fin without a spot.
62b.
Front rays scarcely projecting beyond rear rays when fin is depressed.
Lining of body cavity with speckles well developed.
Dorsal fin not high and pointed.
Base of tail fin usually with a small triangular spot.

63a. *(From 60b.)* Tips of pelvic fins reaching to or beyond front of anal fin; dusky stripe along midside absent or reduced to a few faint speckles; lining of body cavity with dark speckles absent or only faintly developed; sensory canal beneath eye absent or represented by a short section of tube.
Ghost shiner
Notropis buchanani .. **Page 166**

63b. *(From 60b.)* Tips of pelvic fins not reaching front of anal fin; dusky stripe along midside developed on back half of body; lining of body cavity with dark speckles well developed; sensory canal beneath eye complete.
Mimic shiner
Notropis volucellus ... **Page 165**

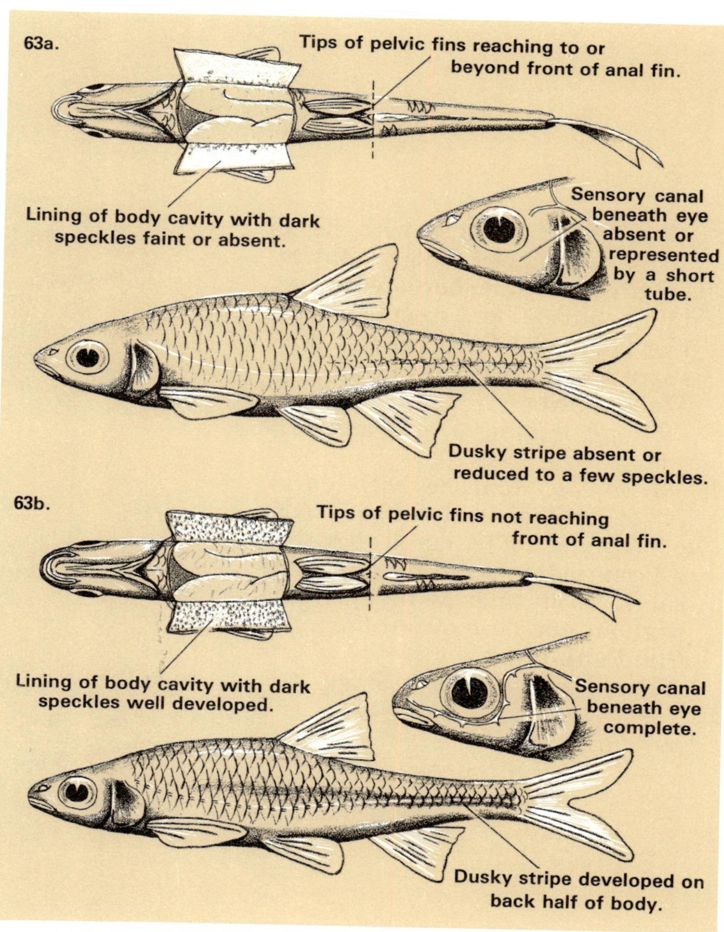

63a.
Tips of pelvic fins reaching to or beyond front of anal fin.
Lining of body cavity with dark speckles faint or absent.
Sensory canal beneath eye absent or represented by a short tube.
Dusky stripe absent or reduced to a few speckles.
63b.
Tips of pelvic fins not reaching front of anal fin.
Lining of body cavity with dark speckles well developed.
Sensory canal beneath eye complete.
Dusky stripe developed on back half of body.

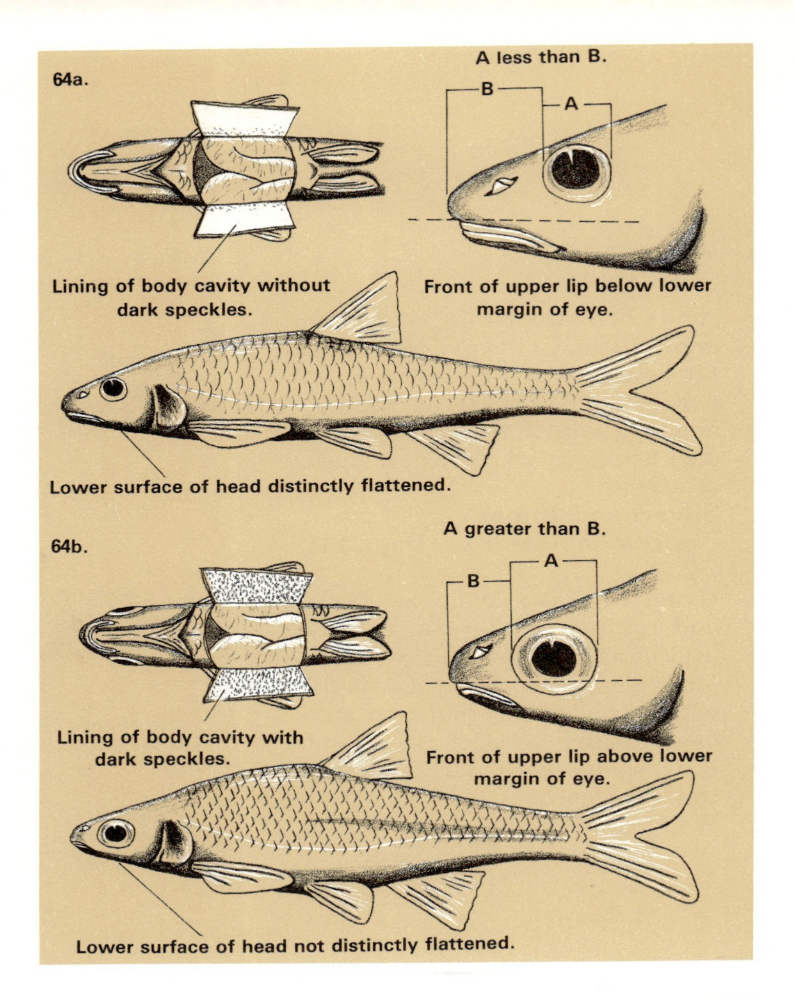
64a.
A less than B.
B
A
Lining of body cavity without dark speckles.
Front of upper lip below lower margin of eye.
Lower surface of head distinctly flattened.
64b.
A greater than B.
B
A
Lining of body cavity with dark speckles.
Front of upper lip above lower margin of eye.
Lower surface of head not distinctly flattened.

64a. *(From 57b.)* Eye small, its diameter (A) less than snout length (B); front of upper lip slightly below lower margin of eye; lining of body cavity without dark speckles; lower surface of head distinctly flattened.
Sabine shiner
Notropis sabinae ..... **Page 161**

64b. *(From 57b.)* Eye larger, its diameter (A) greater than snout length (B); front of upper lip above lower margin of eye; lining of body cavity with dark speckles; lower surface of head not distinctly flattened.
Go to 65

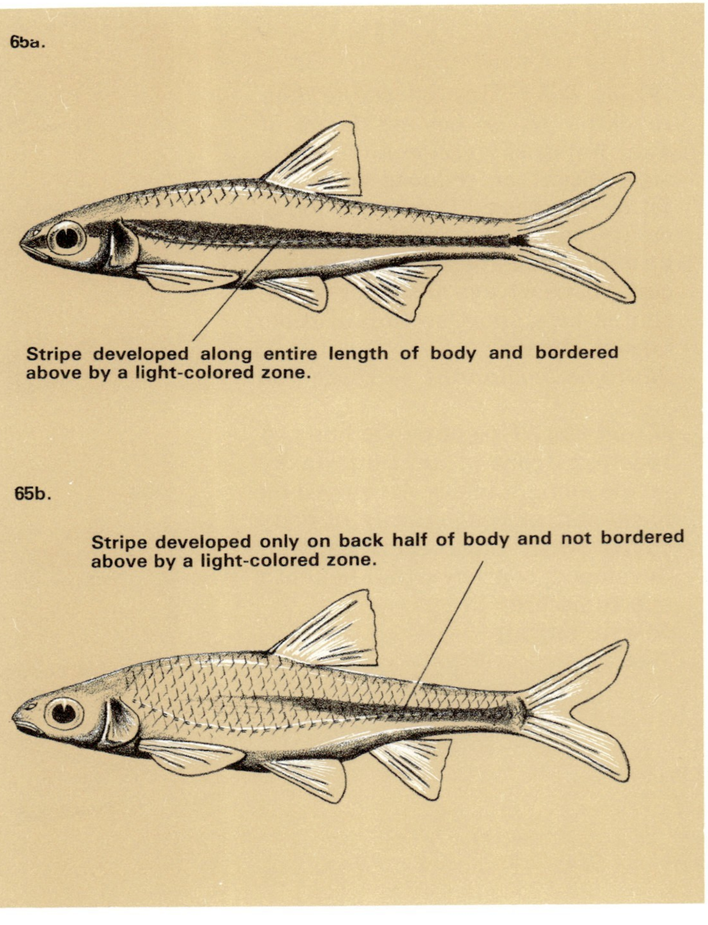
65a.
Stripe developed along entire length of body and bordered above by a light-colored zone.
65b.
Stripe developed only on back half of body and not bordered above by a light-colored zone.

65a. *(From 64b.)* Midside with dark stripe developed along entire length of body and bordered above by a broad light-colored zone; front of dorsal fin closer to tip of snout than to base of tail fin.
Weed shiner
Notropis texanus ..... **Page 151**

65b. *(From 64b.)* Midside with dark stripe developed only on back half of body and not bordered above by a light-colored zone; front of dorsal fin about midway between tip of snout and base of tail fin.
Sand shiner
Notropis stramineus .. **Page 162**

Carp

Cyprinus carpio Linnaeus

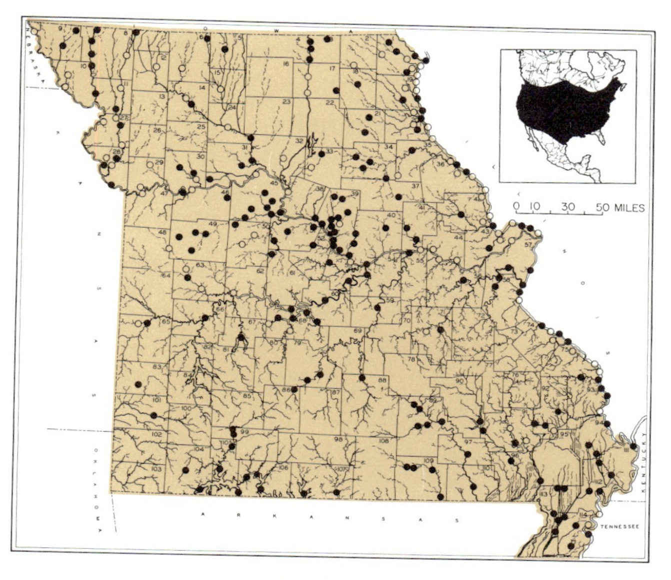

DESCRIPTION

Illustration: Page 95, 2a.

Characters: A heavy-bodied minnow with a long dorsal fin containing 17 to 21 rays, a stout, saw-toothed spine at front of both dorsal and anal fins, and 2 barbels on each side of upper jaw. Lateral line with 35 to 38 scales. Throat teeth 1,1,3-3,1,1; teeth in main row broad and molar-like.

Life colors: Back and sides brassy-olive, belly yellowish-white. Scales of back and sides prominently dark-edged giving a cross-hatched effect. Fins dusky, often overlain by red on tail fin and yellow or orange on lower fins.

Size: Adults are commonly 12 to 25 inches long and weigh 1 to 8 pounds. The largest authenticated specimen from Missouri weighed 47 pounds, 7 ounces. Elsewhere, weights up to 60 pounds have been reported.

Scientific name: *Cyprinus,* ancient Greek name for carp; *carpio,* Latin for carp.

DISTRIBUTION AND HABITAT

The carp is a native of Asia that was introduced into Europe centuries ago and into this country as early as 1876. The first carp were brought to Missouri in the fall of 1879, and over the next 15 years the Missouri Fish Commission reared over 80,000 for stocking in public and private waters throughout the state. The program was discontinued in 1895, largely because the carp had lost its early popularity, but by that time it was firmly established in Missouri waters.

This has proved to be a very adaptable species and is now one of the most widespread and abundant large fishes in the state. In the Missouri and Mississippi rivers the total poundage taken by commercial fishermen consistently exceeds that of any other species. They are also abundant in the Prairie streams of north and west Missouri, in the Lowland ditches of the southeast, and in reservoirs and natural lakes throughout the state. They are least abundant in the clear, high-gradient streams of the central Ozarks, but even here are locally abundant in warm backwaters and in streams polluted by organic wastes.

Invasion of Current and Eleven Point rivers, two of the clearest and least polluted Ozark streams, in recent years demonstrates the adaptability of carp. In previous years they made up only a minor part of the total fish populations, but in 1957 they appeared in large numbers. These carp were of uniform age and their sudden appearance seems to have been the result of population pressure caused by the production of unusually large numbers of young in the lowland sections of these streams in Arkansas. They have remained common in Current and Eleven Point rivers since that time, but their numbers gradually diminished. A few smaller carp were found in 1965 and 1966, indicating limited spawning success or additional recruitment from downstream.

The carp occurs in many kinds of habitats but is most abundant in large streams, natural lakes, and man-made impoundments that are highly productive as a result of natural fertility, runoff from heavily fertilized farmlands, or organic pollutants. In streams adult carp are most often found in the deeper pools around piles of drift, logs, or other submerged cover. In large lakes and reservoirs this fish is occasionally taken at depths of nearly 100 feet, but is more characteristic of shallow waters along the shore.

HABITS AND LIFE HISTORY

Carp do not form large schools but often occur in loose aggregations with no obvious social organization. They feed most actively in late evening or early morning, sometimes in very shallow water. Food is probably located more by taste than by sight. They feed mostly from the bottom, but have been observed sucking in objects floating on the surface. They are very aggressive feeders, uprooting plants and roiling the water by their activities. In early morning hours they may be observed feeding in water so shallow that their dorsal fin is exposed.

Carp are extremely wary and charge away rapidly at the slightest disturbance. They are omnivorous, feeding on a variety of animal and plant material.[4, 135] Most studies indicate that aquatic insects are the most important item in their diet. Plant material is of secondary importance and much dead or decaying plant material may be taken in only incidentally. The seeds, rootlets, and leafy parts of living plants are probably ingested intentionally. Carp commonly concentrate in large numbers where cannery or slaughter house wastes are emptied into streams.

They are not highly migratory, but occasional individuals move for long distances. One tagged in Bear Creek, near Columbia, Missouri, was captured 28 months later 676 stream miles away below Gavins Point Dam, South Dakota.[4]

Carp spawn in Missouri from late March or early April to at least the middle or latter part of June. Ripe males have been taken as late as September and some spawning may occur during all months from early spring to early fall. This fish spawns without preparing a nest and no care is given to the eggs or fry. The eggs are broadcast more or less at random over logs, rocks, or other submerged objects. Often the backs of spawning fish are exposed and the splashing sounds created as they thrash about can be heard for considerable distances.

In Missouri streams carp average 6.5 inches in length at the end of their first year of life and achieve lengths of about 11, 14.2, 16.7, and 18 inches in succeeding years.[52] On the average they weigh 1 pound when 12 inches long, 5 pounds when 21.5 inches long, and 12 pounds when 27.5 inches long. Carp from cool, infertile waters grow more slowly and weigh less at comparable lengths than those from warm, productive waters. Few live more than 12 years in the wild, but in captivity individuals have lived as long as 47 years.

IMPORTANCE

Carp become so abundant in suitable habitats that they are often accused of competing for food and space with more desirable fishes. Their feeding habits frequently result in a general deterioration of the habitat through increased turbidity and the destruction of aquatic vegetation. They have also been reported to eat eggs or otherwise interfere with the reproductive activities of other species. Although there is probably some basis for all these complaints, it seems likely that the carp's nuisance qualities have been considerably overrated.

Carp can put up a fight equal to that of any game fish of similar size and their sporting qualities need to be more generally recognized. Streams providing little suitable habitat for most game species often contain large carp populations, providing fishing opportunities where none would otherwise exist. The total poundage and value of carp in the catch of commercial fishermen in Missouri exceeds that of any other species.

ANGLING

Because of its generalized food habits the carp may be taken on a variety of baits. Probably more are taken on dough balls than any other bait, but many are also caught on whole kernel corn and worms. The bait should be fished on the bottom in areas where they are known to feed. Because the carp has a comparatively small mouth, a small hook should be used.

Goldfish

Carassius auratus (Linnaeus)

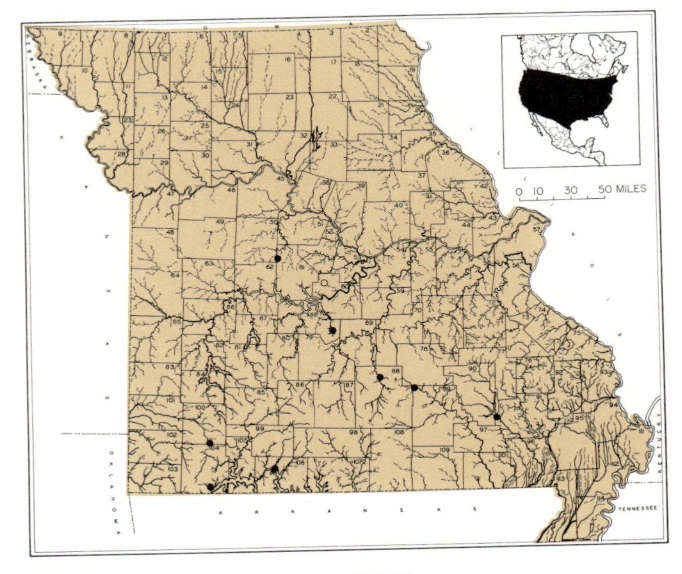

DESCRIPTION

Illustration: Page 95, 2b.

Characters: Resembles the carp in having a long dorsal fin and a stout, saw-toothed spine at front of dorsal and anal fins. However, barbels are absent and there are fewer than 30 scales in the lateral line. Also, the throat teeth are in a single row of 4-4 and lack extensive grinding surfaces.

Life colors: "Wild" goldfish are dark olive-brown above, shading to yellow on lower sides and belly. Scales not prominently dark-edged as in the carp. Cultured varieties of goldfish may be gold, white, red, black, or some combination of these.

Size: Maximum length and weight about 16 inches and 3½ pounds.

Scientific name: *Carassius,* Latinization of the vernacular name for the European Crucian carp; *auratus,* Latin, meaning "gilded", in reference to the color.

DISTRIBUTION AND HABITAT

Like the carp, the goldfish is not native to the United States. No largescale attempts have been made to establish it in Missouri, but the thousands that are released or escape from hatcheries, bait buckets, artificial lakes, and home aquaria have afforded ample opportunity for its establishment. Yet there seem to be no self-sustaining populations of goldfish in natural waters of the state.

It is most often taken in streams below hatcheries, where its numbers are maintained by continuous escape, and in large impoundments, where it is commonly used as bait. There is otherwise little pattern to its distribution, and occasional individuals may be encountered almost anywhere in the state.

HABITS AND LIFE HISTORY

Little has been written about the life history of the goldfish in this country. It is reported to be omnivorous, feeding on much the same type of material as the carp. It spawns at the same time and in the same manner as the carp, and hybrids between them are common in parts of the country where both are firmly established.

Grass Carp

Ctenopharyngodon idella (Valenciennes)

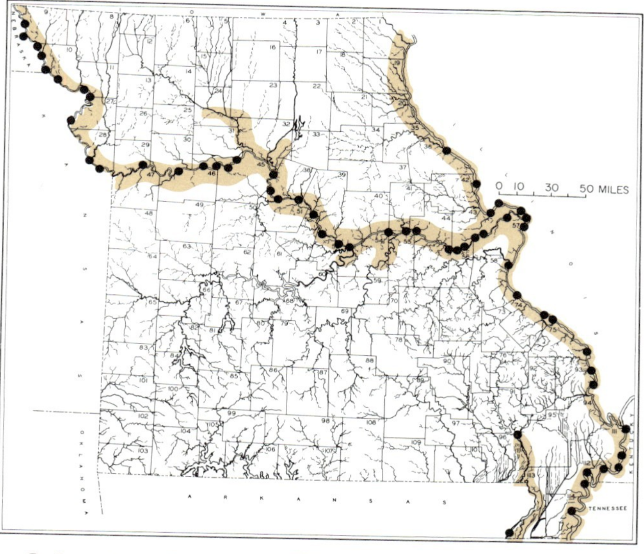

Other local names: White amur

DESCRIPTION

Illustration: Page 95, 3a.

Characters: A thick-bodied, silvery fish with a short, pointed dorsal fin and a broad, blunt head. Scales of back and sides prominently dark-edged, giving a characteristic cross-hatched effect. Dorsal fin with 8 rays. Anal fin closer to tail fin than in native minnows, the distance from front of anal fin base to base of tail fin going more than 2½ times into the distance from anal fin base forward to tip of snout. Throat teeth 2,4-4,2; those in principal row with deep parallel grooves.

Life colors: Back olive-brown, grading to silvery-white on sides and belly. Scales of back and sides outlined by dusky pigment, giving a cross-hatched effect like that which characterizes the carp.

Size: A very large minnow, reported to reach a length of 4 feet and a weight of 100 pounds in its native range. The largest specimen thus far reported from natural waters in Missouri weighed 21 pounds.

Scientific name: *Ctenopharyngodon,* Greek for "comb-like throat-teeth"; *idella,* Greek for "distinct."

DISTRIBUTION AND HABITAT

The grass carp is a native of eastern Asia that was brought into this country as early as 1963 and was introduced into open waters of Arkansas shortly thereafter. Those that gained access to streams have dispersed into areas far from the initial point of release. The first grass carp reported from Missouri waters, a 21-pound specimen, was caught in 1971 from the Mississippi River near Chester, Illinois. Another was caught in 1973 from the Missouri River near Jefferson City. In the summer of 1974 commercial fishermen began reporting grass carp from many localities along the Missouri and Mississippi rivers, and one specimen was caught in the St. Francis River.

The grass carp is reported to be an inhabitant of large rivers. The larger streams of Missouri, particularly the Mississippi and Missouri, appear to provide suitable habitat.

HABITS AND LIFE HISTORY

The grass carp is an active, strong-swimming fish, and will jump spectacularly to avoid a seine. The young feed mainly on small crustaceans and other invertebrates, but a shift in the diet occurs when they attain a length of about 8 inches. Adults exhibit a definite preference for aquatic vegetation, but have been reported to eat a wide variety of plant and animal material.[66] A specimen from the Missouri River contained large quantities of filamentous algae. The grass carp has a voracious appetite and has been reported to consume more than the equivalent of its body weight in a day. However, it is very inefficient in digesting plant material, passing about half of it through undigested.

Spawning occurs in the channels of large rivers, and the eggs hatch as they are carried along by currents. The grass carp grows rapidly under favorable conditions. A specimen caught in the Missouri River had grown from a length of 4.8 inches to 25.8 inches in one year. Twenty specimens caught by commercial fishermen in 1974 ranged from 24 to 34 inches long and from 6 to 14.7 pounds in weight. Most were in their third summer of life.

IMPORTANCE

The grass carp has been imported into this country as a biological control for aquatic vegetation in man-made impoundments. In some countries it is being reared as a food fish. Its flesh is reported to be on a par with that of the common carp. There is strong concern that if the grass carp becomes established in natural waters of the United States it will become a serious pest. Aside from the possibility that it may compete for food and space with native species, there is also a chance that it may destroy fish and waterfowl habitat by eliminating all aquatic vegetation in waters where some vegetation is desirable. The final outcome of the introduction of grass carp into this country may not be known for many years.

Golden Shiner

Notemigonus crysoleucas (Mitchill)

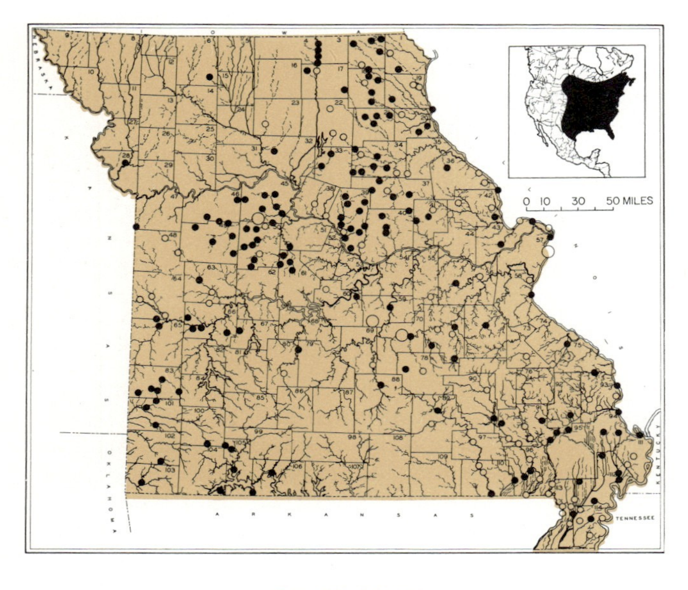

DESCRIPTION

Illustration: Page 96, 4a.

Characters: A deep-bodied, slab-sided minnow with a sickle-shaped outer margin on the anal fin and a strong downward curve in the lateral line. Differs from all other Missouri minnows in having a fleshy, scaleless keel along midline of belly from the anus forward to pelvic fin bases. Mouth strongly upturned (oblique) and small, the upper jaw not reaching front of eye. Barbels absent. Dorsal fin rays 8; anal fin rays 11 to 15. Lateral line scales 45 to 54. Intestine short, with a single S-shaped loop; lining of body cavity silvery, thickly sprinkled with large, dark speckles. Throat teeth 5-5.

Life colors: Back greenish-olive with a faint dusky stripe along midline. Sides golden or silvery. Belly silvery-white. Fins without definite markings. Young individuals from clear waters have a definite dusky stripe along midside.

Size: Adults are commonly 3 to 6 inches long to a maximum of about 8 inches.

Scientific name: *Notemigonus,* Greek, "angled back"; *crysoleucas,* Greek, meaning "golden white", in reference to the body color.

DISTRIBUTION AND HABITAT

The golden shiner is widespread in Missouri, reaching its greatest abundance in the Prairie and Ozark border streams of west-central and northeastern Missouri and the Lowlands of the southeast. The distribution in Ozark streams is sporadic, but the golden shiner is common in backwaters of large Ozark reservoirs. In northwestern Missouri it occurs only as occasional individuals or highly localized populations. It seldom attains the high population densities in Missouri that have been attributed to it elsewhere in its range.

The golden shiner is characteristic of quiet-water habitats, occurring only rarely in stream sections with a noticeable current. The largest populations are found in sloughs, ponds, lakes, impoundments, the quiet pools of low-gradient streams and ditches, and the permanent pools of intermittent upland creeks. It is tolerant of moderate turbidity, but thrives in clear, heavily vegetated habitats.

HABITS AND LIFE HISTORY

The golden shiner lives in small, loosely aggregated schools and is usually found in midwater or near the surface. Its diet is generalized, including plant and animal material in about equal quantities. An early study in Illinois revealed that the diet consisted of about half algae and higher plants, with the other half mostly small crustaceans, snails, and terrestrial insects.[67] Subsequent studies have confirmed these findings.

In Missouri ponds the golden shiner spawns from late April to early June.[68] Spawning begins when the water temperature rises to 70°F and ceases when the temperature exceeds 80°F. Spawning may resume in mid or late summer if the water temperature is sufficiently reduced by a cool rain. The golden shiner does not prepare a nest or guard its eggs. Typically, the adhesive eggs are scattered over filamentous algae or the submerged parts of higher plants. Spawning also occurs over nests of largemouth bass.[69] I have collected breeding adults over green sunfish nests where they evidently spawn. Eggs hatch about 4 days after spawning and soon the young form large schools just below the water surface near shore.

A Michigan study indicates that the golden shiner attains a length of about 3 inches during its second summer, 4 inches its third summer, 4.5 inches its fourth summer, 5 inches its fifth summer, and 5.5 inches its sixth summer.[70] Growth varies considerably with conditions, being most rapid in warmer and fertile waters. Females grow more rapidly and attain a larger maximum size than males. This is one of the largest minnows native to Missouri.

IMPORTANCE

In natural waters the golden shiner often occurs in association with the largemouth bass and the crappies and is commonly used as food by these and other game fishes. It is an excellent bait minnow and is well suited for pond culture. Over 50,000,000 golden shiners with an estimated retail value of $2,000,000 were produced in Missouri in 1965. Large adults are sometimes caught on worms or small artificial baits, but they are seldom specifically sought after by fishermen.

Creek Chub

Semotilus atromaculatus (Mitchill)

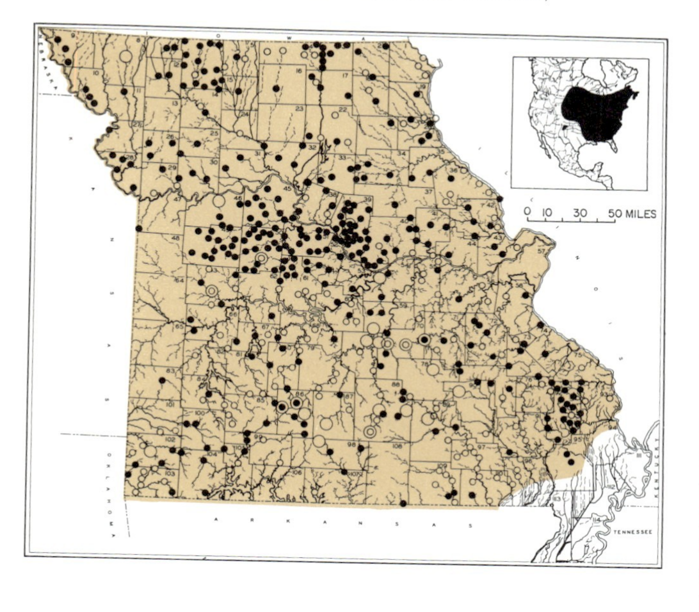

DESCRIPTION

Illustration: Page 109, 30a.

Characters: A slender, cylindrical minnow with a dark blotch at the front of dorsal fin base and a small dark spot at base of tail fin. Mouth moderately oblique and large, the upper jaw reaching behind front of eye. Upper lip wider in middle than on either side. A small, flap-like barbel (sometimes absent on one or both sides) present in groove above upper lip just ahead of corner of mouth. Scales small, especially towards head. Anal fin with 8 rays. Lateral line scales 51 to 64. Intestine short, with a single S-shaped loop; lining of body cavity silvery with a few scattered dark speckles. Throat teeth variable, most often 2,5-4,2.

Life colors: Back dark olive with a broad dusky stripe along midline. Sides silvery with greenish or purplish reflections. A dusky stripe, best developed in small individuals, extends along midside. Belly silvery-white. Fins yellowish or light olive. Breeding males are iridescent apple-green above and rose-red below, with a small red spot near front of dorsal fin base. Large tubercles are scattered over top of head and smaller ones are scattered over parts of body and fins.
Size: The largest minnow native to Missouri, reaching a length of more than 12 inches. The usual adult length is 5 to 7 inches.
Scientific name: *Semotilus,* from the Greek word *sema,* "a banner," (i.e. dorsal fin); the second part of the word was used elsewhere by its author (Rafinesque) to mean "spotted"; *atromaculatus,* Latin, "black spot."

DISTRIBUTION AND HABITAT

The creek chub is one of the most widely distributed Missouri minnows. Its main area of abundance is in the smaller Prairie creeks of central and east-central Missouri. Westward, it becomes increasingly spotty in distribution, but where it does occur it is often abundant. It is present in virtually all the small creeks and spring branches of the Ozarks but is seldom abundant. In the Lowlands it is confined to a few small creeks draining Crowley's Ridge.

The creek chub is well named, for it is most abundant in small headwater creeks where few other fishes are present. These small creeks often cease to flow in dry weather and the creek chub survives in isolated pools or repopulates from below when the creeks again begin to flow. It requires flowing water for spawning but does not thrive in streams with a continuous strong flow. Such streams usually harbor a large variety of fish species and, in this situation, the rather generalized creek chub seems unable to compete successfully. It can tolerate moderately high turbidities, as long as the stream gradient is sufficient to create gravelly stretches for spawning. The scarcity of gravel bottoms in many small streams of northern and western Missouri and in ditches of the Lowlands may be an important factor in limiting the distribution of the creek chub in those regions.

HABITS AND LIFE HISTORY

The creek chub generally occurs in loosely aggregated schools, often mixed with other minnows such as the stoneroller and common shiner. It is an active fish and will move immediately to investigate any small object falling into the water. The creek chub is a generalized carnivore, adapting its diet to whatever is available. The small amounts of plant material commonly found in its stomach probably are ingested incidentally during the feeding process. In the Des Moines River, Iowa, the creek chub feeds to a considerable extent on insects, including both terrestrial and aquatic kinds.[71, 72] Larger creek chubs feed heavily on minnows and other small fishes. Crayfish, worms, and molluscs are also eaten in lesser quantities.

In Missouri the creek chub spawns from early April to the latter part of May. The interesting breeding habits of this minnow were described in detail by Reighard[73] in a classic paper that should be read by anyone interested in studying the habits of fishes. Spawning occurs in nests that are constructed by the males. Nests are located on a gravel bottom, usually at the lower end of a pool where the current begins to quicken. Each nest is the work of a single male and, since he will not tolerate the presence of other males, nests are usually widely separated. The male begins by digging a shallow pit in the stream bottom, piling the stones on its upstream edge. Small stones are transported by the male one or more at a time in his mouth. Stones too large to move in this manner are pushed along the bottom. The pit is gradually lengthened by removing more stones at the lower end, as a low mound of gravel gradually takes form just upstream from it. Most of the stones are deposited at the lower end of the mound and it encroaches upon and fills the pit. Since the pit is continually lengthened, it is never completely filled and is gradually shifted downstream. Sand and silt stirred up by the activities of the male are carried away downstream by the current. The finished nest consists of a long, low ridge of washed gravel lying in a shallow trench with an oval pit at its lower end. The ridge is about a foot in width and rises 2 or 3 inches above the general level of the stream bottom. It may be as much as 18 feet in length but is often much less. The pit is about the same width as the ridge and 2 or 3 inches deep.

Nest construction is interrupted at frequent intervals by nest guarding activities. Other minnow species, and creek chubs smaller than the resident male, are driven off when they attempt to approach the nest. Sometimes other male creek chubs of about the same size or larger than the owner will challenge him for possession of the nest. This may result in a fight in which the males bring their sharp tubercles into play by striking violently at each other with their heads. If the males are of about the same size they often engage in a peculiar ritual referred to by Reighard as "deferred combat." As the intruder approaches "the occupant ranges himself alongside and the two fish swim upstream with great deliberation for a distance of 15 or 20 feet . . . In their course they move slowly and swing their tails from side to side in unison, as though keeping step with them. At the end of their course they settle to the bottom and bring their heads together gently, as though bowing to one another. They then usually separate their heads and bring their tails together, as though about to swim away from one another. They then commonly again bring their heads together and finally separate, the owner to return to his nest, his companion to some near-by shelter."

Spawning may occur any time during the nest building process. Sometimes three or four females approach the nest simultaneously, but ordinarily only one enters. Upon her first approach the female flees when the male turns towards her, but she returns repeatedly, each time approaching a little closer, until finally she enters the pit. At this time she is thrown into a vertical position by the male, who then encircles her with his body. During this brief embrace, lasting only a fraction of a second, a small number of eggs are released and fertilized. The female floats for a moment belly up, then recovers and leaves the nest. The eggs settle to the bottom of the pit, to be covered by gravel when the male resumes his nest building activities. The female will return to this or another nest repeatedly until all her eggs are deposited. Eggs are thus scattered throughout the gravel ridge where they are afforded a considerable measure of protection from predators. The eggs hatch within the nest and the young work their way up through the spaces between the stones. By this time the male has long since abandoned the nest.

In central Missouri streams the creek chub attains a length of 1.5 to 2.5 inches by the end of its first summer of life and is 4 to 8 inches long at maturity. Males grow more rapidly and reach a larger maximum size than females.

IMPORTANCE

The creek chub is a hardy minnow and makes an excellent bait. Because it requires flowing water and gravel for spawning, special techniques are required to propagate it artificially. This minnow rises like a trout to a fly or other small artificial lure and can provide sport when taken on light tackle.

Southern Redbelly Dace

Phoxinus erythrogaster (Rafinesque)

DESCRIPTION

Illustration: Page 97, 6a.

Characters: A slender minnow with two narrow, dusky stripes along the side, separated by a broad, light-colored stripe. Scales so small as to be nearly invisible without magnification. Mouth moderately oblique and small, not extending past front of eye. Barbels absent. Lateral line incomplete. Dorsal and anal fins each with 8 rays. Scales in lateral series 70 to 95. Intestine long, with several loops; lining of body cavity black. Throat teeth 5-5.

Life colors: Back olive-brown with scattered dark spots and a narrow dusky stripe along midline. Side with two black lengthwise stripes, the upper narrower than the lower, separated by a broad, golden or yellowish stripe. Belly white.

Breeding males are among the most beautiful of Missouri fishes. The pattern of light and dark markings is more intense at this time, the undersurface of the head and body are crimson red, the lower fins and undersurface of the caudal peduncle are lemon yellow, and the base of the dorsal fin is crimson or yellow. Small tubercles are scattered over the head, body, and fins.

Size: A small minnow, rarely exceeding a length of 3 inches. Most adults are 1.6 to 2.8 inches long.

Scientific name: *Phoxinus,* Greek, for an unknown river fish; *erythrogaster,* Greek, "red belly."

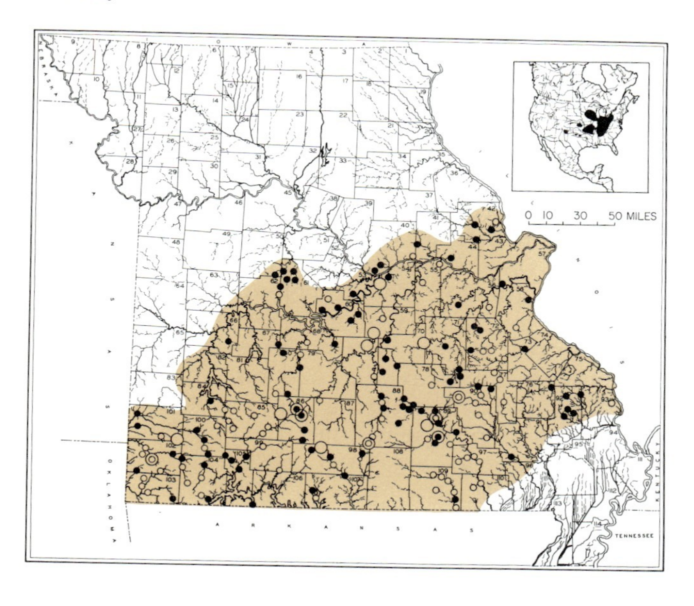

DISTRIBUTION AND HABITAT

The southern redbelly dace is one of the characteristic fishes of the Ozark Uplands and its distribution coincides very closely with the boundaries of that region in Missouri. This fish tends to occur as isolated populations at widely spaced intervals, but it is often one of the most abundant fishes in its preferred habitat.

It is primarily an inhabitant of small creeks and spring branches having a permanent flow of clear, cool water and silt-free, gravelly bottoms. In larger creeks and rivers it occurs only as strays or as highly localized populations in spring pools away from the main channel. Habitats where the southern redbelly dace is found often contain submergent vegetation, but the species is also abundant in habitats where vegetation is sparse.

HABITS AND LIFE HISTORY

The southern redbelly dace lives in schools, often in association with the stoneroller and creek chub. It is usually found near the bottom where it forages over rocks and other submerged objects. The long intestine suggests an herbivorous diet and the meagre information available bears this out. Specimens from Illinois were found to contain mud mixed with algae and occasional traces of microcrustaceans.[67]

Spawning aggregations of this fish have been observed during May. It does not prepare a nest, but rather spawns in nests of other minnows such as the stoneroller and hornyhead chub, or on the clean, gravelly sections of riffles. When spawning, large schools consisting principally of brilliantly colored males gather over the spawning areas, with the females maintaining a position immediately downstream. The males do not guard territories, but jostle vigorously for positions beside the females as they swim up over the spawning site. Ordinarily a single female is clasped firmly between two males while spawning, but occasionally a single male spawns with a female by crowding her against some pebbles and curving his tail over her body.[74] The small, sandpaper-like tubercles of the males assist in holding the female.

In Missouri streams the southern redbelly dace reaches a length of 1.1 to 1.8 inches during its first year of life and is mature when about 2 inches long. Probably few individuals live more than two years.

IMPORTANCE

The southern redbelly dace is very hardy in the bait bucket and on the hook and makes a good panfish bait. Because of its gentle disposition and attractive colors it makes an excellent aquarium fish.

Hornyhead Chub

Nocomis biguttatus (Kirtland)

DESCRIPTION

Illustration: Page 100, 13a; **37.**

Characters: A slender, brownish minnow with small eyes, their diameter much less than snout length, and a large, slightly oblique mouth. Similar to creek chub, page 131, but with larger scales and with a small, conical barbel at corner of mouth. Front of dorsal fin much closer to base of tail fin than to tip of snout. Anal fin with 7 rays. Lateral line scales 38 to 44. Intestine short, with a single S-shaped loop; lining of body cavity black. Throat teeth 1,4-4,1.

Similar to redspot chub, page 135, differing notably only in the absence of tubercles or tubercle spots on body scales in breeding adults. Locality provides the only reliable means for separating many specimens of the hornyhead and redspot chubs.

Life colors: Back and upper sides olive-brown, the scales prominently dark edged giving a cross-hatched effect. Lower sides and belly yellowish-white. Young with a bright orange tail, a dusky stripe along midside, and a small black spot at base of tail fin. These markings fade with age.

Breeding males have a prominent red spot behind eye and large tubercles covering top of head.

Size: A large minnow, reaching a length of at least 10.2 inches. Adults are commonly 5 to 7 inches long.

Scientific name: *Nocomis,* an Indian name applied by Girard to a group of fishes; *biguttatus,* Latin, meaning "two spotted," perhaps in reference to the red spot on each side of the head in breeding males.

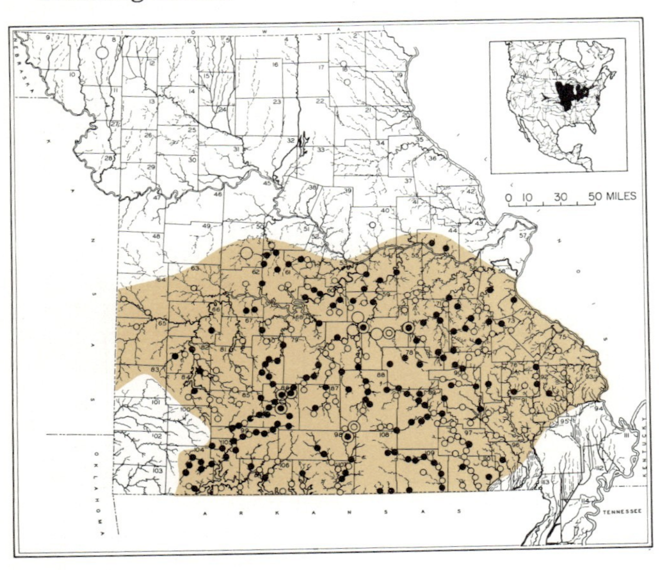

DISTRIBUTION AND HABITAT

The hornyhead chub occurs in all principal stream systems of the Ozarks not occupied by the redspot chub and is one of the common and characteristic Ozark stream fishes. However, it never attains the abundance of some other minnows of the region. The hornyhead chub formerly occurred in the Prairie Region at localities many miles from streams that now support populations. Even in the Ozark Region the hornyhead has suffered some restriction in distribution. It apparently is no longer present in the Bourbeuse River, though it formerly occurred there. Intensive cultivation, with attendant increase in siltation and intermittent flow, may be important factors in the declining abundance of this chub in parts of Missouri.

The hornyhead chub inhabits clear streams having permanent flow and a predominance of clean gravel or rubble bottoms. Adults are most often found near riffles, but not in the swifter current. The young frequent areas without current and are often found in association with higher aquatic plants.

HABITS AND LIFE HISTORY

The hornyhead chub seldom forms large schools, occurring in mixed schools with other minnows such as the bleeding shiner, striped shiner, and the stonerollers. Although the hornyhead's snout is rather well supplied with taste buds, feeding is mainly by sight rather than by taste.[75] The diet consists of about half plant material, including both algae and higher plants, and half animal material, primarily insects.[76]

In Missouri, spawning of the hornyhead chub occurs from late April until about the first week of July, but is most intense in May and early June. Spawning is not continuous, but rather seems to be renewed after each period of high water. In spring and early summer the conspicuous mounds of gravel that are the nests of the hornyhead are a characteristic feature of Ozark streams.

Nests are constructed and guarded by the male who transports stones in his mouth. These stones are often larger than the chub's head and may be carried from points as far as 20 feet from the nest. Nests are roughly circular in outline and are 1 to 3 feet in diameter. They taper upward from the base and rise several inches above the general level of the stream bottom. Nest construction starts with the excavation of a pit. Spawning occurs intermittently during nest construction, in temporary depressions that the male digs and refills. The eggs are thus mixed through the gravel mound.

Only a single male occupies a nest and any other males that venture near are driven away. Sometimes a small male briefly occupies and spawns in the nest of another male when the latter temporarily leaves the nest unguarded. "Deferred combat" and fighting as described for the creek chub, page 131, often occur between males of similar size. Several other species of minnows utilize chub nests for their spawning activities and are tolerated by the male chub. Frequently a veritable swarm of brightly colored bleeding shiners, redbelly dace, and Ozark minnows may be observed over a nest while the male chub industriously transports pebbles, oblivious to the presence of these intruders. Other small minnows, darters, and sunfish also gather near the nest to eat eggs whenever the opportunity presents itself.

The male hornyhead chub grows more rapidly and reaches a larger size than females. In the northeastern United States males reach a mean standard length of 2.2, 3.6, and 4.9 inches at the end of their first, second, and third summers of growth.[249] Females reach a mean length of 1.9, 3.4, and 4.2 inches at the end of the same growth periods. Sexual maturity is reached at 2 or 3 years of age and only an occasional individual survives its fourth summer.

Redspot Chub

Nocomis asper Lachner and Jenkins

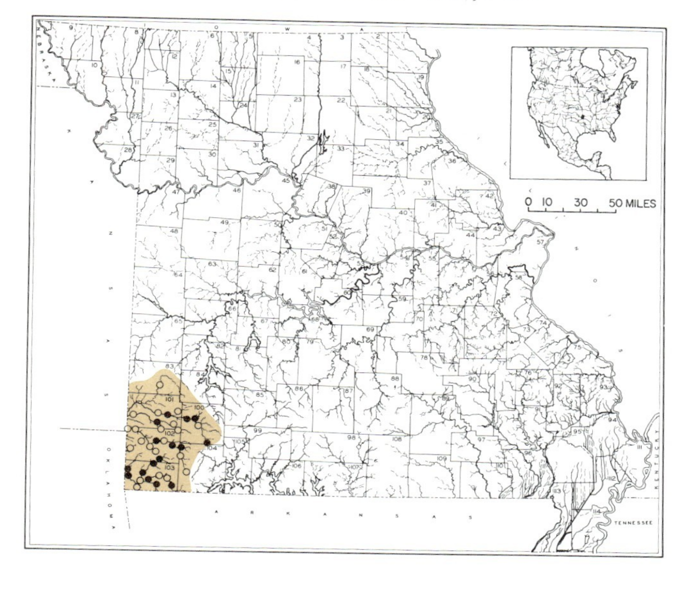

DESCRIPTION

Illustration: Page 100, 13b.

Characters: Similar to hornyhead chub, page 133, differing notably only in the presence of tubercles on body scales in breeding males. Adult females often have light spots on some body scales in a position corresponding to the tubercles in males. Locality provides the only reliable means for separating many specimens of the redspot and hornyhead chubs.

Life colors: Like those of the hornyhead chub, page 133, except that the red spot present behind the eye is better developed in breeding males and is also present in mature females.

Size: Commonly 5 to 7 inches long to a maximum of about 10 inches.

Scientific name: *Nocomis,* an Indian name applied by Girard to a group of fishes; *asper,* Latin, meaning "rough."

DISTRIBUTION AND HABITAT

The redspot chub is restricted to the Elk and Spring stream systems of southwestern Missouri. Its habitat is like that of the hornyhead chub, page 133.

HABITS AND LIFE HISTORY

The habits and life history of this chub are not known in detail, but probably are not notably different from those of the hornyhead chub. Nests of the redspot chub have been observed in southwestern Missouri during June and are used for spawning by the southern redbelly dace, duskystripe shiner, and Ozark minnow.

Silver Chub

Hybopsis storeriana (Kirtland)

DESCRIPTION

Illustration: Page 103, 18b.

Characters: A slender, silvery minnow with rather large eyes—eye diameter nearly equal to length of snout—and a small, nearly horizontal mouth. Mouth with a small, conical barbel at corner. Snout blunt and rounded, projecting distinctly beyond upper lip. Front of dorsal fin much closer to tip of snout than to base of tail fin. Anal fin with 8 rays. Lateral line scales 35 to 40. Intestine short, with a single S-shaped loop; lining of body cavity silvery. Throat teeth 1,4-4,1.

Life colors: Back light olive with silvery reflections; sides and belly silvery white. Lower lobe of tail fin darker than upper lobe. Breeding males without special colors, but with small tubercles along pectoral fin rays.

Size: Reaching a length of nearly 9 inches, but individuals longer than 6 inches are rare. Most adults are 3.5 to 5.3 inches long.

Scientific name: *Hybopsis,* Greek, "rounded face"; *storeriana,* named for D.H. Storer, an early student of North American fishes.

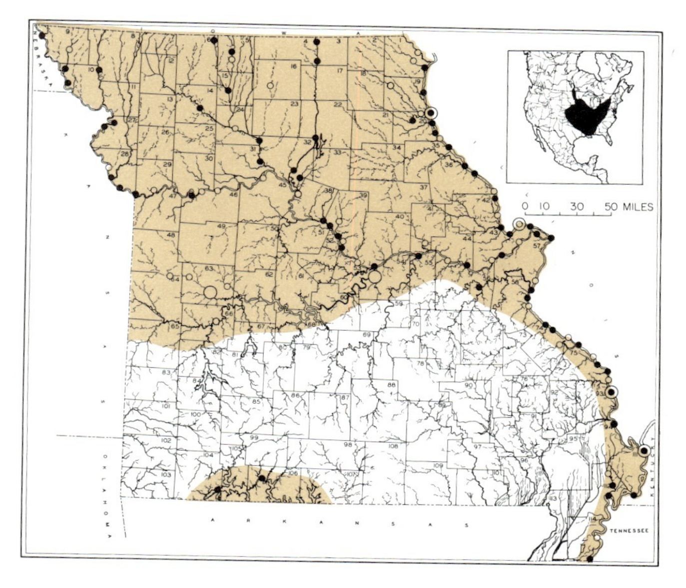

DISTRIBUTION AND HABITAT

The silver chub is one of the common and characteristic minnows in the Missouri and Mississippi rivers. It also occurs in large streams elsewhere in the state, but is seldom abundant. The absence of recent records from the upper Osage and South Grand rivers may be due to inadequate sampling rather than a recent restriction in distribution.

This minnow inhabits the quiet pools and backwaters of large streams. It also occurs in some large reservoirs and, elsewhere in its range, it inhabits natural lakes.

HABITS AND LIFE HISTORY

The silver chub lives on or near the bottom, locating its food by sight as well as by taste.[75] Its food habits have not been studied. The silver chub probably spawns at this latitude in April or May.[42] Its spawning habits are not known.

Bigeye Chub

Hybopsis amblops (Rafinesque)

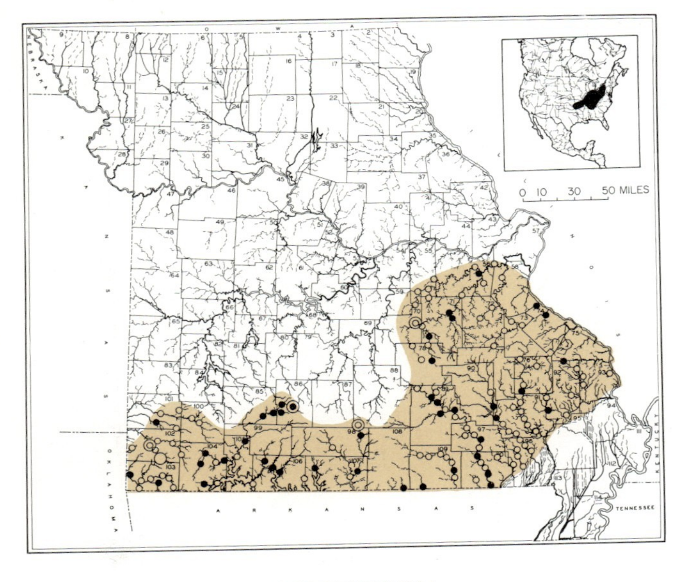

DESCRIPTION

Illustration: Page 103, 18a.

Characters: A slender, silvery minnow with large eyes, and a small, horizontal mouth. Mouth with a small, conical barbel at corner (barbel rarely absent on one or both sides). Snout blunt and rounded, projecting distinctly beyond upper lip. Eye diameter slightly greater than length of snout. Front of dorsal fin about midway between tip of snout and base of tail fin. Anal fin with 8 rays. Lateral line scales 33 to 38. Intestine short, with a single S-shaped loop; lining of body cavity silvery with scattered dark speckles. Throat teeth 1,4-4,1.

Life colors: Back and upper side greenish-yellow with faint dark edgings on scales. Lower sides and belly silvery-white. Midside with a prominent dusky stripe except in individuals from highly turbid waters. Breeding males without special colors but with very small tubercles on top of head and along the pectoral fin rays.

Size: Adults are commonly 2.5 to 3 inches long to a maximum of about 3.5 inches.

Scientific name: *Hybopsis,* Greek, "rounded face"; *amblops,* Greek, meaning "blunt face".

DISTRIBUTION AND HABITAT

The bigeye chub is confined to the Ozarks where it occurs in all the principal stream systems except the Osage and Gasconade. It is still common in the White, Current, and Black River systems but has declined in abundance in the Meramec, Spring, and Elk River systems.

The bigeye chub thrives in clear streams with permanent flow and silt-free gravelly or rocky bottoms. It often occurs near riffles, but not in the main current. Rather, it is found at the base of the riffle where the current slackens, or in quiet pools without current.

HABITS AND LIFE HISTORY

The habits of this minnow are not well known. The scarcity of external taste buds and the large eye suggests that it feeds mostly by sight. This mode of feeding is probably correlated with life in clear waters. Breeding adults have been collected in Missouri in June, indicating a late spring or early summer spawning season. In Missouri the bigeye chub attains a length of nearly 2 inches by the end of its first summer of life and is about 2.5 to 3.2 inches long by the end of its second summer.

Streamline Chub

Hybopsis dissimilis (Kirtland)

DESCRIPTION

Illustration: Page 104, 20a.

Characters: A slender minnow with rather large eyes, a small, horizontal mouth and a series of dark, oval blotches along the midside. Mouth with a small, conical barbel at corner. Snout blunt and rounded, projecting distinctly beyond upper lip. Eye diameter less than length of snout. Front of dorsal fin much closer to tip of snout than to base of tail fin. Anal fin with 7 rays. Lateral line scales 46 to 49. Intestine rather long, with several loops; lining of body cavity black. Throat teeth 4-4.

Life colors: Back pale greenish-yellow with a narrow stripe consisting of alternating golden and dusky areas along its midline (stripe very obvious when fish is in the water). Sides silvery, belly silvery-white. Midside with a series of dark blotches underlain by a faint dusky stripe. Breeding males without special colors but with very small tubercles on head and forward part of body.

Size: Adults commonly 3 to 4 inches long to a maximum of about 4.5 inches.

Scientific name: *Hybopsis,* Greek, "rounded face"; *dissimilis,* Latin, meaning "not similar" (to other shiners).

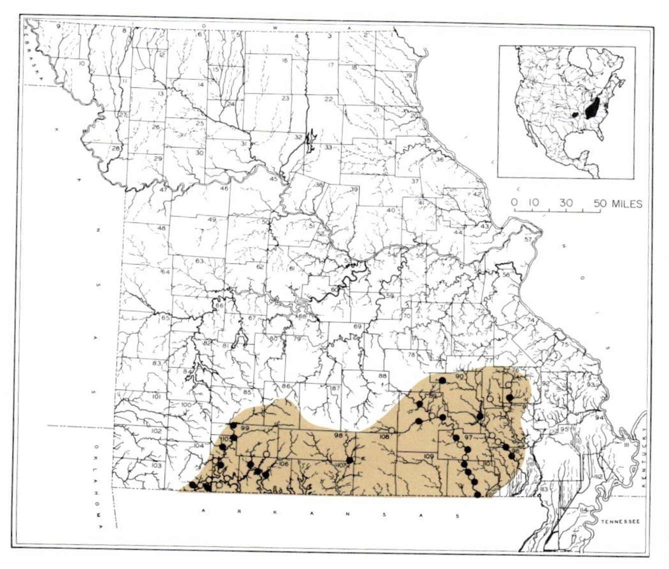

DISTRIBUTION AND HABITAT

The streamline chub is confined to the southern Ozarks where it is the most abundant chub in most large streams.

This minnow inhabits large, high-gradient streams with a continuous strong flow of clear water and clean gravelly or rocky bottoms. It is most often found near riffles or in pools with noticeable current.

HABITS AND LIFE HISTORY

The streamline chub lives close to the bottom and often maintains a position in the current by continuous swimming movements. It probably feeds primarily by sight, assisted by external taste buds.[75] Little else is known of its habits.

Gravel Chub

Hybopsis x-punctata Hubbs and Crowe

DESCRIPTION

Illustration: Page 104, 20b.

Characters: A slender minnow with rather large eyes, a small, horizontal mouth, and scattered X-shaped markings over the back and sides. Mouth with a small, conical barbel at corner. Snout blunt and rounded, projecting well beyond upper lip. Eye diameter less than length of snout. Front of dorsal fin much closer to tip of snout than to base of tail fin. Anal fin with 7 rays. Lateral line scales 40 to 43. Intestine rather long, with several loops; lining of body cavity black. Throat teeth 4-4.

Life colors: Back pale greenish-yellow with a continuous dusky stripe along midline. Sides silvery, sometimes with a faint dusky stripe. Back and upper sides with scattered X-shaped markings. A small, black spot usually present at base of tail fin. Breeding males without special colors, but with very small tubercles on head and forward part of body.

Size: Adults are commonly 2.5 to 3.5 inches long to a maximum of about 4 inches.

Scientific name: *Hybopsis,* Greek, "rounded face"; *x-punctata,* from the Latin word *punctatus,* meaning "spotted." The prefix "x" refers to the characteristic shape of the spots on the sides.

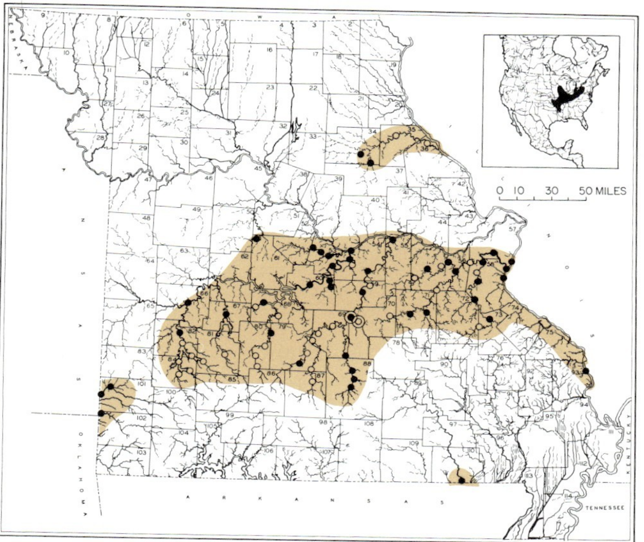

DISTRIBUTION AND HABITAT

The gravel chub is common and widely distributed in the northern and western Ozarks. It is known elsewhere only from the Salt River system of northeast Missouri and from single localities on the lower Mississippi and lower Current rivers. This minnow was first described from specimens collected in the Gasconade River of Missouri.

It inhabits clear to moderately turbid streams with permanent flow and well defined gravelly or rocky riffles. In the Ozarks it tends to be most abundant in the downstream sections of the larger streams where the gradient is less and the water is warmer and less clear than in the headwaters. This fish is most often found in slight to moderate current over a silt-free gravelly or rocky bottom.

HABITS AND LIFE HISTORY

The gravel chub lives on or near the bottom, often resting behind or beneath rocks where it is protected from the main force of the current. It is thought to feed by probing crevices between rocks with its sensitive snout.[75] The gravel chub is reported to spawn at this latitude in early spring on swift gravelly riffles.[42]

Speckled Chub

Hybopsis aestivalis (Girard)

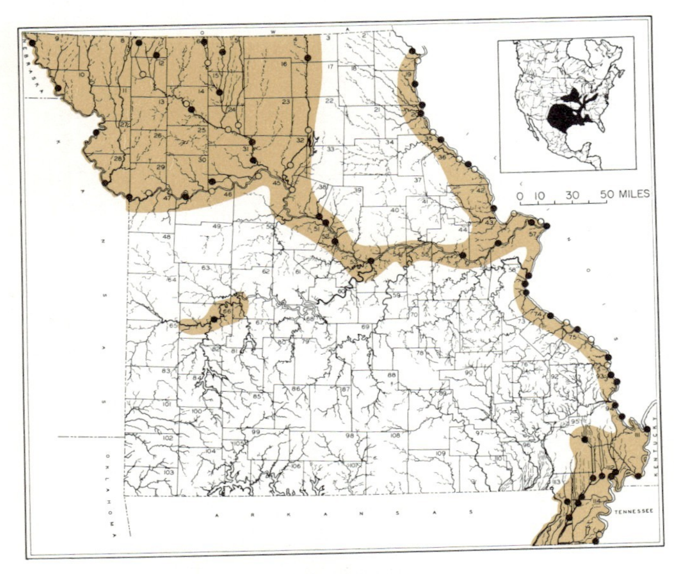

DESCRIPTION

Illustration: Page 103, 19a.

Characters: A slender, pale-colored minnow with rather small eyes, a small, horizontal mouth, and roundish black spots scattered over the back and sides. Mouth with a small, conical barbel at corner. Snout long and bluntly rounded, projecting far beyond upper lip. Eye diameter much less than length of snout. Front of dorsal fin closer to tip of snout than to base of tail fin. Anal fin with 7 or 8 rays. Lateral line scales 34 to 41. Intestine short, with a single S-shaped loop; lining of body cavity silvery with scattered dark speckles. Throat teeth 4-4.

Life colors: Back and upper sides pale yellow with silvery reflections and scattered black spots. Lower sides and belly silvery white. A faint dusky stripe sometimes is present along the midside. Breeding males are without special colors but have very small tubercles over the head and breast and along rays of pectoral fin.

Size: Adults are typically 1.8 to 2.6 inches long to a maximum of about 3 inches.

Scientific name: *Hybopsis,* Greek, "rounded face"; *aestivalis,* Latin, pertaining to summer.

DISTRIBUTION AND HABITAT

The speckled chub is one of the common and characteristic minnows in the Missouri and Mississippi rivers, and also occurs commonly in the larger Prairie streams of northwest Missouri and the main drainage ditches of the Lowlands. It seems to have only recently invaded the Lowland ditches, since it did not occur in collections made there 25 or 30 years ago.

This minnow inhabits the open channels of large, low gradient streams. It is most often found over a bottom of fine sand or small gravel where there is noticeable current. It occurs in streams with continuous high turbidity as well as those that are moderately clear.

HABITS AND LIFE HISTORY

The speckled chub is a sedentary fish, resting quietly on the stream bottom when not moving about in search of food. It is equipped with numerous external taste buds on the head, body, and fins, and food is located more by taste than sight. Eyes are of little value for locating food in the highly turbid water where this minnow often lives. When feeding, the speckled chub swims slowly about with the pectoral fins widespread and the rather long barbels in contact with the bottom. Large quantities of sand are taken into the mouth, sorted for any food it may contain, and then ejected from the mouth and gill openings. The diet consists mostly of immature aquatic insects, along with small quantities of adult insects, small crustaceans, and plant material.[71]

The following information on spawning is taken from an Arkansas study.[77] The spawning season is long; in the Arkansas River, eggs of the speckled chub have been found as early as May 14 and as late as August 28. The spawning habits are unknown, but the eggs are deposited in deep water, where the current is swift, at midday or within an hour or two thereafter. The fertilized eggs are only slightly heavier than water and develop as they drift in the stream currents. Early development is rapid and the eggs hatch about 25 to 28 hours after fertilization. The fry swim erratically at hatching and begin feeding 2 or 3 days thereafter.

The speckled chub is very short-lived, seldom surviving more than 1½ years.[78] Reproduction is, therefore, accomplished primarily by year-old fish. A length of 1 to 2 inches is reached by the end of the first growing season.

Flathead Chub

Hybopsis gracilis (Richardson)

DESCRIPTION

Illustration: Page 102, 17a.

Characters: A slender, silvery minnow with small eyes, a large, slightly oblique mouth, and sickle-shaped (falcate), pointed, pectoral fins.

Head distinctively wedge shaped in profile. Mouth with a small barbel at corner. Snout flattened and rather pointed, projecting slightly beyond upper lip. Eye diameter much less than length of snout. Front of dorsal fin about midway between tip of snout and base of tail fin. Anal fin with 8 rays. Lateral line scales 44 to 56. Intestine short, with a single S-shaped loop; lining of body cavity silvery with scattered dark speckles.

Life colors: Back light brown; sides and belly silvery-white without definite markings. Lower lobe of tail fin darker than upper lobe. Breeding males without special colors, but with very small tubercles on upper surface of head and body and along some rays of all fins except tail fin.

Size: Adults are commonly 3.7 to 7.5 inches long to a maximum of about 9 inches.

Scientific name: *Hybopsis,* Greek, "rounded face"; *gracilis,* Latin, "slender."

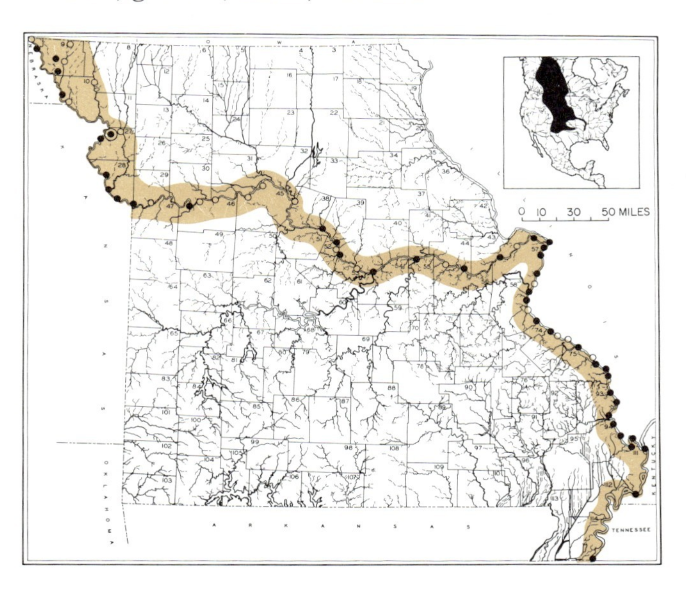

DISTRIBUTION AND HABITAT

The flathead chub is one of the most abundant minnows in the Missouri and lower Mississippi rivers. Like the sicklefin and sturgeon chubs, it does not ascend the Mississippi River above the mouth of the Missouri. The flathead chub enters tributaries only in extreme northwest Missouri.

This minnow inhabits a diverse range of habitats. In the Missouri and Mississippi rivers it is found in more or less continuously turbid waters where the current is swift and the bottom is composed of sand and fine gravel. In northwestern Missouri it occurs in the pools of small creeks with moderately clear waters, little current, and bottoms composed of coarse gravel and bedrock.

In parts of its range two subspecies of the flathead chub have been recognized, one living in large rivers and the other in small creeks. Possibly those occurring in tributary streams of northwest Missouri represent the small-creek subspecies, but they do not appear to be distinguishable morphologically from chubs nearby in the Missouri River.

HABITS AND LIFE HISTORY

The flathead chub is an active minnow, moving about more or less constantly, often in mixed schools with other Big-river minnows. It probably depends largely on external taste buds to locate food in turbid water, but in clear water also feeds by sight. The diet of the flathead chub is reported to consist mostly of terrestrial insects that fall into the water, supplemented by lesser quantities of other small invertebrates and plant material.[79] This fish is thought to spawn at the latitude of Missouri in July or August,[42] but details of the spawning habits are not known. Specimens less than an inch long have been collected in the Missouri River, Boone County, in late May. The presence of several length groups in collections suggests that this fish lives at least 3 or 4 years.

Sturgeon Chub

Hybopsis gelida (Girard)

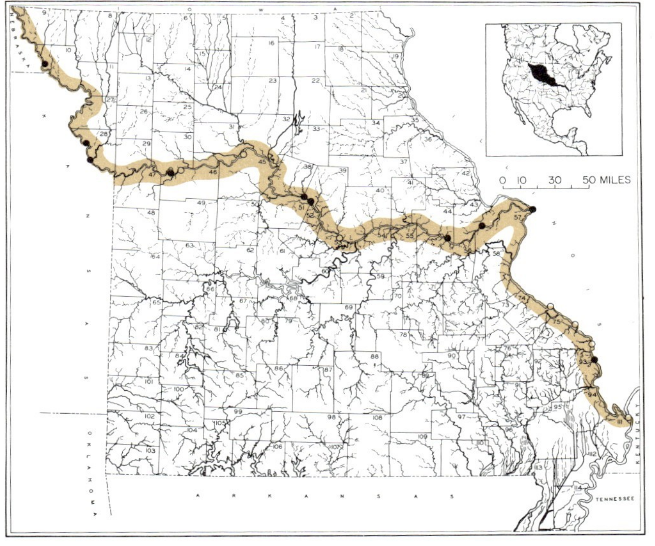

DESCRIPTION

Illustration: Page 102, 16a.

Characters: A slender minnow with small eyes, a small, horizontal mouth, and low ridges or keels on many scales of the back and sides. Mouth with a small, conical barbel at corner. Snout long and somewhat flattened, projecting far beyond upper lip. Eye diameter much less than length of snout. Front of dorsal fin closer to tip of snout than to base of tail fin. Anal fin with 8 rays. Lateral line scales 39 to 45. Intestine short, with a single S-shaped loop; lining of body cavity silvery with scattered dark speckles. Throat teeth 4-4.

Life colors: Back light brown, thickly dusted with fine dark specks. Sides silvery without definite markings. Belly silvery-white. Lower lobe of tail fin darker than upper lobe. Breeding males without special colors, but with small tubercles along rays of pectoral fin.

Size: Adults are typically 1.7 to 2.5 inches long to a maximum of about 3 inches.

Scientific name: *Hybopsis,* Greek, "rounded face"; *gelida,* Latin, meaning "frozen" or "stiff".

DISTRIBUTION AND HABITAT

The sturgeon chub occurs in the Missouri River and the lower Mississippi at least as far downstream as the mouth of the Ohio. Like a number of other fishes characteristic of the Missouri River, it does not enter tributary streams and does not ascend the Mississippi above the mouth of the Missouri. The sturgeon chub is rare in Missouri.

This chub inhabits the open channels of large, silty rivers and occurs in swift current over a bottom of sand or fine gravel.

HABITS AND LIFE HISTORY

The sturgeon chub is well equipped for life in the continuously turbid waters of the Missouri River where sight is of little value. Its eyes are reduced in size, and external taste buds are abundantly developed over the head, body, and fins. These taste buds are probably of primary importance in locating food. The function of the peculiar keels on the scales of the sturgeon chub has not been determined, but perhaps they act as current detectors to aid the fish in orienting itself. The nature of the diet and manner of spawning are not known. Possibly the reproductive habits of this minnow are like those of the speckled chub. In the Missouri River the sturgeon chub attains a length of about 1.1 to 1.4 inches by the end of its first summer of life.

Sicklefin Chub

Hybopsis meeki Jordan and Evermann

DESCRIPTION

Illustration: Page 102, 17b.

Characters: A slender minnow with very small eyes, a small horizontal mouth, and long, sickle-shaped (falcate) fins. Mouth with a small, conical barbel at corner. Pectoral fin longer than in other barbeled minnows, reaching far past base of pelvic fin. Snout blunt and rounded, projecting slightly beyond upper lip. Eye diameter much less than length of snout. Front of dorsal fin closer to tip of snout than to base of tail fin. Anal fin with 8 rays. Lateral line scales 43 to 48. Intestine short, with a single S-shaped loop; lining of body cavity silvery with scattered dark speckles. Throat teeth 4-4.

Life colors: Back and upper sides pale yellowish-brown with silvery reflections. Lower sides and belly silvery-white. Lower lobe of tail fin darker than upper lobe. Breeding males without special colors.

Size: Adults are typically 2.4 to 3.7 inches long to a maximum of about 4 inches.

Scientific name: *Hybopsis,* Greek, "rounded face"; *meeki,* named for Seth Meek, one of the collectors of the type specimens.

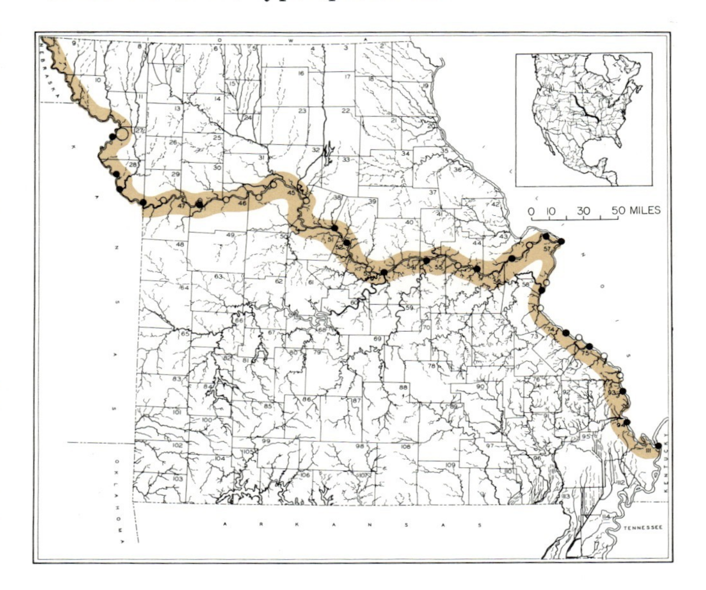

DISTRIBUTION AND HABITAT

The sicklefin chub occurs in the Missouri River and in the Mississippi downstream from the Missouri at least to the mouth of the Ohio River. It is more common than the sturgeon chub, a fish with a similar distribution. The original description of the sicklefin chub is based on specimens collected in the Missouri River near St. Joseph in 1884.

The sicklefin is strictly confined to the main channels of large, turbid rivers where it lives in a strong current over a bottom of sand or fine gravel.

HABITS AND LIFE HISTORY

Like the sturgeon chub, this species is specialized for life in large, turbid rivers. The eyes are even more reduced in size than in the sturgeon chub and are partly covered by skin. External taste buds are less well developed than in the sturgeon chub, but are better developed than in chubs that live in clear waters. The food habits of the sicklefin chub are not known. Probably, it is a bottom feeder and locates its food primarily by taste. The presence of numerous taste buds inside the mouth suggests that food may be sorted and concentrated there from bottom material that is taken rather indiscriminately into the mouth.[75] Young of the sicklefin chub have been collected from the Missouri River in July, suggesting a spring spawning season.

Suckermouth Minnow

Phenacobius mirabilis (Girard)

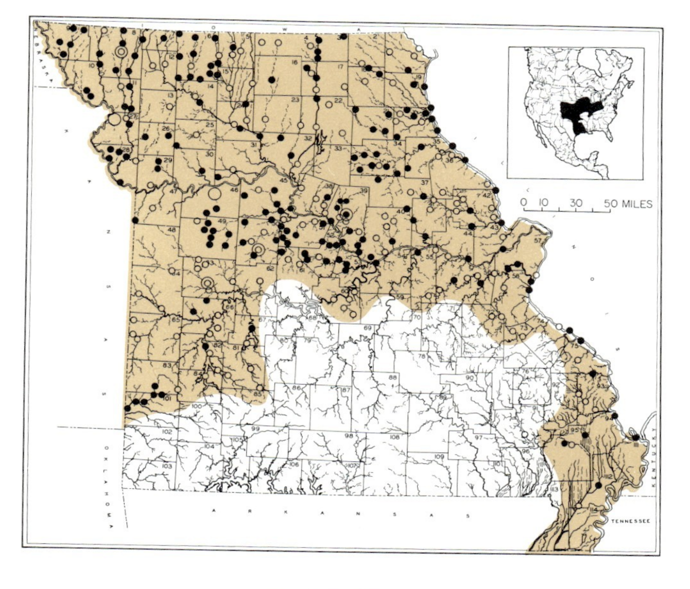

DESCRIPTION

Illustration: Page 108, 29a.

Characters: A slender minnow with small eyes and a horizontal, sucker-like mouth. Barbels absent. Lower lip with a prominent lobe on each side. Eye diameter much less than length of snout. Snout bluntly rounded, projecting distinctly beyond upper lip. Dorsal fin rays 8; anal fin with 6 or 7 rays. Lateral line scales 40 to 48. Intestine short, with a single S-shaped loop; lining of body cavity silvery with scattered dark speckles. Throat teeth 4-4.

Life colors: Back and upper sides dusky-olive with definite dark edgings on scales. Midside with a dusky horizontal stripe, ending in a small but prominent black spot at base of tail fin. Lower sides and belly silvery-white. Breeding males are without special colors but have very small tubercles on head, forward part of body, and rays of pectoral fin.

Size: Adults are commonly 2.2 to 3.5 inches long to a maximum of about 4.5 inches.

Scientific name: *Phenacobius,* Greek, "deceptive life", the appearance suggesting an herbivorous species, which it is not; *mirabilis,* Latin, meaning "wonderful" or "strange".

DISTRIBUTION AND HABITAT

The suckermouth minnow is abundant and widespread in the Prairie streams of north and west Missouri and occurs occasionally in the Lowland ditches of the southeast. This minnow is rather common in warmer streams of the Ozark border, but is absent from the high-gradient streams of the central Ozarks.

It occurs in streams of all sizes, but avoids those with intermittent flow or continuously cool water. It is tolerant of high turbidity as long as there is enough current to keep the riffle areas free of silt. The suckermouth is primarily a riffle fish and is most abundant on the gravelly riffles of warm, rather clear streams with moderate or low gradient.

HABITS AND LIFE HISTORY

The suckermouth minnow lives on the bottom and obtains its food by rooting in gravel and rocks with its sensitive snout and lips. Its diet is reported to consist of the immature stages of aquatic insects, along with small quantities of bottom ooze.[71] Breeding adults have been collected in Missouri from mid-April into June, indicating a spring or early summer spawning season. Little is known about spawning, but it evidently takes place on gravelly riffles.

Pugnose Minnow

Notropis emiliae (Hay)

DESCRIPTION

Illustration: Page 96, 5a.

Characters: A slender minnow with a very small, sharply upturned (nearly vertical) mouth, and a short, blunt snout. Differs from all other Missouri minnows in having 9 principal rays in dorsal fin. Length of upper jaw less than diameter of eye. Often with a small barbel on one or both sides. Lateral line usually incomplete. Anal fin with 8 rays. Scales in lateral series 36 to 39. Intestine short with a single S-shaped loop; lining of body cavity silvery with scattered dark speckles. Throat teeth 5-5.

Life colors: Back and upper sides yellowish with a prominent dusky stripe. Adult males with dusky pigment in dorsal fin, becoming nearly black in breeding males. Breeding males with many small tubercles over snout and chin.

Size: A small minnow, not exceeding a length of 2.5 inches. Adults are commonly 1.4 to 2.3 inches long.

Scientific name: *Notropis,* Greek, "back keel"; *emiliae,* named for Mrs. Emily Hay.

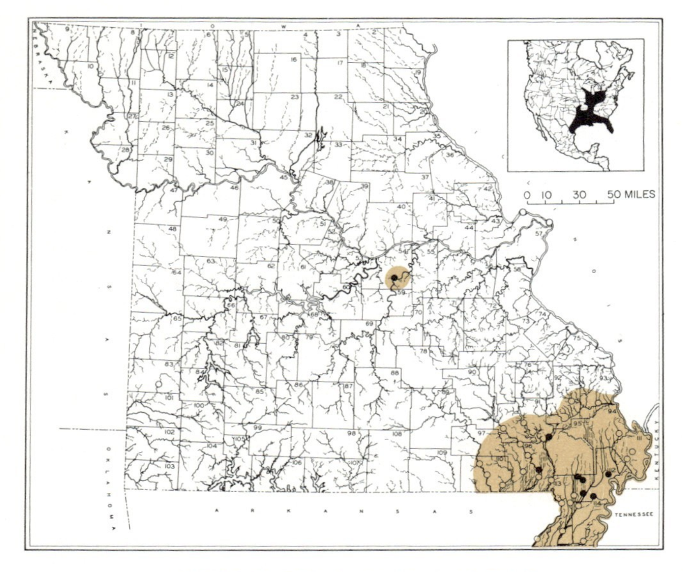

DISTRIBUTION AND HABITAT

The pugnose minnow is largely restricted in Missouri to the Lowlands of the southeast where it is rare. It formerly occurred along the upper Mississippi River and in the Spring River system of southwestern Missouri, but there are no recent records from these areas. A single specimen was taken from the lower Gasconade River by an ichthyology class of the University of Missouri in 1961. Annual seining at that locality since 1961 has yielded no more specimens. The pugnose minnow is less common in the Lowlands than it was in the early 1940's and may be disappearing from the state.

The largest populations are in clear, heavily vegetated waters without noticeable current. Most Missouri collections are from natural lakes, sloughs, borrow pits, and sluggish Lowland ditches.

HABITS AND LIFE HISTORY

Little is known of the biology of this minnow. Its structural adaptations suggest that it is carnivorous, probably feeding on small insects and other aquatic invertebrates. It evidently spawns at this latitude in early summer, since adults in spawning condition are taken at that time of year.

Emerald Shiner

Notropis atherinoides Rafinesque

DESCRIPTION

Illustration: Page 116, 44a.

Characters: A silvery, streamlined minnow with moderately large eyes and a terminal, oblique mouth. Barbels absent. Anal fin with 10 or 11 (occasionally 12) rays. Front of dorsal fin base closer to base of tail fin than to front of eye. Dorsal fin rather high and pointed, its first principal ray longer than second and third. Chin thickly sprinkled with dusky pigment. Lateral line scales 35 to 40; scale rows before dorsal fin 18 to 21. Intestine short, with a single S-shaped loop; lining of body cavity silvery, thickly sprinkled with dark speckles. Throat teeth 2,4-4,2.

Life colors: Back pale yellowish-olive with a faint dusky stripe along its midline. Sides silvery with a narrow, iridescent emerald stripe. Belly silvery-white. Fins plain. Breeding males without special colors, but with small tubercles along rays of pectoral fin.

Size: Adults are commonly 2.5 to 3.5 inches long to a maximum of about 4.2 inches.

Scientific name: *Notropis,* Greek, meaning "back keel"; *atherinoides,* Greek, meaning "silverside-like," in reference to the resemblance to a member of the silverside family.

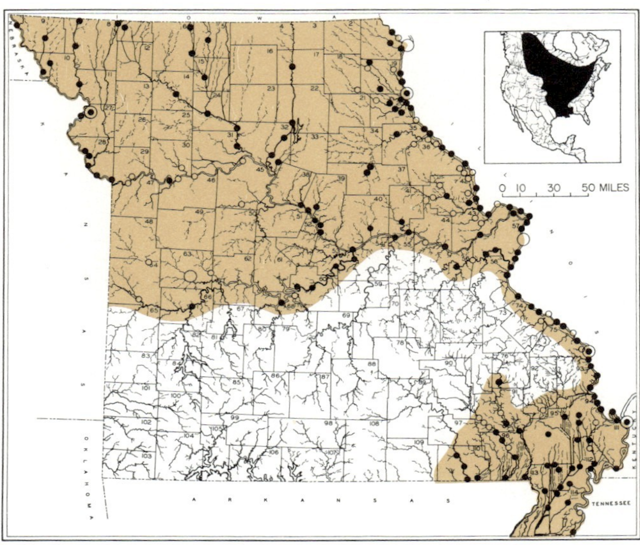

DISTRIBUTION AND HABITAT

The emerald shiner is the most abundant minnow in the Missouri and Mississippi rivers. It is common in large streams and ditches of the Prairie and Lowland regions but avoids the high-gradient streams of the central Ozarks. Its distribution in Missouri may be limited somewhat by competition from the related rosyface shiner, since the two are seldom found together.

The emerald shiner is a characteristic inhabitant of the open channels of large, permanent-flowing streams having moderate or low gradients. It tolerates a wide range of turbidity and bottom types and is usually found where there is noticeable current. Elsewhere in its range it is abundant in reservoirs but has not become firmly established in any Missouri reservoir.

HABITS AND LIFE HISTORY

The emerald shiner lives in large schools in midwater or at the surface. It probably feeds primarily by sight. In reservoirs on the upper Missouri River the diet consists mostly of small crustaceans with lesser quantities of aquatic insects.[80] The diet changes with size. Small individuals feed primarily on algae.

Breeding adults have been taken in the Missouri River from late May through early July, indicating that spawning occurs over a rather long period at this latitude. In western Lake Erie spawning begins in late June and continues for 4 to 6 weeks.[81] Spawning occurs at night, just beneath the surface in shallow water over a bottom of sand or firm mud. The eggs are non-adhesive and sink to the bottom where they hatch in 24 to 36 hours. The fry remain on the bottom for four more days and then congregate in schools at the surface.

Growth is rapid and 55% of the adult size is reached in the first growing season.[80] In South Dakota the emerald shiner averages 2.6 inches in length at the end of its first year of life and 3.3 inches at the end of its second year. Females grow more rapidly and live slightly longer than males. Very few emerald shiners live for 3 years. Most individuals are sexually mature when a year old.

Rosyface Shiner

Notropis rubellus (Agassiz)

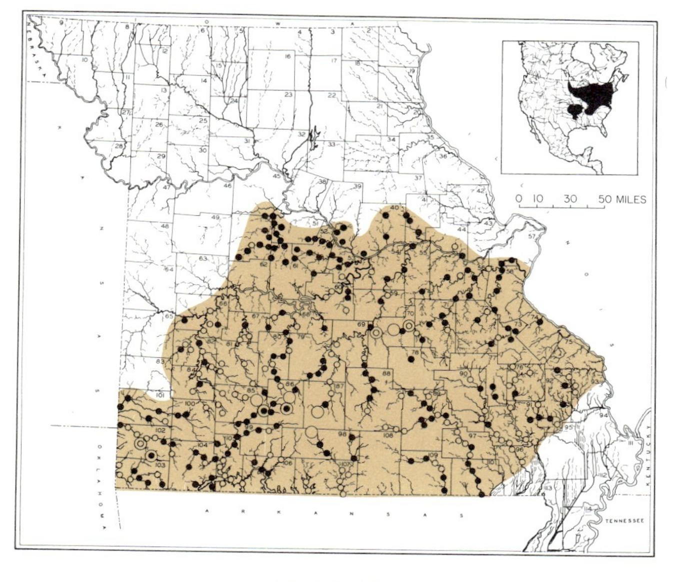

DESCRIPTION

Illustration: Page 115, 43a.

Characters: A slender, silvery minnow with rather small eyes, a short and somewhat rounded dorsal fin, and a terminal, oblique mouth. Barbels absent. Anal fin with 9 or 10 (occasionally 11) rays. Front of dorsal fin base closer to base of tail fin than to front of eye. First principal ray slightly shorter than second and third. Lips dark but chin not sprinkled with dusky pigment. Lateral line scales 36 to 40; scale rows before dorsal fin 17 to 21. Intestine short, with a single S-shaped loop; lining of body cavity silvery, thickly sprinkled with dark speckles. Throat teeth 2,4-4,2.

Life colors: Back dark-olive with a faint, dusky stripe along its midline. Sides silvery with a narrow, iridescent emerald stripe. Belly silvery-white. Fins plain. Head and body flushed with red in breeding males; small tubercles present over head, body, and along rays of pectoral fin. Red colors developed to some extent in breeding females. Base of dorsal fin pink in adults throughout the year.

Size: Adults are commonly 2 to 3 inches long to a maximum of about 3.5 inches.

Scientific name: *Notropis,* Greek, "back keel"; *rubellus,* Latin, meaning "reddish", in reference to the breeding colors.

DISTRIBUTION AND HABITAT

The rosyface shiner is one of the most abundant and generally distributed minnows in the Ozark Uplands.

This fish is an inhabitant of clear streams with permanent flow and moderate or high gradients. It avoids extreme headwater situations and is most abundant in medium-sized to moderately large rivers. It is most often found over a clean, gravelly or rocky bottom, near riffles or in pools with current.

HABITS AND LIFE HISTORY

The rosyface shiner lives in large schools, often in association with the bleeding shiner, telescope shiner and bigeye chub. It feeds at all levels, probably locating its food mostly by sight. During its first year of life the rosyface feeds largely on diatoms and other algae, but thereafter insects are the bulk of its diet.[82, 84] Both aquatic and terrestrial insects are eaten.

This minnow spawns in Missouri from mid-April to early July, but the peak of activity comes in May and early June. The rosyface shiner is one of several species of minnows that characteristically deposits its eggs on the spawning areas of other fishes. Most often it spawns over the gravel piles of the hornyhead chub, but it has also been observed spawning in the pits of the chestnut lamprey and the stoneroller minnow, and over the spawning redds of the longnose gar and several species of redhorse suckers.

Breeding adults gather over the spawning sites in large, compact schools in which the brightly colored males far outnumber the females. Males do not guard territories and show little antagonism towards each other. There is no pairing of males and females during the spawning act. All individuals in the school vibrate in unison as the eggs and sperm are released. The adhesive eggs fall to the bottom where they become lodged in crevices in the gravel. At a temperature of about 70° F. the eggs hatch in 2½ days.[83] Several other minnows, including the common shiner, bleeding shiner, and Ozark minnow, often spawn at the same time and place as the rosyface. Hybrids between all these species occur by cross-matings or the chance meeting of egg and sperm.

The life span of the rosyface shiner is 3 years, and over 70% of the growth is completed during the first year of life.[82] Males grow more rapidly than females the first year, but thereafter the growth of females is most rapid. Females attain a larger maximum size than males.

Silverband Shiner

Notropis shumardi (Girard)

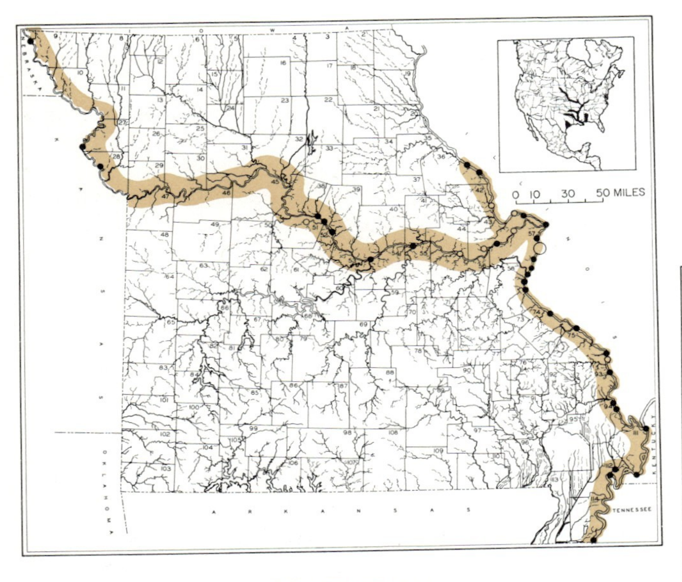

DESCRIPTION

Illustration: Page 125, 62a.

Characters: A silvery, moderately deep and slab-sided minnow with an unusually high and pointed dorsal fin, rather large eyes, and a terminal, oblique mouth. Barbels absent. Anal fin with 8 or 9 (occasionally 10) rays. Front of dorsal fin base about midway between tip of snout and base of tail fin. First principal ray of dorsal fin longer than second and third. Chin without dusky pigment. Lateral line scales 34 to 37. Intestine short, with a single S-shaped loop; lining of body cavity silvery. Throat teeth 2,4-4,2.

Life colors: Back pale olive-yellow with a faint dusky stripe along its midline. Sides silvery. Belly silvery-white. Fins plain. Breeding males without special colors, but with very small tubercles over head and along pectoral fin rays.

Size: Adults are commonly 2 to 3.2 inches long to a maximum of about 3.6 inches.

Scientific name: *Notropis*, Greek, "back keel"; *shumardi*, named for G. C. Shumard, naturalist on the Mexican Boundary Survey.

DISTRIBUTION AND HABITAT

The silverband shiner is a characteristic inhabitant of the Missouri and Mississippi rivers, penetrating only rarely into the lower sections of tributaries. It is fairly common in the lower Mississippi but is rare elsewhere in Missouri. The silverband inhabits the open channels of large rivers and is usually found in a moderate or strong current over a bottom of sand or fine gravel.

HABITS AND LIFE HISTORY

The silverband shiner lives in schools, often in association with the emerald, channel mimic, and river shiners. Females full of eggs have been collected from the Mississippi River in mid-August, indicating a summer spawning season. Little else is known concerning the biology of this fish.

Telescope Shiner

Notropis telescopus (Cope)

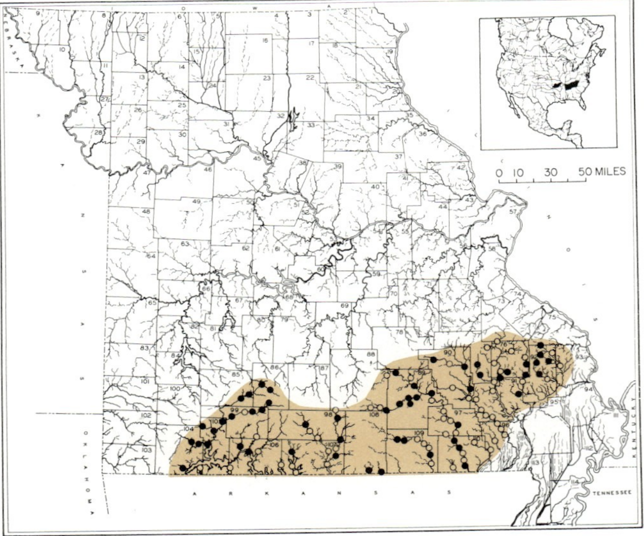

DESCRIPTION

Illustration: Page 118, 48a.

Characters: A slender, silvery minnow with very large eyes and a terminal, oblique mouth. Barbels absent. Anal fin with 9 to 11 (rarely 12) rays. Eye diameter much greater than length of snout, going less than 3 times into head length. Front of dorsal fin base slightly closer to base of tail fin than to tip of snout. Stripe along midline of back intensely dark and broader than dorsal fin base. Upper sides with faint dark lines that converge behind dorsal fin forming V-shaped markings visible when fish is viewed from above. Lateral line scales 35 to 38. Intestine short, with a single S-shaped loop; lining of body cavity black. Throat teeth 2,4-4,2.

Life colors: Back dark olive with a bold black stripe along its midline and prominent dark edgings on the scales. Sides silvery; pores of lateral line prominently outlined by dark pigment. Belly silvery-white. Fins plain. Breeding males are without special colors.

Size: Adults are commonly 2 to 2.8 inches long to a maximum of about 3 inches.

Scientific name: *Notropis,* Greek, "back keel"; *telescopus,* Greek, "far-seeing".

DISTRIBUTION AND HABITAT

The telescope shiner is one of the most abundant and widespread minnows in the southern Ozarks. It is normally found near riffles over a gravelly or rocky bottom. Its habitat is much like that of the rosyface shiner and, within the area where both occur, they are almost invariably found together.

HABITS AND LIFE HISTORY

The telescope shiner lives in schools, commonly in association with the bleeding, duskystripe, and rosyface shiners. The unusually large eyes suggest that this minnow is a sight feeder. The stomach contents of several specimens from Current River consisted almost entirely of insects. Breeding adults were collected from Current River in mid-April, but the place and manner of spawning was not determined.

Redfin Shiner

Notropis umbratilis (Girard)

DESCRIPTION

Illustration: Page 112, 37a; **37.**

Characters: A silvery, slender to moderately deep and slab-sided minnow with rather small eyes and a terminal, oblique mouth. Barbels absent. Anal fin with 9 to 12 (occasionally 13) rays. Front of dorsal fin base closer to base of tail fin than to tip of snout. Dorsal fin usually with a small, dark spot at base of first few rays. Chin thickly sprinkled with dusky pigment. Scales rather small; usually there are 40 to 51 in lateral line and 26 to 30 along midline of back from dorsal fin forward. Intestine short, with a single S-shaped loop; lining of body cavity silvery, sprinkled with dark speckles. Throat teeth 2,4-4,2.

Life colors: Back pale olive-yellow, rather uniformly dusted with fine black specks and with a faint, dusky stripe along its midline. Sides silvery. Belly silvery-white. Dorsal fin with a small, black spot at base of first 2 or 3 rays; fins otherwise plain. Breeding males have top of head powder blue, sides metallic blue, and fins black, red, or a combination of the two; small tubercles are abundantly developed over head, body, and fins.

Size: Adults are commonly 1.5 to 3 inches long to a maximum of about 3.5 inches.

Scientific name: *Notropis,* Greek, "back keel"; *umbratilis,* from the Latin word *umbra,* meaning "shade".

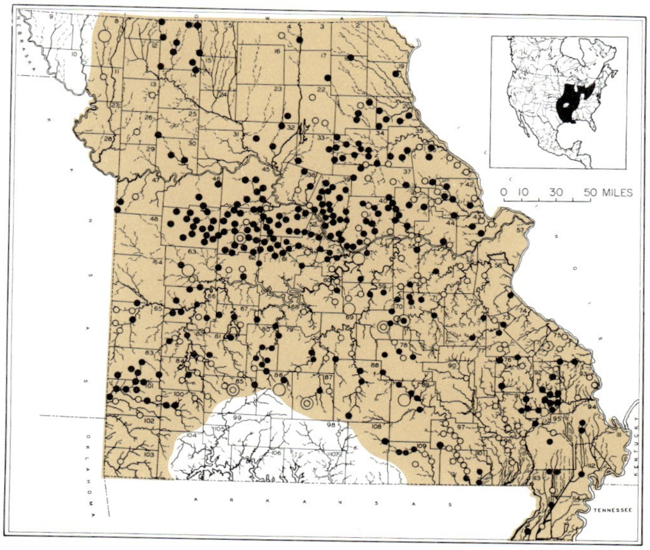

DISTRIBUTION AND HABITAT

The redfin shiner is found over nearly all of Missouri but is absent from the White River system in the southern Ozarks. Its main area of abundance is in a broad zone along the northern and western Ozark border where it is one of the most common minnows. A secondary area of occurrence is in Lowland ditches of southeast Missouri and adjacent parts of the Ozarks. There are only localized populations in the central Ozarks and in the Prairie streams of northwest Missouri.

The redfin shiner may live in a variety of habitats. In the Prairie Region it is most abundant in permanent pools of rocky or gravelly creeks having high gradient and low or intermittent flow. In the Lowlands it inhabits ditches having little current and an abundance of submerged aquatic vegetation. Along the cool, spring-fed streams of the Ozarks it is most often found in weedy backwaters and overflow pools. The common denominators of all these habitats are relatively clear, warm water and absence of strong current.

HABITS AND LIFE HISTORY

The redfin shiner lives in schools in midwater or near the surface. It takes most of its food from the surface, apparently feeding largely by sight. Its diet has not been studied but probably consists mostly of insects. In Missouri this minnow spawns for an extended period from mid-May to early August. It seems invariably to deposit its eggs over the nests of sunfishes, most often those of the green sunfish, but also those of the longear and orangespotted sunfishes. The interesting spawning association between the green sunfish and the redfin shiner has been intensively studied.[85] Spawning of the redfin is most intense where sunfish are just establishing nests or are actively spawning. The shiners are attracted to the nest by the activities of the male sunfish, but are stimulated to spawn by the scent of the milt and ovarian fluid of spawning sunfish. Spawning aggregations of the redfin have been produced experimentally in the absence of both green sunfish and nests by releasing milt and ovarian fluid into the water.

Male redfin shiners gather over the sunfish nests in numbers ranging from 1 to 100 or more. They occupy small territories which are defended against other males. The territories of the largest and most aggressive males are a few inches above the nest, while those of the smaller males are around the edge or above the territories of the larger males. Often the smaller males are so close to the surface that their backs ripple the water. The males are extremely active, continually dashing at other males that enter their territories and engaging in fights for disputed areas. Male sunfish occasionally chase or bite at the shiners, but in general pay little attention to them. Females remain outside the cluster of males except when spawning. At that time a female enters the group of males and is immediately approached by a male who takes a position beside her. Spawning is accomplished as the two fish swim high over the nest. The eggs drop into the nest where they complete their development.

The advantage of this interesting association to the shiner is obvious. The sunfish nest provides a clean, silt-free substrate for development of the eggs, and the presence of the male sunfish prevents other fishes from entering the nest and eating the eggs. The red shiner, *N. lutrensis*, also spawns over sunfish nests, and hybrids between the red shiner and redfin sometimes occur.

In central Missouri the redfin shiner attains a length of about 1.1 inches by the end of its first summer of life and averages about 1.7 inches by the end of its second summer. Most sexually mature adults are in their second or third summer and the life span seldom exceeds three summers. Males grow more rapidly and attain a larger maximum size than females.

Ribbon Shiner

Notropis fumeus Evermann

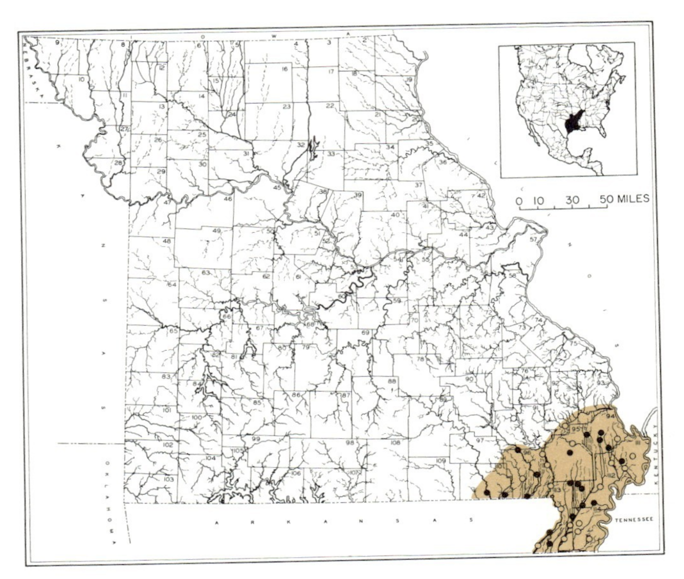

DESCRIPTION

Illustration: Page 116, 45a.

Characters: A slender, silvery minnow with rather large eyes and a terminal, oblique mouth. Barbels absent. Anal fin with 11 to 13 (rarely 10) rays. Front of dorsal fin base closer to base of tail fin than to front of eye. Dorsal fin slightly rounded, its first principal ray shorter than second and third. Chin thickly sprinkled with dusky pigment. Lateral line scales 36 to 41; scale rows before dorsal fin 24 to 26. Intestine short, with a single S-shaped loop; lining of body cavity silvery, sprinkled with dark speckles. Throat teeth 2,4-4,2.

Life colors: Back pale olive-yellow with a faint dusky stripe along its midline. Sides silvery, sometimes with a faint dusky stripe that fades out towards head. Belly silvery-white. Fins plain.

Size: Adults are commonly 1.8 to 2.3 inches long to a maximum of about 2.5 inches.

Scientific name: *Notropis,* Greek, "back keel"; *fumeus,* Latin, meaning "smoky".

DISTRIBUTION AND HABITAT

The ribbon shiner is one of the common and characteristic minnows in the Lowlands of southeastern Missouri. It is an inhabitant of the open channels of large, sparsely vegetated ditches and Lowland rivers. It generally occurs over a sandy bottom, in slight to moderate current.

HABITS AND LIFE HISTORY

Little is known of the habits of this minnow. It lives in schools in midwater or near the surface and probably feeds mostly by sight. Females with eggs were collected in southeastern Missouri in mid-July. Adults collected later in the summer were not in breeding condition. Probably, the ribbon shiner has an early summer spawning season in Missouri.

Bleeding Shiner

Notropis zonatus (Putnam)

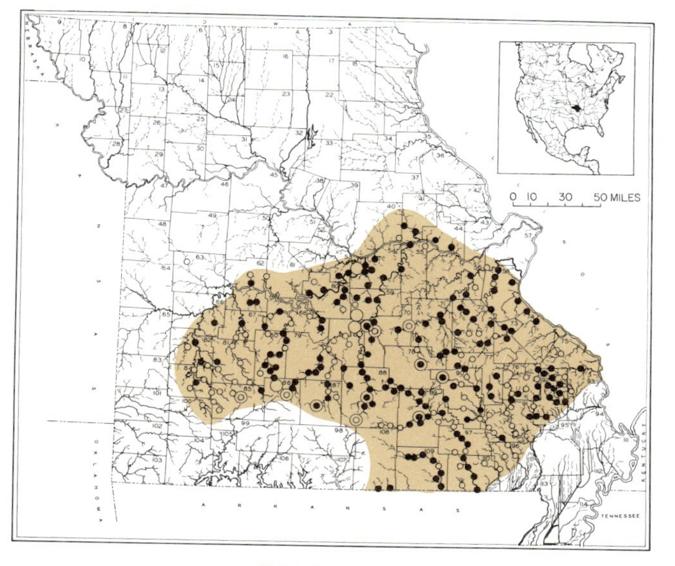

DESCRIPTION

Illustration: Page 119, 50a; **38.**

Characters: A slender, silvery minnow with rather large eyes and a terminal, oblique mouth. Barbels absent. Anal fin with 9 (occasionally 8 or 10) rays. Front of dorsal fin base much closer to tip of snout than to base of tail fin. A prominent black stripe extends forward along midside to tip of snout, paralleled above by a narrow and sometimes rather indistinct secondary stripe. Stripe along midline of back intensely dark and broader than base of dorsal fin. Lateral line scales 38 to 43. Intestine short, with a single S-shaped loop; lining of body cavity black. Throat teeth 2,4-4,2.

Similar to duskystripe shiner, page 148, but with a prominent dark bar along rear margin of gill opening. Also, the prominent stripe along the midside becomes abruptly narrower just behind gill opening and does not touch the lateral line beneath dorsal fin, except in breeding males.

Life colors: Back light olive-brown with a broad dark stripe along its midline. Sides silvery with two horizontal black stripes separated by an iridescent golden stripe. Gill opening with a prominent, crescent-shaped bar. Belly silvery-white. Fins plain. Breeding males with dark markings very intense and with parts of head, body, and fins bright red. Tubercles in breeding males are largest on head, but also are present on forward part of body and on some rays of pectoral and dorsal fins. Breeding colors and tubercles are also somewhat developed in mature females.

Size: A rather large minnow, commonly 3.5 to 4.5 inches long to a maximum of about 4.8 inches.

Scientific name: *Notropis*, Greek, "back keel"; *zonatus*, Latin, meaning "banded."

DISTRIBUTION AND HABITAT

The bleeding shiner is restricted to the Ozark Uplands of Missouri and northeastern Arkansas. In Missouri it occurs in all major drainages not occupied by the closely related duskystripe shiner. Within its area of occurrence the bleeding shiner is the most abundant minnow at many localities.

This minnow inhabits clear, small to medium-sized streams with continuous strong flow. It is typically found over a clean, gravelly or rocky bottom, near riffles, or in pools with noticeable current. The young tend to occupy quieter water than the adults.

HABITS AND LIFE HISTORY

The bleeding shiner occurs in schools in midwater, often in association with the striped, telescope, rosyface, and wedgespot shiners. The rather large eyes suggest that it feeds primarily by sight. It feeds to a considerable extent on insects and other small invertebrates found floating on the water's surface or drifting with the current.

Spawning occurs in Missouri from late April to early July, but is most intense in May and early June. It sometimes spawns in small, pit-like depressions excavated by the males on clean, gravelly riffles. More often spawning occurs over gravel nests of the hornyhead chub or in the spawning pits of stonerollers. On one occasion spawning was observed in the depressions formed where a cow had waded in the stream. When spawning, bleeding shiners gather over the spawning sites in groups of a few to a hundred or more individuals. The brilliantly colored males create a patch of red on the stream bottom that is visible from some distance. The males continually jostle and butt each other as they compete for favored positions over the spawning site. Generally, the larger and more brightly colored males occupy poorly defined pit-like depressions that they construct by flipping out stones with their snout. Typically, all individuals in the spawning group are oriented with their heads upstream, and the males occupying pits are tilted downward at an angle so that the head is lower than the tail. The females remain above and behind the males until ready to spawn, at which time they dip down next to one of the dominant males. During the spawning act the male flips the female into a vertical position and briefly clasps her by throwing his body into a strong U-shaped curve. When released from the spawning embrace, the female shoots vertically towards the surface before she recovers and rejoins the spawning group. The striped shiner, rosyface shiner, Ozark minnow and redbelly dace commonly share the same spawning sites as the bleeding shiner, and hybrids between these species are not uncommon.

In Current River the bleeding shiner attains a length of about 1.3 to 2.3 inches by August of its first summer of life and is about 2.6 to 4 inches long by August of its second summer. Most breeding adults are 3.3 to 4.3 inches long and are in their third summer. Few individuals live beyond three summers. The largest individuals are invariably males.

Duskystripe Shiner

Notropis pilsbryi Fowler

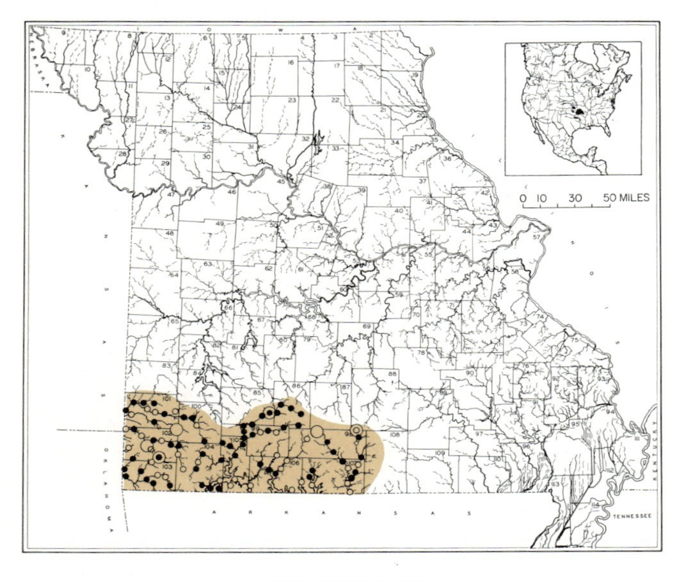

DESCRIPTION

Illustration: Page 119, 50b.

Characters: Similar to bleeding shiner, page 147, but without a dark bar along rear margin of gill cover. Also, the stripe along the midside does not become abruptly narrower just behind gill opening and does touch the lateral line beneath dorsal fin.

Life colors: Like those of bleeding shiner, except as noted under *Characters*. Breeding males differ from those of the bleeding shiner in that red colors are more extensively developed on the fins and body, and the tip of the snout is powder-blue.

Size: About 3.5 to 4.5 inches long to a maximum of about 4.8 inches.

Scientific name: *Notropis,* Greek, "back keel"; *pilsbryi,* named for Dr. H. A. Pilsbry, a conchologist.

DISTRIBUTION AND HABITAT

The duskystripe shiner replaces the closely related bleeding shiner in the White, Elk, and Spring River systems of the southwestern Ozarks. In this region it is one of the most abundant minnows.

This minnow occupies the same type of habitat as the bleeding shiner, page 147.

HABITS AND LIFE HISTORY

The duskystripe's habits are evidently much like those of the bleeding shiner. Spawning has been observed on several occasions and was, in all respects, like that described for the bleeding shiner.

Common Shiner

Notropis cornutus (Mitchill)

DESCRIPTION

Illustration: Page 119, 51b.

Characters: A silvery, rather deep and slab-sided minnow with moderately large eyes and a terminal, oblique mouth. Barbels absent. Anal fin with 9 (occasionally 8) rays. Front of dorsal fin base much closer to tip of snout than to base of tail fin. Stripe along midline of back intensely dark and broader than dorsal fin base. Scales in and near forward part of lateral line very deep and narrow, marked by scattered, crescent-shaped vertical bars—bars most prominent in adults, especially males. Lateral line scales usually 37 to 41. Intestine short, with a single S-shaped loop; lining of body cavity black. Throat teeth 2,4-4,2.

Similar to striped shiner, page 149, but without dusky pigment on chin or V-shaped markings on back and upper sides. Also, there are 22 to 32 scale rows before dorsal fin.

Life colors: Back light olive with a broad dark stripe along its midline. Sides silvery with scattered dark crescents and with an iridescent golden stripe visible at certain angles. Belly silvery-white. Fins plain. Breeding males with head a deep lead blue and body and fins flushed with pink. A broad golden stripe extends along midline of back and another is present along upper side. Breeding tubercles are largest on the head but are also developed on forward part of body and along some rays of pectoral and dorsal fins.

Size: Adults are commonly 3 to 5 inches long to a maximum of about 7 inches.

Scientific name: *Notropis*, Greek, "back keel"; *cornutus*, Latin, meaning "horned."

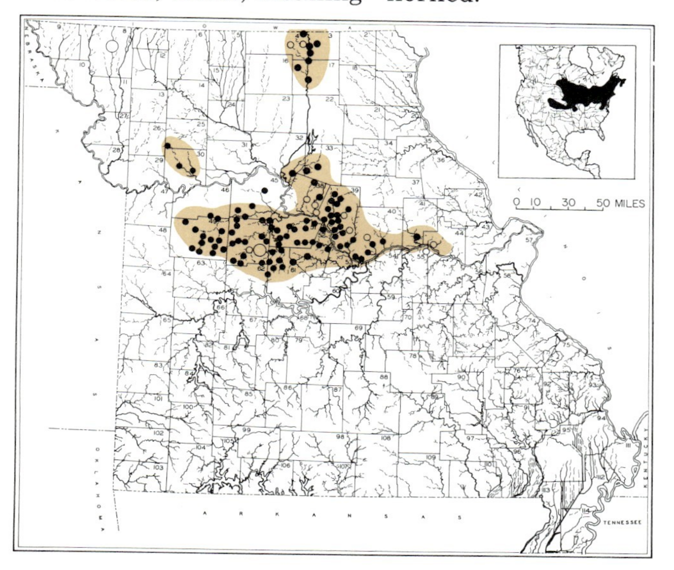

DISTRIBUTION AND HABITAT

The present center of abundance for the common shiner is in short, direct tributaries of the Missouri River in central and west-central Missouri, with isolated populations in a few tributaries of the upper Chariton River. An early report for the common shiner in the Hundred and Two River near Maryville[86] suggests that it formerly had a more widespread distribution in northwestern Missouri. The common shiner is one of the most abundant minnows in the creeks of central Missouri and does not appear to have suffered any further restriction in distribution within the last 30 years.

It inhabits small, moderately clear streams having high gradients and a predominance of gravel, rubble, and bedrock pools. These streams are typically reduced to a series of isolated pools by late summer, but water continues to percolate through the gravel between pools.

HABITS AND LIFE HISTORY

The common shiner occurs in schools in midwater, often in association with the rosyface, red, redfin, sand, and Topeka shiners. It feeds at all levels, but most often in midwater or at the surface. It is generalized in food habits. In the Des Moines River, Iowa, the common shiner feeds principally on aquatic and terrestrial insects, along with lesser quantities of fish, small crustaceans, plant material—mostly filamentous algae—and bottom ooze.[71]

Spawning of the common shiner in Missouri reaches its peak in mid-May but may occur from late April through early June. In other parts of its range the common shiner spawns over the gravel nests of several species of chubs *(Nocomis)*. In Missouri, spawning pits of the creek chub, as well as shallow pits excavated on fine gravel riffles by male common shiners, are often utilized. The males excavate these by dislodging the stones with their snouts. Frequently several males occupy a nest, but a single large male is usually dominant. Males are territorial and engage in frequent fights and "deferred combat" as described for the creek chub, page 131. The spawning act is also much like that of the creek chub. A detailed account of the breeding behavior of the common shiner, including excellent photographs, was given by Raney.[87]

In central Missouri the common shiner reaches a length of 1.5 to 2.7 inches by the end of its first summer of life. Males attain a much larger size than females. Sexual maturity is probably not reached by most individuals before their third summer.

Striped Shiner

Notropis chrysocephalus (Rafinesque)

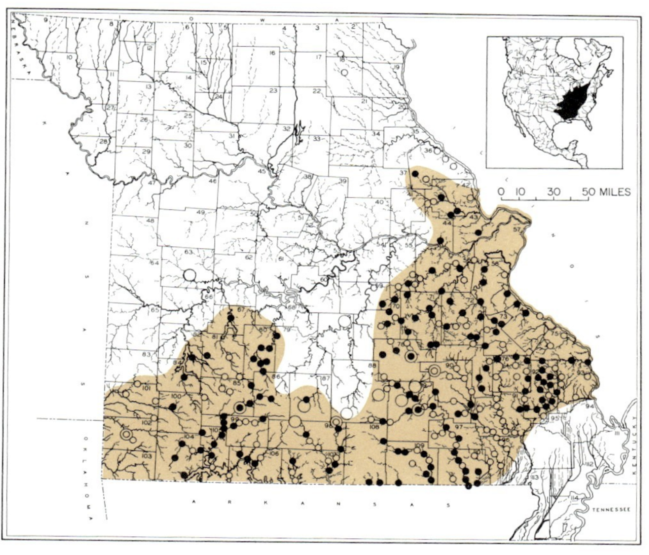

DESCRIPTION

Illustration: Page 119, 51a.

Characters: Similar to common shiner, page 148, but with dusky pigment on chin and faint parallel lines on upper sides that converge behind dorsal fin forming V-shaped markings. Also, there are 13 to 21 scale rows before the dorsal fin.

Life colors: Like those of common shiner except as noted under *Characters*. Breeding males lack the golden stripes that are present along midline of back and upper sides of common shiner.

Size: Adults are commonly 3 to 5 inches long to a maximum of about 7 inches.

Scientific name: *Notropis*, Greek, "back keel"; *chrysocephalus*, Greek, meaning "golden head."

DISTRIBUTION AND HABITAT

The original range of the striped shiner in Missouri included most of the Ozark Uplands and direct tributaries of the upper Mississippi River at least as far north as the Fabius River. However, it is now less widespread than a century ago. It is rare in the Gasconade system, although it was reported "common" by early collectors.[62, 88] In the Spring River system it was reported as "very common"[88] and was still widely distributed there in the early 1940's. However, only one specimen was taken in a series of collections made in 1964. A similar decline may have occurred in parts of the Osage system and in tributaries of the upper Mississippi River. Decline of the striped shiner in the Gasconade system is puzzling, since it remains common just across the divide in the Meramec system where stream conditions seem to be similar. At present the striped shiner is one of the most abundant minnows in the eastern and southern Ozarks.

In Missouri the striped shiner is most abundant in clear, permanent-flowing streams with clean gravelly or rocky bottoms. It is often taken in the same seine hauls as the related bleeding shiner, but in general it occupies warmer and quieter water. The striped shiner is evidently less tolerant of turbidity than the common shiner, judging by their distributional relationships in Missouri. They have not been taken together, although they occur in adjacent tributaries of the Missouri River in southern Warren County.

HABITS AND LIFE HISTORY

In most respects the life history of the striped shiner is not notably different from that of the common shiner, page 148. Spawning of the striped shiner has been observed in Missouri from late April to mid-June. It commonly spawns over the gravel nests of the hornyhead chub in association with the bleeding, duskystripe, and rosyface shiners. Hybrids between the striped shiner and all of these species are common.

Ironcolor Shiner

Notropis chalybaeus (Cope)

DESCRIPTION

Illustration: Page 121, 54a.
Characters: A silvery, rather chubby minnow with moderately large eyes and a terminal, oblique mouth. Barbels absent. Anal fin with 8 (rarely 7 or 9) rays. Front of dorsal fin base much closer to tip of snout than to base of tail fin. Midside with a prominent black stripe extending forward from base of tail fin to tip of snout; stripe bordered above by a light-colored zone in which scales are not dark-edged. Inside of mouth sprinkled with dusky pigment. Lateral line scales 32 to 36. Intestine short, with a single S-shaped loop; lining of body cavity silvery, thickly sprinkled with dark speckles. Throat teeth 2,4-4,2.
Life colors: Back olive-yellow, the scales prominently dark-edged. Sides silvery with a prominent black stripe. Belly silvery-white. Tail fin with a small, irregular-shaped black spot at base; fins otherwise plain. Breeding males have much rose or orange pigment on body and fins, and have moderately large tubercles on chin and lower jaws.
Size: Adults are commonly 1.6 to 2.3 inches long to a maximum of about 2.5 inches.
Scientific name: *Notropis,* Greek, "back keel"; *chalybaeus,* Greek, meaning "iron-colored."

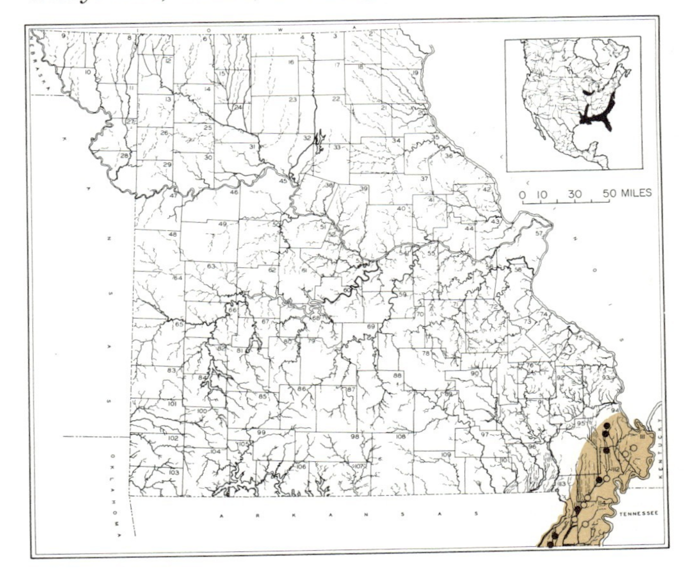

DISTRIBUTION AND HABITAT

The ironcolor shiner is restricted in Missouri to Lowlands of the southeast. Though not widespread it is locally abundant. It formerly occurred in eastern Iowa[89] and, therefore, may have formerly had a continuous distribution northward along the Mississippi River in Missouri. But it has not been taken in Iowa for over 50 years.

This shiner is found only in the clearest Lowland ditches where submerged aquatic vegetation is abundant and there is no noticeable current.

HABITS AND LIFE HISTORY

The ironcolor shiner forms loosely organized schools in midwater and feeds by sight on any animal material small enough to be eaten.[90] However, aquatic insects are the principal item in its diet. Much plant material is present in the intestine but this passes through undigested. Apparently it is food of insects eaten by the ironcolor shiner.

Breeding adults of this minnow have been taken in southeastern Missouri in late June. In Florida it has a very long spawning season, extending from early or mid-April to late September.[90] The ironcolor shiner scatters its eggs over the bottom in sand-bottom pools. During the breeding season males chase the females more or less continuously and the spawning act is completed as the pair dash side by side across the spawning area. The eggs hatch in about 2¼ days at a mean temperature of 62°F.

The young form schools near the surface soon after hatching and join the schools of adults while still in the juvenile stages. The growth of this minnow has not been studied. Females reach a somewhat larger size than males.

Weed Shiner

Notropis texanus (Girard)

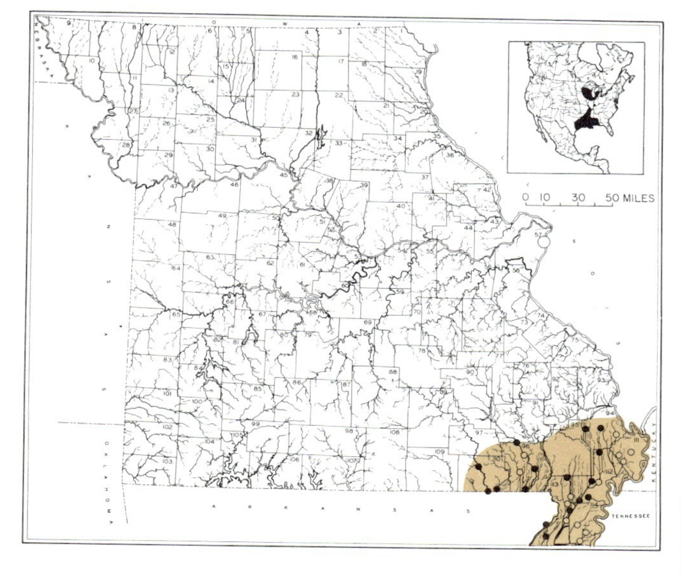

DESCRIPTION

Illustration: Page 121, 55a.

Characters: A silvery, moderately slender minnow with rather large eyes and a terminal, oblique mouth. Barbels absent. Anal fin with 7 (rarely 8) rays. Front of dorsal fin base much closer to tip of snout than to base of tail fin. Midside with a rather prominent dusky stripe extending forward from base of tail fin to tip of snout and chin; stripe bordered above by a broad, light-colored zone in which scales are not dark-edged. Base of tail fin with a small, dark spot that is roundish or irregular in outline. Lateral line scales 31 to 36. Intestine short, with a single S-shaped loop; lining of body cavity silvery, sprinkled with dark speckles. Throat teeth variable, most often 2,4-4,2.

Life colors: Back olive-yellow, the scales prominently dark-edged. Sides silvery with a dusky horizontal stripe. Belly silvery-white. Tail fin with a small, black spot at base; fins otherwise plain. Breeding males have rosy pigment on fins, and tubercles on head, forward part of body, and along rays of pectoral fins. Tubercles are largest on snout and lower jaw.

Size: Adults are commonly 1.8 to 2.5 inches long to a maximum of about 3 inches.

Scientific name: *Notropis,* Greek, "back keel"; *texanus,* "from Texas."

DISTRIBUTION AND HABITAT

The weed shiner is widely distributed in the Lowlands of southeastern Missouri and penetrates into adjacent sections of the Ozarks along the major streams. It is more widespread in the Lowlands than the ironcolor shiner but does not attain as high a population density. An old record from near St. Louis indicates it formerly had a more widespread distribution in eastern Missouri.

The weed shiner occurs most abundantly in large ditches and Lowland rivers having noticeable current, a sandy bottom, and little or no aquatic vegetation. Therefore, it is well separated ecologically from the ironcolor shiner.

HABITS AND LIFE HISTORY

This minnow lives in schools in midwater, often in association with the ribbon, emerald and blacktail shiners. Its habits and life history have not been studied.

Spottail shiner

Notropis hudsonius (Clinton)

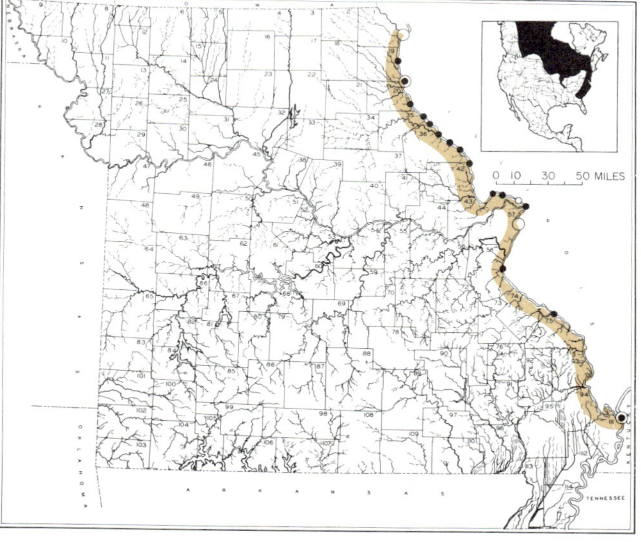

DESCRIPTION

Illustration: Page 111, 34b.

Characters: A silvery, moderately deep and slab-sided minnow with large eyes and a slightly subterminal, moderately oblique mouth. Barbels absent. Anal fin with 8 (rarely 9) rays. Front of dorsal fin base much closer to tip of snout than to base of tail fin. Tail fin with a large, roundish, black spot at base. Snout bluntly rounded, projecting slightly beyond upper lip. Lateral line scales 36 to 40. Intestine short, with a single S-shaped loop; lining of body cavity silvery with scattered dark speckles. Throat teeth variable, most often 2,4-4,2.

Life colors: Back olive-yellow with a rather distinct dusky stripe along midline of back. Sides silvery. Belly silvery-white. Tail fin with a prominent black spot at base; fins otherwise plain. Breeding males are without bright colors, but have very small tubercles on head and along pectoral fin rays.

Size: Adults are commonly 3 to 5 inches long to a maximum of about 6 inches.

Scientific name: *Notropis,* Greek, "back keel"; *hudsonius,* named for the Hudson River where it was first discovered.

DISTRIBUTION AND HABITAT

This northern species is restricted to the Mississippi River where the mouth of the Ohio River marks the downstream limit of its distribution. It is nowhere abundant but is more common upstream from the mouth of the Missouri River than below.

In Missouri the spottail shiner is a fish of the larger rivers. Elsewhere in its range it occurs abundantly in lakes. It is generally found over a firm bottom of sand, gravel, and rubble, and avoids strong current.

HABITS AND LIFE HISTORY

The spottail shiner lives in schools in midwater, often in association with the river and emerald shiners. It feeds at all levels, probably mostly by sight. Its diet is variable, including adult and immature insects, small crustaceans, water mites, an occasional fish, the fibres and seeds of higher plants, and algae.[91, 92] Animal life is more important than plants in its diet. Spottail shiner eggs have been reported from stomachs of many adults taken during the spawning season.

In Clear Lake, Iowa, the spottail spawns in May and early June, with some indication of a second spawning in early August of some years.[91, 93] The spawning habits are not known.

It attains a mean length of 3, 3.9 and 4.3 inches at the end of the first, second, and third summers of life.[91] Females grow more rapidly and live longer than males.[92] The maximum life span is 4 years.

River Shiner

Notropis blennius (Girard)

DESCRIPTION

Illustration: Page 122, 56a.

Characters: A slender, silvery minnow with moderately small eyes and a terminal, oblique mouth. Barbels absent. Anal fin with 7 (rarely 8) rays. Front of dorsal fin base about equidistant between tip of snout and base of tail fin. Dark stripe along midline of back well defined and uniform in width. Body uniformly darkened along base of dorsal fin. Dusky stripe along midside faint or absent, fading out towards head. Lateral line scales 34 to 37. Intestine short, with a single S-shaped loop; lining of body cavity silvery with faint dark speckles. Throat teeth 2,4-4,2 (a tooth is commonly missing on one or both sides).

Life colors: Back olive-yellow with a well defined dusky stripe along its midline. Sides silvery, sometimes with a very faint dusky stripe. Belly silvery-white. Fins plain. Breeding males are without special colors, but have minute tubercles along rays of pectoral fin.

Size: Adults are commonly 2 to 3.5 inches long to a maximum of about 4 inches.

Scientific name: *Notropis,* Greek, "back keel"; *blennius,* from the Greek term *blennos,* meaning slime or mucus.

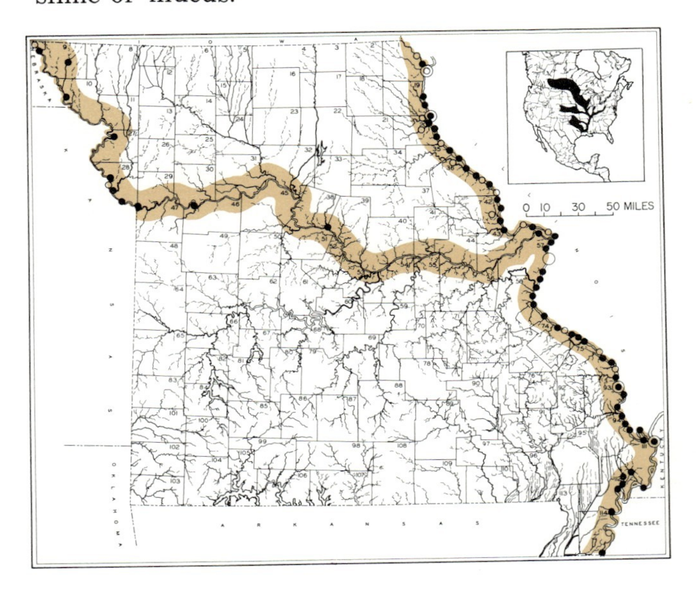

DISTRIBUTION AND HABITAT

The river shiner is primarily a fish of the Missouri and Mississippi rivers, occurring only rarely in tributary streams. In the Mississippi it is exceeded in abundance only by the emerald shiner. In the Missouri this fish has an unusual distribution. It is common in the river from the northern border of the state downstream to Lexington, but occurred in only one collection between Lexington and the river mouth, 322 miles downstream. The reasons for this peculiar pattern are not known.

As its name implies, the river shiner is primarily an inhabitant of large rivers. It is usually found in the main channel of the river but avoids areas of strong current. It occurs over a variety of bottom types and is tolerant of continuous high turbidity.

HABITS AND LIFE HISTORY

The river shiner lives in schools in midwater and is commonly found in association with the emerald and silverband shiners. Its food habits have not been studied, but it probably feeds by sight on insects and other animal material. Adults in spawning condition have been collected in Missouri from early June to late August, indicating a prolonged summer spawning season.

Wedgespot Shiner

Notropis greenei (Hubbs and Ortenburger)

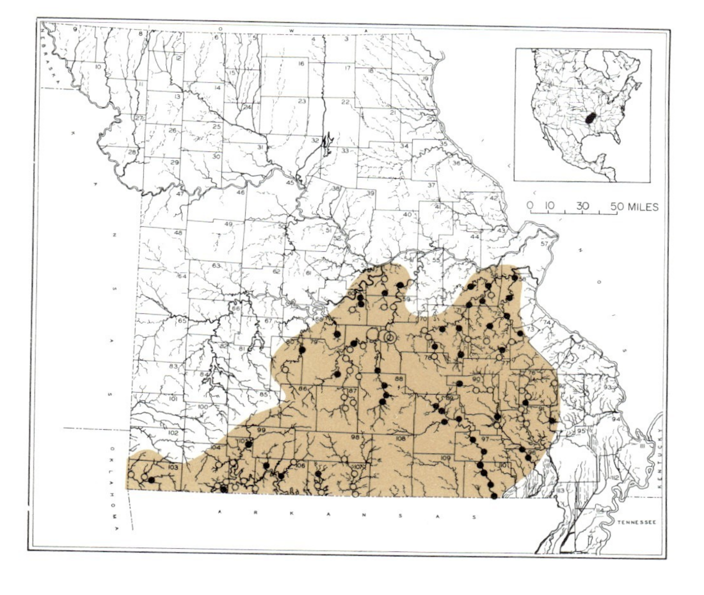

DESCRIPTION

Illustration: Page 125, 62b.
Characters: A slender, silvery minnow with rather large eyes and a terminal or slightly subterminal, oblique mouth. Barbels absent. Anal fin with 8 (often 9, rarely 7) rays. Front of dorsal fin base equidistant between tip of snout and base of tail fin. Tail fin with a small, wedge-shaped black spot at base—occasionally faint or poorly defined. Dusky stripe along midside fading out towards head. Scales in forward part of lateral line with exposed margins not much deeper or narrower than scales on adjacent parts of side. Lateral line scales 35 to 38. Intestine short, with a single S-shaped loop; lining of body cavity silvery, heavily sprinkled with dark speckles. Throat teeth 2,4-4,2.
Life colors: Back dark olive, the scales rather prominently dark-edged. Sides silvery; lateral line pores outlined by dark pigment. Belly silvery-white. Tail fin with a black spot at base; fins otherwise plain. Breeding males are without special colors, but have numerous small tubercles over head, forward part of body, and along pectoral fin rays.
Size: Adults are commonly 1.8 to 2.5 inches long to a maximum of about 3 inches.
Scientific name: *Notropis,* Greek, "back keel"; *greenei,* named for C.W. Greene, a student of C.H. Hubbs who was studying Wisconsin fishes.

DISTRIBUTION AND HABITAT

The wedgespot shiner is restricted to the Ozark Uplands. It is common over much of the Missouri Ozarks but is not as abundant as other minnows characteristic of the region. It is rare in the Osage River system where it is not known to occur farther west than the Niangua River.

The wedgespot shiner inhabits clear, permanent-flowing streams ranging in size from medium-sized creeks to moderately large rivers. It never occurs in small headwater creeks. It is usually found near riffles or in the adjacent parts of pools, over a bottom of sand, gravel or rubble.

HABITS AND LIFE HISTORY

The wedgespot shiner lives in schools in midwater, often in association with the rosyface, bleeding, striped, mimic, and telescope shiners. Adults in spawning condition have been collected in Missouri from late May to late August, indicating a prolonged spawning season. This fish spawns over clean gravel riffles in a swift current. Nothing is known of its food habits or growth.

Bigmouth Shiner

Notropis dorsalis (Agassiz)

DESCRIPTION

Illustration: Page 120, 52a.

Characters: A slender, silvery minnow with small eyes and a slightly subterminal, nearly horizontal mouth. Barbels absent. Anal fin with 8 (occasionally 7, rarely 9) rays. Front of dorsal fin base closer to base of tail fin than to tip of snout. Head long, its lower surface broad and flat. Eye directed slightly upward rather than immediately to side, so that lower margin of pupil is visible when fish is viewed from directly above. Mouth large, the length of upper jaw greater than eye diameter. Lateral line scales 34 to 37. Intestine short, with a single S-shaped loop; lining of body cavity silvery, sometimes faintly sprinkled with dark speckles. Throat teeth 1,4-4,1.

Life colors: Back olive-yellow with a narrow

dusky stripe of uniform width along its midline. Sides silvery, often with a faint dusky stripe that fades out towards head; pores of lateral line outlined by dark pigment. Belly silvery-white. Fins plain. Breeding males are without special colors, but have very small tubercles on head, forward part of body, and along rays of pectoral fin.

Size: Adults are usually 2.1 to 2.6 inches long to a maximum of about 3 inches.

Scientific name: *Notropis,* Greek, "back keel"; *dorsalis,* Latin, "pertaining to the back."

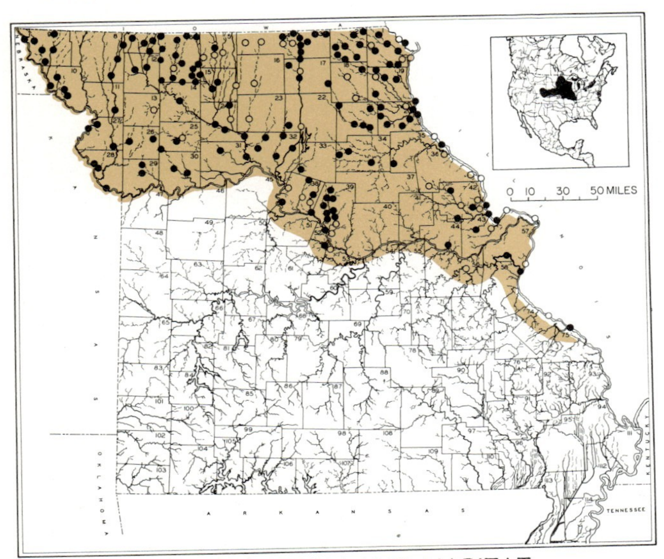

DISTRIBUTION AND HABITAT

The bigmouth shiner is one of the most common and widely distributed minnows in Prairie streams north of the Missouri River. Except for one questionable early report for South Grand River in Henry County,[86] it has never been found more than a few miles south of the Missouri River. Failure of early collectors to report the bigmouth shiner from Missouri, with the one exception, and its absence from collections made in northwest Missouri 30 years ago, strongly suggests that it is now more widespread and abundant than was formerly the case.

It occurs most abundantly in small streams having permanent flow and unstable, sandy bottoms. It is usually found where there are broad expanses of shallow water and a slight current. It is uncommon in the larger Prairie streams where it is replaced by the sand shiner. Extensive channelization of Prairie streams in north Missouri over the past several decades created conditions favorable to the bigmouth shiner, accounting for the increase in its abundance during that period.

HABITS AND LIFE HISTORY

The bigmouth shiner lives in schools just off the bottom and is commonly found in association with the sand and red shiners. It takes its food only from on or near the bottom. Sight is apparently less important than taste in locating food. Specimens I have kept in aquaria swam about rapidly over the bottom when food was introduced, taking in mouthfuls of sand from which they sorted out the food. The sand was then forcefully rejected from the mouth or gill openings. In the Des Moines River they fed primarily on aquatic insects, along with lesser amounts of bottom ooze and plant material.[71] Small crustaceans occurred in the diet in significant quantities during the winter months.

Breeding adults have been collected in Missouri during June and July, indicating a summer spawning season. Spawning has not been observed. In central Missouri this minnow reaches a length of about 0.8 to 1.6 inches by the end of its first summer of life and probably reaches maturity during its second summer.

Bigeye Shiner

Notropis boops Gilbert

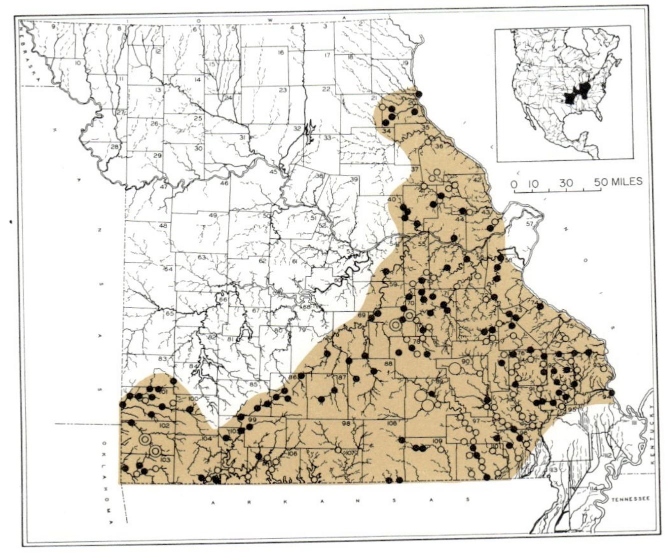

DESCRIPTION

Illustration: Page 123, 59b.

Characters: A moderately slender, silvery minnow with very large eyes and a terminal, oblique mouth. Barbels absent. Anal fin with 8 (occasionally 9, rarely 7) rays. Front of dorsal fin about equidistant between tip of snout and base of tail fin. Midside with a prominent dusky stripe extending forward from base of tail fin to tip of snout and chin; stripe bordered above by a light-colored zone in which scales are not dark-edged. Mouth large, the upper jaw extending past front of eye. Dorsal fin high and pointed. Lateral line scales 34 to 38. Intestine short, with a single S-shaped loop; lining of body cavity black. Throat teeth 1,4-4,1.

Life colors: Back olive-yellow, the scales prominently dark-edged. Sides silvery with a prominent dusky stripe; pores of lateral line outlined by dark pigment. Belly silvery-white. Fins plain. Breeding males are without bright colors but have numerous small tubercles on head, body—except caudal peduncle—and along some rays of dorsal, anal, and pectoral fins.

Size: Adults are commonly 1.2 to 2.6 inches long to a maximum of about 3 inches.

Scientific name: *Notropis,* Greek, "back keel"; *boops,* Greek, meaning "ox-eyed," probably a reference to the large eyes.

DISTRIBUTION AND HABITAT

The bigeye shiner occurs over most of the Ozark Uplands and in tributaries of the Mississippi River northward to Lewis County. It is one of the most abundant minnows in streams of the Spring and Meramec River systems. The most unusual feature of its distribution is its rarity in the Gasconade River system and complete absence from the Osage River system. Both of these stream systems appear to have plenty of habitat of the type inhabited by the bigeye shiner elsewhere. In this respect the distribution of the bigeye shiner parallels that of the striped shiner, a species with which it is commonly associated. Unlike the striped shiner, the bigeye has suffered no recent restrictions in distribution.

The bigeye shiner inhabits moderately clear streams having large, permanent pools, bottoms composed mostly of clean sand, gravel, or rock, and an abundance of aquatic vegetation. It avoids strong currents and water that is continuously cool. Ideal habitat is found in small creeks of the Ozark border. These streams are not spring-fed and consist of a series of warm, quiet pools with little flow between during drier seasons of the year. Along Ozark streams cooled by many springs the bigeye shiner tends to occur as isolated populations in backwaters and overflow pools that are several degrees warmer than the main stream.

HABITS AND LIFE HISTORY

The bigeye shiner lives in schools in midwater or at the surface. It feeds extensively on small insects hovering a few inches above the water, jumping gracefully into the air to capture them.[94] This minnow has a prolonged spawning season. Adults in spawning condition have been collected in Missouri from early June to late August. Spawning habits and growth have not been studied.

Pallid Shiner

Notropis amnis Hubbs and Greene

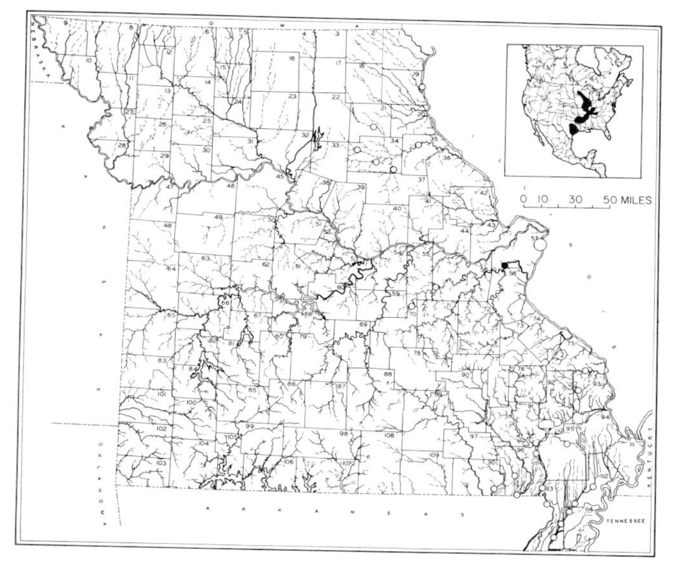

DESCRIPTION

Illustration: Page 124, 61a.

Characters: A slender, silvery minnow with large eyes and a small, nearly horizontal mouth. Barbels normally absent. Anal fin with 8 (occasionally 7, rarely 9) rays. Front of dorsal fin base closer to tip of snout than to base of tail fin. Upper jaw not reaching front of eye. Snout bluntly rounded, projecting well beyond upper lip. Dark stripe along midline of back faint or absent. Dorsal fin high and pointed. Scales in forward part of lateral line not greatly heightened. Lateral line scales 34 to 37. Intestine short, with a single S-shaped loop; lining of body cavity silvery, sometimes with a few faint dark speckles. Throat teeth 1,4-4,1.

Life colors: Back pale olive-yellow, the scales faintly dark-edged. Sides silvery. Belly silvery-white. Fins plain. Breeding males are without special colors but have minute tubercles on head, forward part of body, and along pectoral fin rays.

Size: Adults are commonly 1.5 to 2.2 inches long to a maximum of about 2.7 inches.

Scientific name: *Notropis,* Greek, "back keel"; *amnis,* Latin, meaning "of the river," in reference to the habitat of the typical subspecies.

DISTRIBUTION AND HABITAT

Little is known concerning the early abundance and distribution of the pallid shiner in Missouri, but as recently as the early 1940's it was widespread in the eastern part of the state. Its main area of occurrence seems to have been in the Lowland streams and ditches of the southeast, but it was also common in the Salt River and some other direct tributaries of the Mississippi. Efforts have been made in recent years to collect the pallid shiner at localities where it formerly occurred, but they have been unsuccessful. The last specimens known to have been collected in Missouri were from the Meramec River in 1956. No other Missouri fish has shown such a marked decline in abundance during the past 30 years. It probably is on the verge of being eliminated from the state if it is not already gone.

The pallid shiner occurs principally in streams of medium to large size. Although it is essentially a Lowland species it also occurs in sluggish streams draining level uplands. It seems intolerant of excessive siltation and turbidity and avoids strong currents. The reasons for its decline in Missouri are not known, but possibly result from increased siltation associated with changing land use patterns.

HABITS AND LIFE HISTORY

Nothing is known about the habits and life history of this species.

Steelcolor Shiner

Notropis whipplei (Girard)

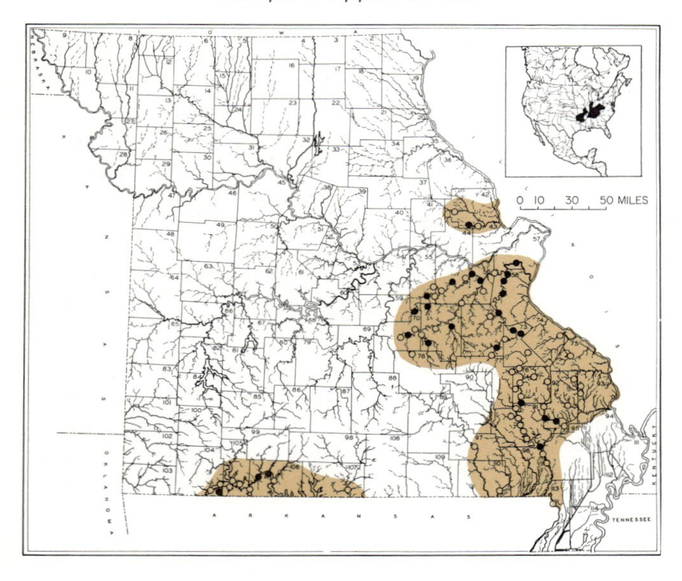

DESCRIPTION

Illustration: Page 114, 41b.

Characters: A moderately slender, slab-sided minnow with small eyes and a terminal, oblique mouth. Barbels absent. Anal fin with 9 (rarely 8 or 10) rays. Front of dorsal fin base slightly closer to base of tail fin than to tip of snout. Large young and adults with a dusky or black blotch on last 2 or 3 membranes of dorsal fin; other dorsal membranes thickly dusted with fine, dark specks. Base of tail fin not marked by a black spot or white patches. Dusky stripe (visible only after preservation) along side of caudal peduncle broad and faint, poorly defined above and centered on lateral line. Lateral line scales 37 to 39. Intestine short, with a single S-shaped loop; lining of body cavity silvery, thickly sprinkled with black speckles. Throat teeth 1,4-4,1.

Life colors: Back yellowish-olive with definite dark edgings on scales and a narrow, dusky stripe along midline. Sides silvery with blue reflections, the scales dark-edged nearly to belly forming a characteristic pattern of diamond-shaped cross-hatchings. Dorsal fin marked as indicated under *Characters;* fins otherwise plain. Breeding males a brilliant steel-blue on back and sides, the snout brick red, and the fins mostly lemon-yellow fringed with white; dorsal fin greatly enlarged; tubercles developed over much of head, body and fins; tubercles largest on snout and top of head.

Size: Adults are commonly 2.5 to 4.5 inches long to a maximum of about 5.5 inches.

Scientific name: *Notropis,* Greek, "back keel"; *whipplei,* named for Captain A. W. Whipple who collected the types.

DISTRIBUTION AND HABITAT

The steelcolor shiner is common and widespread in the Meramec, Headwater Diversion, and St. Francis stream systems and occurs occasionally in the southern Ozarks as far west as the White River system. North of the Missouri River it occurs only in the Cuivre River system. It is more common in the Meramec system than elsewhere.

This minnow inhabits clear, permanent-flowing streams with moderate or high gradients. It prefers streams of medium size, avoiding both small headwater creeks and large main streams such as the Mississippi River. It is most often found near rocky or gravelly riffles in a moderate or swift current. The steelcolor shiner seems less tolerant of turbidity than the related spotfin shiner.

HABITS AND LIFE HISTORY

The steelcolor shiner lives in schools in midwater or near the surface. It is most often found in association with the spotfin, whitetail, rosyface, and bleeding shiners. It feeds by sight on material drifting with the current at the surface or in midwater, and to a lesser extent on small invertebrates gleaned from the bottom. Insects, both terrestrial and aquatic, make up the bulk of its diet. The remainder of its food is composed almost exclusively of animal material, including mites, earthworms and small crustaceans.

The steelcolor shiner spawns in Missouri from

late May or early June to mid-August. The eggs are deposited in the crevices of submerged objects, most often on logs or tree roots where there is a moderate or swift current.[95] The males occupy small territories which they guard against other males. Many males are commonly present around a single spawning site. The females occupy a position in the current below the spawning site. When ready to spawn a female moves up over the spawning site and briefly pairs with one of the males. The male takes a position above or beside the female as spawning occurs.

Studies by the writer in Ohio indicate that few steelcolor shiners live more than three summers, but a few females complete four summers. Males grow more rapidly than females and the fastest-growing males are larger at the end of their second summer than the largest females are at the end of three summers. A few individuals mature their second summer but most do not spawn before their third summer.

Spotfin Shiner

Notropis spilopterus (Cope)

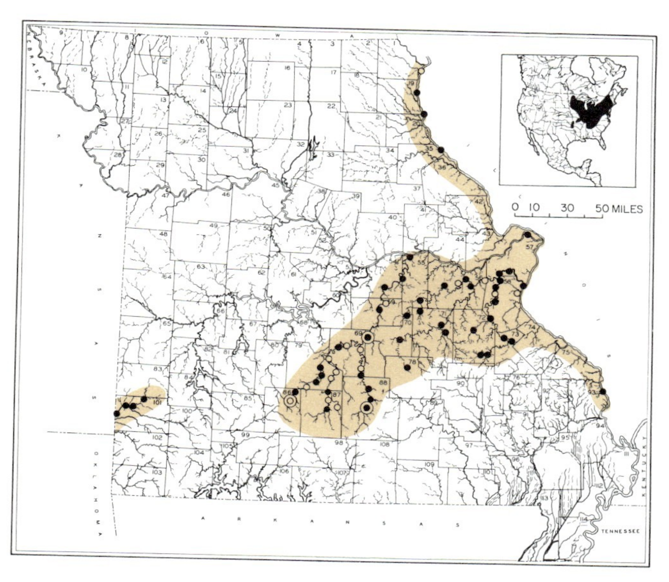

DESCRIPTION

Illustration: Page 113, 39a.

Characters: A moderately slender, slab-sided minnow with small eyes and a moderately oblique mouth. Barbels absent. Anal fin with 8 (occasionally 9) rays. Front of dorsal fin base closer to base of tail fin than to tip of snout. Large young and adults have a dusky or black blotch on last 2 or 3 membranes of dorsal fin; other dorsal membranes are clear in young and half-grown specimens, becoming thickly dusted with fine dark specks only in breeding males. Tail fin without a black spot or white patch at its base. Dusky stripe (visible only after preservation) along side of caudal peduncle narrow and distinct, sharply defined above, and centered below lateral line. Lateral line scales 35 to 38. Intestine short, with a single S-shaped loop; lining of body cavity silvery, thickly sprinkled with dark speckles. Throat teeth 1,4-4,1.

Life colors: Like those of steelcolor shiner, page 156, except as indicated under *Characters*. Also, the snout of breeding males is not red and the dorsal fin is not enlarged.

Size: Average size about the same as the steelcolor shiner, 2.5 to 4.5 inches, but maximum somewhat less, about 4.8 inches in Missouri.

Scientific name: *Notropis*, Greek, "back keel"; *spilopterus*, Greek, meaning "spotfin," in reference to the prominent blotch in the dorsal fin.

DISTRIBUTION AND HABITAT

The spotfin shiner is common in the Gasconade and Meramec River systems and occurs sparingly in the upper Mississippi and the Spring River system of southwestern Missouri. Occasional individuals have been collected in the lower Missouri and lower Mississippi as far south as Cape Girardeau County. Populations in the Spring River system are isolated from the main part of the species range, indicating a more widespread distribution at some time in the past.

The habitat requirements of this minnow are similar to those of the steelcolor shiner and where their ranges overlap they are often taken together. However, the spotfin seems to be more tolerant of turbidity and occurs more frequently in large streams such as the Mississippi River.

HABITS AND LIFE HISTORY

Studies of the spotfin shiner and the steelcolor shiner by the writer in Ohio revealed no major differences in their habits and life histories. The spawning season is the same for both, but the peak of spawning activity comes slightly earlier in the summer for the spotfin.[95] Spawning groups of the two species usually remain separate, even when spawning in close proximity. Breeding adults of the spotfin shiner produce sounds during courtship.[96] These sounds, along with visual clues such as differences in breeding colors of the males, may be helpful in permitting individuals to recognize others of their own species. Hybrids between these species have been produced in aquaria but evidently occur rarely, if ever, in nature. The spotfin shiner grows less rapidly than the steelcolor, but the growth patterns and longevity are about the same for the two species.

Blacktail Shiner

Notropis venustus (Girard)

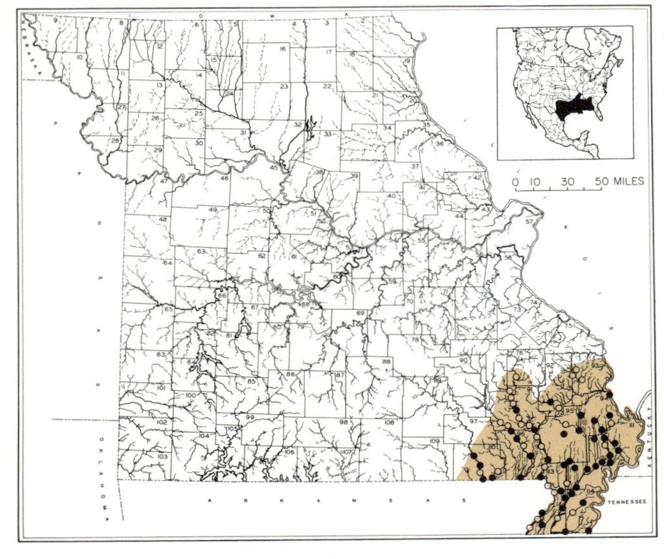

DESCRIPTION

Illustration: Page 111, 34a.

Characters: A moderately slender, slab-sided minnow with small eyes and a terminal, oblique mouth. Barbels absent. Anal fin with 8 (occasionally 9) rays. Front of dorsal fin base slightly closer to base of tail fin than to tip of snout. Large young and adults with a dusky blotch on last 2 or 3 membranes of dorsal fin; other dorsal membranes thickly dusted with fine dark specks. Tail fin with a large and prominent black spot at base. Lateral line scales 36 to 39. Intestine short, with a single S-shaped loop; lining of body cavity silvery, thickly sprinkled with dark speckles. Throat teeth 1,4-4,1.

Life colors: Similar to steelcolor shiner, page 156, but with a prominent black spot at base of tail fin. Also, the snout of breeding males is not red and the dorsal fin is not enlarged.

Size: Adults are usually 2.5 to 4.5 inches in length.

Scientific name: *Notropis,* Greek, "back keel"; *venustus,* Latin, meaning "beautiful, like Venus."

DISTRIBUTION AND HABITAT

The blacktail shiner is the most abundant minnow in the Lowlands. It also occurs sparingly in the lower reaches of Ozark streams entering the Lowlands.

This minnow occupies a variety of habitats but shows a decided preference for flowing waters. It is most abundant in large, sparsely vegetated Lowland ditches and streams where there is a strong current and a sand or gravel bottom.

HABITS AND LIFE HISTORY

The life history of the blacktail shiner is not known in detail but is probably not greatly different from that of the related steelcolor shiner, page 156. It lives in schools in midwater and commonly occurs in association with the ribbon, emerald, and weed shiners. In Missouri it spawns over an extended period from June into August, depositing its eggs in the crevices of submerged objects. Spawning females produce sounds to which the males respond. They are able to distinguish these sounds from those produced by the related red shiner.[97] These sounds apparently serve to bring the spawning fish together and permit the male to recognize females of his own species.

Whitetail Shiner

Notropis galacturus (Cope)

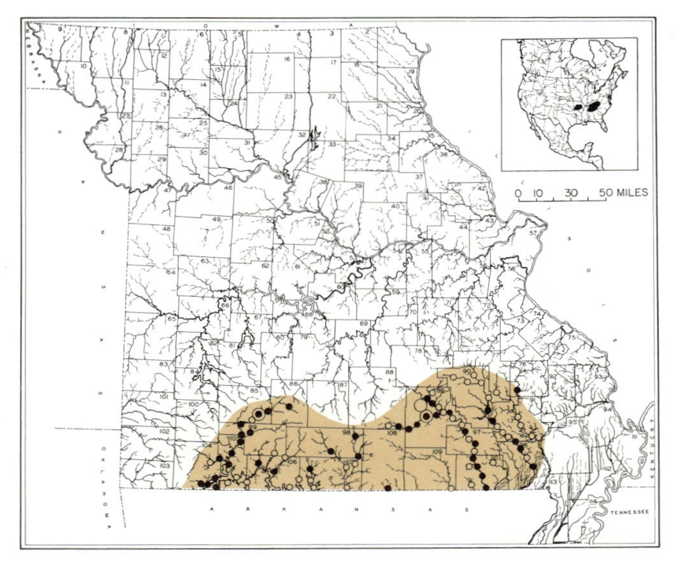

DESCRIPTION

Illustration: Page 114, 40a; **38.**

Characters: A slender, slab-sided minnow with small eyes and a terminal, oblique mouth. Barbels absent. Anal fin with 9 (rarely 8 or 10) rays. Front of dorsal fin base slightly closer to base of tail fin than to tip of snout. Large young and adults have a dusky or black blotch on last 2 or 3 membranes of dorsal fin; other dorsal membranes thickly dusted with fine, dark specks. Tail fin with two broad white patches at base. Lateral line scales 39 to 41. Intestine short, with a single S-shaped loop; lining of body cavity silvery, thickly sprinkled with dark speckles. Throat teeth 1,4-4,1.

Life colors: Like those of steelcolor shiner, page 156, but with two broad, white patches across base of tail fin. Also, breeding males have fins salmon-pink instead of yellow.

Size: Adults are commonly 3 to 5 inches long to a maximum of about 6 inches.

Scientific name: *Notropis,* Greek, "back keel"; *galacturus,* Greek, meaning "milk tail".

DISTRIBUTION AND HABITAT

The whitetail shiner is one of the common and characteristic minnows in large streams of the southern Ozarks. It is absent from most of the Eleven Point River, perhaps as a result of the influence of Greer and other large springs on water temperature.

This minnow inhabits clear, high-gradient streams with continuous, strong flow and firm, silt-free bottoms. It is particularly characteristic of boulder strewn pools with noticeable current. The whitetail shiner avoids stream sections kept continuously cool by discharge from large springs.

HABITS AND LIFE HISTORY

The whitetail shiner occurs singly or in small, loosely organized groups. It is an active minnow, moving about swiftly and more or less constantly from place to place. It seems always to be on the lookout for food and is quick to move in and feed on insects and other aquatic invertebrates stirred up by swimmers or fishermen wading in the stream. Most of its food probably is obtained as it drifts with the stream currents. Insects, including both terrestrial and aquatic kinds, are the principal item in the diet of the whitetail shiner.[98]

In the Missouri Ozarks this minnow spawns over an extended period from early June to mid-August. Its spawning habits are much like those of the steelcolor shiner, page 156. I have observed whitetail shiners depositing eggs beneath the bark of submerged logs, and also in the crevices of bedrock. In the latter situation the rocks were polished clean by the activities of the spawning fish.

In Current River the whitetail attains a length of about 1.5 to 2.8 inches by the end of its first summer of life. Most individuals do not mature until their third summer. Males grow more rapidly and achieve a larger size than females.

Bluntface Shiner

Notropis camurus (Jordan and Meek)

DESCRIPTION

Illustration: Page 114, 41a.

Characters: A rather deep and slab-sided minnow with small eyes and a terminal, oblique mouth. Barbels absent. Anal fin with 9 (rarely 8 or 10) rays. Front of dorsal fin base slightly closer to base of tail fin than to tip of snout. Large young and adults with a dusky or black blotch on last 2 or 3 membranes of dorsal fin; other dorsal membranes thickly dusted with fine dark specks. Tail fin with a narrow vertical white patch—not always conspicuous—across base. Dusky stripe (visible only after preservation) along side of caudal peduncle broad and faint, poorly defined above, and centered on lateral line. Lateral line scales 35 to 37. Intestine short, with a single S-shaped loop; lining of body cavity silvery, thickly sprinkled with dark speckles. Throat teeth 1,4-4,1.

Life colors: Like those of steelcolor shiner, page 156, except that tail fin has a narrow, vertical white patch across base. Also, fins of breeding males salmon-pink instead of yellow.

Size: Adults are usually 2.5 to 4.3 inches long to a maximum of about 4.5 inches.

Scientific name: *Notropis,* Greek, "back keel"; *camurus,* Latin, meaning "blunt-faced."

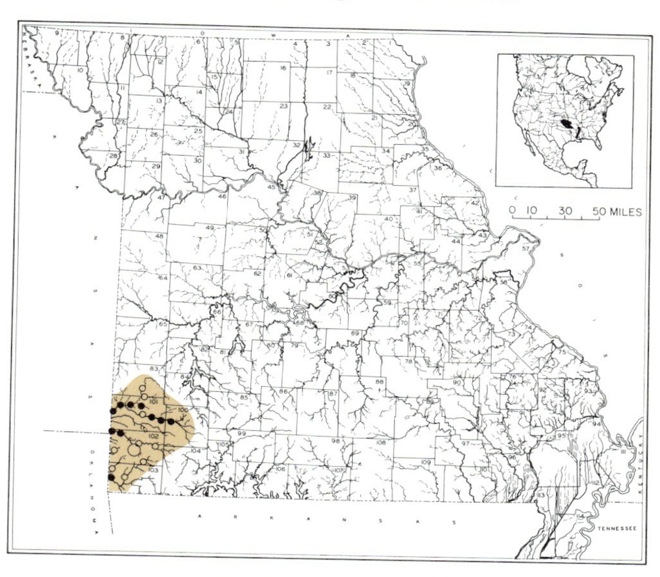

DISTRIBUTION AND HABITAT

The bluntface shiner is common and generally distributed in the Spring and Elk River systems of southwest Missouri. It has been reported from the White River system in Missouri,[99] but this report is attributable to faulty locality data.

This shiner inhabits moderately clear, permanent-flowing streams with moderate or high gradients and gravel or rubble bottoms. It is most often found near riffles where there is noticeable current.

HABITS AND LIFE HISTORY

The life history of the bluntface shiner has not been studied but probably is not greatly different from that of the steelcolor shiner, page 156. Adults in spawning condition have been collected in Missouri from late May into July, indicating an extended late-spring and early-summer spawning season.

Red Shiner

Notropis lutrensis (Baird and Girard)

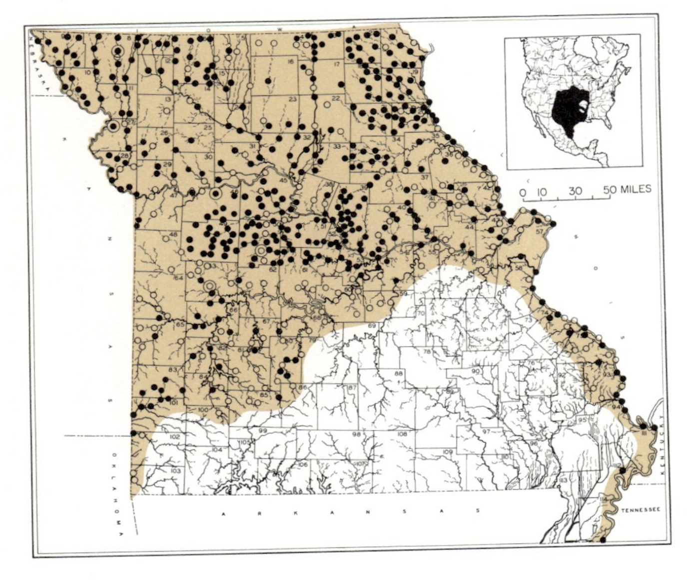

DESCRIPTION

Illustration: Page 113, 38a.

Characters: A deep and slab-sided minnow with small eyes and a terminal, oblique mouth. Barbels absent. Anal fin with 9 (occasionally 8 or 10) rays. Front of dorsal fin base about equidistant between tip of snout and base of tail fin. Large young and adults with all membranes of dorsal fin more or less uniformly dusted with fine dark specks—not concentrated into a dusky or black blotch on last 2 or 3 dorsal membranes. Tail fin without a black blotch or white patch at base. Lateral line scales 32 to 36. Intestine short, with a single S-shaped loop; lining of body cavity silvery, thickly sprinkled with dark speckles.

Life colors: Like those of steelcolor shiner, page 156, except with dorsal fin marked as indicated under *Characters*. Breeding males are a beautiful metallic blue, with top of head and all fins except dorsal bright red, and a pink vertical bar on body behind pectoral fin.

Size: Adults are commonly 1.8 to 3 inches long to a maximum of about 3.5 inches.

Scientific name: *Notropis*, Greek "back keel"; *lutrensis*, from *lutra*, Latin for otter; the species was first known from Otter Creek, Arkansas.

DISTRIBUTION AND HABITAT

The red shiner is the most abundant and widely distributed minnow in the Prairie Region of north and west Missouri. It is common in most streams of the northern and western Ozark border and occurs southward along the Mississippi River to the southern boundary of the state. Its distribution largely complements that of its close relatives—whitetail, bluntface, blacktail, spotfin, and steelcolor shiners—suggesting that competition from these species is an important factor in controlling its distribution.

The red shiner occurs in streams of all sizes but is most abundant in large creeks and rivers. Although it sometimes thrives when introduced into impoundments, in natural waters it is primarily a stream fish. The red shiner inhabits a variety of habitats, including quiet pools and backwaters as well as riffles. It is tolerant of high turbidity and siltation but avoids waters that are continuously clear or cool.

HABITS AND LIFE HISTORY

The red shiner lives in schools in midwater or near the surface and is most often found in association with the sand, redfin, bigmouth, Topeka, and ghost shiners. It is an extremely active fish, commonly breaking the surface of the water while feeding. It feeds primarily by sight and takes its food at all levels. Its diet has not been studied but probably consists mostly of insects and other small invertebrates.

The red shiner spawns over an extended period from late May to early September in Missouri, with the peak in June and July. No other Missouri fish is so adaptable in its spawning requirements. In central Missouri the eggs are most often deposited over nests of the green and orangespotted sunfishes, but spawning also commonly occurs on clean, gravelly riffles or on submerged objects such as logs and tree roots. In clear ponds I have seen the red shiner spawning near the surface over beds of submerged aquatic plants.

Spawning activity around sunfish nests is most intense when the sunfish are depositing their eggs or shortly thereafter. Male red shiners occupy small territories around the margins of the sunfish nests and guard these vigorously against the intrusion of other males. The Topeka and redfin shiners have similar spawning habits and all three minnow species commonly spawn simultaneously on the same sunfish nest. The redfin shiner normally spawns in midwater over the nest while the red shiner and Topeka shiner spawn near the bottom, around the edges of the nest.

In central Missouri the red shiner averages 0.9 inches in length by the end of its first summer of life and 1.8 inches by the end of its second summer. Most adults mature in their second or third summer; few live beyond three summers. Growth in new impoundments is much more rapid than in streams.

Sabine Shiner

Notropis sabinae Jordan and Gilbert

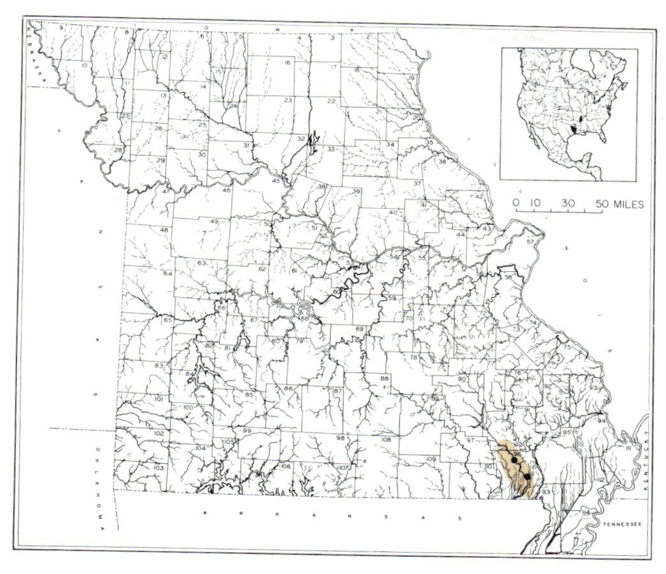

DESCRIPTION

Illustration: Page 126, 64a.

Characters: A slender, silvery minnow with small eyes and a rather large, nearly horizontal mouth. Barbels absent. Anal fin with 7 (rarely 6 or 8) rays. Front of dorsal fin base much closer to tip of snout than to base of tail fin. Undersurface of head distinctly flattened. Snout bluntly rounded, projecting slightly beyond upper lip. Upper jaw reaching past front of eye. Eyes directed slightly upward, rather than to sides, so that lower margin of pupil is visible when fish is viewed from above. Lateral line scales 31 to 34. Intestine short, with a single S-shaped loop; lining of body cavity silvery, sprinkled with faint dark speckles. Throat teeth 4-4.

Life colors: Back pale olive-yellow without a definite streak along midline or dark edgings on scales. Sides silvery. Belly silver-white. Fins plain. Breeding males are without special colors but have small tubercles on snout, cheeks, and jaws.

Size: Adults are commonly 1.8 to 2.2 inches long to a maximum of about 2.5 inches.

Scientific name: *Notropis,* Greek, "back keel"; *sabinae,* named for the Sabine River, Texas, from which the species was first known.

DISTRIBUTION AND HABITAT

The Sabine shiner has been collected in Missouri only from Black River near the point where it descends into the Lowlands. In 1964 the Sabine shiner was found to be fairly common a few miles below Poplar Bluff, but only a single specimen was taken in a collection made several miles farther upstream. None occurred in collections from Black River below these localities.

Black River at the point the Sabine shiner was collected is clear and deep with a bottom composed of fine, silt-free sand. It was collected over sand bars in slight to moderate current.

HABITS AND LIFE HISTORY

The habits of this minnow are not well known. It lives on or near the bottom. In Black River it was found in association with the blacktail shiner, emerald shiner, silvery minnow, and bullhead minnow. It probably feeds on animal life taken from the bottom. Adults collected in July were in spawning condition indicating a summer spawning season.

Topeka Shiner

Notropis topeka Gilbert

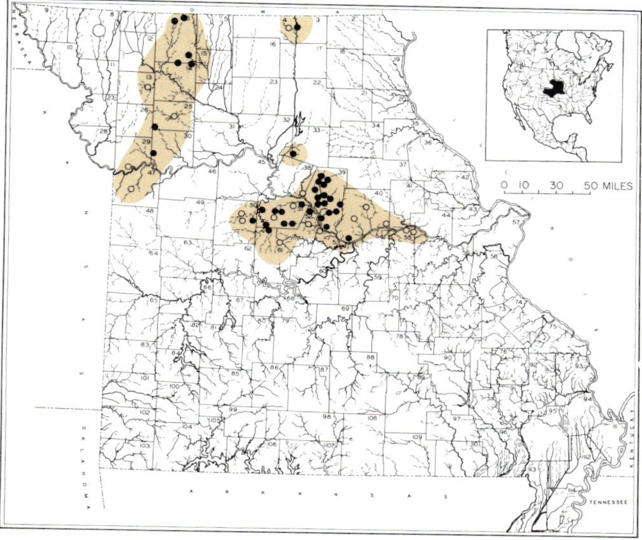

DESCRIPTION

Illustration: Page 121, 55b.

Characters: A chubby, rather slab-sided minnow with moderately small eyes and a small, oblique mouth. Barbels absent. Anal fin with 7 (rarely 6 or 8) rays. Front of dorsal fin base closer to tip of snout than to base of tail fin. Tail fin with a small, wedge-shaped black spot at base. Dark stripe along midline of back broad and distinct ahead of dorsal fin but often indistinct or absent behind. Dusky stripe along midside quite distinct, extending forward onto head; stripe not bordered above by a light-colored zone. Upper jaw not reaching past front of eye. Lateral line scales 32 to 36. Intestine short, with a single S-shaped loop; lining of body cavity silvery, sometimes with a few faint, dark speckles. Throat teeth 4-4.

Life colors: Back olive-yellow, the scales prominently dark-edged. Sides silvery, with a well defined dusky stripe. Belly silvery-white. Tail fin with a wedge-shaped black spot at base; fins otherwise plain. Breeding males with all fins orange-red and head and body tinged with orange; tubercles present over much of head and body and along some rays of pectoral and dorsal fins; tubercles largest on snout and top of head.

Size: Adults are commonly 1.6 to 2.6 inches long to a maximum of about 3 inches.

Scientific name: *Notropis,* Greek, "back keel"; *topeka,* named for Topeka, Kansas, the type locality.

DISTRIBUTION AND HABITAT

The distribution of the Topeka shiner in Missouri is centered in the streams of Boone, Cooper, Moniteau, and Callaway Counties with isolated populations northwestward in the Prairie Region. An early report from the Hundred and Two River near Maryville[86] suggests a former more widespread distribution in northwest Missouri. The Topeka shiner is not abundant at any location but is a characteristic element in the fish fauna of small streams in central Missouri.

This minnow inhabits quiet pools of small, clear, upland creeks having bottoms composed mostly of sand, gravel, or rubble. These streams may cease to flow during dry seasons but permanent pools are maintained by the percolation of water through the stream bed. Increased siltation as a result of intensive cultivation may have reduced the amount of this type of habitat in Missouri. At present the Topeka shiner is largely restricted to direct tributaries of the Missouri River having sufficient gradient to prevent extensive deposition of silt.

HABITS AND LIFE HISTORY

The Topeka shiner occurs in schools in midwater or near the surface. It is most often found with the redfin, sand, common, and red shiners, and the bluntnose minnow. It is probably carnivorous but its food habits have not been studied. Spawning has been observed in central Missouri from late May to mid-July. Like the redfin and red shiners, it spawns over the nests of the green and orangespotted sunfishes. The males occupy small territories around the periphery of sunfish nests. Males follow females by swimming beneath them rather than above or to one side, as in most other shiners. The details of the spawning act have not been observed.

The Topeka shiner attains a length of 0.8 to 1.6 inches by the end of its first summer of life and 1.4 to 2.2 inches by the end of its second summer.[42] The normal life span does not exceed three summers and sexual maturity is reached during the second summer. Males grow more rapidly and attain a larger size than females.

Sand Shiner

Notropis stramineus (Cope)

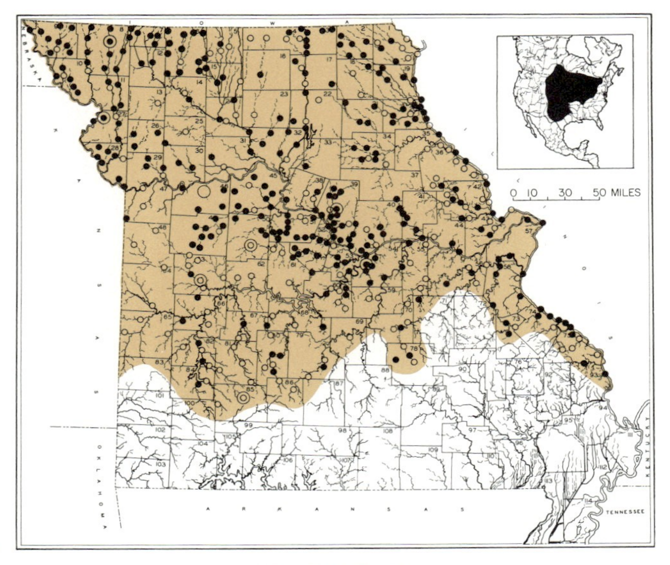

DESCRIPTION

Illustration: Page 122, 56b.

Characters: A moderately slender, silvery minnow with rather large eyes and a small, slightly oblique mouth. Barbels absent. Anal fin with 7 (rarely 6 or 8) rays. Front of dorsal fin base about equidistant between tip of snout and base of tail fin. Dark stripe along midline of back narrow but rather well defined and expanded into a wedge-shaped spot at front of dorsal fin; along dorsal fin base stripe is darkest near rear part of fin. Upper jaw not reaching past front of eye. Dusky stripe along midside fading out towards head. Dark spot at base of tail fin poorly defined and irregular in outline. Lateral line scales 31 to 36. Intestine short, with a single S-shaped loop; lining of body cavity silvery with scattered dark speckles. Throat teeth 4-4.

Life colors: Back olive-yellow, the scales prominently dark-edged. Sides silvery with pores of lateral line marked by dark pigment. Belly silvery-white. Tail fin sometimes with a faint dusky spot at base; fins otherwise plain. Breeding males are without special colors but have very small tubercles on head and along rays of pectoral fins.

Size: Adults are commonly 1.7 to 2.6 inches long to a maximum of about 2.8 inches.

Scientific name: *Notropis,* Greek, "back keel"; *stramineus*, Latin, meaning "made of straw," probably in reference to the color.

DISTRIBUTION AND HABITAT

The sand shiner occurs throughout the Prairie Region. In many Prairie streams it is the most abundant minnow or is second in abundance only to the red shiner. The distribution of these two species is remarkably similar, differing only in the absence of the sand shiner from the Spring River of southwest Missouri and the greater abundance and more widespread distribution of this species in the Gasconade and Meramec drainages.

As its name implies, the sand shiner shows a strong affinity for sandy bottoms. It occurs in streams of all sizes but is seldom abundant in the largest rivers. It is replaced towards the headwaters of many Prairie streams by the bigmouth shiner, another minnow with an affinity for sandy bottoms. The sand shiner is most abundant in the shallow, sandy pools of medium-sized creeks having permanent flow, moderately clear water, and low or moderate gradient.

HABITS AND LIFE HISTORY

The sand shiner lives in schools in midwater or near the bottom. It is most often found with the red, redfin, bigmouth, common and Topeka shiners. The sand shiner takes most of its food on or near the bottom. Its food habits are rather generalized. An Iowa study revealed that immature aquatic insects and bottom ooze, along with small quantities of adult insects, small crustaceans, and plant material make up its diet.[71]

In central Missouri streams the sand shiner reaches a length of 0.8 to 1.5 inches by the end of its first summer of life and 1.6 to 2.3 inches by the end of its second summer. Maturity is reached in the second or third summer.

Taillight Shiner

Notropis maculatus (Hay)

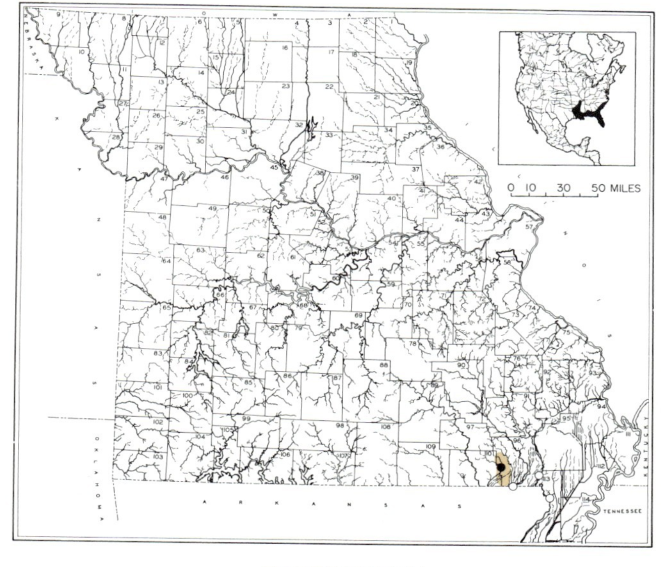

DESCRIPTION

Illustration: Page 110, 33a.

Characters: A very slender minnow with moderately large eyes and a small, slightly oblique mouth. Barbels absent. Anal fin with 8 (rarely 7 or 9) rays. Front of dorsal fin base slightly closer to tip of snout than to base of tail fin. Tail fin with a very large and prominent roundish black spot at base. Midside with a narrow dusky stripe that extends forward onto snout and chin. Snout blunt and rounded, projecting slightly beyond upper lip. Lateral line incomplete, developed only on about 8 or 10 scales towards head. Scales along midside 34 to 39. Body depth going more than 5 times into standard length. Intestine short, with a single S-shaped loop; lining of body cavity silvery, often with a few faint, dark speckles. Throat teeth 4-4.

Life colors: Back pale olive-yellow, the scales prominently dark-edged. Sides silvery with a narrow dusky stripe. Belly silvery-white. Tail fin with a prominent black spot at base; fins otherwise plain or dusted with small dark specks. In breeding males the dorsal fin is almost completely black.

Size: Adults are commonly 1.9 to 2.4 inches long to a maximum of about 2.7 inches.

Scientific name: *Notropis,* Greek, "back keel"; *maculatus,* Latin, meaning "spotted."

DISTRIBUTION AND HABITAT

The taillight shiner is presently known only from the Little Black River. It was collected from three localities on the lower Black and St. Francis rivers more than 30 years ago.

The habitat of this fish is the sluggish pools of Lowland rivers and creeks.

HABITS AND LIFE HISTORY

Nothing is known about the habits and life history of the taillight shiner in Missouri. It is reported to have a one-year life cycle in Florida.[252]

Blacknose Shiner

Notropis heterolepis Eigenmann and Eigenmann

DESCRIPTION

Illustration: Page 123, 59a.

Characters: A slender, silvery minnow with rather large eyes and a small, nearly horizontal mouth. Barbels absent. Anal fin with 8 (rarely 7 or 9) rays. Front of dorsal fin base slightly closer to tip of snout than to base of tail fin. Midside with a dusky stripe that extends forward to tip of snout; stripe bordered above by a light-colored zone in which the scales are not dark-edged. Lower lip and chin without dusky pigment. Dark borders of lateral line pores often expanded into small, crescent-shaped vertical bars. Lateral line complete or lacking a few pores. Lateral line scales 33 to 38. Intestine short, with a single S-shaped loop; lining of body cavity silvery with scattered dark speckles. Throat teeth 4-4.

Life colors: Back pale olive-yellow, the scales prominently dark-edged. Sides silvery with a prominent dusky stripe; pores of lateral line with dark borders that are often expanded into vertical crescents. Belly silvery-white. Fins plain. Breeding males are without special colors but have very small tubercles on upper surface of head and along pectoral fin rays.

Size: Adults are commonly 1.8 to 2.5 inches long to a maximum of about 2.8 inches.

Scientific name: *Notropis,* Greek, "back keel"; *heterolepis,* Greek, meaning "various scale," in reference to the variation in the shape of the scales.

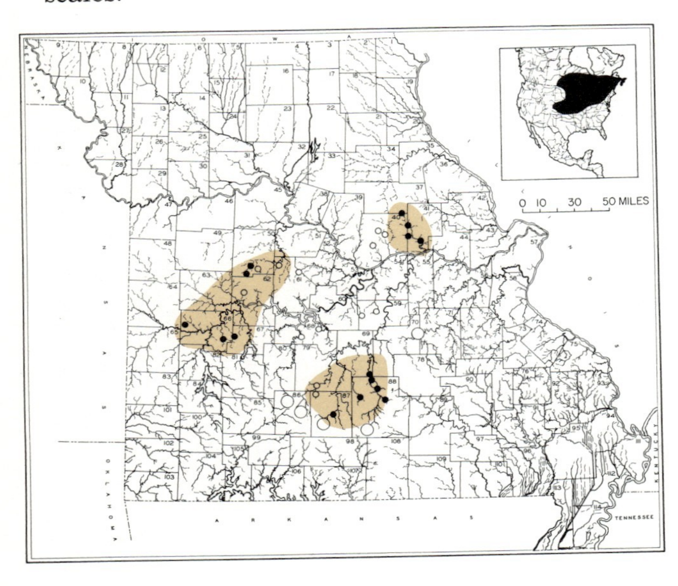

DISTRIBUTION AND HABITAT

The blacknose shiner is not abundant anywhere in Missouri. The only streams in which we have found it to be at all common are Flat Creek in southern Pettis County, Hagies Creek in Hickory County, and the Loutre River and its tributaries in Montgomery and Callaway counties. Although the blacknose shiner was reported as "scarce in southern Missouri" by one early collector,[88] it must have been more common and widely distributed then than it is today since it was reported from localities where it is not now known to occur. Its apparent absence from streams in Callaway County where it was present as recently as 25 or 30 years ago indicates that its range and abundance may still be decreasing. If this trend continues the blacknose shiner may soon be eliminated from Missouri.

This minnow is found with greatest frequency in small, moderately clear, Prairie streams, in quiet pools having considerable amounts of aquatic vegetation and bottoms of muck and organic debris, often overlying sand, gravel, or rock. A secondary area of occurrence is in the quiet, heavily vegetated pools and backwaters of Ozark streams. This minnow seems intolerant of continuous turbidity. Increased siltation and tendency for the smaller Prairie creeks to dry up as a result of intensive cultivation seem to be important factors in its declining abundance. The largest remaining populations are in streams of the Ozark border that drain level uplands underlain by thin, rocky soils. These soils are not conducive to intensive cultivation and extensive areas of the uplands were, until recently, covered by native grasses that retard siltation. However, the acreage in native grasses becomes less each year. This is certain to have an effect on the chances for long-term survival of the blacknose shiner in Missouri.

HABITS AND LIFE HISTORY

The blacknose shiner lives in schools in midwater and often occurs in association with the golden shiner, redfin shiner and bluntnose minnow. It is reported to spawn at this latitude in June or July.[24] In central Missouri it reaches a length of about 0.8 to 1.5 inches by the end of its first summer of life. Nothing more is known of its habits or life history.

Ozark Shiner

Notropis ozarcanus Meek

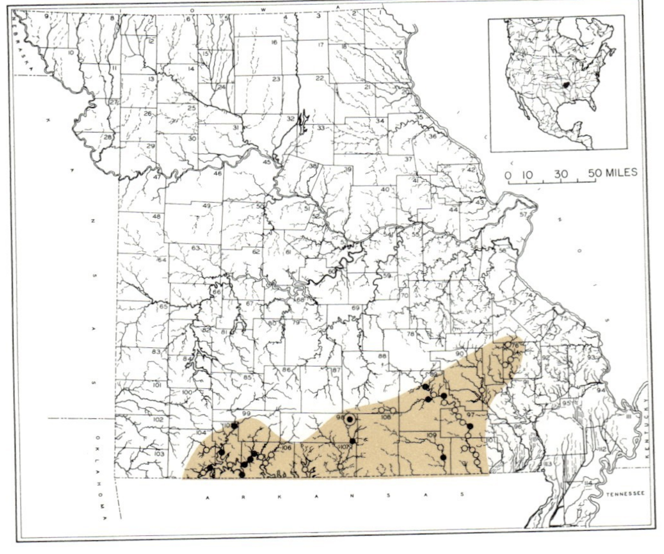

DESCRIPTION

Illustration: Page 112, 36a.

Characters: A very slender minnow with rather large eyes and a small, nearly horizontal mouth. Barbels absent. Anal fin with 8 (rarely 7 or 9) rays. Front of dorsal fin base closer to base of tail fin than to tip of snout. Dorsal fin with a small, dusky blotch near base of first 2 or 3 rays; membranes of all fins often dusted with fine dark specks in adults. Snout blunt and rounded, projecting slightly beyond upper lip. Scales in forward part of lateral line much deeper than those on adjacent parts of sides. Lateral line scales 34 to 38. Intestine short, with a single S-shaped loop; lining of body cavity silvery with scattered dark speckles. Throat teeth 4-4.

Life Colors: Back pale yellow, the scales prominently dark-edged. Sides silvery with a faint, dusky stripe that fades out towards head. Belly silvery-white. Fins marked as indicated under *Characters.* Breeding males with fins black; tubercles absent, but the first ray of pectoral fin is thickened and roughened.

Size: Adults are commonly 1.8 to 2.5 inches long to a maximum of about 2.8 inches.

Scientific name: *Notropis,* Greek, "back keel"; *ozarcanus,* "from the Ozarks."

DISTRIBUTION AND HABITAT

The Ozark shiner is found only in the Ozark Uplands of southern Missouri and northern Arkansas. In Missouri it is common in the Current and North Fork rivers but it is rare elsewhere. It was formerly abundant in sections of the White River now inundated by Table Rock and Bull Shoals reservoirs. The original description of this minnow is based on specimens collected from the North Fork of White River in Missouri in 1891.[88]

It inhabits large, clear streams having high gradients and permanent strong flow. It occurs most abundantly near riffles in a slight to moderate current over a silt-free bottom.

HABITS AND LIFE HISTORY

The Ozark shiner lives in schools in midwater and is commonly found in association with the telescope, rosyface, duskystripe, striped and whitetail shiners. Adults in spawning condition have been collected in Missouri from late May to late August, indicating a long spawning season. Nothing else is known of its habits or life history.

Mimic Shiner

Notropis volucellus (Cope)

DESCRIPTION

Illustration: Page 125, 63b.

Characters: A slender to moderately chubby minnow with rather large eyes and a small, oblique mouth. Barbels absent. Anal fin with 8 (rarely 7 or 9) rays. Front of dorsal fin base about equidistant between tip of snout and base of tail fin. Depth of scales in lateral line becoming greater toward the head. Sensory canal beneath eye complete. Tips of pelvic fins not reaching front of anal fin. Dusky stripe along midside faint, fading out toward head. Lateral line scales 33 to 38. Intestine short, with a single S-shaped loop; lining of body cavity silvery with scattered dark speckles. Throat teeth 4-4.

Life Colors: Back pale olive-yellow, the scales prominently dark-edged. Sides silvery, often with a faint dusky stripe. Belly silvery-white. Fins plain. Breeding males are without special colors but have very small tubercles over top of head and along rays of pectoral fin.

Variation: Two recognized subspecies of the mimic shiner occur in Missouri. These are the northern mimic shiner, *N. v. volucellus* (Cope), and the channel mimic shiner, *N. v. wickliffi* Trautman. The northern mimic shiner is darker in color, is more slender, and the scales in the forward part of the lateral line are deeper than in the channel mimic shiner. Mimic shiners from Spring River in southwestern Missouri are smaller and chubbier than those from elsewhere and may represent an as yet unnamed subspecies.

Size: Adults are commonly 1.8 to 2.5 inches long to a maximum of about 2.8 inches. Individuals from southwest Missouri are smaller, not known to exceed a length of 2.3 inches.

Scientific name: *Notropis,* Greek, "back keel"; *volucellus,* Latin, meaning "winged or swift."

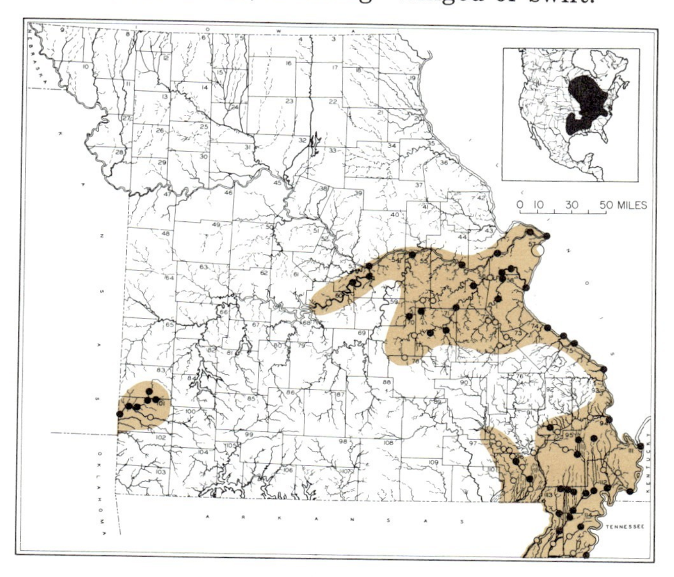

DISTRIBUTION AND HABITAT

The channel mimic shiner occurs in the Missouri and lower Mississippi rivers, possibly intergrading with the northern mimic shiner in the lower few miles of major tributary streams. The northern mimic shiner is found in the larger Lowland ditches of southeastern Missouri, in the lower sections of some Ozark streams entering the Lowlands, and in the Osage and Meramec systems of east-central Missouri. The unnamed subspecies is common in the lower part of Spring River and its tributaries in southwestern Missouri.

The subspecies of the mimic shiner occupy quite different habitats. The channel mimic shiner inhabits the main channels of very large, moderately clear to highly turbid rivers. It may have only recently invaded the lower Missouri River. The northern mimic shiner inhabits clear streams ranging in size from medium-sized creeks to rather large rivers. It occurs most abundantly near riffles in noticeable current. The habitat of the mimic shiner in Spring River is like that described for the northern mimic shiner.

HABITS AND LIFE HISTORY

The mimic shiner lives in schools in midwater or near the surface. The channel mimic shiner is most often found with the ghost, emerald, silverband and river shiners. The northern mimic shiner commonly occurs with the wedgespot, rosyface, bleeding, weed and ribbon shiners. In Indiana lakes the northern mimic shiner feeds mostly on small crustaceans and insects, and some algae.[101]

In Missouri adults of the mimic shiner in spawning condition have been collected from early June to late July, indicating an early summer spawning season. The spawning habits are not known. Females of the northern mimic shiner grow more rapidly and attain a larger size than males.[101] The maximum life span in Indiana is 2 years with most of the spawning population made up of fish in their second summer.

Ghost Shiner

Notropis buchanani Meek

DESCRIPTION

Illustration: Page 125, 63a.

Characters: A very pale, rather deep and slab-sided minnow with large eyes and a small, oblique mouth. Barbels absent. Anal fin with 8 (rarely 7 or 9) rays. Front of dorsal fin base about equidistant between tip of snout and base of tail fin. Depth of scales in lateral line becoming greater toward the head. Tips of pelvic fins reaching to or beyond front of anal fin (except in females swollen with eggs). Dorsal fin very high and pointed. Sensory canal beneath eye absent or represented only by a short section of tube. Lateral line scales 30 to 35. Intestine short, with a single S-shaped loop; lining of body cavity silvery, without dark speckles. Throat teeth 4-4.

Life colors: Back pale yellowish-white, the scales sometimes faintly dark-edged. Sides and belly silvery-white, usually with no dark markings of any kind. Fins plain. Breeding males are without special colors but have small tubercles over most of head, forward part of body, and along rays of pectoral fin; tubercles largest on snout and top of head.

Size: Most adults are 1.5 to 2.0 inches long. The ghost shiner is one of the smallest Missouri minnows, not known to exceed a length of 2.0 inches.

Scientific name: *Notropis,* Greek, "back keel"; *buchanani,* named for Dr. J. L. Buchanan, then president of Arkansas Industrial University.

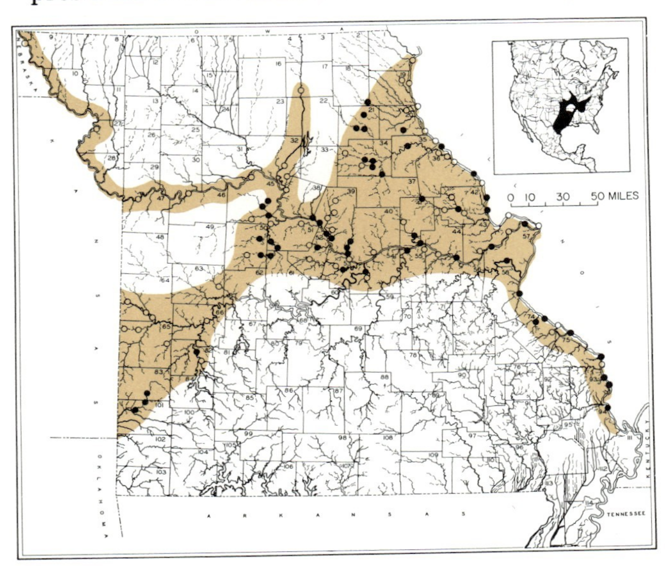

DISTRIBUTION AND HABITAT

The ghost shiner occurs in streams along a broad, northeastward-trending band from the Spring River in the southwest to the Salt and Mississippi rivers in the northeast. In the Mississippi the ghost shiner occurs at least as far south as Cape Girardeau. It is seldom abundant but is more common in the Prairie streams of central and northeastern Missouri than elsewhere.

This minnow is characteristic of the low-gradient sections of large creeks and rivers having permanent flow and moderately clear water. It is a quiet-water species, inhabiting larger pools and protected backwaters without noticeable current.

HABITS AND LIFE HISTORY

The ghost shiner lives in schools in midwater and is most often found in association with the mimic, red, and redfin shiners. Its diet has not been studied, but probably consists mostly of insects and other small invertebrates. Spawning in Missouri occurs from late April to early July over sluggish riffles composed of sand or fine gravel. In central Missouri the ghost shiner reaches a length of 1 to 1.5 inches by the end of its first summer, and 1.5 to 2.0 inches by the end of its second summer. Most spawning adults are in their second summer, but a few are in their third summer. Three summers seems to be the maximum life span. Females attain a larger size than males.

Ozark Minnow

Dionda nubila (Forbes)

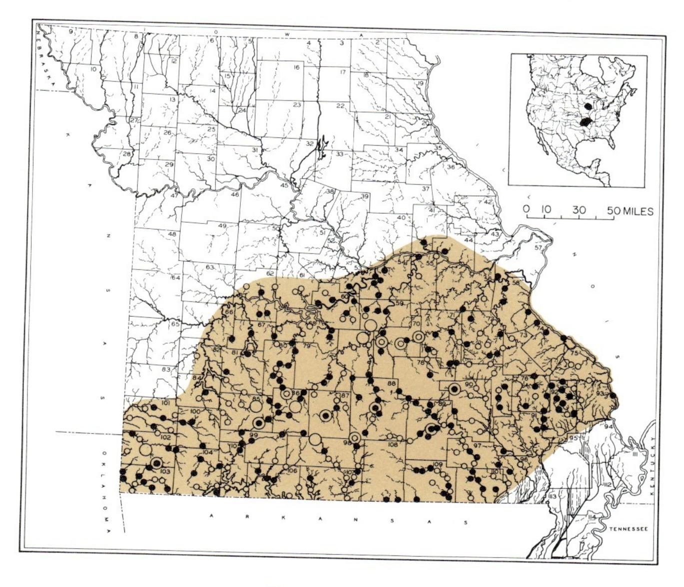

DESCRIPTION

Illustration: Page 106, 24a.
Characters: A slender, silvery minnow with rather large eyes and a terminal, oblique mouth. Barbels absent. Anal fin with 8 rays. Front of dorsal fin base about equidistant between tip of snout and base of tail fin. Midside with a prominent dusky stripe that extends forward onto snout. Dark stripe along midline of back very distinct. Superficially similar in appearance to some shiners (*Notropis*), but differs in having a long, many-looped intestine. Lining of body cavity uniformly black. Lateral line scales 33 to 37. Throat teeth 4-4; teeth short and hooked near tips.
Life colors: Back and upper sides dark yellowish-olive, the scales faintly dark-edged. Midline of back with a prominent dusky stripe overlain by a series of golden spots that are quite conspicuous when fish is in the water. Side silvery with a prominent dusky stripe. Belly silvery-white. Tail fin sometimes with a small black spot at base; fins otherwise plain. In breeding males lower half of body and all fins are tinged with yellowish-orange; granular tubercles are present over most of head, body, and all fins except tail fin. Breeding colors and tubercles somewhat developed in females.
Size: Adults are commonly 2.2 to 2.8 inches long to a maximum of about 3 inches.
Scientific name: *Dionda,* Greek from *Dione,* a name for the mother of Venus; *nubila,* Latin meaning "dusky" in reference to the body color.

DISTRIBUTION AND HABITAT

The Ozark minnow is well named, for it is one of the most common and characteristic minnows in the Ozark Uplands. It occurs in all the principal Ozark stream systems and its range corresponds closely to the limits of that region in Missouri. It is almost invariably found with either the bleeding shiner or duskystripe shiner and its distribution in the state parallels the combined distribution of these two closely related species to a remarkable degree. Thus, both the Ozark minnow and bleeding shiner are abundant and widespread in the Meramec system, but neither occurs in the Bourbeuse River or the Dry Fork of the Meramec.

The Ozark minnow inhabits streams with a predominance of gravelly or rocky bottoms and permanent strong flow. It is most often found in protected backwaters near riffles or in pools immediately below riffles where the current slackens.

HABITS AND LIFE HISTORY

The Ozark minnow lives in schools near the bottom and is most often found in association with the bleeding, duskystripe, rosyface, telescope, and wedgespot shiners, and the largescale and central stonerollers. Its food habits have not been studied, but the long intestine and the presence of grinding surfaces on the teeth suggest a diet containing much plant material.

Spawning of the Ozark minnow in Missouri occurs from late April to early July but reaches a peak in May and June. Like the bleeding shiner, this minnow spawns over nests of the hornyhead chub. The Ozark minnow and bleeding shiner often spawn at the same time and place, and hybrids are common. Spawning groups of the two species usually remain separate, with those of the Ozark minnow being beneath or downstream from those of the bleeding shiner. Breeding males of the Ozark minnow are less territorial than males of the bleeding shiner. Growth of the Ozark minnow has not been studied. Females attain a larger size than males.

Silverjaw Minnow

Ericymba buccata Cope

DESCRIPTION

Illustration: Page 109, 31a.
Characters: A slender, silvery minnow with large eyes and a small, nearly horizontal mouth.

Barbels absent. Anal fin with 8 (occasionally 7) rays. Head long, its undersurface distinctly flattened. Undersurface and lower sides of head with numerous internal tubular channels that appear externally as translucent or whitish streaks. Front of dorsal fin base slightly closer to tip of snout than to base of tail fin. Intestine short, with a single S-shaped loop; lining of body cavity silvery with a few scattered dark speckles. Throat teeth 4-4 or 1,4-4,1.

Life colors: Back pale olive-yellow, the scales faintly dark-edged. Sides silvery, sometimes with an indistinct dusky stripe that fades out towards head. Belly silvery-white. Fins plain. Breeding males are without special colors or tubercles.

Size: Adults are commonly 1.7 to 2.5 inches long to a maximum of about 3 inches.

Scientific name: *Ericymba,* Greek, "cavity," a reference to the development of channels in the head; *buccata,* Latin, meaning "cheek."

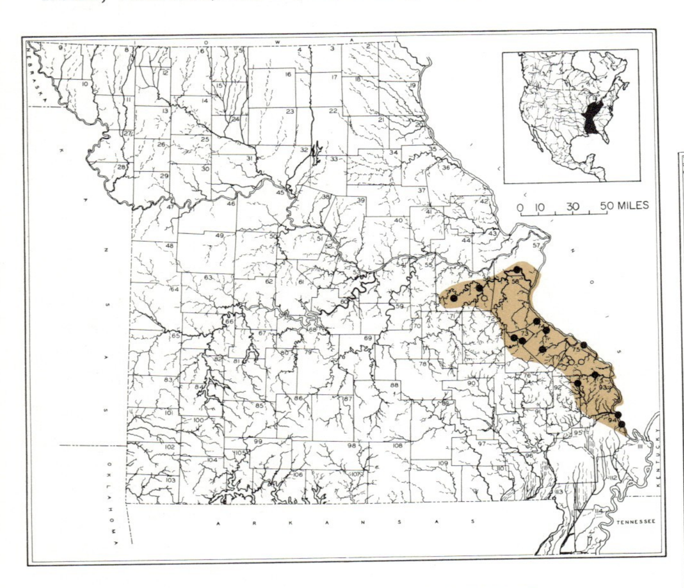

DISTRIBUTION AND HABITAT

The silverjaw minnow occurs at a few scattered localities in the Meramec River system and southward in direct tributaries of the Mississippi River to the Headwater Diversion. Although not widely distributed, it is common at most localities where it occurs.

The silverjaw is found over the shallow, sandy stretches of small, clear, permanent-flowing streams. It seems to be the ecological counterpart of the plains-inhabiting bigmouth shiner and replaces that species in the clearer and more stable streams of the Mississippi Valley from Missouri eastward.

HABITS AND LIFE HISTORY

The silverjaw minnow lives in schools on or near the bottom. In Missouri it is commonly found in association with the sand shiner, bigeye shiner, bigeye chub, and bluntnose minnow. In Kentucky the silverjaw minnow feeds from the layer of algae growing over the stream bottom, in mixed species groups that include the bluntnose minnow and stoneroller.[102] The latter two species feed on the algae while the silverjaw minnow feeds on insect larvae exposed by their feeding activities. Midges and mayflies are the principal insects eaten.

In Kentucky this species spawns from March through June with a peak of activity in April.[103] Actual spawning has not been observed but presumably occurs in shallow areas above gravelly or sandy riffles. In Kentucky the silverjaw averages 1.9 inches when one year old and averages 2.6 and 3 inches in succeeding years.[104] Some individuals are sexually mature when one year of age but most do not mature until their second year. The normal life span is 3 years.

Central Silvery Minnow

Hybognathus nuchalis Agassiz

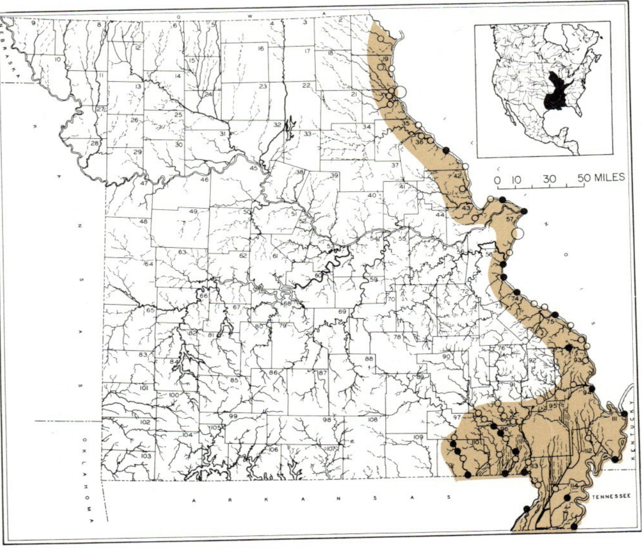

DESCRIPTION

Illustration: Page 108, 28b.

Characters: A rather stout, silvery minnow with moderately small eyes and a small, slightly oblique mouth (front of upper lip below middle of eye). Barbels absent. Anal fin with 8 rays. Midline of back with a prominent dark stripe broader than dorsal fin base. No prominent dusky stripe along midside. Dorsal fin distinctly pointed at tip. Scales in adults with about 10 radiating lines (radii). Front of dorsal fin base usually slightly closer to tip of snout than to base of tail fin. Lateral line scales 34 to 40. Intestine long, with many loops; lining of body cavity uniformly black. Throat teeth 4-4; teeth long and not hooked near tips.

Very similar to western silvery minnow, page 169, and plains minnow, page 170, but differing in the following respects: eye slightly larger, its diameter going 3.6 to 4.2 times into head length; diameter of eye greater than width of mouth opening; basioccipital process (a backward extension of bone at lower rear margin of skull) broad and blade-like, its back margin deeply concave; greatest width of basioccipital process going 0.9 to 1.3 times into its greatest length; muscles of pharyngeal arches widely separate at point of attachment to rear part of basioccipital process.

Life colors: Back yellowish-olive, with emerald reflections and a broad dusky or greenish-golden stripe along its midline. Sides silvery, sometimes with scattered dusky flecks towards head but without a dusky stripe. Belly silvery-white. Fins plain. Breeding males are without special colors but have very small tubercles on head, forward part of body, and on all fins except tail fin.

Size: Adults are commonly 3 to 5 inches long to a maximum of about 6 inches.

Scientific name: *Hybognathus*, Greek, "swollen jaw"; *nuchalis*, Latin, pertaining to the nape.

DISTRIBUTION AND HABITAT

The central silvery minnow is abundant in the lower Current, Black, and St. Francis rivers, and the lower sections of some of the larger ditches of the Lowlands. It occurs along the full length of the Mississippi River but is far more common below the mouth of the Ohio River than above. It now seems rare in the upper Mississippi River and its tributaries but occurred commonly in collections made in that area 30 years ago. The reasons for this decline are not known.

The central silvery minnow is most abundant in the low-gradient sections of clear, moderately large streams. It seems intolerant of continuous high turbidity, as indicated by marked reduction in abundance in the Mississippi River above the point where that stream receives the clear waters of the Ohio River. It avoids strong currents and occurs most abundantly in pools and backwaters over a silt or sand bottom.

HABITS AND LIFE HISTORY

The central silvery minnow lives near the bottom in large schools and is most often found in association with the bullhead minnow and the blacktail, ribbon, and weed shiners. It feeds by scraping up mud and bottom ooze from which it digests out the algae and other living or dead organic matter.[24]

Its breeding habits have not been studied but are probably like those of its east coast relative, *Hybognathus regius* Girard. This minnow is unique in that the non-adhesive eggs are deposited in quiet water over a silt bottom.[105] Males do not hold territories and do not seem to be aggressive towards each other. When spawning, the females may be accompanied by as many as 10 males, but usually only one male on either side of her participates in the spawning act. Spawning is accompanied by rapid vibrations that stir the bottom and muddy the water. Adults of the central silvery minnow in spawning condition have been taken in early June at the latitude of Missouri.[24] In southeast Missouri this minnow reaches a length of about 1.4 to 2.6 inches by the end of its first summer of life and is 3 to 3.5 inches long by the end of its second summer.

Western Silvery Minnow

Hybognathus argyritis Girard

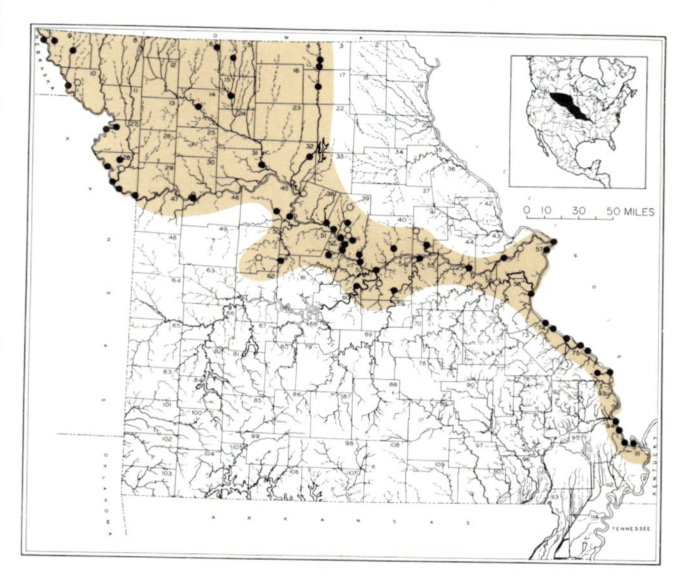

DESCRIPTION

Illustration: Page 108, 28a.

Characters: Very similar to central silvery minnow, page 168, but differing in the following respects: eye slightly smaller, its diameter going 4 to 4.8 times into head length; diameter of eye less than or equal to width of mouth opening; basioccipital process (a backward extension of bone at lower rear margin of skull) broad and blade-like, its back margin straight or only slightly concave; greatest width of basioccipital process going 1.2 to 1.8 times into its greatest length; muscles of pharyngeal arches moderately well separated at point of attachment to rear part of basioccipital process.

Life colors: Like those of central silvery minnow, page 168.

Size: Adults are commonly 3 to 5 inches long. Maximum length in Missouri about 5.4 inches.

Scientific name: *Hybognathus*, Greek, "swollen

jaw"; *argyritis,* Greek for "silvery," in reference to the color.

DISTRIBUTION AND HABITAT

The western silvery minnow occurs most commonly in the Missouri River and its larger tributaries of the Prairie Region. It also occurs in the Mississippi downstream from the mouth of the Missouri at least to Scott County, but it is rare there. This minnow is decidedly less abundant than the closely related plains minnow in the Missouri River and in the larger prairie streams from Grand River westward. Eastward, it is more abundant than the plains minnow in most tributary streams.

Habitat requirements are similar to those of the central silvery minnow, page 168, except that it seems more tolerant of high turbidity. It is generally found over a silt or sand bottom in the backwaters and pools of large streams and in the quiet lower reaches of their tributaries.

HABITS AND LIFE HISTORY

The habits and life history of this minnow are not well known but are probably similar to those of the central silvery minnow. It lives in schools near the bottom and is often found in association with the plains minnow, silver and flathead chubs, and the red, sand, and emerald shiners. Adults in breeding condition have been collected in Missouri in late June. Young collected in late August average slightly smaller than those of the central silvery minnow, suggesting a later spawning season or slower growth.

Plains Minnow

Hybognathus placitus Girard

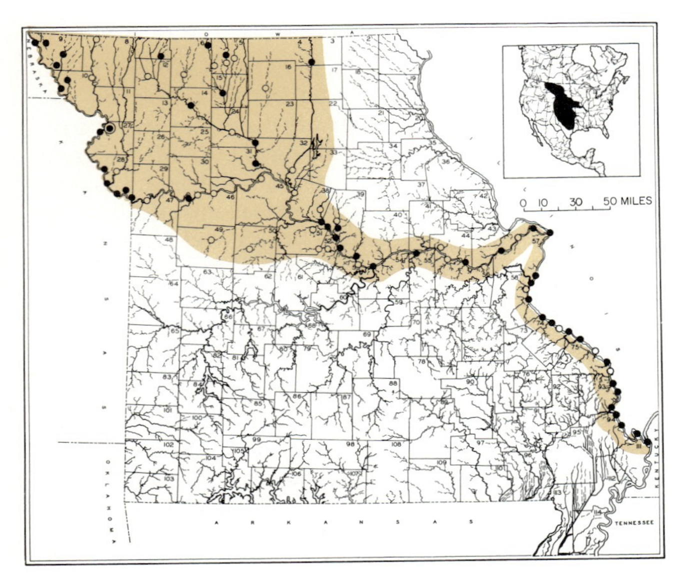

DESCRIPTION

Illustration: Page 107, 27a.

Characters: Very similar to central silvery minnow, page 168, but differing in these respects: eye smaller, its diameter going 4.4 to 4.9 times into head length; diameter of eye much less than width of mouth opening; basioccipital process (a backward extension of bone at lower rear margin of skull) narrow and peg-like, its back margin nearly straight; greatest width of basioccipital process going 2.4 to 4 times into its greatest length; muscles of pharyngeal arches nearly touching at point of attachment to basioccipital process.

Life colors: Like those of central silvery minnow, page 168.

Size: About the same as central silvery minnow.

Scientific name: *Hybognathus,* Greek, "swollen jaw"; *placitus,* Greek, meaning "a broad surface," perhaps in reference to the thickish snout.

DISTRIBUTION AND HABITAT

The distribution of the plains minnow is similar to that of the western silvery minnow, differing notably only in that it is somewhat more widespread in western tributaries of the Missouri River and enters tributary streams from the Chariton River eastward less frequently than the western silvery minnow. The plains minnow is the most abundant minnow in the upper Missouri River but undergoes a gradual decline in abundance downstream. It is uncommon in the lower Mississippi, reaching the downstream limit of its distribution near the mouth of the Ohio River.

Although the plains and western silvery minnows occur at the same localities they tend to be segregated ecologically; the plains minnow predominates in the river channel where there is a sandy bottom and some current, whereas the western silvery minnow is more abundant in protected areas with little current and a silt bottom.

HABITS AND LIFE HISTORY

The habits and life history of the plains minnow are not known in detail but seem to be like those of the silvery minnows. It lives in schools near the bottom and occurs in association with the same species as the western silvery minnow. The plains minnow spawns in Kansas from April into August, probably utilizing shallow backwaters for this purpose.[42] In Grand River it reaches a length of about 1.1 to 1.7 inches by early September of its first summer of life.

Cypress Minnow

Hybognathus hayi Jordan

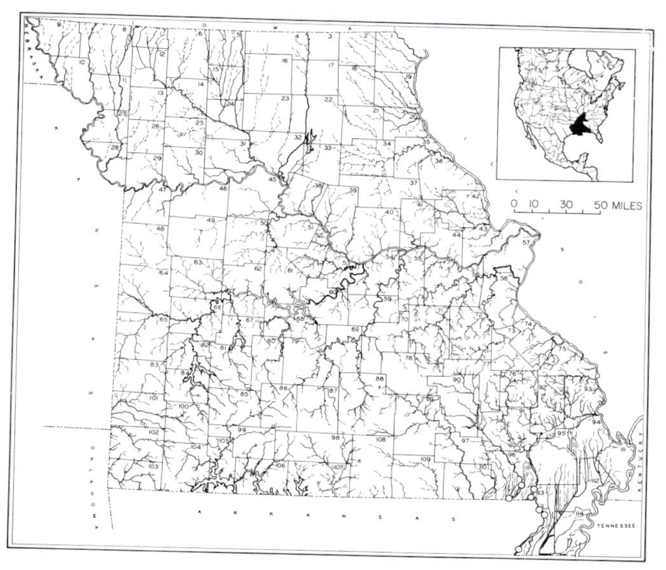

DESCRIPTION

Illustration: Page 107, 26a.

Characters: Very similar to central silvery minnow, page 168, but with the following differences: body deeper and more slab-sided; mouth more oblique, the front of upper lip above middle of eye; eye larger, its diameter going 3.4 to 3.8 times into head length; scales on forward part of side more distinctly dark-edged, forming a diamond-shaped pattern of cross-hatchings; basioccipital process (extension of bone at lower rear margin of skull) more or less intermediate in size and shape between central silvery minnow and western silvery minnow.

Life colors: Like central silvery minnow, page 168, except as noted under *Characters.*

Size: About the same as central silvery minnow.

Scientific name: *Hybognathus,* Greek, "swollen jaw"; *hayi,* named for Dr. O. P. Hay, discoverer of the species.

DISTRIBUTION AND HABITAT

The cypress minnow formerly occurred in the lower Black and St. Francis rivers where it was more common than the central silvery minnow. However, it has not been collected there for many years and probably no longer occurs in the state.

It is a Lowland species inhabiting the sluggish pools of low-gradient streams. It commonly occurs with the central silvery minnow, indicating that their habitat requirements are similar.

HABITS AND LIFE HISTORY

No information is available on the habits and life history of this minnow.

Brassy Minnow

Hybognathus hankinsoni Hubbs

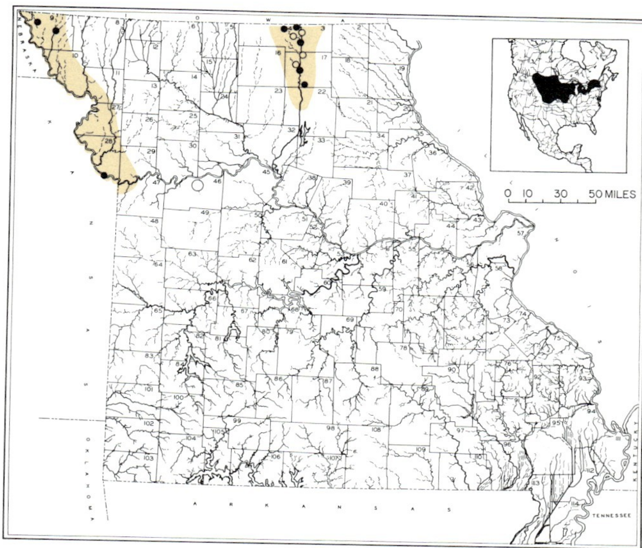

DESCRIPTION

Illustration: Page 106, 25a.

Characters: Similar to central silvery minnow, page 168, but with the following differences: dorsal fin distinctly rounded at tip; scales in adults with about 20 radiating lines (radii); color in life usually brassy-yellow; basioccipital process (an extension of bone at lower rear margin of skull) similar in shape to that of western silvery minnow but slightly narrower.

Life colors: Like those of central silvery minnow, page 168, except as noted under *Characters.*

Size: Smaller than central silvery minnow. Adults are commonly 2.4 to 3.3 inches long to a maximum of about 3.5 inches.

Scientific name: *Hybognathus,* Greek, "swollen jaw"; *hankinsoni,* named for T. L. Hankinson, known for his studies of the breeding habits of freshwater fishes.

DISTRIBUTION AND HABITAT

The brassy minnow is common in a few small tributaries of the upper Chariton River and occurs rarely in the Missouri River and its tributaries westward in the Prairie Region.

It inhabits small, moderately clear prairie streams having permanent pools and sandy or gravelly bottoms.

HABITS AND LIFE HISTORY

The brassy minnow lives in schools on or near the bottom. It commonly occurs in association with the fathead minnow and the bigmouth, red, and sand shiners. This minnow ingests the thin layer of organic-rich ooze that forms over the stream bottom from which it digests out the algae and other organic material.[71] It evidently spawns early in the spring, since young ranging in length from 1.2 to 1.8 inches have been collected from tributaries of the Chariton River in late June.

Bullhead Minnow

Pimephales vigilax (Baird and Girard)

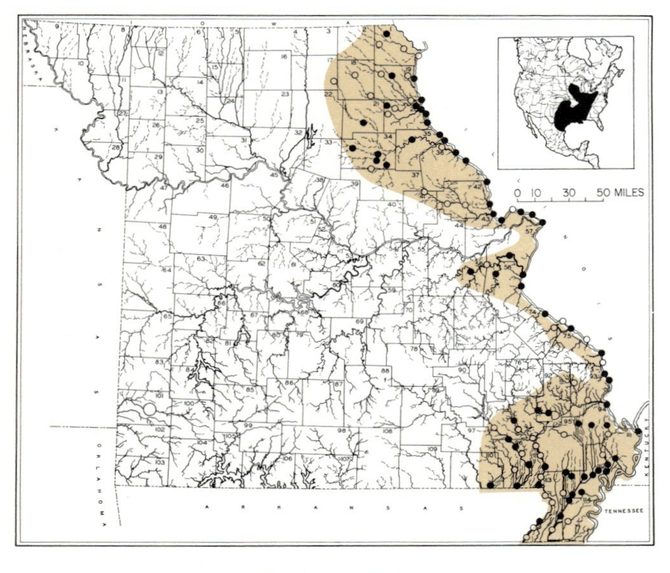

DESCRIPTION

Illustration: Page 98, 9a.

Characters: A stout-bodied minnow with a blunt, rounded snout and short, rounded fins. Barbels absent. Anal fin with 7 rays. Body surface in front of dorsal fin broad, rather flat, and covered with scales that are much smaller and more crowded than those on adjacent parts of sides. Tail fin with a prominent dark spot at base; dorsal fin with a dusky or black blotch near front, about a third of way up from base (blotch absent in small young). Short ray at front of dorsal fin thickened, rather than splint-like, and separated from first principal ray by a membrane. Mouth terminal and slightly oblique. Lateral line complete with 37 to 42 scales. Intestine short, with a single S-shaped loop; lining of body cavity silvery with scattered dark speckles. Throat teeth 4-4.

Similar to slim minnow, page 173, but with the following differences: scales above lateral line 7 or 8 (rarely 6); upper lip only slightly thickened at middle; dusky stripe along underside of caudal peduncle broader and less distinct than in slim minnow; body width about equal to distance from ridge of back to lateral line.

Life colors: Back pale yellowish-olive without definite dark edgings on scales or a prominent dusky stripe along midline. Sides silvery with distinct dark borders on lateral line pores. Dusky stripe along midside faint or absent. Snout with a distinctive crescent-shaped dark mark on each side above upper lip. Dorsal and tail fins marked as indicated under *Characters;* fins otherwise plain. Breeding males are dark, the head nearly black, and have 2 rows of large tubercles on snout and a fleshy, whitish pad on forward part of back.

Size: Adults are commonly 1.5 to 3 inches long to a maximum of about 3.5 inches.

Scientific name: *Pimephales,* Greek, "fat head"; *vigilax,* Latin, meaning "watchful."

DISTRIBUTION AND HABITAT

The bullhead minnow is widespread in the Lowlands and occurs northward in the Mississippi River and its tributaries to the Iowa line. In the Lowlands it is second in abundance only to the blacktail shiner. Elsewhere in its Missouri range it is common at most localities. This minnow is known in the Spring River of southwest Missouri only from a single old collection but is common in adjacent streams of Kansas.

It inhabits sluggish pools and backwaters of medium-sized to large streams having continuous flow and low to moderate gradients. It avoids strong current but is fairly tolerant of turbidity and siltation.

HABITS AND LIFE HISTORY

The bullhead minnow lives in schools, occurring in association with the central silvery minnow, the silver chub, and the blacktail, emerald, river, and red shiners. It feeds on or near the bottom and its diet consists mostly of insects.[71] Some plant material, including the seeds and fruits of higher plants, are also eaten.

Spawning occurs in late spring and early summer in a cavity excavated by the male beneath a stone, tree limb, or other object lying on the bottom.[106] The eggs are attached to the upper surface of the nest cavity and are guarded continuously by the male until they hatch. The male is very aggressive, driving other fish away by butting them with the tubercle-covered snout. The eggs are kept free of sediments by brushing them with the fleshy pad on the back. At a temperature of 79-83°F the eggs hatch in about 4½ days.

In Missouri the bullhead minnow reaches a length of 0.9 to 2.2 inches by the end of its first summer of life. Males grow more rapidly and attain a larger size than females.

Slim Minnow

Pimephales tenellus (Girard)

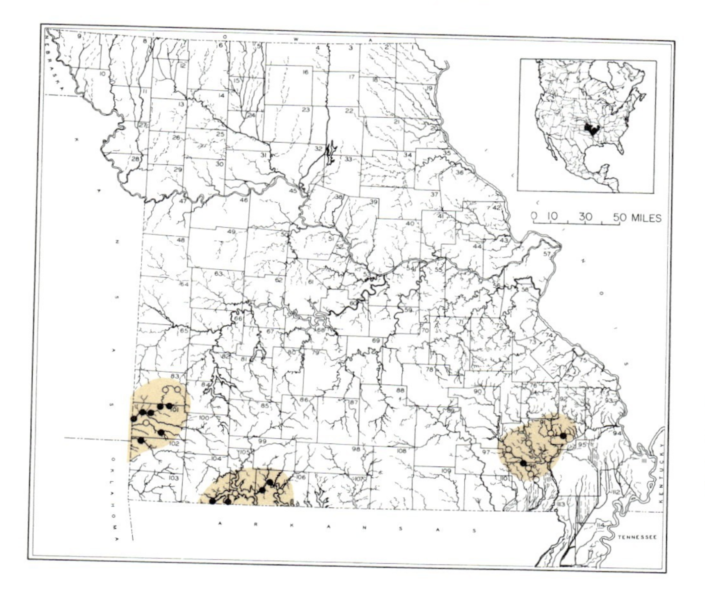

DESCRIPTION

Illustration: Page 98, 9b.

Characters: Similar to bullhead minnow, page 172, but with the following differences: scales above lateral line 6 (rarely 5 or 7); upper lip considerably thickened at middle; dusky stripe along underside of caudal peduncle narrower and more distinct than in bullhead minnow; body width about one scale heighth greater than distance from ridge of back to lateral line.

Variation: Two well-marked subspecies of the slim minnow occur in Missouri. These are the western slim minnow, *P. t. tenellus* (Girard), and the eastern slim minnow, *P. t. parviceps* (Hubbs and Black). The eastern slim minnow is more slender, the body depth usually going more than 5 times into the standard length. Also, the snout projects slightly beyond the upper lip in the eastern subspecies, while the upper lip is terminal in the western subspecies.

Life colors: Like those of the bullhead minnow, page 172, except that the scales of the back are more prominently dark-edged, the dusky stripe along the midside is more prominent, and fins are often tinged with orange. Also, the pectoral fin of breeding males is mostly black with its leading edge white, whereas the pattern is reversed in the bullhead minnow.

Size: Adults are commonly 1.5 to 2.5 inches long to a maximum of about 2.7 inches.

Scientific name: *Pimephales,* Greek, "fat-head"; *tenellus,* Latin, meaning "delicate," perhaps in reference to the slender form.

DISTRIBUTION AND HABITAT

The western slim minnow is confined to the Spring River and its larger tributaries of southwestern Missouri, while its eastern counterpart occurs in the White, Black, St. Francis, and Castor rivers to the east. The western slim minnow is common within its area of occurrence in the state. The eastern slim minnow is rare and may have been eliminated from the White River by impoundment of Bull Shoals and Table Rock reservoirs.

The streams in which the western slim minnow occurs are warmer and more sluggish than typical Ozark streams. Its habitat preferences are much like those of the bullhead minnow but it tends to occupy smaller streams. The eastern slim minnow inhabits clearer, swifter streams than its western counterpart. Both subspecies are usually found in quiet water over a sandy, gravelly, or rocky bottom.

HABITS AND LIFE HISTORY

The slim minnow lives in schools in midwater or near the bottom. Breeding adults have been collected in Kansas from May to July and spawning presumably occurs on swift riffles.[42] Nothing else is known of the habits and life history of this minnow.

Bluntnose Minnow

Pimephales notatus (Rafinesque)

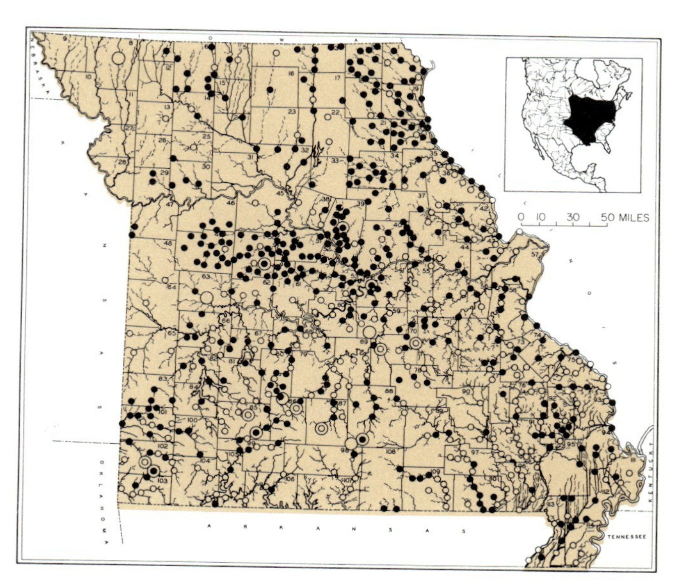

DESCRIPTION

Illustration: Page 99, 10a.

Characters: A slender minnow with a blunt, rounded snout and short, rounded fins. Barbels absent (breeding males have a barbel-like projection at corner of mouth). Anal fin with 7 rays. Body squarish in cross-section. Body surface in front of dorsal fin broad, rather flat, and covered with scales that are smaller and more crowded than those on adjacent parts of sides. Tail fin with a prominent black spot at base; dorsal fin often with a dusky blotch near front about a third of way up from base. Short ray at front of dorsal fin thickened, rather than splint-like, and separate from first principal ray. Mouth slightly over-hung by snout and nearly horizontal. Upper lip about same width at middle as on either side. Lateral line complete. Lateral line scales 39 to 44. Intestine long, with several loops; lining of body cavity black. Throat teeth 4-4.

Life colors: Back olive-yellow, the scales prominently dark-edged; no dusky stripe along midline. Sides silvery with a well developed dusky stripe; scales dark-edged almost to belly forming a characteristic cross-hatched pattern. Belly silvery-white. Dorsal and tail fins marked as indicated under *Characters;* fins otherwise plain. Breeding males very dark, the head nearly black, with 3 rows of large tubercles on snout and a fleshy, whitish pad on forward part of back.

Size: Adults are commonly 1.5 to 3.3 inches long to a maximum of about 3.7 inches.

Scientific name: *Pimephales,* Greek, "fat-head"; *notatus,* Latin, meaning "marked or spotted".

DISTRIBUTION AND HABITAT

The bluntnose minnow is one of the most common and generally distributed Missouri fishes, occurring throughout the state except for the extreme northwest. Only the green sunfish has occurred in more collections. The bluntnose reaches its greatest abundance along the Ozark border and in the northeastern part of the Prairie Region.

This minnow is found in a variety of habitats but is most numerous in the quiet pools and backwaters of medium-sized to moderately large streams having clear, warm waters, permanent flow, and moderate amounts of aquatic vegetation. In the cooler Ozark streams it is most often found in backwaters that are a few degrees warmer than the main channel. In the more turbid and intermittent prairie streams it is largely replaced by the fathead minnow, and in the larger rivers and Lowland ditches it is far outnumbered by the bullhead minnow.

HABITS AND LIFE HISTORY

The bluntnose minnow lives in schools in midwater or near the bottom. Its food habits are generalized and include both plant and animal life.[107] The most important items in its diet are aquatic insects, small crustaceans and algae.

It has a long spawning season, extending in Missouri from early May to about mid-August. The peak of spawning is in late May and June. The breeding habits are similar to those of the bullhead minnow.[108, 109] The eggs are deposited on almost any object lying on the bottom that has a flat undersurface. Usually sand or gravel, rather than a mud bottom, is selected for a nest site. Nest construction consists of excavating a small cavity beneath the object selected and cleaning the undersurfaces where the eggs will be deposited. In excavating the cavity, silt, fine sand, and pebbles are swept away by violent motions of the tail fin and larger objects are pushed out with the tuberculate snout. The roof of the cavity is cleaned by the male with his mouth and the spongy pad on his back. Only a single male occupies a nest but several males often nest in close proximity beneath a single object. Several females may spawn in a single nest which may contain more than 5,000 eggs. Eggs are usually deposited in a single compact layer but occasionally two layers are present. Since spawning may occur at widely spaced intervals, eggs in several stages of development are sometimes present in the same nest. Eggs hatch in 6 to 14 days, depending on water temperature. The male remains on the nest throughout the incubation period, driving away all other fish except females ready to spawn.

In central Missouri streams the bluntnose minnow reaches a length of about 0.9 to 1.8 inches by early November of its first year of life. Males grow more rapidly and attain a larger maximum size than females. Sexual maturity is reached during the second or third summer of life.

IMPORTANCE

This minnow is well suited for propagation in ponds and is often raised for use as bait. It is less prolific and less hardy than the fathead minnow, and therefore is less desirable as a bait species. It thrives in habitats where game fish are abundant and is an important forage fish.

Fathead Minnow

Pimephales promelas Rafinesque

DESCRIPTION

Illustration: Page 99, 10b.

Characters: A chubby, slab-sided minnow with a blunt, rounded snout and short, rounded fins. Barbels absent. Anal fin with 7 rays. Body surface in front of dorsal fin broad, rather flat, and with scales that are smaller and more crowded than those on adjacent parts of sides. Midline of back with a definite dusky stripe. Dark spot at base of tail fin and dusky blotch in forward part of dorsal fin faint or absent. Short ray at front of dorsal fin thickened, rather than splint-like, and separate from first principal ray. Mouth terminal, small, and distinctly oblique. Lateral line incomplete. Scales along midside 42 to 48. Intestine long, with several loops; lining of body cavity black. Throat teeth 4-4.

Life colors: Back pale brown or yellowish-olive, the scales not dark-edged; a definite dusky stripe is developed along its midline. Sides silvery, often with a narrow dusky stripe. Belly silvery-white. Fins without definite markings. Breeding males are mostly black with a broad, yellowish bar encircling body behind head and a similar bar beneath dorsal fin; large tubercles developed on chin and in 3 rows on snout; forward part of back with a fleshy pad.

Size: Adults are commonly 1.6 to 2.8 inches long to a maximum of about 3.2 inches.

Scientific name: *Pimephales,* Greek, "fat-head"; *promelas,* Greek, meaning "before black," perhaps in reference to the darkened head in breeding males.

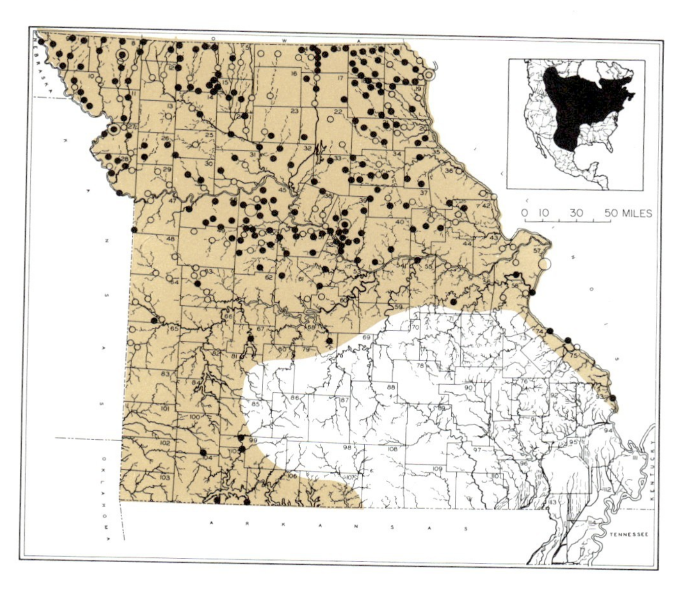

DISTRIBUTION AND HABITAT

The fathead minnow is one of the common and characteristic minnows of the Prairie Region. Most records in the Ozarks are probably based on bait bucket releases or individuals that have escaped from minnow hatcheries. The fathead minnow is rare in natural waters of that region.

This minnow occurs in streams of all sizes but is abundant only in the pools of small, intermittent Prairie creeks. Because of its tolerance for high temperature, extreme turbidity, and low oxygen, the fathead minnow is well suited for survival in the stagnant pools that provide the only refuge for fish in many small Prairie streams during extended dry periods. In such situations the fathead minnow, along with a few other hardy species such as the creek chub, black bullhead, and green sunfish, often comprise the entire fish population. The fathead minnow seems intolerant of competition and is seldom abundant in habitats that support a variety of other fishes.

HABITS AND LIFE HISTORY

The fathead minnow lives in schools in midwater or near the bottom. Its food consists mostly of algae and other plant material, but aquatic insects are also eaten.[71, 110] Spawning occurs in Missouri from the second week of May to early August. Like the bluntnose and bullhead minnows, this species deposits its eggs on submerged objects and the male remains with them until they hatch.[111, 112] A diversity of objects, including boards, rocks, tree roots, or even the underside of lily pads, may be utilized for spawning. As many as 12,000 eggs have been found in a single nest. A female may spawn 12 or more times in a single summer and produce 4,000 or more offspring. In Iowa streams the fathead minnow reaches a length of 1.2 to 2.5 inches by the end of its first year of life and 1.7 to 2.8 inches by the end of its second year.[113] The largest individuals are invariably males. Fry hatched in May sometimes grow to maturity and spawn during their first summer of life, but most do not spawn until their second summer.[112] Spawning mortality is high and the maximum life span seems to be three summers.

IMPORTANCE

The fathead minnow is well suited for propagation in ponds and is produced in large numbers for use as bait. It seldom is sufficiently abundant in waters containing large populations of game fish to be of much value as a forage fish.

Central Stoneroller

Campostoma anomalum (Rafinesque)

DESCRIPTION

Illustration: Page 105, 23a; **38.**

Characters: A slender to moderately stout, brownish-colored minnow with small eyes, and short, rounded fins. Snout bluntly rounded, projecting beyond the nearly horizontal mouth. Barbels absent. Lower jaw with a hard, shelf-like extension (best seen by opening mouth) separated from lower lip by a groove. Anal fin with 7 rays. Scales readily visible without magnification and about as large on back as on adjacent parts of sides. Intestine very long and spirally looped around air bladder. Lining of body cavity black. Throat teeth 4-4.

Very similar to largescale stoneroller but with the following differences: lateral line scales usually 47 to 55; scale rows around body just in front of dorsal fin usually 40 to 55; sum of preceding two counts usually 88 to 101; body stouter. Breeding males have black in anal fin and a row of 1 to 3 tubercles on each side of snout between nostrils.
Life colors: Back and upper sides tan or light brown, often with scattered, blackish scales; lower sides and belly silvery-white. Small young often have a dusky stripe along midside. Fins plain, often tinged with yellow in adults. Breeding males with sides orange-tinged, much orange and black in fins, lips swollen and white, and iris of eye orange-red. Breeding tubercles are better developed in stonerollers than in other Missouri minnows, occurring over most of upper body and head (where they are largest), along some rays of dorsal, tail, and pectoral fins, and on under-surface of head.
Size: Adults are commonly 3 to 6.5 inches long to a maximum of about 7.9 inches.
Scientific name: *Campostoma,* Greek, "curved mouth"; *anomalum,* Latin, meaning "extraordinary."

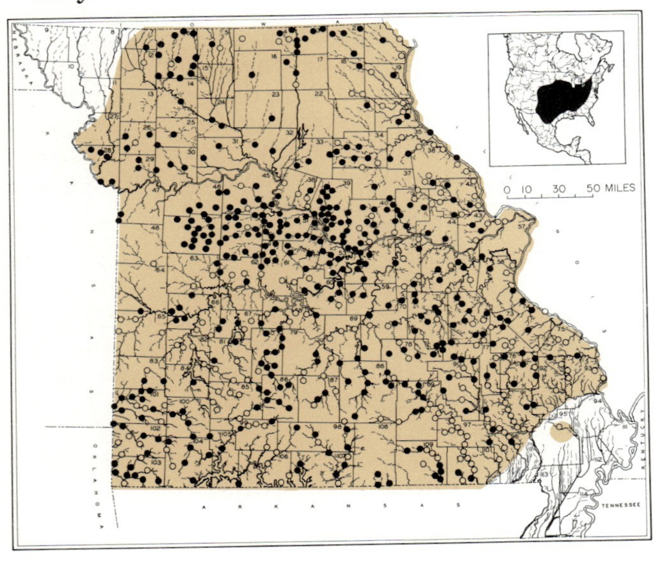

DISTRIBUTION AND HABITAT

The central stoneroller occurs over all of Missouri except the Lowlands and the extreme northwestern part of the Prairie Region. It is one of the most abundant fishes in the Ozarks and adjacent parts of the Prairie Region. It is generally outnumbered by the largescale stoneroller in large to medium-sized Ozark streams but often is the only stoneroller in small headwater creeks.

This minnow occurs most abundantly in streams having moderate or high gradients, well-defined gravel, rubble or bedrock riffles, and permanent flow. It is generally found on riffles or in short, rocky pools where riffles and pools alternate in rapid succession. It seems more tolerant of high turbidity than the largescale stoneroller.

HABITS AND LIFE HISTORY

The central stoneroller lives in schools near the bottom. It feeds primarily on algae and bottom ooze that it scrapes from rocks, logs, and other submerged objects with the blade-like extension of its lower jaw.[248] The large, compact schools of stonerollers grazing slowly over the bottom are one of the characteristic features of Ozark streams.

This fish has the odd habit of coming to the surface of the water at frequent intervals where it leaps vertically clear of the water and sinks again from sight. Where large schools are present stonerollers may often be seen surfacing in this manner almost continuously. This behavior seems to be more frequent on warm days in late fall and early spring than at other times.

The central stoneroller begins spawning earlier in the spring than most other minnows. In Missouri spawning extends from mid-March to late May. The eggs are deposited in shallow pits dug by the males. Pits are located in water ranging from a few inches to a foot or more in depth. Often the pits are on riffles where there is a swift current, but are sometimes in quiet pools. Commonly, the pits are dug in riffles so shallow that the backs of the males are continuously exposed as they work. The main requirements for a spawning site seem to be a bottom composed of small gravel, and a nearby area of deeper water into which the males can retreat when frightened. Individual pits are irregular in outline and several inches across. Usually many males work in close proximity and the pits merge to form a large area of clean gravel with scattered deeper depressions.

Pit construction is accompanied by violent swimming motions in which the males seem to be trying to drive their heads into the bottom. This activity serves to loosen the gravel and brings the finer materials into suspension where it is carried away by the currents. Males then transport gravel from the pits with their mouths or nudge it out with their snouts. Males compete vigorously for favored locations in the pits but do not establish permanent territories. Females remain in deeper water near the spawning area, entering the pits individually or in small groups to deposit their eggs. Spawning occurs as one or more males press against the female. The adhesive eggs become lodged in the gravel and are abandoned before they hatch.

In Big Piney River the central stoneroller reaches a length of about 1.4 to 2.3 inches by late August of its first summer of life. Maturity is reached in the second or third summer. Males grow more rapidly and attain a much larger size than females.

IMPORTANCE

This minnow is an excellent bait for bass and other game fish but is seldom propagated in ponds because it requires flowing water for spawning. It is probably one of the most important forage fishes in Ozark streams. Because of its herbivorous habit it does not compete for food with game fishes and is efficient in converting the basic productivity of the stream into a form that can be used by the smallmouth bass and other desirable stream fishes.

Largescale Stoneroller

Campostoma oligolepis Hubbs and Greene

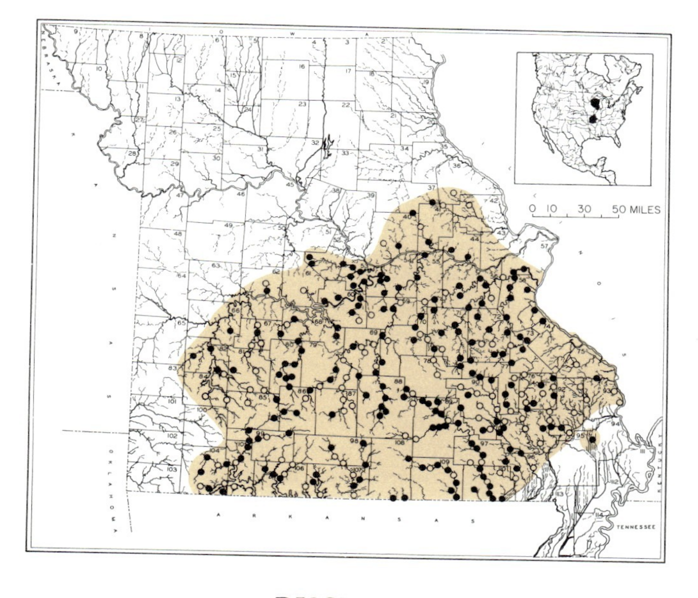

DESCRIPTION

Illustration: Page 105, 23b.

Characters: Very similar to central stoneroller, page 175, but with the following differences: lateral line scales usually 43 to 49; scale rows around body just in front of dorsal fin usually 32 to 39; sum of these two counts usually 75 to 87; body more slender. Breeding males usually without black in anal fin and without a row of tubercles on each side of snout between nostrils.

Life colors: Similar to central stoneroller but slightly darker and more bicolored, the dark upper parts contrasting more sharply with the whitish undersurface. Breeding males differ as indicated under *Characters* and have less orange on the sides; base of the dorsal fin whitish instead of bright orange.

Size: Length range similar to the central stoneroller, page 175.

Scientific name: *Campostoma,* Greek, "curved mouth"; *oligolepis,* Greek, meaning "few scales."

DISTRIBUTION AND HABITAT

The largescale stoneroller is more restricted in distribution than the central stoneroller, being almost strictly an Ozark species in Missouri. It occurs in all the principal stream systems of the Ozarks except the Spring and Elk River systems of southwestern Missouri. The largescale stoneroller is the most abundant fish in many large to medium sized Ozark streams.

The habitat requirements of this minnow are similar to those of the central stoneroller, page 175, except for the preference of the latter species for smaller streams. In the Ozark Uplands the largescale stoneroller is far more abundant than the central stoneroller in the larger rivers, with a shift in abundance favoring the central stoneroller towards the headwaters. I have found no localities in the Ozarks where the largescale stoneroller occurs to the complete exclusion of the central stoneroller.

HABITS AND LIFE HISTORY

The habits and life history of this minnow are much like those of the central stoneroller. It lives in large schools near the bottom and feeds primarily on attached algae scraped from submerged objects. Spawning has been observed in May and the breeding habits are like those of the central stoneroller.

Growth during the first summer of life in Big Piney River does not differ significantly for the two species. Fry of the largescale stoneroller placed by themselves in a small, unfertilized pond near Columbia in mid-May averaged 4.5 inches in length by the following October. This is far more rapid growth than is normally achieved in streams.

SUCKERS

Catostomidae

Except for two or three Asiatic species, the sucker family is restricted to North America. About 100 species are known, of which 18 occur in Missouri.

They are soft-rayed fishes with toothless jaws, a scaleless head, cycloid (smooth-edged) scales on the body, a forked tail fin and a single, continuous dorsal fin. None has more than 10 rays in the anal fin. Suckers are superficially similar to some members of the minnow family but differ in several respects. First of all, they almost always have 10 or more rays in the dorsal fin, whereas native minnows have 8 (in one species 9) rays.

Two introduced minnows, the carp and goldfish, are like the suckers in this character but differ in having a stout, saw-toothed spine at the front of the dorsal and anal fin. In suckers the anal fin is farther back so that the distance from its base to the base of the tail fin goes more than 2½ times into the distance from the anal fin forward to the tip of the snout; in native minnows it goes less than 2½ times. Here again the carp and goldfish are like the suckers rather than the other minnows. The grass carp, another introduced minnow, also resembles the suckers in this character. Both suckers and minnows have teeth in the throat but the teeth of suckers are always in a single row of 20 or more.

The suckers range in size upward from about the point where native minnows leave off. The smallest sucker is the creek chubsucker. It reaches a length of about 9 inches and a weight of about half a pound. The bigmouth buffalo is the giant of the clan. It is reported to reach a length of 3 feet and a weight of over 80 pounds.

Suckers are one of the dominant groups of large fishes in Missouri waters. In streams their total poundage commonly exceeds that of all other fishes combined. Each kind of sucker has its own particular habitat preference. Carpsuckers are the most abundant group in the turbid Prairie streams of north Missouri, while in clear Ozark streams the hogsucker and the redhorse suckers are the most abundant. The white sucker is especially characteristic of spring branches and headwater streams. The buffalofishes are found principally in large streams and lakes.

As their name implies, suckers feed mostly by sucking up material from the bottom. Typically, the mouth is located on the underside of the head and is equipped with fleshy, protrusile lips. The food of most species consists of burrowing insects and small mollusks, along with lesser amounts of plant material. Some suckers take in large quantities of mud from which they extract nonliving organic material and the associated microscopic plant and animal life. Species with more terminal mouths and longer gill rakers feed to a large extent on "water fleas" as well as other small animals and plants that are strained from the water.

Suckers are seldom caught on hook and line but many are taken by snagging and gigging, especially during their spring spawning runs. The buffalofishes rank second in importance to the carp in the commercial fishery of the Mississippi and Missouri rivers. The carpsuckers, redhorse suckers, and the blue sucker are also part of the commercial fishery of these streams. In general, the flesh of suckers has a good flavor, but numerous small bones detract from its value as food. Small suckers are an important source of forage for game fishes. Carpsuckers are sometimes so abundant they are thought to compete for food with more desirable fishes.

Key to the Suckers

1a. Dorsal fin long, with 20 or more principal rays.
Go to 2

1b. Dorsal fin short, with 18 or fewer principal rays.
Go to 8

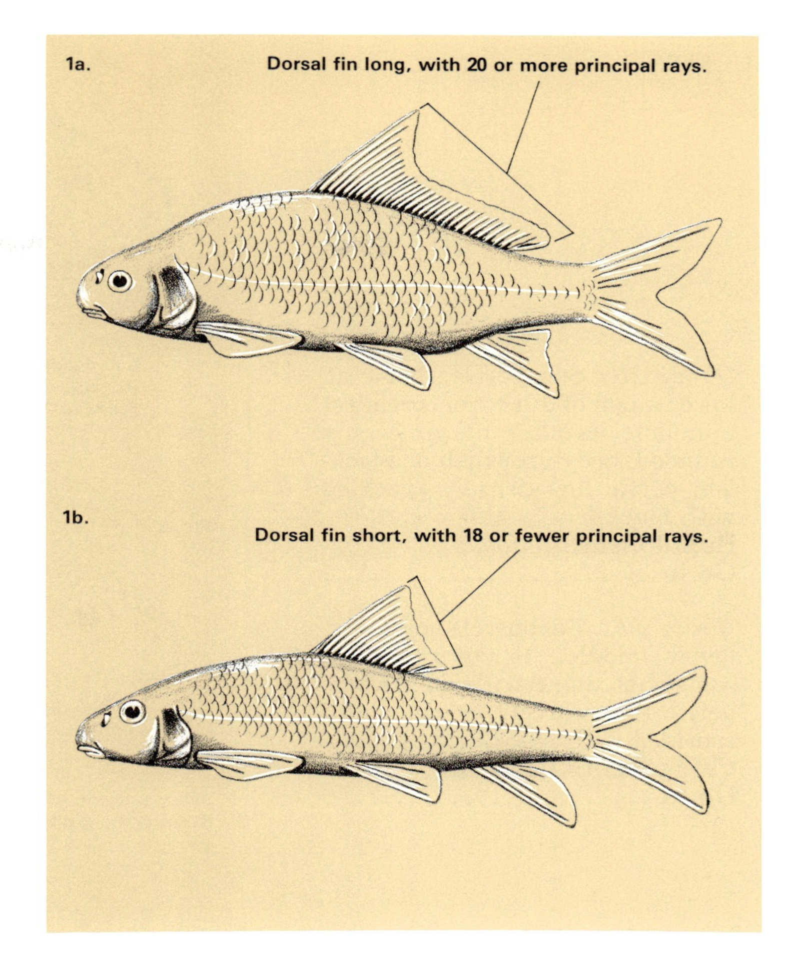
1a.
Dorsal fin long, with 20 or more principal rays.
1b.
Dorsal fin short, with 18 or fewer principal rays.

2a. *(From 1a.)* Snout length (A) greater than distance from back of eye to rear margin of gill cover (B); body slender; lateral line scales more than 50; lips with wart-like projections.
Blue sucker
Cycleptus elongatus **... Page 187**

2b. *(From 1a.)* Snout length (A) less than distance from back of eye to rear margin of gill cover (B); body moderately deep; lateral line scales fewer than 50; lips smooth or with shallow striations.
Go to 3

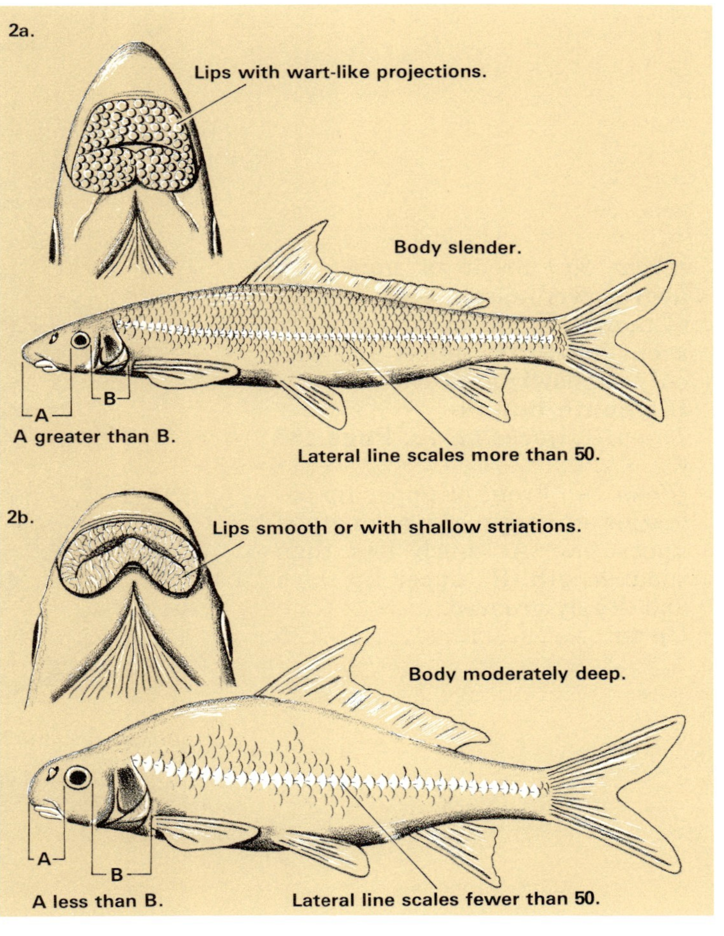
2a.
Lips with wart-like projections.
Body slender.
A
B
A greater than B.
Lateral line scales more than 50.
2b.
Lips smooth or with shallow striations.
Body moderately deep.
A
B
A less than B.
Lateral line scales fewer than 50.

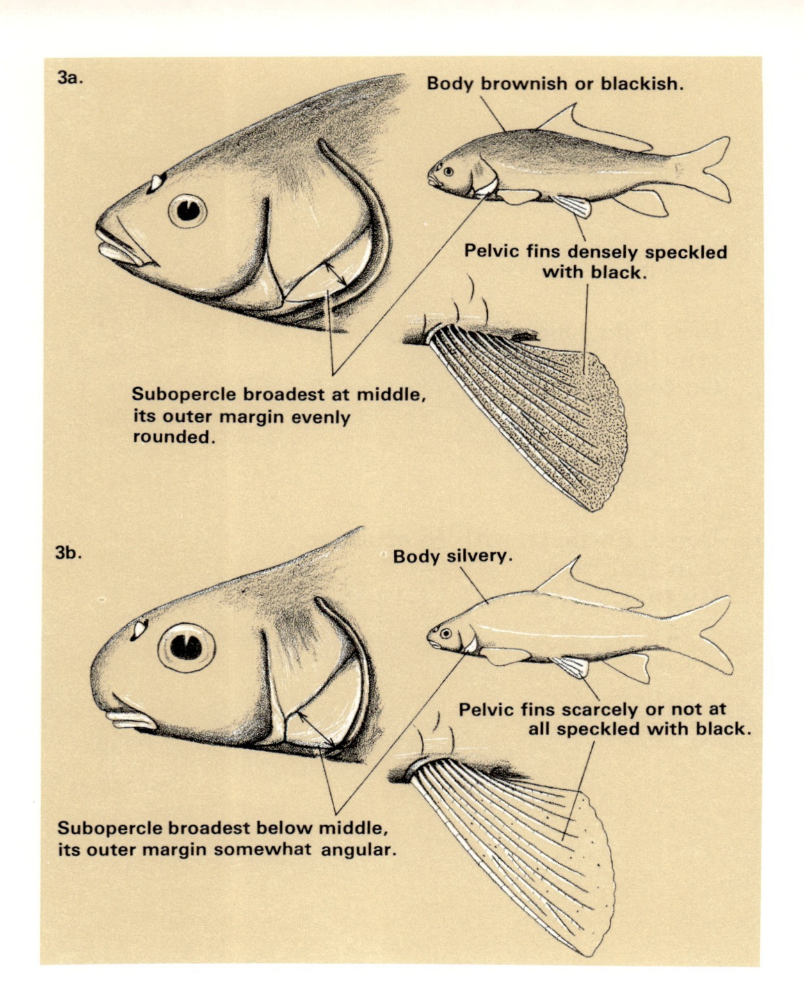
3a.
Body brownish or blackish.
Pelvic fins densely speckled with black.
Subopercle broadest at middle, its outer margin evenly rounded.
3b.
Body silvery.
Pelvic fins scarcely or not at all speckled with black.
Subopercle broadest below middle, its outer margin somewhat angular.

3a. *(From 2b.)* Subopercle (bone at lower angle of gill cover) broadest at middle, its outer margin evenly rounded; body brownish or blackish; pelvic fins densely speckled with black.
Buffalofishes, *Ictiobus*
Go to 4

3b. *(From 2b.)* Subopercle broadest below middle, its outer margin somewhat angular; body silvery; pelvic fins scarcely or not at all speckled with black.
Carpsuckers, *Carpiodes*
Go to 6

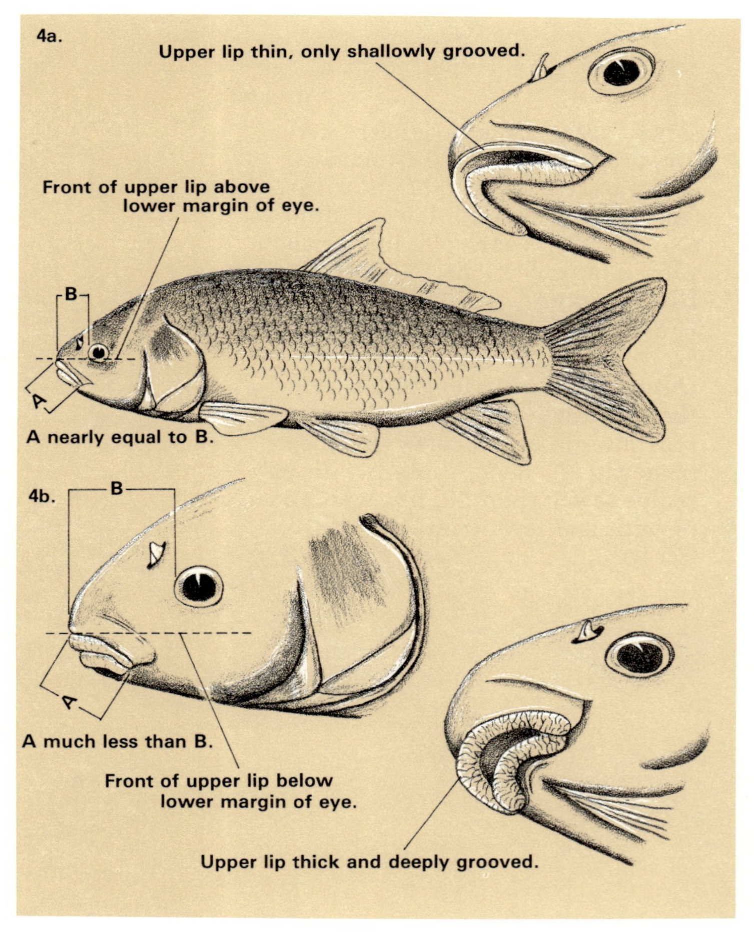
4a.
Upper lip thin, only shallowly grooved.
Front of upper lip above lower margin of eye.
B
A
A nearly equal to B.
4b.
B
A
A much less than B.
Front of upper lip below lower margin of eye.
Upper lip thick and deeply grooved.

4a. *(From 3a.)* Front of upper lip above lower margin of eye; length of upper jaw (A) nearly equal to snout length (B); upper lip thin, only shallowly grooved.
Bigmouth buffalo
Ictiobus cyprinellus **... Page 187**

4b. *(From 3a.)* Front of upper lip below lower margin of eye; length of upper jaw (A) much less than snout length (B); upper lip thick and deeply grooved.
Go to 5

5a. *(From 4b.)* Body depth (A) usually going more than 2.8 times into standard length (B); body width (C) about equal to distance from upper end of gill opening to tip of snout (D); body surface in front of dorsal fin rounded or only weakly keeled.
Black buffalo
Ictiobus niger .... **Page 188**

5b. *(From 4b.)* Body depth (A) usually going 2.8 times or less into standard length (B); body width (C) less than distance from upper end of gill opening to tip of snout (D); body surface in front of dorsal fin strongly keeled.
Smallmouth buffalo
Ictiobus bubalus ..... **Page 189**

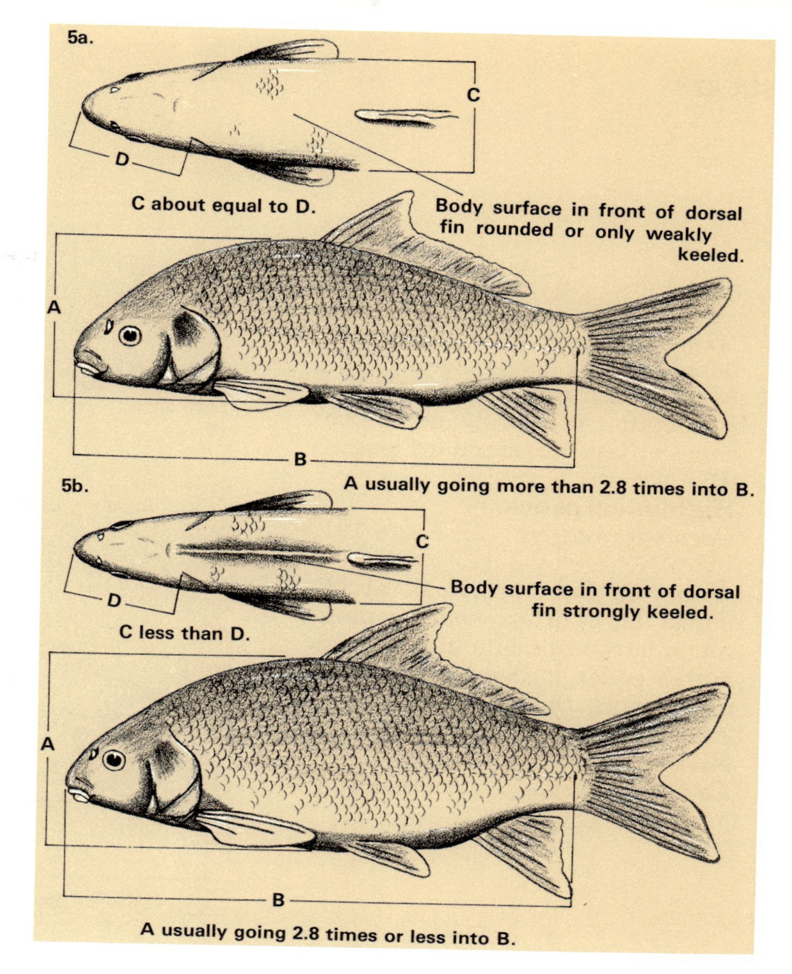

5a.
C
D
C about equal to D.
Body surface in front of dorsal fin rounded or only weakly keeled.
A
B
A usually going more than 2.8 times into B.
5b.
C
D
Body surface in front of dorsal fin strongly keeled.
C less than D.
A
B
A usually going 2.8 times or less into B.

6a. *(From 3b.)* No nipple-like projection at middle of lower lip; upper jaw not extending backward beyond front of eye; snout long, its length (A) about equal to distance from back of eye to upper end of gill opening (B); lateral line scales usually 36 or 37.
Quillback
Carpiodes cyprinus ... **Page 191**

6b. *(From 3b.)* A nipple-like projection at middle of lower lip; upper jaw extending backward beyond front of eye; snout short, its length (A) less than distance from back of eye to upper end of gill opening (B); lateral line scales usually 34 to 36.
Go to **7**

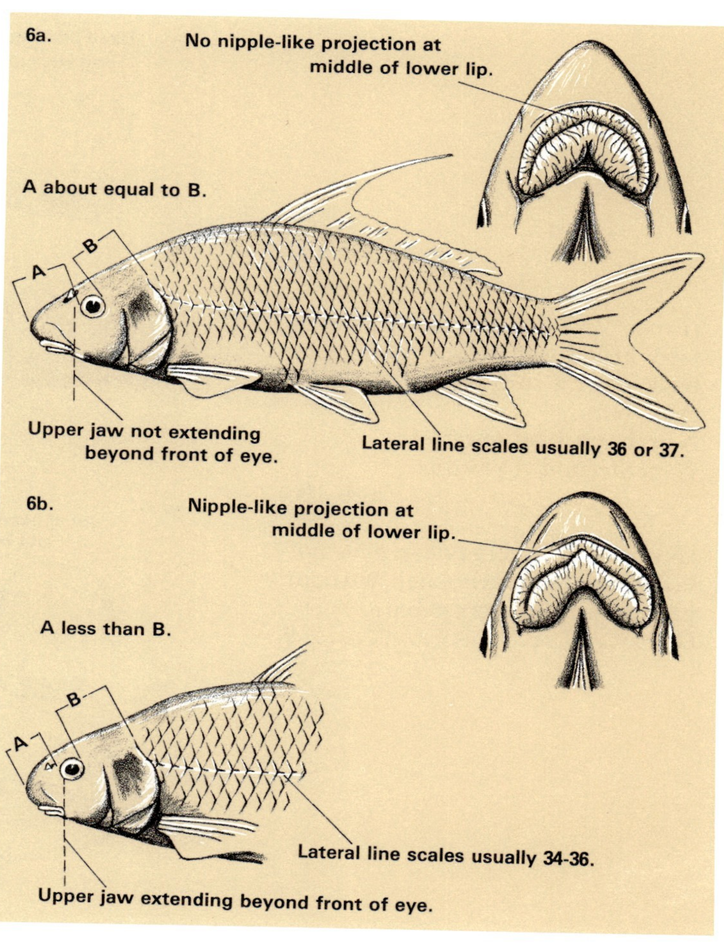

6a.
No nipple-like projection at middle of lower lip.
A about equal to B.
A
B
Upper jaw not extending beyond front of eye.
Lateral line scales usually 36 or 37.
6b.
Nipple-like projection at middle of lower lip.
A less than B.
A
B
Lateral line scales usually 34-36.
Upper jaw extending beyond front of eye.

7a. *(From 6b.)* First principal ray of dorsal fin very long, reaching to or beyond back of fin; body deeper, its depth (A) usually going 2.6 times or less into standard length (B).
Highfin carpsucker
Carpiodes velifer ..... **Page 191**

7b. *(From 6b.)* First principal ray of dorsal fin shorter, not reaching much beyond middle of fin; body more slender, its depth (A) usually going more than 2.6 times into standard length (B).
River carpsucker
Carpiodes carpio ..... **Page 190**

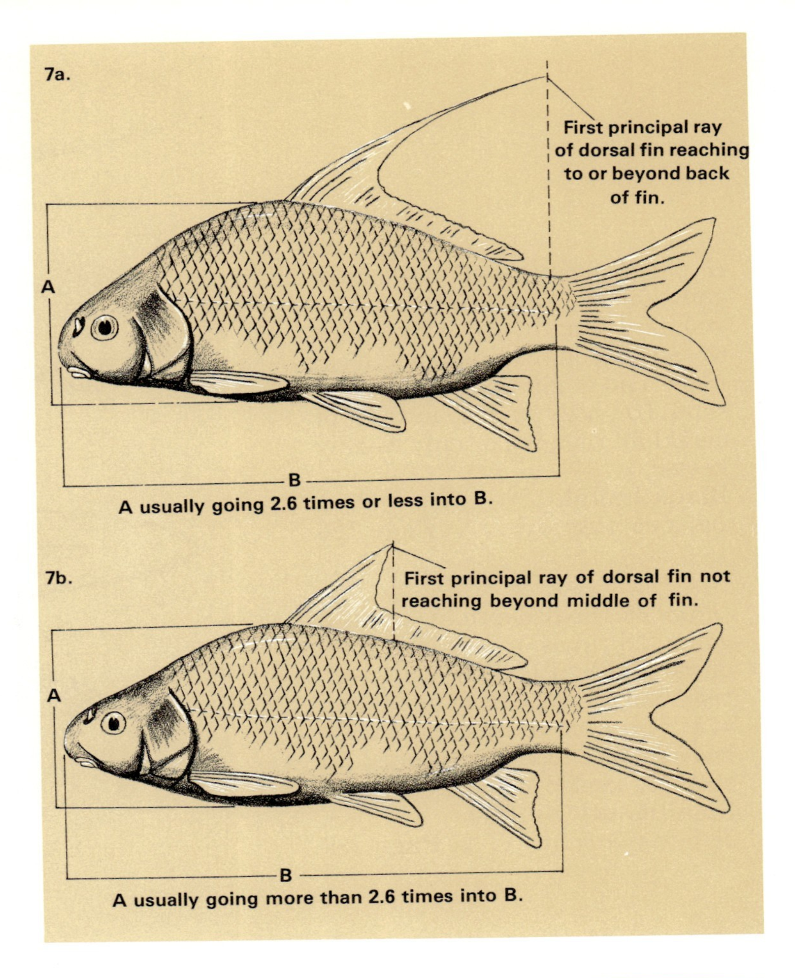
7a.
First principal ray of dorsal fin reaching to or beyond back of fin.
A
B
A usually going 2.6 times or less into B.
7b.
First principal ray of dorsal fin not reaching beyond middle of fin.
A
B
A usually going more than 2.6 times into B.

8a. *(From 1b.)* Head between eyes very broad and strongly concave; back with 4 to 6 prominent dark cross-bars.
Northern hog sucker
Hypentelium nigricans
.... **Page 193**

8b. *(From 1b.)* Head between eyes not broad and concave; back without prominent dark cross-bars.
Go to **9**

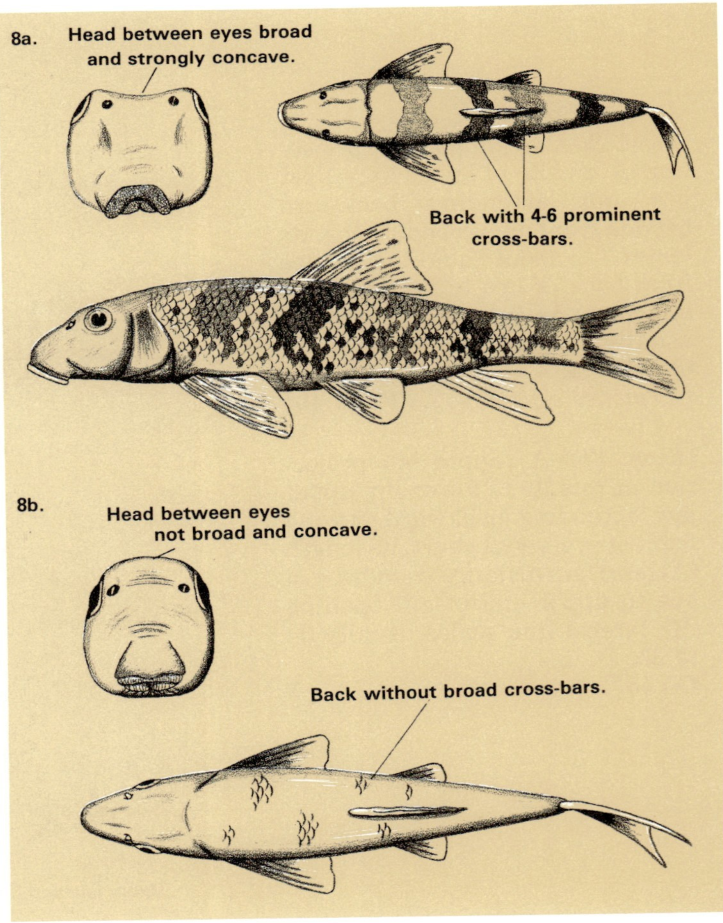
8a.
Head between eyes broad and strongly concave.
Back with 4-6 prominent cross-bars.
8b.
Head between eyes not broad and concave.
Back without broad cross-bars.

9a. *(From 8b.)* Scales small, especially towards head, and with 55 or more in lateral line; lips with numerous small wart-like projections.
White sucker
Catostomus commersoni
.... **Page 192**

9b. *(From 8b.)* Scales larger with fewer than 50 in lateral line; lips with numerous parallel folds.
Go to **10**

9a.
Lips with numerous small wart-like projections
Scales small, 55 or more in lateral line.
9b.
Scales large, fewer than 50 in lateral line.
Lips with numerous parallel folds.

10a. *(From 9b.)* Lateral line complete; air bladder with 3 chambers.
Go to **11**

10b. *(From 9b.)* Lateral line incomplete or absent; air bladder with 2 chambers.
Go to **15**

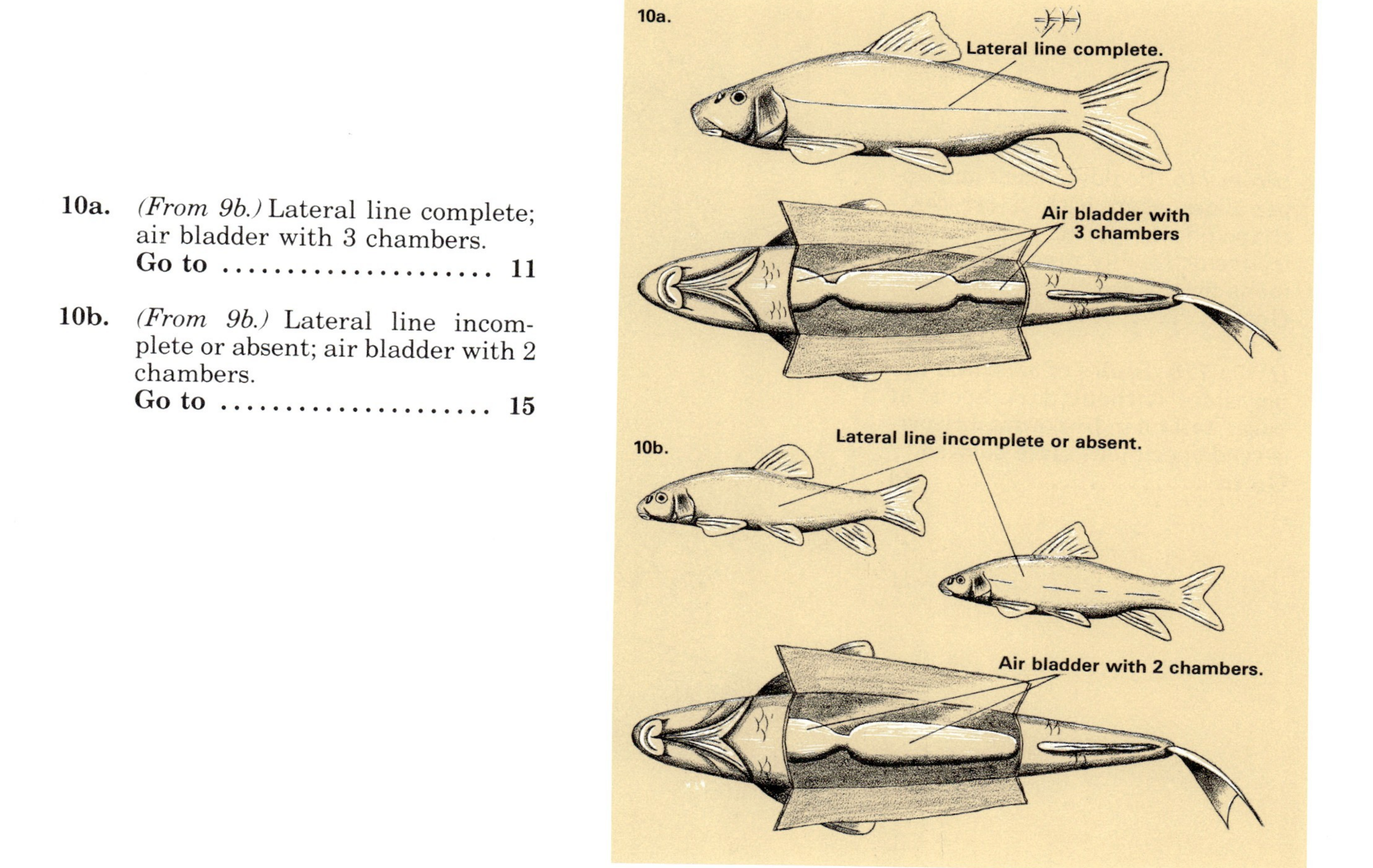

10a.
Lateral line complete.
Air bladder with 3 chambers
10b.
Lateral line incomplete or absent.
Air bladder with 2 chambers.

11a. *(From 10a.)* Dorsal fin rays usually 14 or 15, occasionally 16; rear margin of lower lip forming an acute angle.
Silver redhorse
Moxostoma anisurum **Page 196**

11b. *(From 10a.)* Dorsal fin rays usually 12 or 13, rarely 14 or 15; rear margin of lower lip nearly straight, or forming a slight to moderate angle.
Go to 12

11a.
Rear margin of lower lip forming an acute angle.
Dorsal fin rays usually 14 or 15, occasionally 16.

11b.
Dorsal fin rays usually 12 or 13, rarely 14 or 15.
Rear margin of lower lip nearly straight, or forming a slight to moderate angle.

12a. *(From 11b.)* Scales of back and upper sides each with a crescent-shaped dark spot at base; tail fin in live or freshly preserved specimens bright red.
Go to 13

12b. *(From 11b.)* Scales of back and upper sides without dark spots at bases; tail fin in live or freshly preserved specimens slate colored.
Go to 14

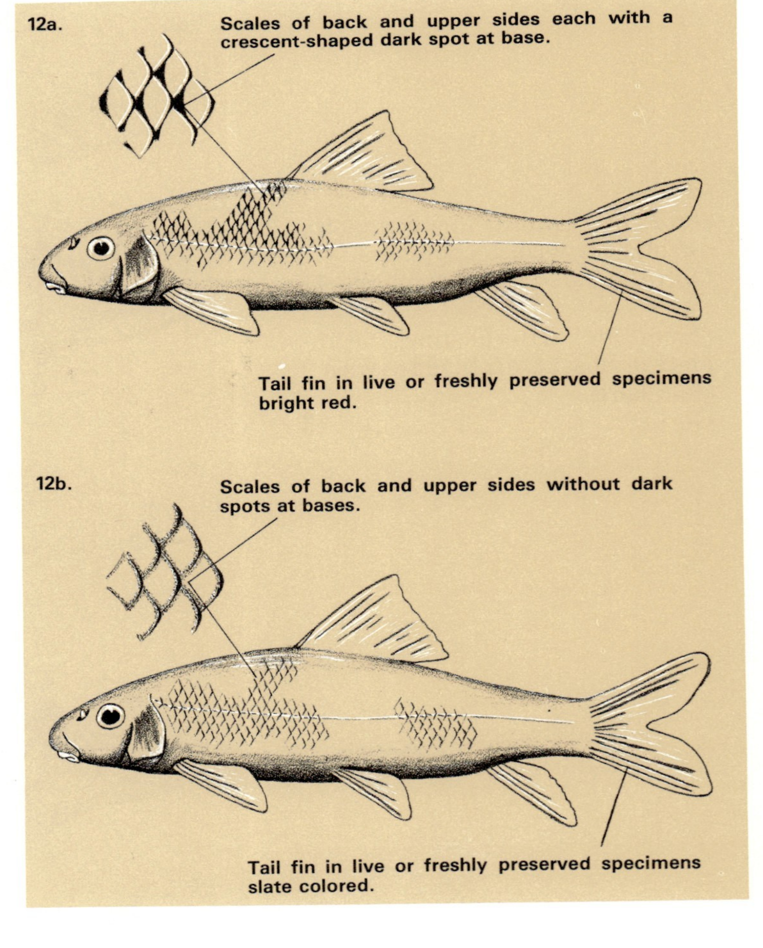
12a.
Scales of back and upper sides each with a crescent-shaped dark spot at base.
Tail fin in live or freshly preserved specimens bright red.
12b.
Scales of back and upper sides without dark spots at bases.
Tail fin in live or freshly preserved specimens slate colored.

13a. *(From 12a.)* Rear margin of lower lip nearly straight; head short, its length (A) going 4.5 times or more into standard length (B); upper lip often with a pea-shaped swelling at middle (absent in some populations); pharyngeal arch thin, with slender teeth in comb-like series.
Shorthead redhorse
Moxostoma macrolepidotum
.... **Page 197**

13b. *(From 12a.)* Rear margin of lower lip forming a definite V-shaped angle; head longer, its length (A) going less than 4.5 times into standard length (B); upper lip never with a pea-shaped swelling at middle; pharyngeal arch thick, with molar-like teeth.
River redhorse
Moxostoma carinatum **Page 198**

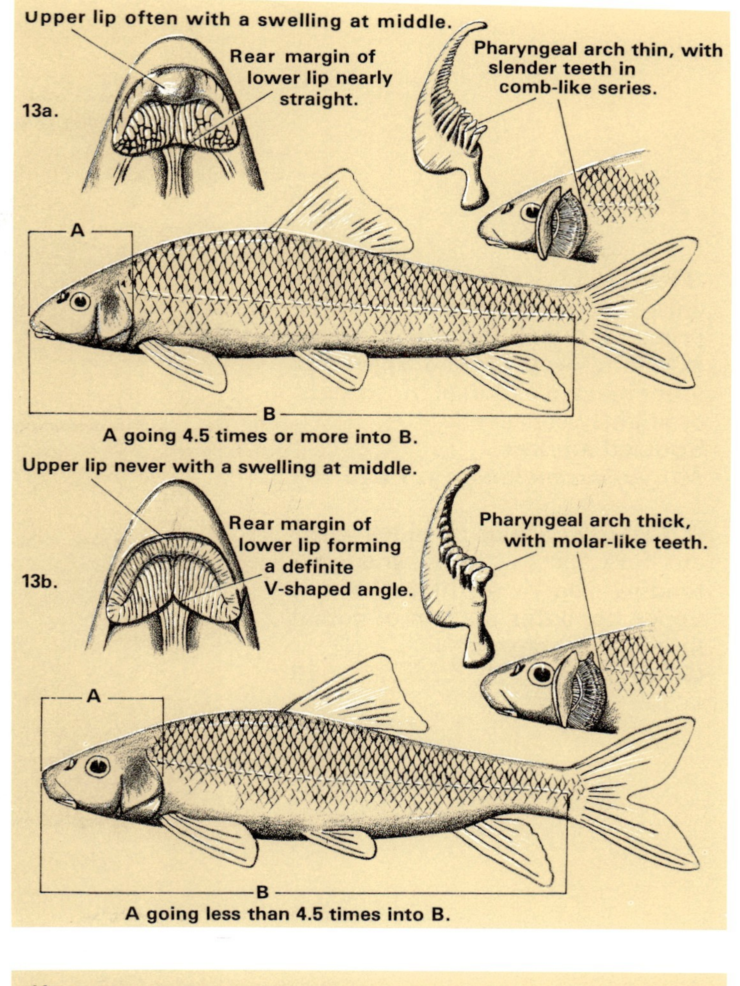
Upper lip often with a swelling at middle.
Rear margin of lower lip nearly straight.
Pharyngeal arch thin, with slender teeth in comb-like series.
13a.
A
B
A going 4.5 times or more into B.
Upper lip never with a swelling at middle.
Rear margin of lower lip forming a definite V-shaped angle.
Pharyngeal arch thick, with molar-like teeth.
13b.
A
B
A going less than 4.5 times into B.

14a. *(From 12b.)* Lateral line scales usually 44 to 47; caudal peduncle slender, its least depth (A) going 2 times or more into distance from base of tail fin to front of anal fin base (B); pelvic fin rays usually 10, often 9 or 11; breeding males without tubercles on head.
Black redhorse
Moxostoma duquesnei
.... **Page 194**

14b. *(From 12b.)* Lateral line scales usually 39 to 42; caudal peduncle deeper, its least depth (A) going less than 2 times into distance from base of tail fin to front of anal fin base (B); pelvic fin rays usually 9, often 8 or 10; breeding males with tubercles on head.
Golden redhorse
Moxostoma erythrurum
.... **Page 195**

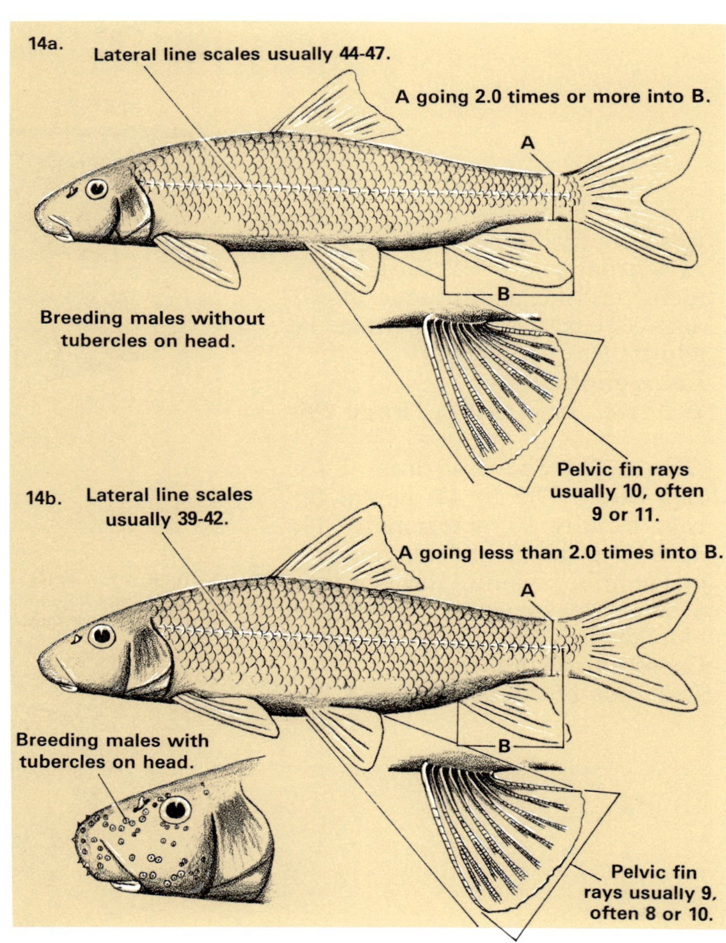
14a.
Lateral line scales usually 44-47.
A going 2.0 times or more into B.
A
B
Breeding males without tubercles on head.
Pelvic fin rays usually 10, often 9 or 11.
14b.
Lateral line scales usually 39-42.
A going less than 2.0 times into B.
A
B
Breeding males with tubercles on head.
Pelvic fin rays usually 9, often 8 or 10.

15a. *(From 10b.)* Scales on sides with dark spots at bases, forming prominent parallel lines; snout extending well beyond upper lip; outer margin of dorsal fin straight or slightly concave.
Spotted sucker
Minytrema melanops . **Page 199**

15b. *(From 10b.)* Scales on sides without dark spots at bases; snout extending only slightly beyond upper lip; outer margin of dorsal fin slightly convex.
Go to 16

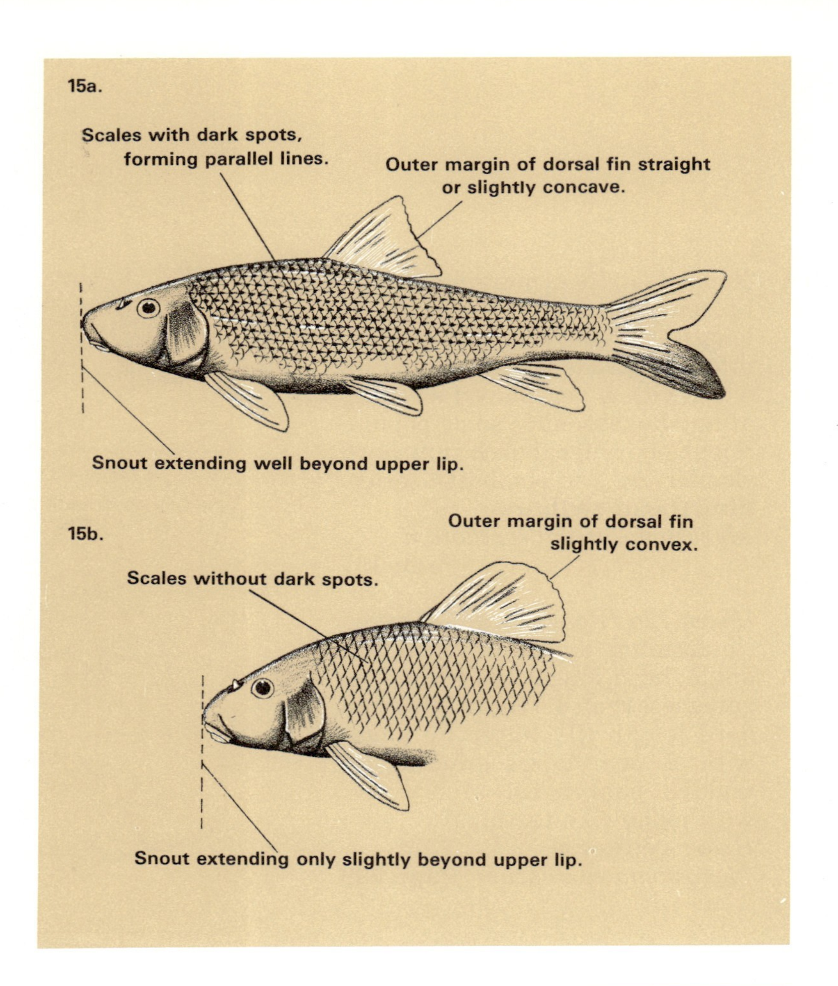
15a.
Scales with dark spots, forming parallel lines.
Outer margin of dorsal fin straight or slightly concave.
Snout extending well beyond upper lip.
15b.
Outer margin of dorsal fin slightly convex.
Scales without dark spots.
Snout extending only slightly beyond upper lip.

16a. *(From 15b.)* Scales in lateral series usually 35 to 37; dorsal fin rays usually 11 or 12; dark stripe along midside continuous at all ages (stripe often indistinct in adults).
Lake chubsucker
Erimyzon sucetta ..... **Page 200**

16b. *(From 15b.)* Scales in lateral series usually 39 to 41; dorsal fin rays usually 10, occasionally 11; dark stripe along midside continuous only in juveniles, broken into a series of somewhat connected blotches in adults.
Creek chubsucker
Erimyzon oblongus ... **Page 199**

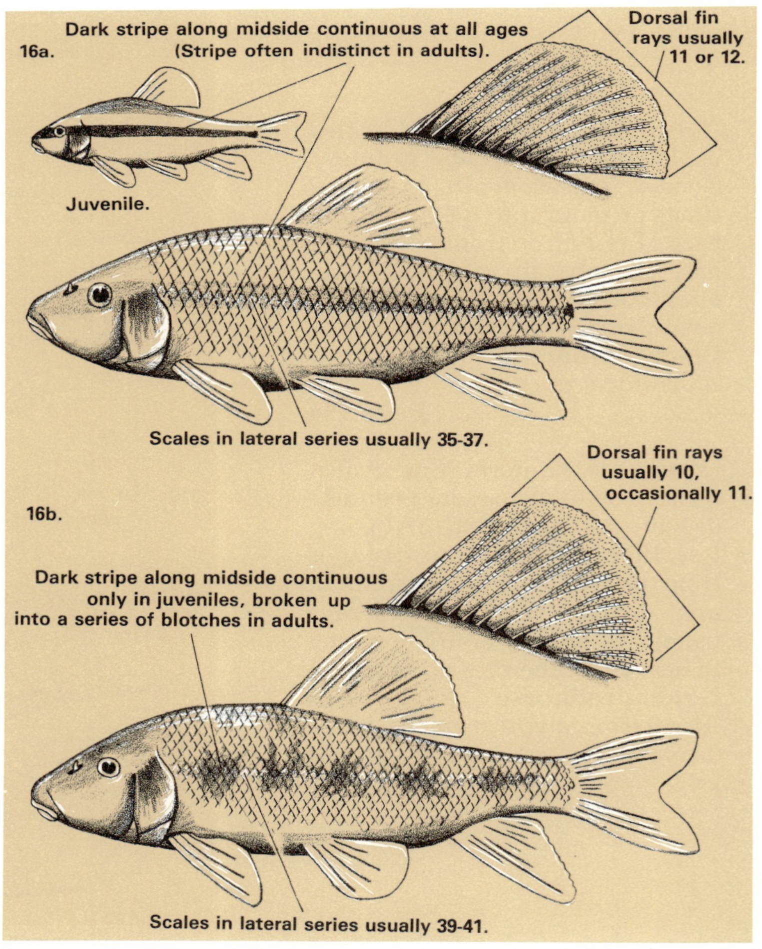
16a.
Dark stripe along midside continuous at all ages (Stripe often indistinct in adults).
Dorsal fin rays usually 11 or 12.
Juvenile.
Scales in lateral series usually 35-37.
16b.
Dorsal fin rays usually 10, occasionally 11.
Dark stripe along midside continuous only in juveniles, broken up into a series of blotches in adults.
Scales in lateral series usually 39-41.

Blue Sucker

Cycleptus elongatus (Lesueur)

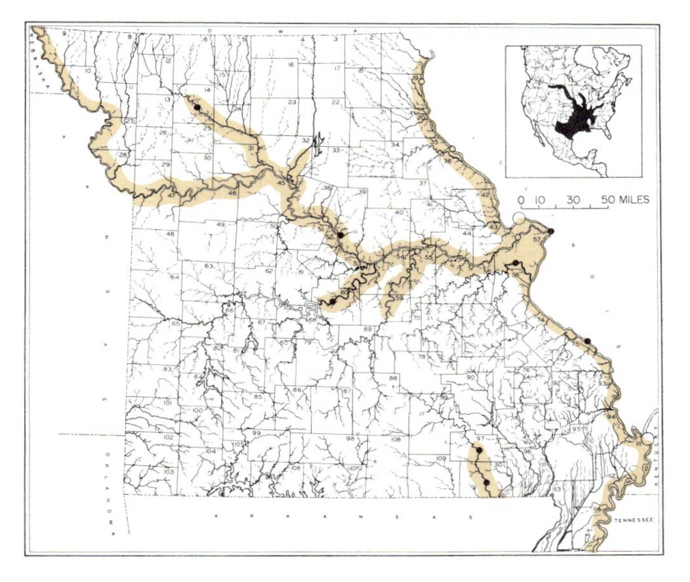

Other local names: Missouri sucker, Slender-headed sucker, Blackhorse, Gourdseed sucker, Schooner

DESCRIPTION

Illustration: Page 179, 2a.

Characters: A slender, dark-colored sucker with a small head and a long, sickle-shaped dorsal fin. Eyes small and closer to rear margin of gill cover than to tip of snout. Mouth small, horizontal, and distinctly overhung by snout. Lips covered by numerous wart-like papillae. Lateral line complete, containing 55 to 58 scales. Body depth going about 4 to 5 times into standard length. Dorsal fin with 28 to 33 rays.

Life colors: Back and sides blue-black or dark olive with brassy reflections; belly white. Fins dusky or black. Breeding males are very dark and have small tubercles over most of head, body, and fins.

Size: According to commercial fishermen, blue suckers weighing up to 20 pounds were formerly common in the Missouri River. Most specimens taken in recent years were 16 to 24 inches long and weighed 1½ to 3 pounds.

Scientific name: *Cycleptus,* reported by its author to mean "small round mouth"; *elongatus,* "elongate."

DISTRIBUTION AND HABITAT

The blue sucker is rare but widespread in the Missouri and Mississippi rivers and the lower sections of their larger tributaries. It seems to have declined in abundance since 1900.

This sucker inhabits the deep, swift channels of large rivers over a bottom of sand, gravel, or rock. It is tolerant of high turbidity if there is sufficient current to prevent deposition of silt. Construction of dams, with the attendant decrease in current velocity that permits siltation, has been unfavorable to the blue sucker.

HABITS AND LIFE HISTORY

The habits of this distinctive sucker are not well known. The streamlined body and sickle-shaped fins are adaptions for maintaining a position in swift currents. The blue sucker probably feeds on insect larvae and other small invertebrates taken from the bottom. It is a highly mobile fish. Formerly there were important spring runs and lesser fall runs of the blue sucker in the upper Mississippi River.[22] Adults in breeding condition have been taken in Current River as early as February and March, but spawning is said to occur in May and June at this latitude.[24] A larval blue sucker was collected from the Missouri River, Boone County, in mid-June. In Lake Texoma, Oklahoma, two-year-old fish were about 15 inches standard length.[114]

IMPORTANCE

The blue sucker is said to be the best food fish of all the suckers and was formerly of some commercial importance along the Missouri and Mississippi rivers. It is still taken in small numbers by commercial fishermen, most often by drifting trammel nets with the current.

Bigmouth Buffalo

Ictiobus cyprinellus (Valenciennes)

Other local names: Gourdhead, Redmouth buffalo, Common buffalo

DESCRIPTION

Illustration: Page 180, 4a.

Characters: A dark-colored sucker with a deep, rather thick body and a long, sickle-shaped dorsal fin. Eyes small and closer to tip of snout than to rear margin of gill cover. Lower fins with much dusky pigment. Subopercle (bone at lower back margin of gill cover) broadest at middle, its outer margin gently rounded. Lateral line complete, containing 32 to 40 scales. Dorsal fin with 23 to 32 rays.

Similar to smallmouth and black buffaloes but with a large, oblique mouth, and thinner, less strongly grooved (striate) lips. Front of upper lip about on a level with lower margin of eye. Length of upper jaw much greater than diameter of eye.

More slender than smallmouth buffalo, the body depth going about 2.5 to 3.3 times into standard length. Forward part of back rounded or only weakly keeled.

Life colors: Back and sides brownish or blackish with coppery and greenish reflections, the scales not prominently dark-edged. Belly whitish or pale yellow. All fins blackish, the lower fins often whitish along free margins. Breeding males are slightly darker but do not develop tubercles.

Size: The largest Missouri sucker. Adults are commonly 15 to 27 inches long and weigh 2 to 14 pounds. Individuals weighing up to 30 pounds are not uncommon and the maximum weight reported is about 80 pounds.

Scientific name: *Ictiobus,* Greek, meaning "bull fish"; *cyprinellus,* Latin, meaning "small carp".

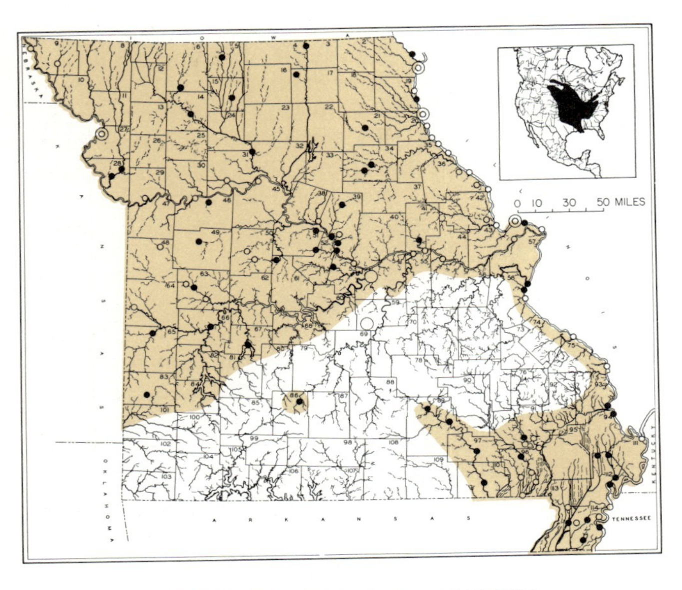

DISTRIBUTION AND HABITAT

The bigmouth buffalo occurs over much of the state and is most abundant in the Missouri River and its larger Prairie tributaries. Here it outnumbers the other buffalofishes about three to one at most localities. It is also abundant along the Mississippi River and in the larger Lowland ditches and streams of the southeast, but in these areas it is usually outnumbered by one of the other buffalofishes.

The bigmouth buffalo is primarily an inhabitant of the deeper pools of large streams, natural lowland lakes, and man-made impoundments. It sometimes enters rather small creeks to spawn and the young remain in the smaller streams during their first summer of life. The habitat requirements of the three species of buffalofishes are similar but their distributional relationships in Missouri and elsewhere suggest that the bigmouth buffalo is more tolerant of high turbidity than the other species.

HABITS AND LIFE HISTORY

The bigmouth buffalo commonly occurs in schools in midwater or near the bottom. A South Dakota study reveals that young feed principally on midges and other bottom-dwelling invertebrates, while the food of older individuals is primarily small crustaceans that live in midwater.[115] The large, terminal mouth and numerous slender gill rakers are efficient devices for straining small crustaceans from the water.

In the Missouri River near Columbia buffalofishes thought to be this species were observed spawning in late May on rock rip-rap in a quiet backwater. The eggs were broadcast over rocks in water so shallow that the backs of the spawning fish were exposed. The eggs hatch in 9 or 10 days at a water temperature of about 62°F.[163] Recently hatched young have been collected in central Missouri from late May to early July. In Reelfoot Lake, Tennessee, the average lengths and weights achieved by the bigmouth buffalo through the first eight summers of life are as follows:[116]

Age in Summers	Length (inches)	Weight (pounds)
2	13.2	1.5
3	15.2	2.1
4	16.7	2.5
5	17.9	3.1
6	20.8	5.3
7	23.5	7.4
8	26.3	13.8

Growth in weight increases progressively during the first eight summers, indicating that fish in their eighth summer are still in a fast-growing period of life.

IMPORTANCE

The buffalofishes are seldom taken on hook and line but are fine food fishes. Most are caught with trammel nets and other commercial fishing gear. They are well suited for artificial propagation and in some southern states are raised in rotation with rice. A pond method for propagation is described by Brady and Hulsey.[117]

Black Buffalo

Ictiobus niger (Rafinesque)

Other local names: Mongrel buffalo, Round buffalo, Blue rooter, Current buffalo.

DESCRIPTION

Illustration: Page 181, 5a.

Characters: Similar to bigmouth buffalo but with a small, nearly horizontal mouth and thicker, more strongly grooved (striate) lips. Front of upper lip well below level of lower margin of eye. Length of upper jaw equal to or slightly greater than diameter of eye. Body not as deep but thicker than in smallmouth buffalo, its depth going about 2.6 to 3.2 times into standard length and its width greater than distance from tip of snout to upper end of gill opening. Forward part of back rounded or only weakly keeled.

Life colors: Like those of bigmouth buffalo, page 187, but averaging slightly darker.

Size: Said to be a somewhat larger species than the smallmouth buffalo, reaching a weight of 50 pounds.

Scientific name: *Ictiobus,* Greek, meaning "bull fish"; *niger,* Latin, meaning "dark" or "black".

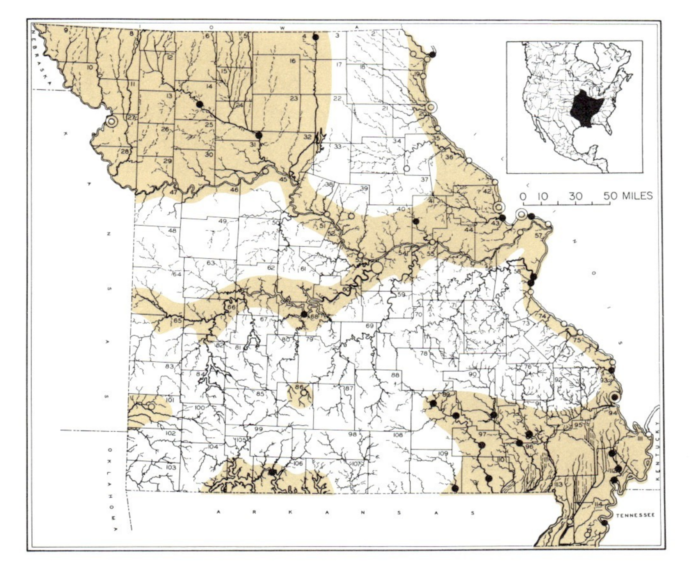

DISTRIBUTION AND HABITAT

The black buffalo is less widespread in Missouri than the other two buffalofishes. In our collections it has outnumbered the other two species only in the lower Current River. It is somewhat more common than the bigmouth buffalo in streams and ditches of the Lowlands, but is less abundant there than the smallmouth buffalo. In the Mississippi River it is more abundant in the unimpounded section below the mouth of the Missouri River than in the canalized section above.[32]

The habitat requirements of this species are like the other buffalofishes, but it occurs more often in strong currents. This difference in habitat is recognized by commercial fishermen who often refer to the black buffalo as the "current buffalo."

HABITS AND LIFE HISTORY

The habits and life history of the black buffalo are not well known. Spawning was observed in the state of Mississippi the third week of April along the margin of a flooded swamp.[118] Several hundred adults participated in the spawning activity. They did not show their customary timidity and continually broke the water's surface as they milled about. Three days later, when the water had receded about a foot, numerous masses of drying eggs were found on fallen tree tops and logs and the lower branches of bushes. In a Kansas impoundment the black buffalo grew more slowly than the bigmouth buffalo.[119]

Smallmouth Buffalo

Ictiobus bubalus (Rafinesque)

Other local names: Roach-back, Razor-backed buffalo, Hump-backed buffalo, Liner, Blue pancake.

DESCRIPTION

Illustration: Page 181, 5b.

Characters: Similar to bigmouth buffalo, page 187, but with a small, nearly horizontal mouth, and thicker, more strongly grooved (striate) lips. Front of upper lip well below level of lower margin of eye. Length of upper jaw greater than diameter of eye. Body deeper and thinner than in other buffaloes, its depth going about 2.2 to 2.8 times into standard length and its width less than distance from tip of snout to upper end of gill opening. Forward part of back usually strongly keeled.

Life colors: About as in bigmouth buffalo, but averaging lighter. Larger individuals often a rather uniform slate-grey, without coppery or greenish reflections.

Size: Reported to be the smallest of the buffalofishes, reaching a weight of about 40 pounds. Adults are commonly 15.3 to 30.8 inches in length and weigh 2.2 to 17.6 pounds.

Scientific name: *Ictiobus,* Greek, meaning "bull fish"; *bubalus,* Greek for "buffalo".

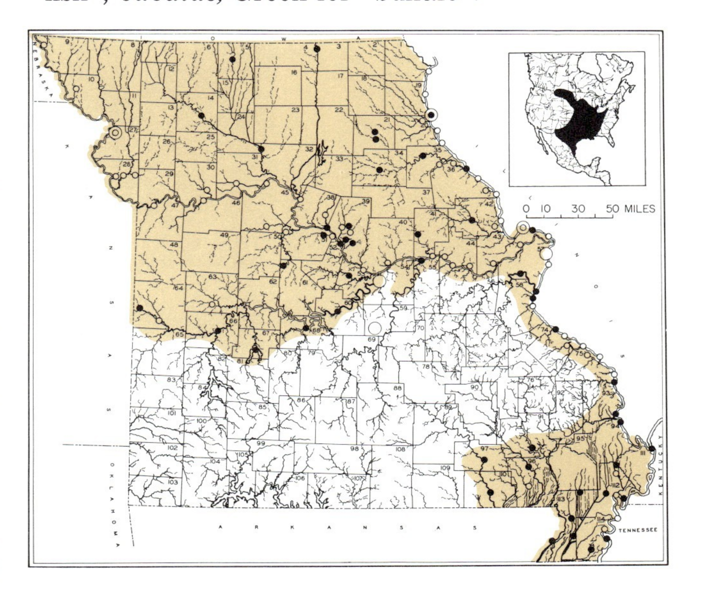

DISTRIBUTION AND HABITAT

The smallmouth buffalo is nearly as common and widespread in Missouri as the bigmouth buffalo. It is the most abundant buffalofish in the Mississippi River and its major tributaries in northeast Missouri, in the Lowland streams and ditches of the southeast, and in large Ozark reservoirs.

This fish seems to prefer clearer water than the bigmouth buffalo and is found less often in strong currents than the black buffalo.

HABITS AND LIFE HISTORY

The smallmouth buffalo is primarily a bottom feeder, as indicated by the high frequency of insect larvae, attached algae, and associated detritus and sand in its diet.[120] The breeding habits of this fish are not known. Males in breeding condition have been taken from the Chariton River in late June, suggesting an early summer spawning season. Growth of the smallmouth buffalo in Reelfoot Lake, Tennessee, is comparable to that of the bigmouth buffalo.[121] In that study the oldest individuals were in their 13th summer, and were still growing rapidly. They averaged 32.9 inches in length and 25.5 pounds in weight.

River Carpsucker

Carpiodes carpio (Rafinesque)

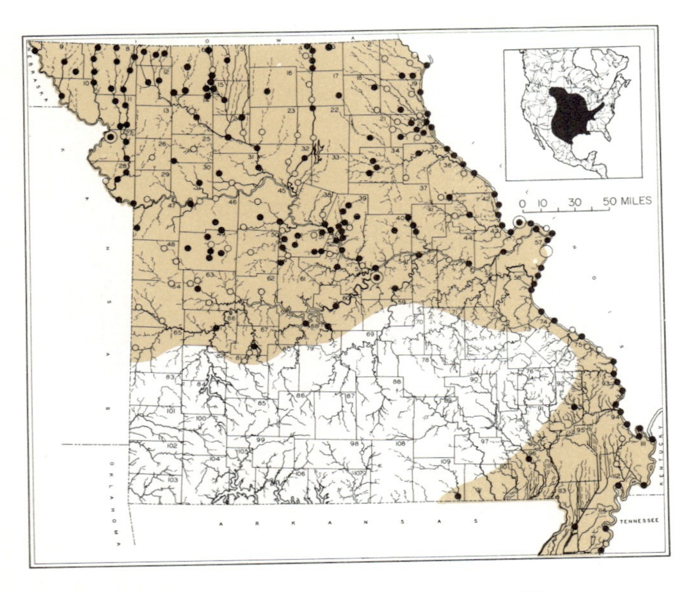

Other local names: White carp, Silver carp, Quillback.

DESCRIPTION

Illustration: Page 182, 7b.

Characters: A silver-colored sucker with a deep, rather thick body and a long, sickle-shaped dorsal fin. Eyes moderately large and closer to tip of snout than to rear margin of gill cover. Lower fins whitish, not dark as in buffalofishes. Subopercle (bone at lower angle of gill cover) broadest below middle, its outer margin somewhat angular. Lateral line complete. Dorsal fin with 23 to 30 rays.

Similar to quillback, page 191, but with a nipple-like projection at middle of lower lip. Also, the snout is shorter, its length less than distance from rear margin of eye to upper end of gill opening, and the mouth is farther back, the upper jaw extending past front of eye. Lateral line with 34 or 35 (occasionally 36) scales. Most like the highfin carpsucker, page 191, but with first principal ray of dorsal fin shorter, not reaching much beyond middle of fin. Also, the body is not as deep but is thicker, its width usually going 2 times or less into its depth.

Life colors: Back brown or slate with silvery reflections. Sides silvery, the scales rather prominently dark-edged. Belly, undersurface of head, and lips milk-white. Dorsal and tail fins dusky; lower fins white, sometimes with a faint dusky or orange-yellow tinge. Breeding males are without special colors but have very small tubercles on top and sides of head, forward part of back, and upper surfaces of paired fins.

Size: Adults are commonly 12 to 15 inches long and weigh 0.8 to 1.5 pounds. Maximum length and weight in Missouri about 18.5 inches and 3 pounds. Elsewhere, individuals weighing 10 pounds or more have been reported.[94]

Scientific name: *Carpiodes,* Latin, meaning "carp-like"; *carpio,* Latin, "carp".

DISTRIBUTION AND HABITAT

The river carpsucker is by far the most abundant and widely distributed carpsucker in Missouri. Its main center of occurrence is the Prairie Region of north and west Missouri. In the larger streams of that region the river carpsucker is the most abundant large fish or is second in abundance only to the carp or gizzard shad. Elsewhere in the state it is common in the Missouri and Mississippi rivers, and occurs occasionally in the Lowlands.

Preferred habitat of the river carpsucker is the quiet, silt-bottomed pools, backwaters, and oxbows of large streams having moderate or low gradients. It also occurs in the deeper pools of small Prairie creeks and often thrives in impoundments. The river carpsucker seems to prefer waters that are turbid much of the time and is replaced in clearer waters by the quillback or highfin carpsucker.

HABITS AND LIFE HISTORY

The river carpsucker lives in large schools and feeds from the bottom. In Lake of the Ozarks this species browses extensively on the attached filamentous algae, consuming large quantities of single-celled algae, protozoans, and small crustaceans associated with the attached algae.[122]

Other items in its diet include immature aquatic insects, aquatic worms, mollusks, and miscellaneous parts of higher plants. Adults of the river carpsucker in breeding condition have occurred in Missouri collections from mid-May to late June. In the Des Moines River, Iowa, spawning is underway by early June and continues until late July or August.[123] The place and manner of egg deposition are not known. In Missouri streams this fish averages 3.2 inches in length by the end of its first year of life and averages 6.5, 9, 11, 12.3 and 13.7 inches in succeeding years.[52] The maximum life span is at least 10 years.

IMPORTANCE

Carpsuckers are rarely taken on hook and line and are little valued as food because of their soft, tasteless flesh. A few carpsuckers, of which most are the river carpsucker, are marketed by commercial fishermen along the Missouri and Mississippi rivers. The young are probably of some importance as forage, but at an early age the river carpsucker is too large to be eaten by most game fish. In some reservoirs this species is thought to compete for food or space with more desirable fishes.

Highfin Carpsucker

Carpiodes velifer (Rafinesque)

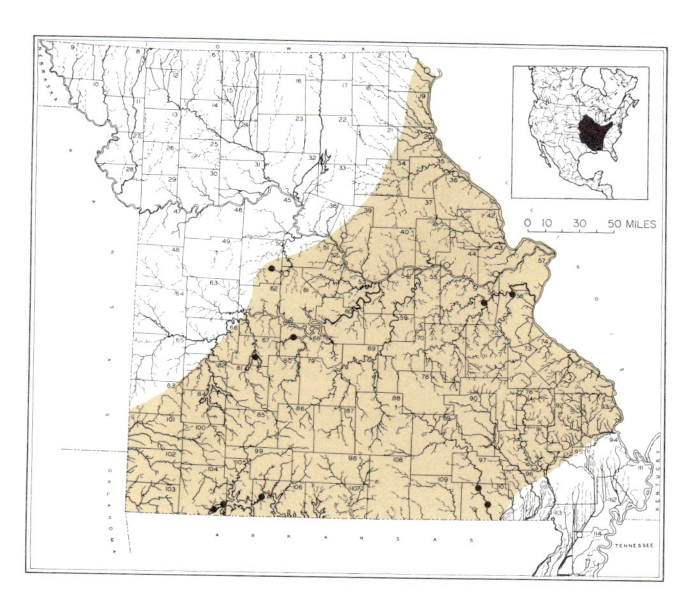

DESCRIPTION

Illustration: Page 182, 7a.

Characters: Agrees with the river carpsucker, page 190, in most characters, but with first principal ray of dorsal fin very long, reaching far beyond back of fin base unless broken off. Also, body is deeper and thinner, its width going more than 2 times into its depth.

Life colors: About the same as the river carpsucker. Breeding males have larger tubercles than the river carpsucker; tubercles are present over most of head, body, and fins.

Size: A small carpsucker, seldom exceeding a length of 12 inches or a weight of 1 pound. Most adults are 9 to 11 inches long.

Scientific name: *Carpiodes,* Latin, meaning "carp-like"; *velifer,* Latin, meaning "sail bearer," in reference to the elongate dorsal fin.

DISTRIBUTION AND HABITAT

The highfin carpsucker is rare in Missouri and may now be less common than in former years. Recent collecting in northeast Missouri has failed to reveal the presence of this fish in some streams where it occurred 30 years ago. At present the highfin carpsucker is largely confined to the Ozarks where it is more common in large reservoirs than in streams.

This fish prefers clearer waters and firmer bottoms than the river carpsucker. It is much less tolerant of turbidity and siltation than the other carpsuckers. This intolerance probably explains its present restricted distribution in Missouri.

HABITS AND LIFE HISTORY

The habits and life history of the highfin carpsucker are not well known. It has the curious habit of "skimming" along near the water's surface with its dorsal fin and part of its back exposed, and it frequently jumps clear of the water.[94] Adults in breeding condition were collected from the Meramec River in late July over deep, gravelly riffles; presumably they were spawning. In the Des Moines River, Iowa, this species grew more slowly than the river carpsucker or quillback.[124]

Quillback

Carpiodes cyprinus (Lesueur)

DESCRIPTION

Illustration: Page 181, 6a; **39.**

Characters: Similar to river and highfin carpsuckers, but without a nipple-like extension on lower lip, and with 36 to 38 (rarely 35) scales in lateral line. Also, the snout is longer, its length about equal to distance from rear margin of eye to upper end of gill opening, and the mouth is farther forward, the upper jaw not extending past front of eye. Body not as deep and thicker than highfin carpsucker, its width usually going 2 times or less into its depth.

Variation: In some specimens the first principal ray of the dorsal fin is long, reaching to or beyond the hind margin of the fin base, while in others it is nearly as short as in the river carpsucker. In general, specimens with a long dorsal ray have narrower and deeper bodies, shorter heads, and smaller eyes than those with a short dorsal ray. Some authorities consider these types to be different species, reserving the name quillback for the type with the long dorsal ray, and calling those with the short ray the plains carpsucker, *Carpiodes forbesi* Hubbs. Both types occur in Missouri, often at the same localities. Some individuals are not readily assignable to either type and until the problem receives a more thorough study it seems best to treat all as members of a single, variable species.

Life colors: Similar to river carpsucker, page 190, but the sides often have a tinge of golden yellow. Breeding tubercles are larger than in river carpsucker and are developed over most of head and body, except belly, and on upper surfaces of paired fins.

Size: Adults are commonly 12 to 17 inches in length and weigh 0.8 to 2.3 pounds. The maximum size in Missouri streams is about 19.2 inches and 3.7 pounds.

Scientific name: *Carpiodes,* Latin, meaning "carp-like"; *cyprinus,* after the generic name for the carp, an allusion to its similarity to that species.

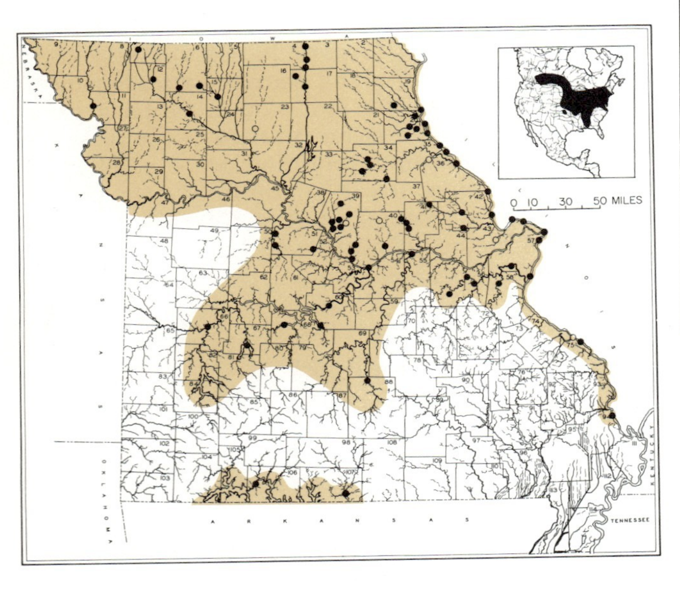

DISTRIBUTION AND HABITAT

The quillback is most abundant in the clearer prairie streams of central and northeastern Missouri. It is fairly common in the upper Mississippi and in large reservoirs of the Ozark Uplands. At most localities in the Prairie Region it is less numerous than the river carpsucker.

This fish is characteristic of moderately clear, highly productive streams having large, permanent pools and stable bottoms composed of gravel and other coarse material. Like other carpsuckers, the quillback inhabits quiet water except when spawning. It is most abundant in moderately large streams, but also occurs in creeks if large, permanent pools are present.

HABITS AND LIFE HISTORY

Adults of the quillback in breeding condition have been collected in Missouri from early April to late May, suggesting an earlier spawning season than for other carpsuckers. These adults were collected near the lower ends of deep, gravelly riffles. In the Des Moines River, Iowa, the quillback grows more slowly than the river carpsucker for the first 6 years, after which growth of the quillback is most rapid.[124]

White Sucker

Catostomus commersoni Lacépède)

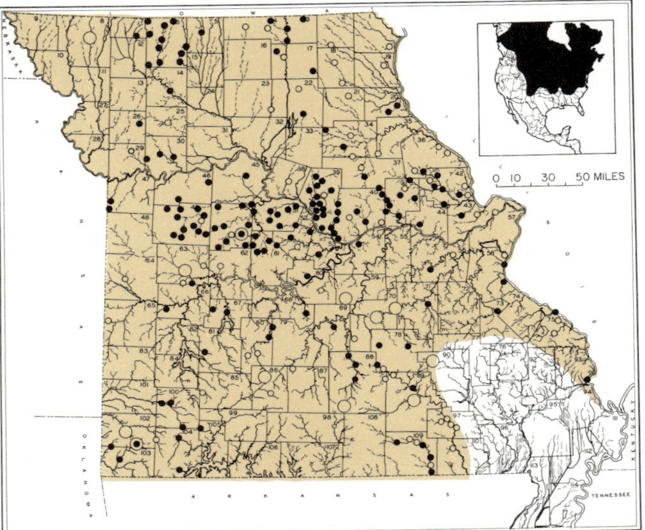

Other local names: Black sucker.

DESCRIPTION

Illustration: Page 183, 9a.

Characters: A slender, fine-scaled sucker with a short dorsal fin having 11 to 13 rays. Scales largest near tail fin, becoming smaller towards head. Lateral line complete, with 57 to 76 scales. Eye about midway between tip of snout and rear margin of gill cover. Interspace between eyes flat or slightly rounded outward. Lips covered with small, wart-like bumps (papillae). Air bladder with 2 chambers.

Life colors: Back and sides greenish with a brassy or silvery luster; belly white. Dorsal and tail fins dusky or clear; lower fins white, often tinged with yellow or orange. Breeding males are darker and are distinctly bicolored (nearly black above, white below), with a pink band along the side; small tubercles are present on head, body and fins. Tubercles best developed on anal fin, lower lobe of tail fin, and underside of caudal peduncle. Young white suckers often have a series of dusky blotches along the midside.

Size: Adults are commonly 10 to 16 inches long and weigh 0.5 to 1.7 pounds. Maximum length and weight in Missouri streams is about 18 inches and 2.8 pounds.

Scientific name: *Catostomus,* Greek, meaning "subterminal mouth"; *commersoni,* named for Phelebert Commerson, an early French naturalist.

DISTRIBUTION AND HABITAT

The white sucker is common in the clearer Prairie and Ozark border streams of central and northeastern Missouri and is locally common but spotty in distribution in the Ozarks. It is absent from the Lowlands and adjacent streams of the Ozarks.

This is decidedly a small-creek fish, occurring only rarely in major rivers. In the Prairie Region it is abundant in high-gradient headwater streams having gravelly or rocky bottoms and well-defined riffles. These streams tend to be intermittent, but permanent pools are maintained by seepage through gravel of the stream bed. In the Ozarks this fish occurs in spring branches and in heavily vegetated spring pools along large streams. The habitats in which the white sucker is abundant are largely devoid of other suckers. Perhaps competition from these is an important factor limiting its distribution. The habitat requirements of the white sucker are much like those of the creek chub, a minnow with which it is commonly associated.

HABITS AND LIFE HISTORY

The white sucker lives in schools near the bottom. Its feeding habits and diet vary with age.[125] For 10 or 11 days after hatching the young suckers have terminal mouths and feed near the surface on bloodworms, small crustaceans, protozoa, and other microscopic life. Soon they develop the subterminal, horizontal mouth of the adults, and from then on they feed almost entirely on the bottom. Fingerling white suckers feed primarily on organic-rich bottom ooze; adults have rather generalized food habits but subsist mostly on immature aquatic insects.

The white sucker is an early spring spawner. In central Missouri the spawning season extends from late March through April. The spawning habitat is gravelly areas near the lower ends of pools, in quiet water or where the current begins to quicken. Many individuals occupy a single site and create a large area of clean, silt-free gravel by their activities. The males remain more or less continuously over the spawning area, but the females enter only when ready to spawn. Two or more males crowd against the sides of the female as the eggs are deposited. Spawning is accompanied by violent vibrations that raise clouds of silt and bury the eggs in the gravel. The eggs hatch in 18 or 20 days at a temperature of about 50°F.[125]

In the Salt River of northeast Missouri the white sucker averages 3.8 inches in length by the end of its first year of life and attains lengths of 6.8, 9, and 11.7 inches in succeeding years.[126] Growth here is more rapid than that reported for streams elsewhere in its range.

Northern Hog Sucker

Hypentelium nigricans (Lesueur)

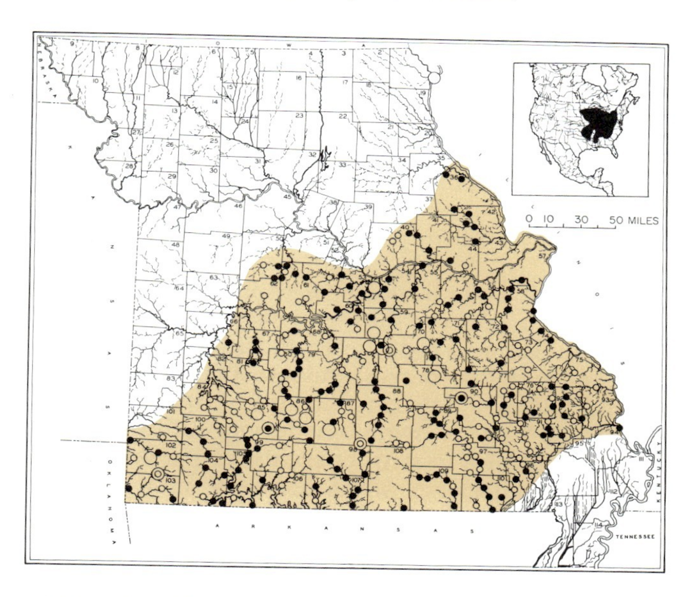

Other local names: Hog molly, Boxhead

DESCRIPTION

Illustration: Page 182, 8a; **39.**

Characters: A mottled, brownish sucker with a large, bony head that tapers abruptly into a slender body. Eye much closer to rear margin of gill cover than to tip of snout. Head squarish in cross-section; interspace between eyes broad and distinctly depressed (curved inward). Dorsal fin short, containing 10 to 12 rays. Lateral line complete, with 46 to 51 scales. Lips covered with small, wart-like bumps (papillae). Air bladder with 2 chambers.

Life colors: Back reddish-brown mottled with darker brown, and with about four dark cross-bars that extend obliquely forward onto sides. Sides lighter, with a brassy luster. Belly silvery-white. Fins mostly plain with a few dark specklings; lower fins often tinged with orange. Breeding males are without special colors, but have large tubercles on lower fins and lower lobe of tail fin.

Size: Adults are commonly 8 to 15 inches in length and weigh 0.3 to 1.4 pounds. Maximum length and weight in Missouri about 17 inches and 2.2 pounds.

Scientific name: *Hypentelium,* Greek, meaning "below 5 lobes," supposedly in reference to the 5-lobed lower lip; *nigricans,* Latin, meaning "blackish."

DISTRIBUTION AND HABITAT

The hog sucker is one of the most abundant and widely distributed stream fishes in the Ozarks. Among suckers of that region it is exceeded in abundance at many localities only by the black redhorse. The distribution of the hog sucker and black redhorse is remarkably similar in Missouri, indicating the close association between these two species.

This fish is an inhabitant of streams having clean gravelly or rocky bottoms and permanent flow. It is most often found in riffles or in pools having noticeable current.

HABITS AND LIFE HISTORY

In habit and structure this species is more like an oversize darter than a sucker. It is strictly a bottom fish, resting quietly on the stream bottom when it is not moving about. The heavy bony head, slender tapering body, enlarged pectoral fins, and reduced swim bladder permit it to maintain a position in swift currents with a minimum of effort. Because of its strongly mottled and barred coloration the hog sucker is nearly invisible as it lies among the rocks. When disturbed it darts off rapidly for a short distance, seeming to disappear as it comes to rest abruptly and again blends into the background. The hog sucker is an aggressive feeder, overturning rocks and stirring up the bottom as it forages for immature aquatic insects and other bottom life with its fleshy, sucking lips. Other fishes, especially the smallmouth bass, longear sunfish, and various minnows commonly follow foraging hog suckers to feed on the small organisms exposed by these activities. It is less a schooling fish than most other suckers, occurring alone or in small, loosely organized groups.

In Missouri the hog sucker spawns in April or early May near the heads of gravelly riffles. Each female is attended by one or more males. Spawning is accompanied by strong vibrations that stir the finer material into suspension and form a slight depression in which eggs are deposited. The female and attending males remain over the spawning site for an extended period, spawning at irregular intervals until the female is spent. The spawning fish lose much of their customary shyness and sometimes may be approached and even picked up with little difficulty.

In Missouri streams the hog sucker reaches a length of about 3.4 inches by the end of its first year of life and averages 6.5, 9.7, 11.8, and 13 inches its second through fifth years respectively.[52] Females grow more rapidly than males after the fifth year and attain a larger maximum size.[127]

IMPORTANCE

The hog sucker is seldom taken on a baited hook but may be caught by gigging, snagging and snaring. It is not a desirable food fish because most of its bulk is made up of the bony head and, as a result, there is little usable meat.

Black Redhorse

Moxostoma duquesnei (Lesueur)

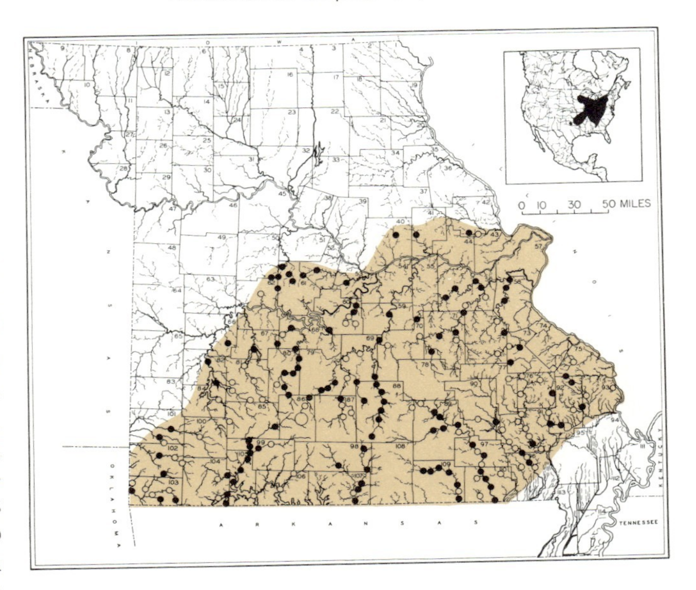

Other local names: White sucker, Blackhorse, Blue sucker

DESCRIPTION

Illustration: Page 185, 14a.

Characters: A slender, coarse-scaled sucker with a short dorsal fin containing 12 or 13 (rarely 14) rays. Lateral line complete. Lower lips consisting of parallel folds (plicae). Rear margin of lower lip forming a broad, V-shaped angle. Outer margin of dorsal fin curved inward (concave). Scales of back and sides without dark spots at bases. Tail fin olive or slate-colored in life. Throat teeth on lower half of arch numerous, blade-like, and without flattened grinding surfaces. Air bladder with 3 chambers.

Similar to golden redhorse, page 195, but usually with 44 to 47 scales in lateral line. Also, the caudal peduncle is more slender, its least depth going 2 or more times into its length. Breeding males do not have tubercles on head.

Life colors: Back dark olive-brown without definite dark edgings on scales. Sides lighter and more silvery. Belly white. Dorsal and tail fins olive or slate-colored; lower fins plain or with an orange tinge. Breeding males are without special colors, but have tubercles on all fins except dorsal (tubercles largest on anal fin and lower lobe of tail fin).

Size: Adults are commonly 9.3 to 15 inches long and weigh 0.3 to 1.3 pounds. In Missouri streams few black redhorse exceed a length of 17 inches or a weight of 2 pounds. However, an individual 25.9 inches long and weighing 7 pounds was taken in the Eleven Point River.

Scientific name: *Moxostoma,* Greek, meaning "mouth to suck"; *duquesnei,* named for Fort Duquesne, near Pittsburgh.

DISTRIBUTION AND HABITAT

The black redhorse is restricted to the Ozarks where it occurs in all the principal stream systems. In many Ozark streams the total poundage of this fish and the related golden redhorse equals that of all other large fishes combined.

The black redhorse inhabits clear streams having permanent flow and clean gravelly or rocky bottoms. It is most abundant in streams of medium size, being replaced by the white sucker in headwater creeks and spring branches, and by the northern redhorse and golden redhorse in the larger rivers. Generally it is more abundant than the golden redhorse in the cooler and swifter streams. Where the two occur together the black redhorse tends to predominate in short, rocky pools with current, whereas the golden redhorse is most abundant in larger pools and backwaters without noticeable current.

HABITS AND LIFE HISTORY

The black redhorse lives in large schools that are commonly observed foraging slowly over the bottom in riffles or the adjacent parts of pools.[128] The individuals in the feeding school are all oriented into the current and each leaves a trail of muddy water as it sucks in bottom material and selectively rejects the silt and other material unsuitable for food. The black redhorse feeds most actively in late evening. As is commonly the case with suckers, young black redhorse have a more terminal mouth and different food habits than the adults. Individuals less than 3 inches in length feed in backwater areas on algae and small crustaceans. As they grow larger they shift their feeding activities to riffles where they forage for aquatic insect larvae and other small bottom-dwelling invertebrates.

The black redhorse spawns in the Missouri Ozarks in late April or early May.[128] Spawning occurs on riffles 6 inches to 2 feet in depth over a bottom of small rubble mixed with lesser amounts of small gravel and sand. With the approach of the spawning season breeding adults congregate in pools adjacent to the spawning areas. The start of spawning activity is signalled by much jumping while the fish are still in deep water. About 2 hours after they begin jumping the males drift onto the spawning area, tail first, where they establish small territories. When ready to spawn, the females drift onto the spawning area individually from the pool above. The spawning act is essentially like that of the white sucker, page 192. On any given riffle spawning is completed within about 4 days.

In Missouri streams the black redhorse averages 3.5 inches in length by the end of its first year of life and averages 6.5, 9.3, 11 and 12.1 inches by the end of succeeding years.[52] The maximum life span is about 10 years.

IMPORTANCE

Redhorse suckers may be caught on small worms and other live bait, but most are taken by gigging, snagging, or snaring. The clear streams of the Missouri Ozarks are uniquely suited for gigging, and redhorse suckers make up the bulk of the fish taken by this method. Snagging and snaring are most successful during the spring spawning season when large numbers of redhorse are concentrated in shallow water. When redhorse suckers are scored and fried in deep fat the numerous small bones disappear and the flesh has a sweet, delicate flavor that ranks with that of the finest food fishes.

Golden Redhorse

Moxostoma erythrurum (Rafinesque)

Other local names: Yellow sucker, Golden sucker

DESCRIPTION

Illustration: Page 185, 14b; **39.**

Characters: A moderately chubby, coarse-scaled sucker with a short dorsal fin containing 12 or 13 (rarely 14) rays. Lateral line complete. Lower lips broken up into parallel folds (plicae). Rear margin of lower lip forming a moderately acute, V-shaped angle. Outer margin of dorsal fin slightly curved inward (concave). Scales of back and sides without dark spots at bases. Tail fin olive or slate-colored in life. Throat teeth on lower half of arch numerous, blade-like, and without flattened grinding surfaces. Air bladder with 3 chambers.

Similar to black redhorse but with 39 to 42 scales in lateral line. Also, the caudal peduncle is deeper, its least depth going less than 2 times into its length. Breeding males have tubercles on head.
Life colors: Back olive-brown without definite dark edgings on scales. Sides a rich golden yellow. Belly white. Dorsal and tail fins olive or slate-colored; lower fins plain or with an orange tinge. Breeding males have a broad, yellowish stripe along the upper side, and tubercles over much of the head and on all fins except dorsal (tubercles largest on snout, anal fin, and lower lobe of tail fin).
Size: Adults are commonly 8.6 to 14.4 inches in length and weigh 0.3 to 1.2 pounds. The maximum length and weight in Missouri streams is about 16.6 inches and 2.3 pounds.
Scientific name: *Moxostoma,* Greek, meaning "mouth to suck"; *erythrurum,* Greek, meaning "red tailed."

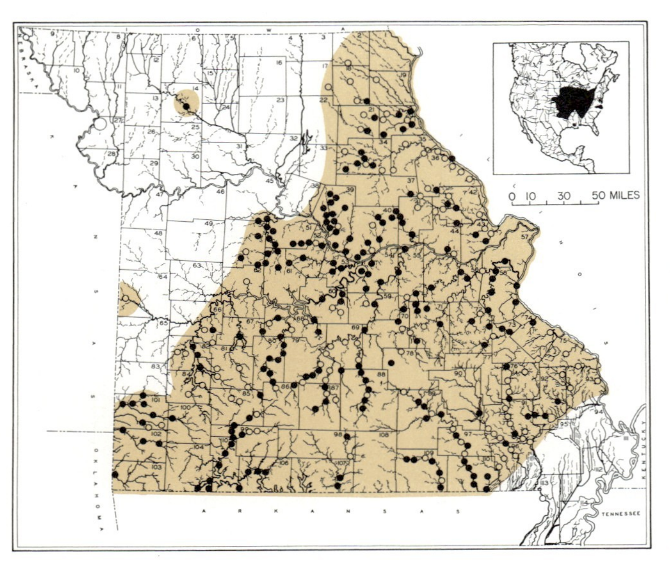

DISTRIBUTION AND HABITAT

The golden redhorse occurs throughout the Ozark Uplands and penetrates northeastward into Prairie streams of the upper Mississippi drainage. It has been collected only rarely in the Lowlands and the northwestern part of the Prairie Region. It is the most abundant redhorse in most streams of central and northeastern Missouri but is generally outnumbered by the black redhorse in Ozark streams.

The habitat requirements of this fish are similar to those of the black redhorse, page 194, except that the golden redhorse prefers slightly warmer waters, less current, and is more tolerant of turbidity and intermittent flow. The golden redhorse is most abundant in moderately clear, unpolluted streams having large, permanent pools and well defined rocky or gravelly riffles.

HABITS AND LIFE HISTORY

The habits and life history of this species are so similar to those of the black redhorse, page 194, that they need not be reported in detail here. The spawning season in central Missouri extends from about the third week of April to the middle of May (occasionally into early June), and is often preceded by movements into smaller and higher gradient streams. Golden redhorse appear in the smaller streams as soon as these begin to warm in early spring and disappear with the first rise after spawning is completed.

Growth in length is somewhat slower than that of the black redhorse during the early years of life but by the fifth or sixth year the two species are nearly equal. At any given length the golden redhorse is heavier. It averages 3.1 inches in length at the end of its first year of life and is about 5.9, 8.6, 10.7, and 12.2 inches in length at the end of succeeding years.[52] The life span does not usually exceed 6 or 7 years, but a few individuals live 11 years or more.

Silver Redhorse

Moxostoma anisurum (Rafinesque)

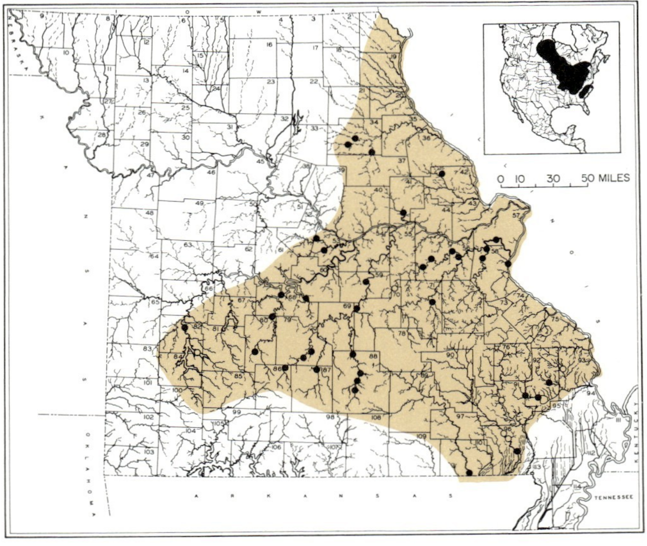

DESCRIPTION

Illustration: Page 184, 11a.
Characters: A chubby, coarse-scaled sucker with a short dorsal fin; distinguished from other redhorse by the presence of 14 or 15 (occasionally 16) rays in the dorsal fin. Lateral line complete, usually containing 42 to 45 scales. Lower lips covered by many small, wart-like bumps (papillae). Rear margin of lower lip forming an acute, V-shaped angle. Outer margin of dorsal fin straight or

slightly curved outward (convex). Scales of back and sides without dark spots at bases. Tail fin olive or slate-colored in life. Throat teeth on lower half of first arch numerous, blade-like, and without flattened grinding surfaces. Air bladder with 3 chambers.

Life colors: About as in the black redhorse, page 194.

Size: Adults are commonly 10.6 to 20 inches in length and weigh 0.5 to 3.5 pounds. The largest Missouri specimen was 22 inches long and weighed 4.3 pounds.

Scientific name: *Moxostoma,* Greek, meaning "mouth to suck"; *anisurum,* Greek, meaning "unequal tail."

DISTRIBUTION AND HABITAT

The silver redhorse is widespread but seldom abundant in the northern and eastern Ozarks. It seems to be more abundant in the Salt River system than elsewhere and is the dominant species of redhorse in some streams of that system. The silver redhorse may be abundant in other tributaries of the Mississippi River in northeastern Missouri, but these have not been sampled with the kind of gear necessary to properly collect large redhorse suckers.

The silver redhorse inhabits the larger and deeper pools of medium to large streams having moderately clear water, rocky or gravelly bottoms, and permanent flow. It avoids spring-fed streams having high gradients and those that are excessively turbid. It is most numerous in streams that are transitional between the Ozark and Prairie regions.

HABITS AND LIFE HISTORY

The diet of the silver redhorse consists principally of immature aquatic insects and is not notably different from that of the golden redhorse and shorthead redhorse from the same waters.[129] Spawning has been observed in central Missouri in early April, somewhat ahead of the black redhorse and golden redhorse. The spawning adults gather in large schools over shallow gravelly riffles, as is typical of other redhorse species that have been studied. Growth in Missouri streams is more rapid than that of other redhorse suckers. In the St. Francis River the silver redhorse averages 4.5 inches in length by the end of its first year of life, and is about 7.9, 10.6, 12.3, 13.8, 15.2 and 16.3 inches long by the end of succeeding years.[52] The maximum life span is at least 10 years.

Shorthead Redhorse

Moxostoma macrolepidotum (Lesueur)

Other local names: Redhorse, Redfin sucker

DESCRIPTION

Illustration: Page 185, 13a.

Characters: A slender, coarse-scaled sucker with a short dorsal fin containing 12 or 13 (rarely 14) rays. Lateral line complete, containing 41 to 45 scales. Lower lips broken up into parallel folds (plicae). Missouri specimens often have a distinctive "pea" shaped swelling at middle of upper lip. Rear margin of lower lip nearly straight. Head shorter than in other redhorse suckers, its length going more than 4.2 times into standard length. Outer margin of dorsal fin strongly curved inward (concave). Scales of back and upper sides each with a crescent-shaped dark spot at base. Tail fin bright red in life. Throat teeth on lower half of first arch numerous, blade-like, and without flattened grinding surfaces. Air bladder with 3 chambers.

Life colors: Back and upper sides olive brown with golden reflections, the scales rather prominently dark-edged. Remainder of sides a rich golden yellow. Belly white. Dorsal fin olive or slate; tail fin bright red; lower fins plain or with orange tinge. Breeding males without special colors but with tubercles on pelvic, anal, and tail fins.

Size: Adults are commonly 9 to 16.1 inches in length and weigh 0.3 to 1.5 pounds. The largest Missouri specimen examined weighed 4.2 pounds.

Scientific name: *Moxostoma,* Greek, meaning "mouth to suck"; *macrolepidotum,* Greek, meaning "large scaled."

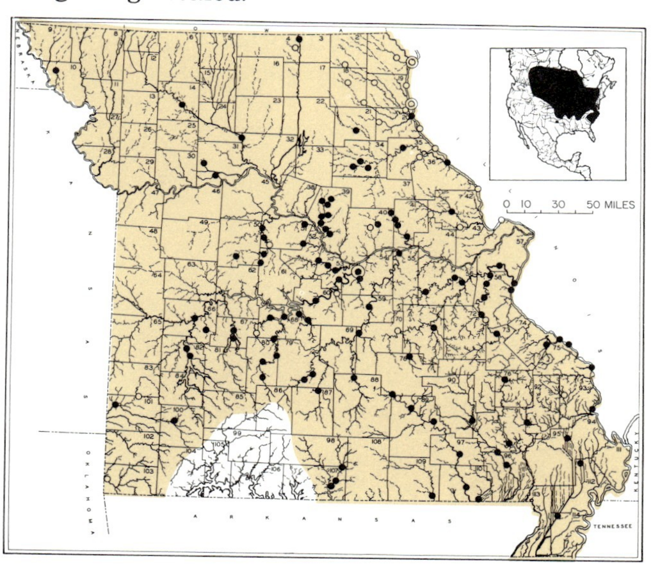

DISTRIBUTION AND HABITAT

The shorthead redhorse is common and widespread in the Ozarks but is absent from much of the White River system. It is the most abundant redhorse in downstream sections of the largest Ozark rivers and is exceeded in abundance only by the golden redhorse and black redhorse in many other streams of that region. This species is also abundant in the northeastern part of the Prairie Region where it frequents smaller streams than in the Ozarks.

The shorthead redhorse inhabits a diversity of stream types but is most abundant in moderately large rivers having a predominance of gravelly or rocky bottoms and a permanent strong flow. In large streams the shorthead redhorse frequents the swifter water near riffles; in small streams it is also found in pools without noticeable current. No other Missouri redhorse is as adaptable in its habitat requirements as the shorthead redhorse.

HABITS AND LIFE HISTORY

The life history of the shorthead redhorse is not notably different from that of other redhorse suckers. Its food in the Des Moines River, Iowa, consisted entirely of immature aquatic insects.[129] Spawning schools of the shorthead redhorse have been observed on gravelly riffles in central Missouri during late April. These schools remained separate from those of the golden redhorse that were spawning on the same riffle. Growth of the shorthead redhorse in Missouri streams is more rapid than that of the golden and black redhorse, but is slightly slower than that of the silver redhorse. A length of about 4.2 inches is achieved the first year and average lengths at the end of succeeding years are 7.6, 10.4, 12.0 and 13.2 inches.[52] The maximum life span is 9 years or more.

River Redhorse

Moxostoma carinatum (Cope)

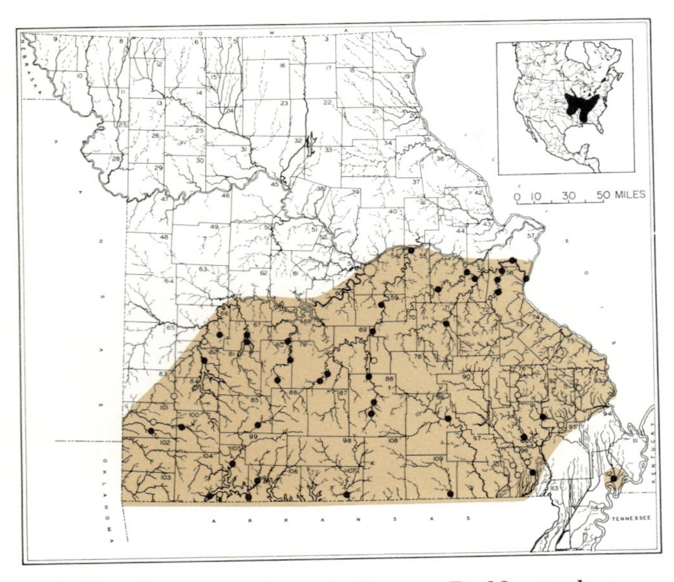

Other local names: Redhorse, Redfin sucker

DESCRIPTION

Illustration: Page 185, 13b.

Characters: A moderately chubby, coarse-scaled sucker with a short dorsal fin containing 12 or 13 (rarely 14) rays. Lateral line complete, with 41 to 46 scales. Lower lips broken up into parallel folds (plicae). Rear margin of lower lip forming a slight V-shaped angle. Outer margin of dorsal fin straight or slightly curved outward (convex). Scales of back and upper sides each with a crescent-shaped dark spot at base. Base of tail fin with a thin pencil-line of black along margin of last row of scales. Tail fin bright red in life. Throat teeth on lower half of first arch few in number, broad and molar-like, and with flattened grinding surfaces. Air bladder with 3 chambers.

Life colors: About like those of shorthead redhorse, page 197.

Size: Adults are commonly 10.4 to 22 inches long and weigh 0.5 to 4 pounds. Maximum size reported for Missouri streams is 26.1 inches and 8 1/4 pounds.

Scientific name: *Moxostoma,* Greek, meaning "mouth to suck"; *carinatum,* Latin, meaning "keel."

DISTRIBUTION AND HABITAT

The river redhorse occurs throughout the Ozarks but is not abundant at any location. In many Ozark streams it is exceeded in abundance by all other redhorse suckers except the silver redhorse. Elsewhere in its range this sucker has undergone a marked decline in abundance, but in the Ozarks there have been no discernable changes in its distribution and abundance over the past 30 years. Nothing is known of its abundance in Missouri prior to 1940.

The river redhorse inhabits the pools of clear, medium-sized streams having gravelly or rocky bottoms and continuous strong flow. It seems less tolerant of turbidity, siltation, and intermittent flow than other redhorse suckers found in Missouri.

HABITS AND LIFE HISTORY

The large, molar-like throat teeth that distinguish the river redhorse from other Missouri redhorse are an adaptation for crushing the shells of molluscs. An Alabama study revealed that the diet of this redhorse consisted mostly of molluscs, especially the Asiatic clam *Corbicula.*[130] This clam is not abundant in most Ozark streams and perhaps river redhorse in these streams feed on snails and the young of native unionid clams. In the Ozarks the river redhorse spawns a little earlier than the black redhorse, with spawning preceded by upstream movements. The spawning habits are like those of other redhorse suckers. Growth in Ozark streams is slower than for other redhorse during the first few years of life, but eventually the river redhorse overtakes and then surpasses the other species. In the St. Francis River a length of 2.4 inches is reached the first year and lengths of about 5.3, 8.1, 10.4 and 11.7 inches are reached in succeeding years.[52] The maximum life span in Missouri is at least 12 years.

Spotted Sucker

Minytrema melanops (Rafinesque)

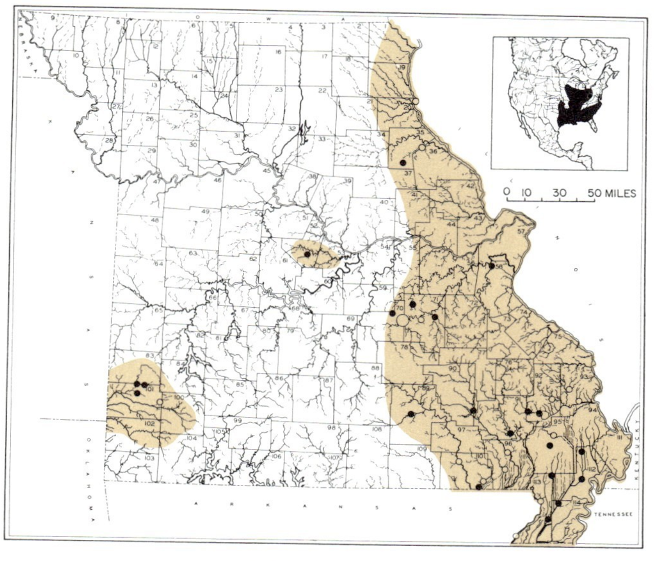

DESCRIPTION

Illustration: Page 186, 15a.

Characters: A moderately slender, coarse-scaled sucker with a short dorsal fin containing 11 or 12 (occasionally 10 or 13) rays. Lateral line absent or developed only on a few scales; scales in lateral series 42 to 46. Distinguished from other Missouri suckers by the presence of several parallel rows of prominent dark spots along the side (spots faint or absent in small individuals). Mouth distinctly subterminal and horizontal. Rear margin of lower lip forming a rather acute, V-shaped angle. Outer margin of dorsal fin straight or curved inward (concave).

Life colors: Back olive-brown without definite dark edgings on scales. Sides silvery or brassy yellow; each scale with a squarish black or dark green spot at base forming lengthwise streaks along body. Belly silvery-white. Dorsal and tail fins olive or slate-colored; lower fins whitish. Breeding males have two dark stripes separated by a pinkish band along midside, and have large tubercles on snout and anal fin.

Size: Adults are commonly 9.2 to 15.9 inches long and weigh about 0.3 to 2 pounds. The maximum length and weight in Missouri streams is about 16.2 inches and 2.2 pounds.

Scientific name: *Minytrema,* Greek, meaning "reduced aperture," in reference to the reduction in the lateral line; *melanops,* Greek, meaning "black appearance."

DISTRIBUTION AND HABITAT

The spotted sucker is rather common and generally distributed in the Lowlands of southeastern Missouri and occurs at scattered localities northward in the Ozarks and in the northeastern part of the Prairie Region. It has been collected on two occasions in recent years from the Moreau River; this is the only documented locality for the spotted sucker in the Missouri River system of Missouri.

The spotted sucker is an inhabitant of clear, warm waters having no noticeable current, an abundance of submerged aquatic vegetation, and soft bottoms containing large quantities of organic debris. In the Lowlands it is found principally in the clearer and more sluggish ditches. In the Ozarks the spotted sucker is most abundant in the deeper pools of small creeks draining level uplands along major stream divides, and in the quiet backwaters and overflow pools of larger streams.

HABITS AND LIFE HISTORY

The food of the spotted sucker has not been studied in detail but probably consists mostly of molluscs and insect larvae.[24] In Oklahoma spawning occurs from the last week of April through May on riffles above large pools.[131] The eggs hatch in 7 to 12 days, depending on temperature. The spotted sucker attains a length of about 6.1 inches its first year and averages 11.3, 13.3, 16.1, and 17.3 inches at the end of succeeding years.[131] Maturity is reached at 3 years of age, and the maximum life span is about 5 years.

Creek Chubsucker

Erimyzon oblongus (Mitchill)

DESCRIPTION

Illustration: Page 186, 16b.

Characters: A small, chubby sucker with a short dorsal fin containing 10 (occasionally 11) rays. Lateral line absent. No parallel rows of dark spots along sides. Mouth nearly terminal and somewhat oblique. Rear margin of lower lips forming an acute V-shaped angle. Outer margin of dorsal fin usually strongly curved outward (convex).

Similar to lake chubsucker, page 200, but usually with fewer dorsal fin rays and with more scales in the lateral series (usually 39 to 41). Also, the dark stripe along midside is continuous only in small individuals.

Life colors: Back and upper sides olive-brown, the scales prominently dark-edged. Midside marked by a series of more or less connected blotches. Lower sides and belly yellowish or white. Dorsal and tail fins olive or slate-colored; lower fins yellowish-white. Breeding males are without special colors but have a long, sickle-shaped anal fin and 3 large tubercles on each side of snout.

Size: This species is the smallest Missouri sucker. Adults are commonly 4.5 to 7 inches long to a maximum of about 9.3 inches.

Scientific name: *Erimyzon,* Greek, meaning "to suck"; *oblongus,* Latin, meaning "oblong."

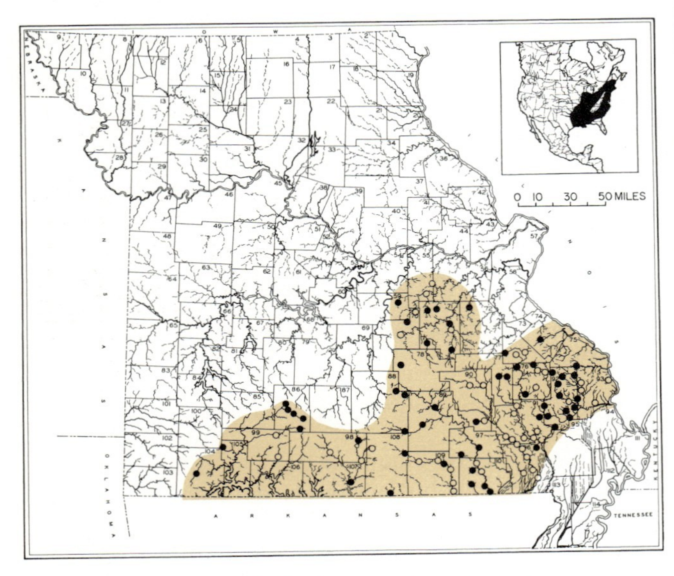

DISTRIBUTION AND HABITAT

The creek chubsucker is widespread in the eastern and southern Ozarks but is seldom very abundant. It avoids the Lowlands where the lake chubsucker occurs, and is absent from Ozark streams of the Missouri and Spring River systems.

This fish is an inhabitant of clear, quiet waters having thick growths of submergent vegetation and bottoms composed of sand or silt mixed with organic debris. It commonly occurs in the deeper and more sluggish pools of small creeks, but is more often found in protected inlets and overflow pools. As its name suggests, it is more characteristic of small creeks than of rivers.

HABITS AND LIFE HISTORY

The food habits of the creek chubsucker have not been studied but the diet is probably similar to that of the lake chubsucker. The terminal mouth of this species may indicate that it is less a bottom feeder than many suckers. Spawning occurs at this latitude in March or April on the gravelly shoals of streams.[132] The spawning act is like that of the white sucker, page 192. In southern Illinois the creek chubsucker averages 2 inches in length at the end of its first year, and 4 inches at the end of its second year.[133]

Lake Chubsucker

Erimyzon sucetta (Lacépède)

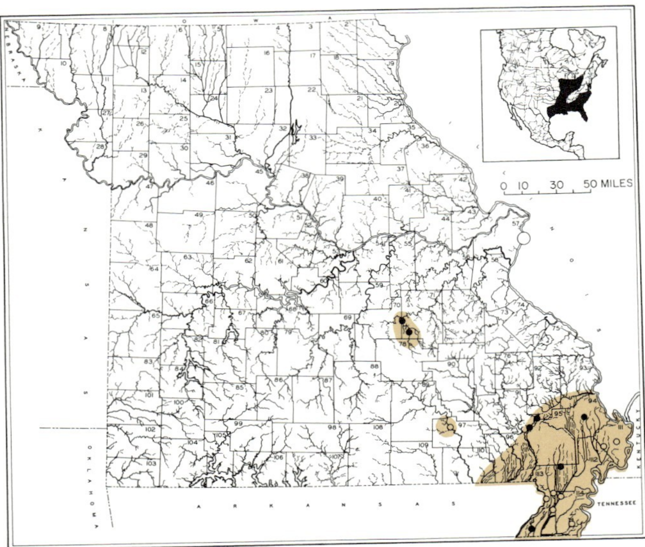

DESCRIPTION

Illustration: Page 186, 16a.

Characters: Similar to creek chubsucker, page 199, but with more dorsal fin rays (usually 11 or 12, occasionally 10 or 13), and with fewer scales in the lateral series (usually 35 to 37). Also, the dark stripe along midside is continuous at all ages (stripe often indistinct in adults).

Life colors: About as in the creek chubsucker, except as noted under *Characters.*

Size: Adults are commonly 5 to 10 inches long to a maximum of about 11 inches.

Scientific name: *Erimyzon,* Greek, meaning "to suck"; *sucetta,* from the French *sucet,* "a sucker," or "sucking fish."

DISTRIBUTION AND HABITAT

The lake chubsucker is largely restricted to the Lowland Faunal Region but has also been collected along the Current and Meramec rivers in the eastern Ozarks. A very old (1853) record for the lake chubsucker near St. Louis suggests a former more widespread distribution along the Mississippi River. It is not abundant anywhere in Missouri and seems to have declined in abundance during the past 30 years.

It is most often found in clear, quiet pools having much submerged aquatic vegetation and bottoms composed of sand or silt mixed with organic debris. In the Lowlands it is found in the clearer and more sluggish ditches. In the Ozarks it has been collected in overflow pools away from the main channel of large streams. The habitat requirements of the lake chubsucker and the creek chubsucker are similar and their largely complementary patterns of distribution in Missouri may result from competition.

HABITS AND LIFE HISTORY

A limited study of the food habits of the lake chubsucker in Ohio indicates that it feeds primarily on "water fleas" and other small crustaceans, along with lesser quantities of immature aquatic insects.[134] In ponds near Columbia where the lake chubsucker was stocked it spawned in May. The eggs are scattered over submergent vegetation and hatch in 6 or 7 days at a water temperature of 72 to 85°F.[136]

CATFISHES

Ictaluridae

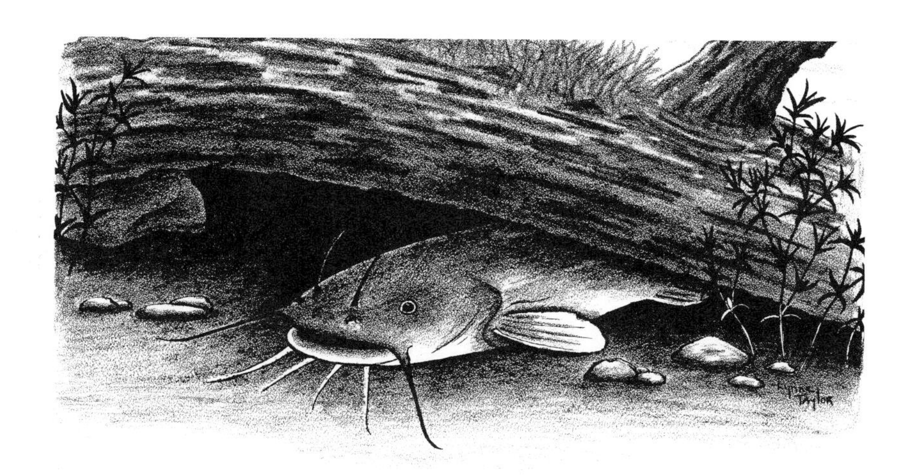

Many kinds of catfishes occur in tropical regions and the sea, but all belong to different fish families than our native species. The catfish family Ictaluridae includes 37 species, all restricted to North America. Fifteen species occur in Missouri, among them such popular food and game fishes as the channel catfish, flathead catfish, and the bullheads. Also included are nine lesser-known species collectively referred to as "madtoms." These small, secretive catfish are rarely seen unless a special effort is made to capture them.

Catfishes are such easily recognized and familiar fishes that a detailed description is unnecessary. The name, "catfish" results from the presence of four pairs of long, slender barbels near the mouth that somewhat resemble the "whiskers" of a cat. All have a smooth, scaleless skin. The fins are supported by soft rays, except for a stout, sharp spine at the front of the dorsal fin and each of the pectoral fins. A small, rayless adipose fin is present on the midline of the back just ahead of the tail fin. In all the catfishes commonly taken by fishermen the adipose fin forms a free, flap-like lobe. In the smaller and less familiar "madtom" catfishes the adipose fin forms a low, keel-like ridge without a free, flap-like lobe behind.

Like their namesakes the cats, catfishes are most active at night. During the daylight hours they often hide in natural cavities and crevices or remain quietly in the deeper parts of pools. However, if there is a sudden sharp rise in the stream level they go on a feeding spree and forage actively at all hours of the day or night. Catfishes have many external taste buds which are most abundant on the barbels. If a piece of meat is brought into contact with the side of a bullhead it will immediately turn and swallow it, and the same kind of response can be elicited by directing a stream of juices from the meat against the side. No doubt taste and touch play a more important role than sight in feeding and general orientation to the environment of catfishes.

Parental care is quite highly developed in catfishes. So far as is known all species spawn in natural cavities or construct a nest and remain with the eggs until they hatch. Some, such as the bullheads, even attend the young for a considerable time after they are free-swimming. One or both parents may participate in these activities.

A noteworthy feature of the madtoms is that they possess a mild venom that is associated with the pectoral and dorsal spines. When introduced into a puncture wound produced by the spine, this venom causes a painful reaction. The spines are often erected and locked in place when the madtom is alarmed, increasing the chance of a puncture. The venom is not considered dangerous to man and the chances of being "spined" are not great if the possibility is kept in mind while handling a madtom. This venom is not restricted to madtoms, being developed to varying degrees in other North American catfishes.

Key to the Catfishes

1a. Adipose fin a free lobe which is widely separate from tail fin.
Go to **2**

1b. Adipose fin a low keel-like ridge, connected to tail fin or with, at most, a slight notch between them.
Madtoms, *Noturus*
Go to **7**

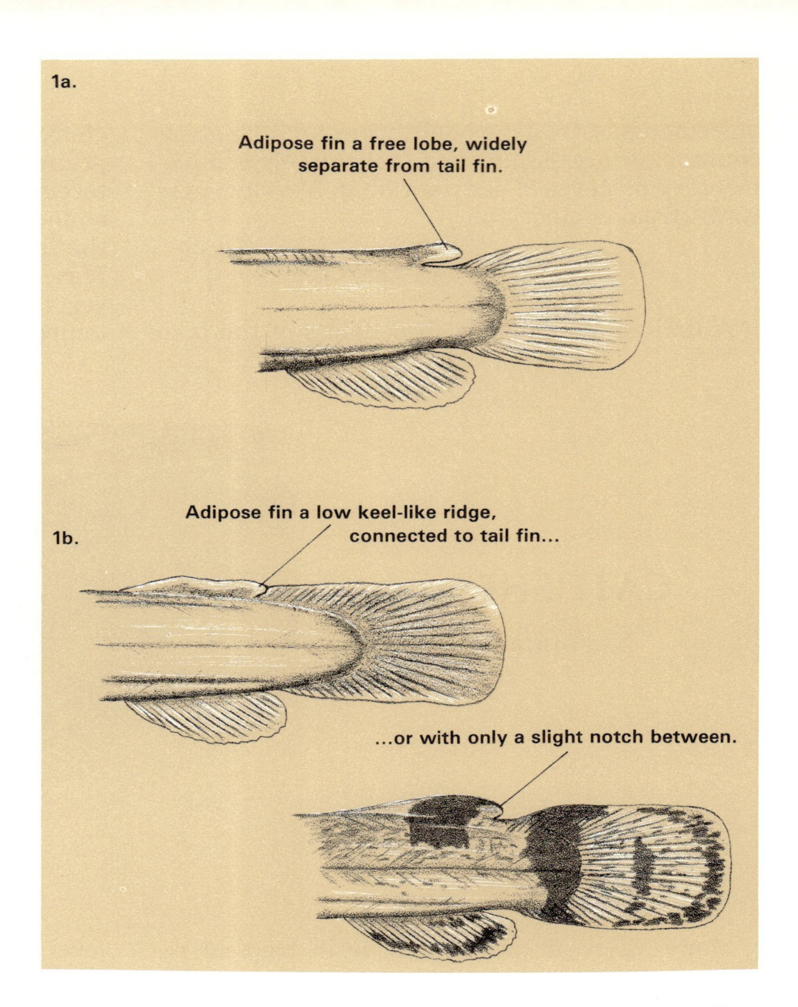
1a.
Adipose fin a free lobe, widely separate from tail fin.
1b.
Adipose fin a low keel-like ridge, connected to tail fin...
...or with only a slight notch between.

2a. *(From 1a.)* Tail fin deeply forked; head wedge-shaped in profile.
Go to **3**

2b. *(From 1a.)* Tail fin not deeply forked, its rear margin at most slightly notched; head blunter, not wedgeshaped in profile.
Go to **4**

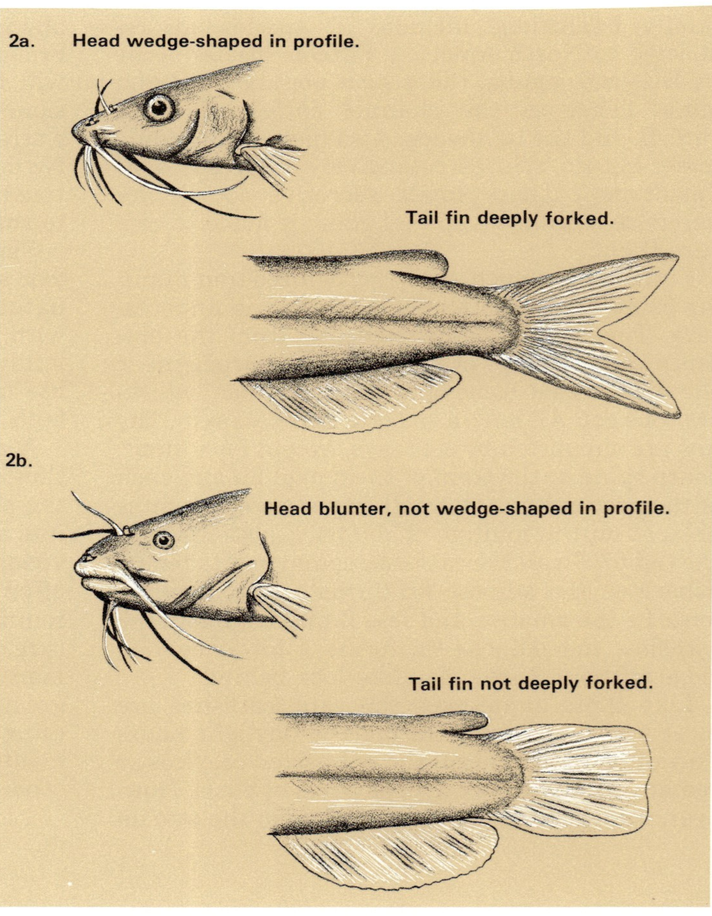
2a.
Head wedge-shaped in profile.
Tail fin deeply forked.
2b.
Head blunter, not wedge-shaped in profile.
Tail fin not deeply forked.

3a. *(From 2a.)* Outer margin of anal fin rounded; anal fin rays 24 to 29; body with dark spots, except in large adults and small young; air bladder without a definite constriction.
Channel catfish
Ictalurus punctatus .. **Page 211**

3b. *(From 2a.)* Outer margin of anal fin straight; anal fin rays 30 to 35; body without dark spots at all ages; air bladder with a definite constriction.
Blue catfish
Ictalurus furcatus .... **Page 213**

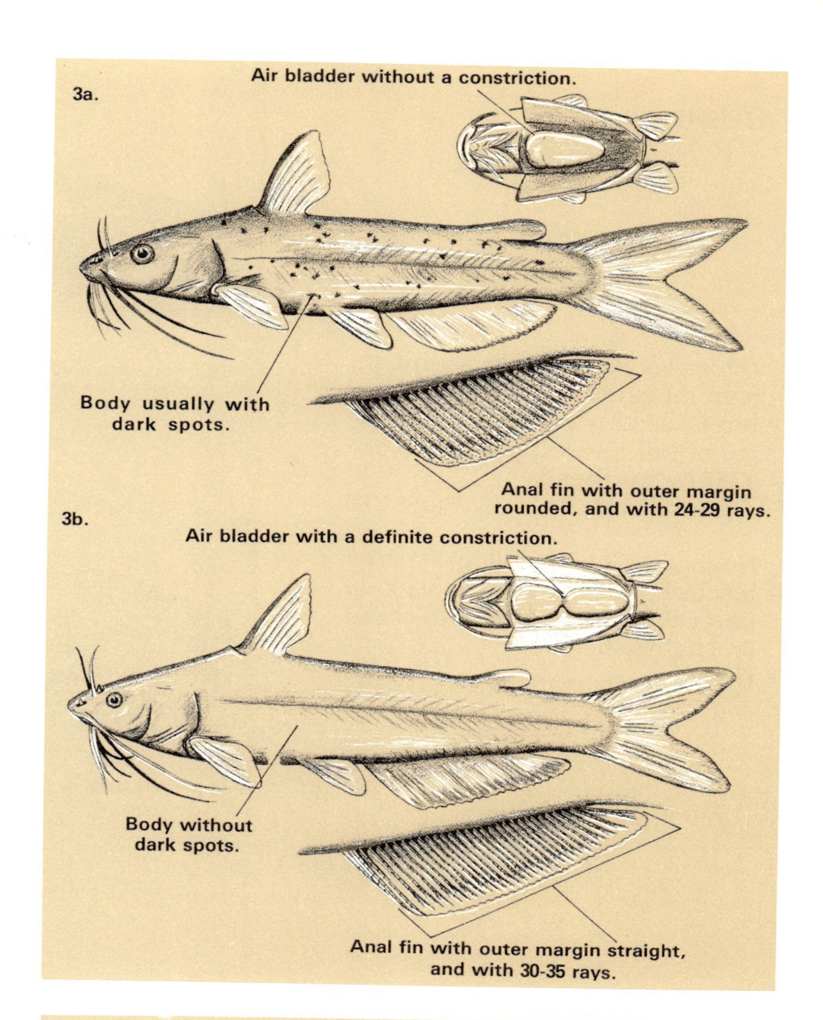
3a.
Air bladder without a constriction.
Body usually with dark spots.
Anal fin with outer margin rounded, and with 24-29 rays.
3b.
Air bladder with a definite constriction.
Body without dark spots.
Anal fin with outer margin straight, and with 30-35 rays.

4a. *(From 2b.)* Lower jaw projecting far beyond upper jaw except in smallest young; anal fin short, the length of its base (A) less than distance from back of eye to rear margin of gill cover (B); upper tip of tail fin lighter in color than rest of fin; pad of teeth in upper jaw with a backward extension on each side.
Flathead catfish
Pylodictis olivaris .... **Page 220**

4b. *(From 2b.)* Lower jaw not projecting beyond upper jaw; anal fin longer, the length of its base (A) greater than distance from back of eye to rear margin of gill cover (B); upper tip of tail fin not lighter in color than rest of fin; pad of teeth in upper jaw without backward extensions.
Go to **5**

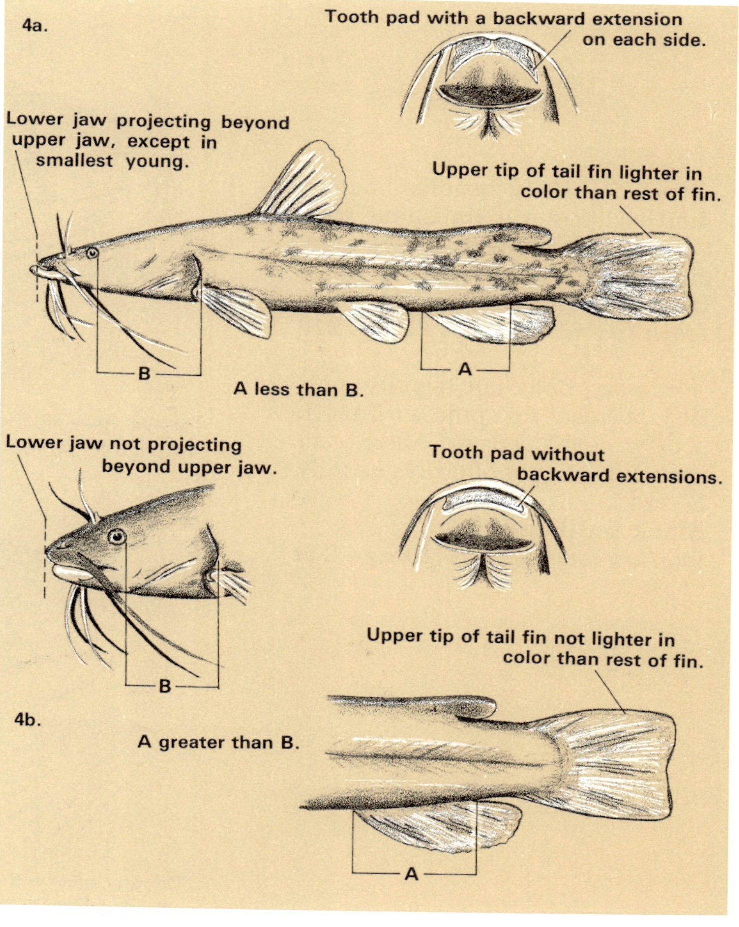
4a.
Tooth pad with a backward extension on each side.
Lower jaw projecting beyond upper jaw, except in smallest young.
Upper tip of tail fin lighter in color than rest of fin.
B
A
A less than B.
Lower jaw not projecting beyond upper jaw.
Tooth pad without backward extensions.
Upper tip of tail fin not lighter in color than rest of fin.
B
4b.
A greater than B.
A

5a. *(From 4b.)* Chin barbels whitish; anal fin rays (including rudimentaries) usually 24 to 27; rear margin of tail fin nearly straight.
Yellow bullhead
Ictalurus natalis ..... **Page 210**

5b. *(From 4b.)* Chin barbels grayish or blackish; anal fin rays usually fewer than 24; rear margin of tail fin slightly notched.
Go to 6

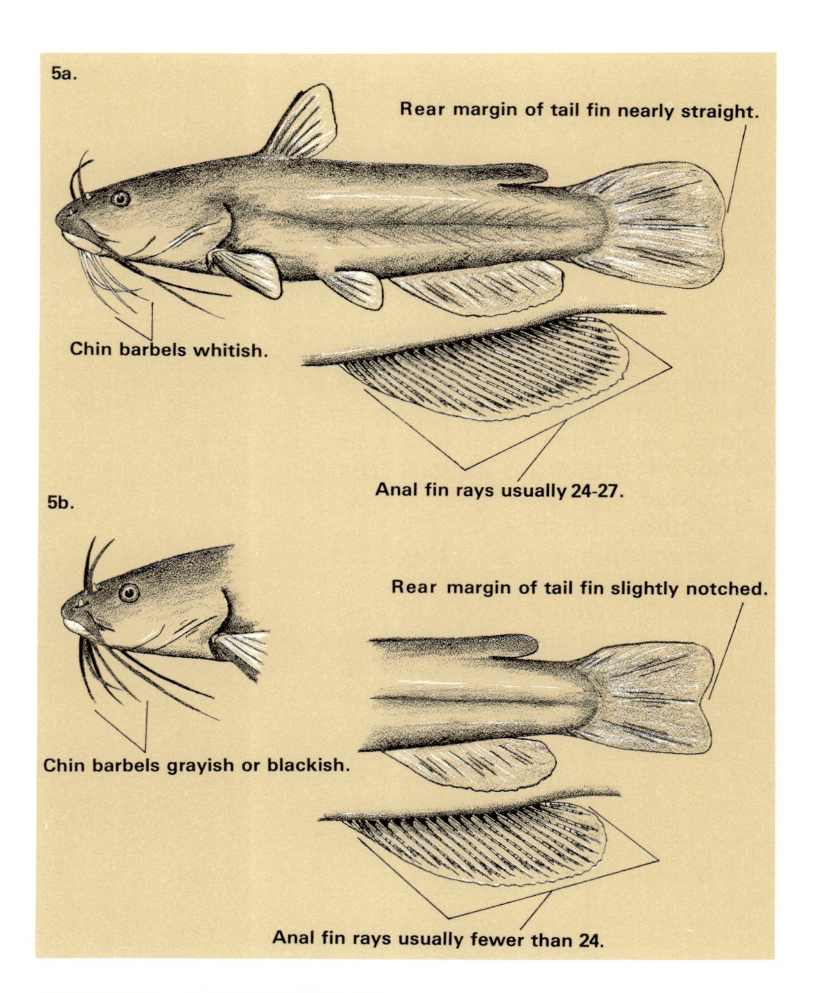
5a.
Rear margin of tail fin nearly straight.
Chin barbels whitish.
Anal fin rays usually 24-27.
5b.
Rear margin of tail fin slightly notched.
Chin barbels grayish or blackish.
Anal fin rays usually fewer than 24.

6a. *(From 5b.)* Body usually heavily mottled; pectoral fin spine with teeth well developed on back margin; anal fin rays usually 22 or 23.
Brown bullhead
Ictalurus nebulosus ... **Page 210**

6b. *(From 5b.)* Body not heavily mottled; pectoral fin spine with teeth poorly developed or absent on back margin; anal fin rays usually 17 to 21.
Black bullhead
Ictalurus melas ...... **Page 209**

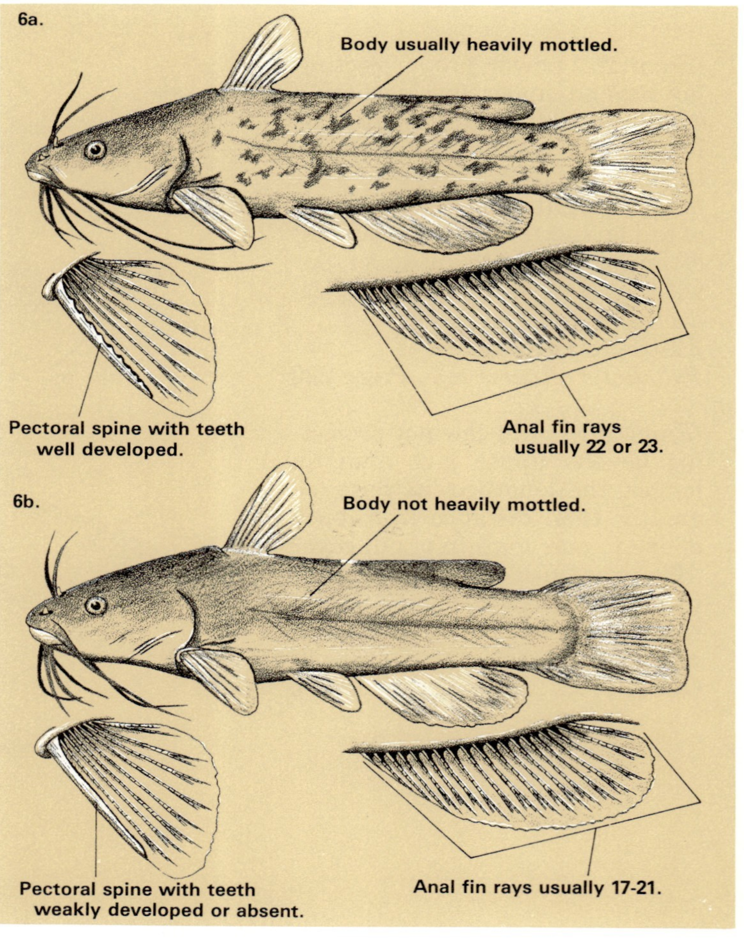
6a.
Body usually heavily mottled.
Pectoral spine with teeth well developed.
Anal fin rays usually 22 or 23.
6b.
Body not heavily mottled.
Pectoral spine with teeth weakly developed or absent.
Anal fin rays usually 17-21.

7a.

Upper jaw not projecting beyond lower jaw.

7b.

Upper jaw projecting beyond lower jaw.

7a. *(From 1b.)* Upper jaw not projecting beyond lower jaw, the two jaws about equal length.
Go to **8**

7b. *(From 1b.)* Upper jaw projecting well beyond lower jaw.
Go to **9**

8a. *(From 7a.)* Anal, tail, and dorsal fins dark-edged; pectoral fin spine with well developed teeth on back margin; body more slender, its depth (A) going more than 4.5 times into standard length (B).
Slender madtom
Noturus exilis .... **Page 215**

8b. *(From 7a.)* Anal, tail, and dorsal fins not dark-edged; pectoral fin spine without teeth on back margin; body deeper, its depth (A) going less than 4.5 times into standard length (B).
Tadpole madtom
Noturus gyrinus ...... **Page 214**

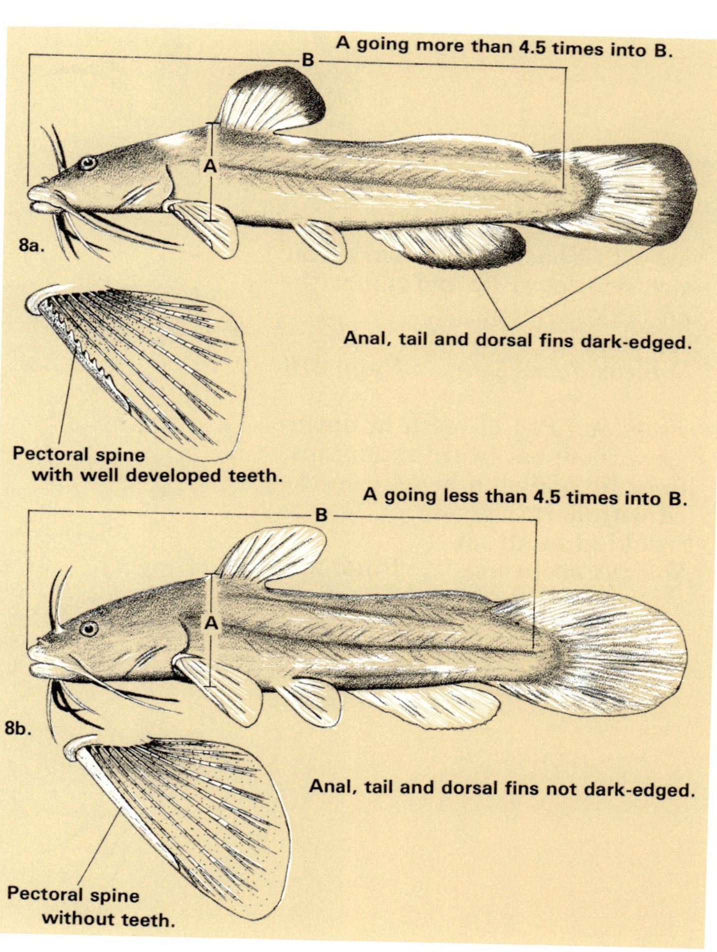
A going more than 4.5 times into B.
B
A
8a.
Anal, tail and dorsal fins dark-edged.
Pectoral spine
with well developed teeth.
A going less than 4.5 times into B.
B
A
8b.
Anal, tail and dorsal fins not dark-edged.
Pectoral spine
without teeth.

9a.

Body without distinct blotches or bars.

Pectoral spine without teeth.

9b.

Body with distinct blotches or bars.

Pectoral spine with saw-like teeth.

9a. *(From 7b.)* Pectoral fin spine without teeth on back margin; body rather uniformly colored, without distinct blotches or bars.
Go to **10**

9b. *(From 7b.)* Pectoral fin spine with saw-like teeth on back margin; body with distinct blotches or bars.
Go to **11**

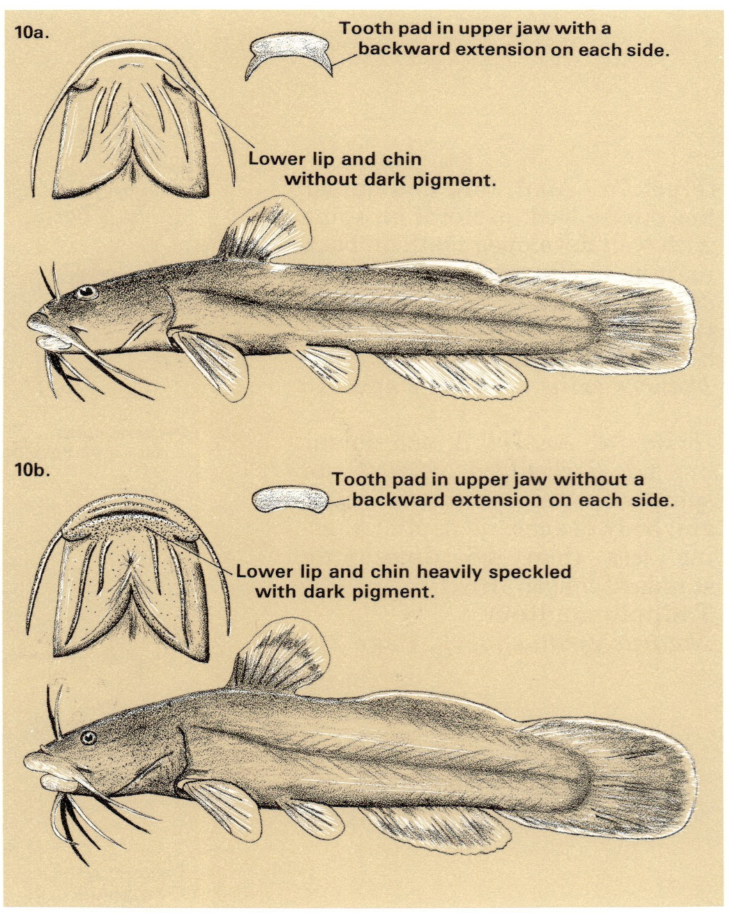
10a.
Tooth pad in upper jaw with a backward extension on each side.
Lower lip and chin without dark pigment.
10b.
Tooth pad in upper jaw without a backward extension on each side.
Lower lip and chin heavily speckled with dark pigment.

10a. *(From 9a.)* Pad of teeth in upper jaw with a backward extension on each side; lower lip and chin without dark pigment.
Stonecat
Noturus flavus .... **Page 216**

10b. *(From 9a.)* Pad of teeth in upper jaw without backward extensions; lower lip and chin heavily speckled with dark pigment.
Freckled madtom
Noturus nocturnus ... **Page 215**

11a. *(From 9b.)* Head length (A) going 3.5 times or more into standard length (B); distance from tip of tail fin to adipose fin notch (C) going more than 2 times into distance from adipose fin notch to front of dorsal fin base (D); pectoral rays usually 9 (occasionally 8 or 10).
Ozark madtom
Noturus albater ...... **Page 217**

11b. *(From 9b.)* Head length (A) going less than 3.5 times into standard length (B); distance from tip of tail to adipose fin notch (C) going less than 2 times into distance from adipose fin notch to front of dorsal fin base (D); pectoral rays usually 8 (occasionally 7 or 9).
Go to **12**

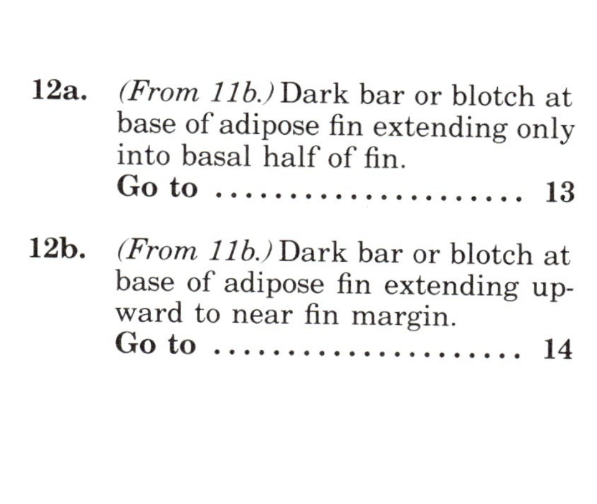

12a. *(From 11b.)* Dark bar or blotch at base of adipose fin extending only into basal half of fin.
Go to **13**

12b. *(From 11b.)* Dark bar or blotch at base of adipose fin extending upward to near fin margin.
Go to **14**

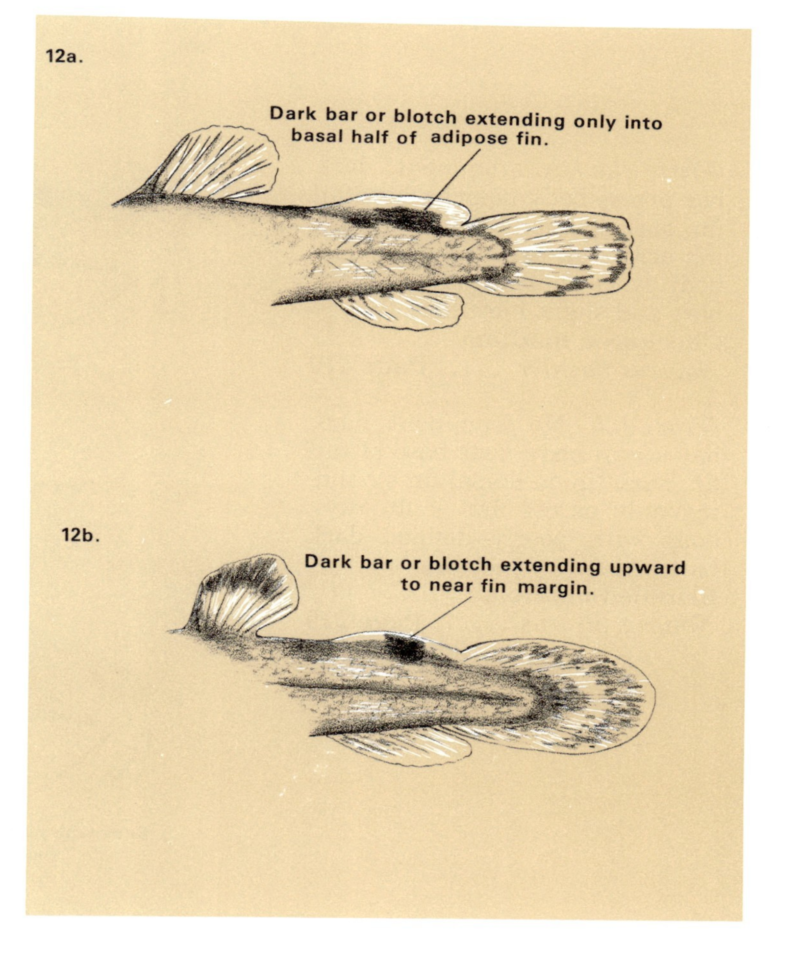
12a.
Dark bar or blotch extending only into basal half of adipose fin.
12b.
Dark bar or blotch extending upward to near fin margin.

13a. *(From 12a.)* With a dark crescent-shaped bar across middle of tail fin; small saw-like teeth poorly developed on front margin of pectoral fin spine.
Neosho madtom
Noturus placidus ..... **Page 219**

13b. *(From 12a.)* No dark crescent-shaped bar across middle of tail fin; small saw-like teeth well developed on front margin of pectoral fin spine.
Mountain madtom
Noturus eleutherus ... **Page 218**

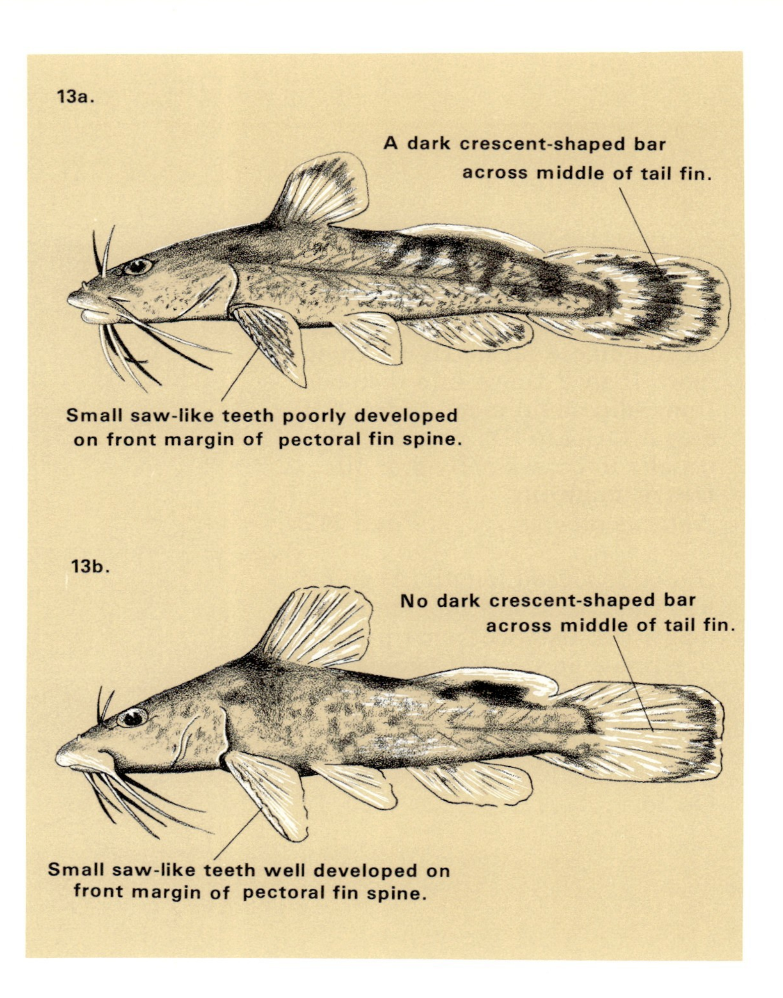
13a.
A dark crescent-shaped bar across middle of tail fin.
Small saw-like teeth poorly developed on front margin of pectoral fin spine.
13b.
No dark crescent-shaped bar across middle of tail fin.
Small saw-like teeth well developed on front margin of pectoral fin spine.

14a. *(From 12b.)* A prominent, dark bar across body near base of tail fin; dark tip on dorsal fin extending across all except last fin ray; body with sharply defined dark bars and slight mottling.
Checkered madtom
Noturus flavater ..... **Page 219**

14b. *(From 12b.)* No prominent, dark bar across body near base of tail fin; dark tip on dorsal fin extending only across first 4 fin rays; body with poorly defined dark bars and heavy mottling.
Brindled madtom
Noturus miurus ...... **Page 218**

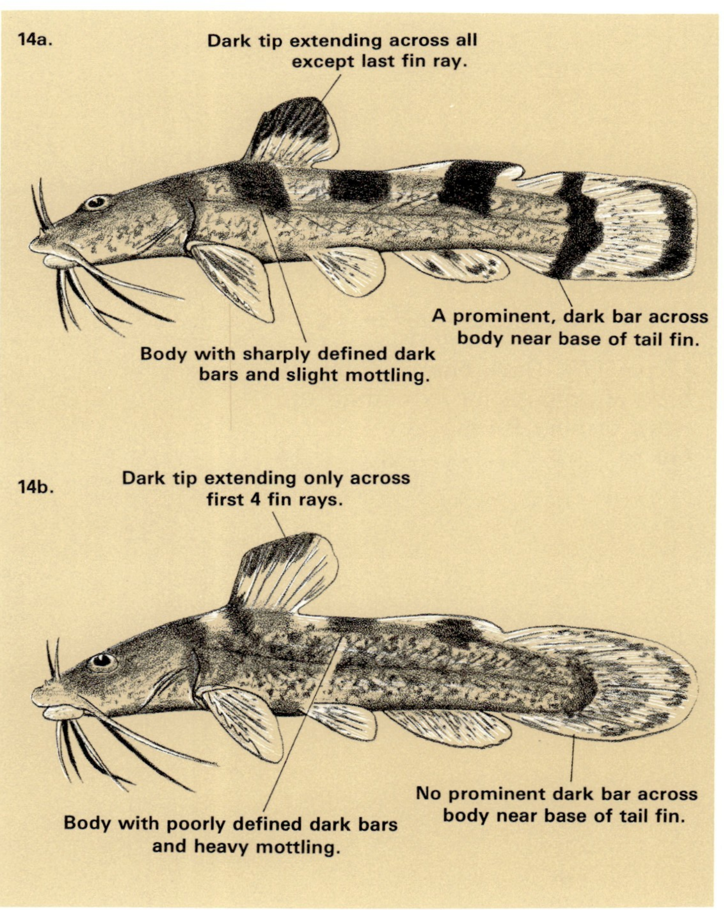
14a.
Dark tip extending across all except last fin ray.
A prominent, dark bar across body near base of tail fin.
Body with sharply defined dark bars and slight mottling.
14b.
Dark tip extending only across first 4 fin rays.
No prominent dark bar across body near base of tail fin.
Body with poorly defined dark bars and heavy mottling.

Black Bullhead

Ictalurus melas (Rafinesque)

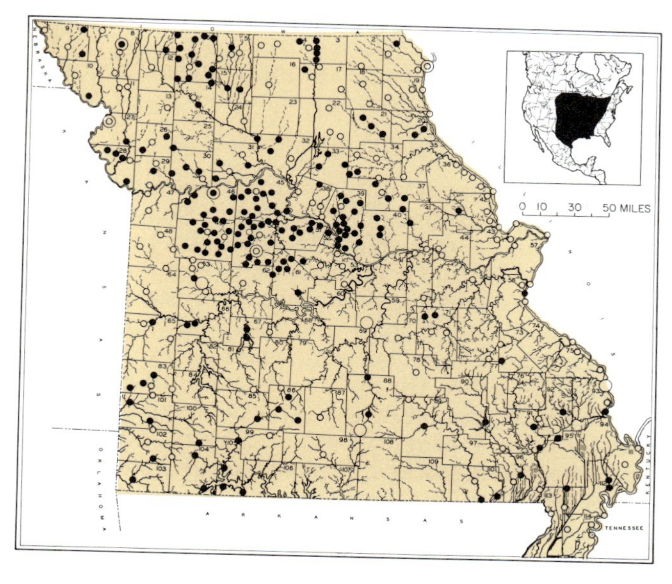

Other local names: Mud cat

DESCRIPTION

Illustration: Page 204, 6b.

Characters: A chubby catfish with the tail fin slightly notched, but not deeply forked, and with the adipose fin forming a free, flap-like lobe. Upper jaw projecting beyond lower jaw. Tooth pad on upper jaw without backward extensions. Upper tip of tail fin never lighter in color than remainder of fin.

Similar to yellow bullhead and brown bullhead, but without saw-like teeth on rear margin of pectoral spine and with fewer rays in anal fin—usually 17 to 21. Chin barbels dusky or black—never uniformly white; back and sides not strongly mottled with darker color. Barbel at corner of mouth not reaching farther back than base of pectoral fin. Length of anal fin base less than length of head. Rear margin of tail fin slightly notched.

Life colors: Back and sides a uniform yellowish-brown, dark olive, or black, with a pale vertical bar often evident across base of tail fin (bar never present in other bullheads). Belly yellowish or white. Fins dusky or black, the membranes much darker than the rays.

Size: Adults seldom exceed a length of 16 inches or a weight of 2.3 pounds. The largest authenticated specimen from Missouri weighed 3 pounds, 2 ounces.

Scientific name: *Ictalurus,* Greek, meaning "fish cat"; *melas,* Greek for "black"

DISTRIBUTION AND HABITAT

The black bullhead is nearly statewide in distribution but is better represented in the Prairie Region of north and west Missouri than elsewhere. It is the most abundant bullhead in many Prairie streams. In the Ozark and Lowland regions it is less numerous than the yellow bullhead. This fish occurs in a variety of habitats but is most abundant in habitats with turbid water, a silt bottom, no noticeable current or strong flow, and a lack of diversity in the fish fauna. Especially favorable habitats are the permanent pools of small, intermittent creeks and the muddy oxbows and backwaters of large streams in the Prairie Region. Here the black bullhead and a few other hardy species, such as the fathead minnow and green sunfish, sometimes comprise the bulk of the fishes present.

HABITS AND LIFE HISTORY

The black bullhead feeds primarily from the bottom on a variety of plant and animal material. In an Iowa study the diet of adult black bullheads was principally immature aquatic insects, while the young up to an inch in length fed almost exclusively on small crustaceans.[137]

Black bullheads spawn at this latitude in May or June in saucer-shaped nests fanned out by one or both parent fish. Nests are often located beneath logs or other large objects elevated above the stream bottom, but sometimes no overhead cover is present. The eggs are deposited as a golden-yellow mass in the bottom of the nest. One of the parent fish remains continuously over the eggs, warding off predators and providing aeration with fanning motions of its fins. Often large numbers of minnows and sunfish hover about the nest, rushing in to eat eggs whenever the opportunity arises. Upon leaving the nest the young bullheads move about in a compact, ball-like school, accompanied by one or both adults. The conspicuous balls of coal-black young are easily observed from shore as they move along near the water's surface. The young are abandoned by the adults when about an inch long but persist in schooling throughout the first summer of life.[137]

In Oklahoma waters the black bullhead averages 3.7 inches in length by the end of its first year of life and is about 6.7, 9, 10.8, 12.3, and 13.8 inches long at the end of succeeding years.[138] However, growth varies drastically from one situation to another, being slowest in overpopulated ponds and streams and fastest in new impoundments. In fast-growing populations they sometimes grow to 10 inches the first year. In slow-growing populations this length may not be achieved until the fifth or sixth year. Few individuals live more than 5 years, but the maximum life span is 10 years or more. The black bullhead does not reach as large a size as the other bullheads.

IMPORTANCE AND ANGLING

Although the purist may turn up his nose at the idea of angling for bullheads, this fish provides many hours of fishing pleasure in waters where few fishing opportunities would otherwise exist. The black bullhead may be caught almost anywhere in the state but makes up a larger proportion of the creel in the smaller Prairie creeks of north and west Missouri than elsewhere. Still-fishing with cane pole or rod and reel is the most popular method for catching them. Almost any kind of live or prepared bait may be used, but worms are one of the best. The black bullhead is an eager biter and little skill is required to catch it. The main thing to remember in fishing for bullheads is to fish on or close to the bottom.

Brown Bullhead

Ictalurus nebulosus (Lesueur)

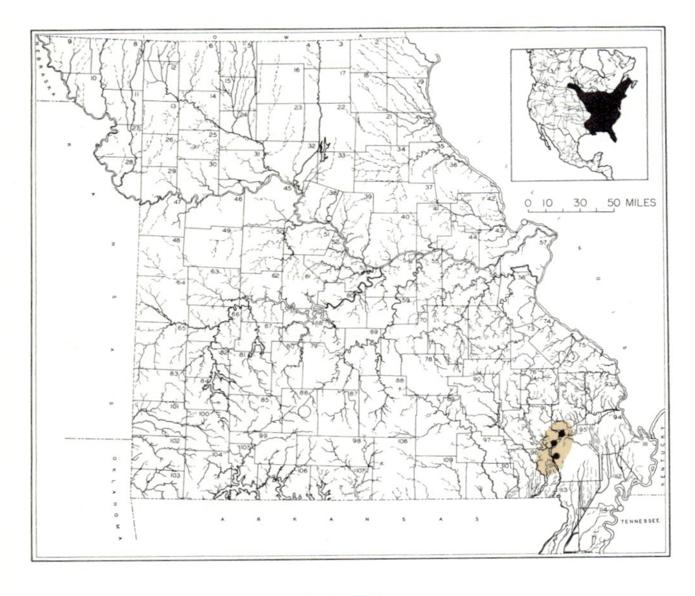

DESCRIPTION

Illustration: Page 204, 6a; **41.**

Characters: Similar to black bullhead and yellow bullhead, but with back and sides usually strongly mottled rather than uniformly colored, and with barbel at corner of mouth longer, reaching well behind base of pectoral fin in adults. Saw-like teeth strongly developed on rear margin of pectoral spine (teeth can be detected by grasping spine between thumb and forefinger and pulling outward). Rays in anal fin usually 22 or 23 (occasionally 21 or 24). Chin barbels dusky or black—never uniformly white. Length of anal fin base less than length of head. Rear margin of tail fin slightly notched, as in black bullhead.

Life colors: Back and sides dark yellowish-brown, usually strongly mottled with darker brown or black. Belly yellowish or white. Fins dusky or black, the membranes often darker than the rays.

Size: Adults are commonly 7 to 15 inches long and weigh 0.3 to 2.2 pounds. Maximum length and weight about 18 inches and 3.7 pounds.

Scientific name: *Ictalurus,* Greek, meaning "fish cat"; *nebulosus,* Latin, meaning "clouded," in reference to the mottled coloration.

DISTRIBUTION AND HABITAT

The only self-sustaining natural population of brown bullheads presently known in Missouri occurs at Duck Creek Wildlife Area and the adjacent Mingo National Wildlife Refuge in Bollinger and Wayne counties. Most other records shown on the accompanying map are based on published reports that I have not confirmed by examining specimens. Since the bullheads have often been confused, some published reports may have resulted from misidentification. The brown bullhead has been stocked in ponds around the state in recent years, but these stockings are not known to have resulted in the establishment of populations in natural waters.

The brown bullhead seems to prefer quiet, clear waters with moderate or large amounts of submerged aquatic vegetation. Its habitat requirements are much like those of the yellow bullhead, but it is found less frequently in flowing waters.

HABITS AND LIFE HISTORY

The general habits and life history of this fish are similar to those of the black bullhead. The food and growth of the young have been studied by Raney and Webster,[139] and the reproductive habits were described by Breder.[140, 141]

Yellow Bullhead

Ictalurus natalis (Lesueur)

Other local names: Yellow cat

DESCRIPTION

Illustration: Page 204, 5a; **40.**

Characters: Similar to black bullhead and brown bullhead, but with chin barbels uniformly white, often slightly dusky in large adults from Ozark streams, and with more rays in anal fin, usually 24 to 27. Length of anal fin base about equal to head length. Saw-like teeth moderately developed on rear margin of pectoral spine (teeth can be detected by grasping spine between thumb and forefinger and pulling outward). Barbel at corner of mouth not reaching much farther back than base of pectoral fin. Back and sides usually not strongly mottled. Rear margin of tail fin nearly straight.

Life colors: Back and sides usually uniformly yellowish-brown, often faintly mottled with darker brown in adults from clear, weedy water. Belly yellowish or white. Fins dusky, the membranes similar in color to the rays.

Size: Adults are commonly 7 to 13.5 inches long and weigh 0.2 to 1.3 pounds. Maximum length and weight in Missouri streams about 16.8 inches and 2 pounds.

Scientific name: *Ictalurus,* Greek, meaning "fish cat"; *natalis,* Latin, meaning "having large buttocks."

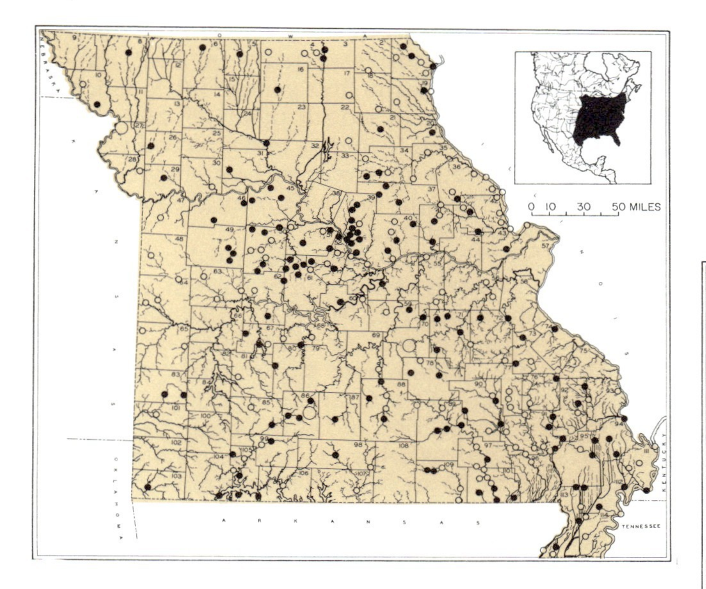

DISTRIBUTION AND HABITAT

The yellow bullhead is nearly as widespread in Missouri as the black bullhead. It is the commonest bullhead in the Ozark and Lowland faunal regions and is nearly as common as the black bullhead in the clearer Prairie streams of central and northeastern Missouri. The yellow bullhead seldom occurs in the high population densities sometimes achieved by the black bullhead. This species prefers clearer water than the black bullhead and is usually found in or near streams with permanent flow. Like the other bullheads, it avoids strong currents. In the Ozarks the yellow bullhead is almost invariably found in quiet, heavily vegetated backwaters and overflow pools. Elsewhere it is less restricted and often occurs in open pools of the stream channel.

HABITS AND LIFE HISTORY

The habits and life history of this species are not much different from those of the black bullhead. The yellow bullhead relies on an acute sense of smell to find its food. The sense of smell is also important in social behavior.[142] In experiments, blinded catfish were able to distinguish one individual of their species from another, but lost this ability when deprived of the sense of smell. In Reelfoot Lake, Tennessee, the yellow bullhead averages 7.2 inches long at the end of its first year of life and achieves lengths of about 13.1, 14.6, 15.6 and 16.9 inches in succeeding years.[143]

IMPORTANCE AND ANGLING

In Missouri the yellow bullhead is less important as a hook-and-line fish than the black bullhead because it is seldom abundant. However, this disadvantage is partly offset by the fact that, on the average, yellow bullheads taken by fishermen are larger than black bullheads. Methods used in catching yellow bullheads do not differ from those described for the black bullhead.

Channel catfish

Ictalurus punctatus (Rafinesque)

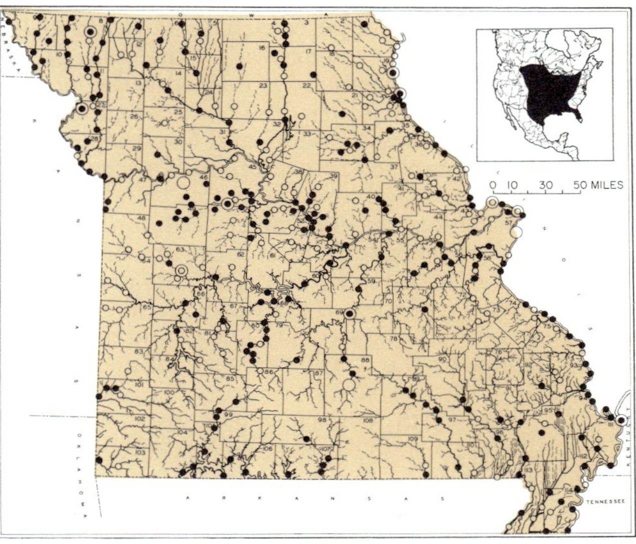

Other local names: Spotted cat, Blue cat, Fiddler, Lady cat, Chucklehead cat, Willow cat.

DESCRIPTION

Illustration: Page 203, 3a; **40.**

Characters: A slender catfish with a deeply forked tail fin and with the adipose fin forming a free, flap-like lobe. Upper jaw projecting beyond lower jaw. Tooth pad on upper jaw without backward extensions.

Similar to blue catfish but differs in having scattered dark spots on back and sides (spots often absent in smallest young and large adults), and in having the outer margin of the anal fin rounded outward (convex) rather than straight. Also, the anal fin contains fewer rays—usually 24 to 29—and has a shorter base (length of base usually going 3.4 to 3.7 times into standard length). The

profile of the back from the dorsal fin forward is gently sloping and slightly rounded outward so that the head and forward part of the body are less distinctly wedge-shaped than in the blue catfish.
Life colors: Back and sides olive-brown or slate-blue, usually with few to many roundish black spots. Belly silvery-white. Fins yellowish or dusky, often with a narrow black fringe. Breeding males are a deep blue-black on the back and sides, with the head swollen and knobby and the lips thickened and fleshy.

Size: Adults are commonly 12 to 32 inches long and weigh 0.8 to 15 pounds. The present state record is 29¾ pounds.
Scientific name: *Ictalurus,* Greek, meaning "fish cat"; *punctatus,* Latin, meaning "spotted," in reference to the dark spots on the body.

DISTRIBUTION AND HABITAT

The channel catfish is the most abundant and widely distributed large catfish in Missouri. Although it occurs over nearly all of the state, it is especially characteristic of the Prairie Region of north and west Missouri. The channel catfish is also common in the Missouri and Mississippi rivers and in man-made impoundments throughout the state.

This catfish occurs in a variety of habitats, but is especially characteristic of large streams having low or moderate gradients. Adults are found in the larger pools, in deep water or about submerged logs and other cover. The young often occur in riffles or the shallower parts of pools.

HABITS AND LIFE HISTORY

During daylight hours adult channel catfish retire to deep water or lie about drift piles, submerged logs, or other cover. At night they move onto riffles or into the shallows of pools to feed. Food is located primarily by taste and to a lesser extent by sight. It takes most of its food from the bottom. Its diet is varied, including fish, insects, crayfish, mollusks, and plant material. The channel catfish also consumes quantities of slaughterhouse and rendering plant wastes along rivers where these are being dumped. The extreme variability of this fish's diet is indicated by the presence of insects belonging to 50 different families in the stomachs of channel catfish from the Des Moines River.[144] This study showed that the diet varied markedly with size. Catfish less than 4 inches long fed almost entirely on small insects; larger catfish ate larger food items and had a more varied diet.

The channel catfish spawns in Missouri from about the last week of May through the third week of July.[145] Often there are two peaks of spawning activity during this period. Prior to spawning the male catfish selects and cleans out a nest site. Natural cavities about piles of drift, logs, or undercut banks, and the burrows of muskrats and beavers are favored nest sites. Semidarkness and seclusion are major factors in the choice of nest sites.[145] Females do not normally participate in the selection of nest sites or in care of the eggs or young. However, pairing sometimes occurs before the female is ready to spawn.[146] The eggs are deposited in the bottom of the nest as a gelatinous mass having the appearance and consistency of a large golden-yellow mound of tapioca. They hatch in about a week and the fry remain in the nest for 7 or 8 more days. The male guards the fry only until they leave the nest. Survival of young during the first year of life is much lower in clear than in turbid ponds,[145] and this relationship between turbidity and survival probably also holds true in streams. Low survival in clear waters is thought to result from greater susceptibility to predation.

In lower Salt River the channel catfish averages 2.6 inches in length at the end of its first year of life and is about 5.3, 8.1, 10.2, 11.7, 13.4 and 15.7 inches long at the end of succeeding years.[126] Growth in the middle and upper parts of Salt River and in Lake of the Ozarks[147] is slower. In the Missouri-Illinois section of the Mississippi River this catfish matures when 4 or 5 years old at a length of 12 to 15 inches.[32] The channel catfish sometimes lives more than 10 years but the life span does not usually exceed 6 or 7 years.

IMPORTANCE

The channel catfish is one of Missouri's most highly prized game and food fishes. As a sport fish it has no rival in the larger Prairie streams of northwest Missouri where other game fish are scarce. During one year this fish made up 40% of the creel in Salt River and the average for 6 years was 20%.[126] The channel catfish also figures prominently in the creel in streams and reservoirs elsewhere in Missouri and is widely stocked in farm ponds. It is one of the important commercial fishes along the Missouri and Mississippi rivers. The propagation of channel catfish for sale as live or dressed fish is an important industry in Missouri. In 1971 nearly 9,000,000 catfish valued at more than $4,000,000 were produced.

ANGLING

Channel catfish may be caught on set lines, by jugging, or by still-fishing with rod and reel. A variety of live, cut, or prepared baits, including fish, crayfish, chicken entrails, blood, cheese, and commercial concoctions are used to catch this fish. Occasionally it is taken on spinners, small spoons, and other artificial lures retrieved slowly near the bottom. Fishing is best near dusk and in the early part of the night, or on a rise following a heavy rain.

Blue Catfish

Ictalurus furcatus (Lesueur)

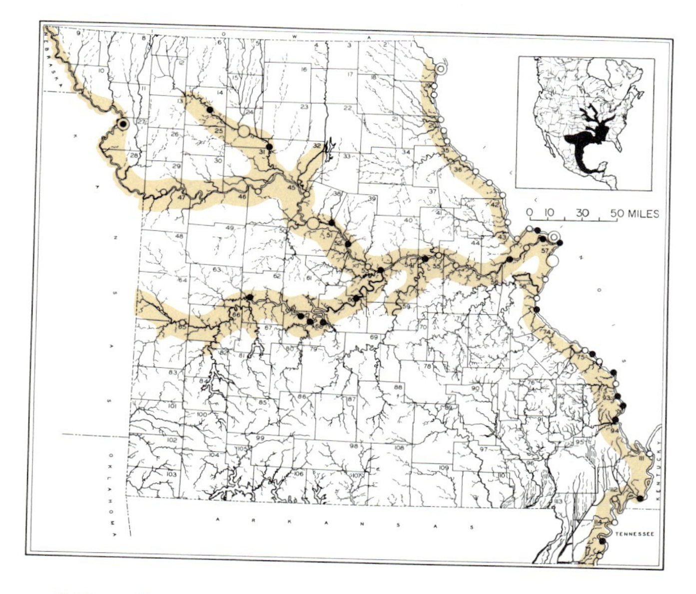

Other local names: White cat, Silver cat, Blue fulton, White fulton, Blue channel cat.

DESCRIPTION

Illustration: Page 203, 3b; **40.**

Characters: Similar to channel catfish but differs in never having dark spots on back and sides and in having outer margin of anal fin straight and tapered like a barber's comb. Also, the anal fin contains more rays—usually 30 to 35—and has a shorter base (length of base usually going 2.9 to 3.3 times into standard length). The profile of the back from the dorsal fin forward is steeply sloping and straight, giving the head and forward part of the body a distinctive wedge-shaped appearance.

Life colors: Back and upper sides pale bluish-silver, grading to silver-white on lower sides and belly. Fins clear or whitish, often dusky towards outer margin.

Size: Adult blue catfish commonly are 20 to 44 inches long and weigh 3 to 40 pounds. The largest specimen taken in Missouri in recent years weighed 117 pounds.

Scientific name: *Ictalurus,* Greek, meaning "fish cat"; *furcatus,* Latin, meaning "forked," in reference to the tail fin.

DISTRIBUTION AND HABITAT

The blue catfish is decidedly a Big-river fish, occurring only in the Missouri and Mississippi rivers and their principal tributaries. In these streams it is less abundant at most localities than the other large catfishes and has declined in abundance since 1900. This decline has been greatest in the impounded portion of the Mississippi River upstream from St. Louis. Presently the most substantial populations are in the lower Mississippi River and in the upper Osage River and Lake of the Ozarks. The latter population may be adversely affected by Truman Dam and Reservoir now under construction on the Osage River near Warsaw.

The blue catfish is principally an inhabitant of swift chutes and of pools having noticeable current.

HABITS AND LIFE HISTORY

The blue catfish is said to be somewhat migratory, undertaking seasonal movements in response to changes in water temperature. In the lower Mississippi River it moves farther down river where the water is warmest in winter, running upstream in summer.[148] Formerly the blue catfish was abundant in the Mississippi River near Keokuk, Iowa, during the warmer months, but none were ever seen in winter.[22] Movements in this section of the river are now largely blocked by dams.

As with catfish in general, the sensitive barbels of the blue catfish are probably more important than sight in locating food. The nature of its diet suggests that this fish feeds mostly on or near the bottom and to a lesser extent in midwater. It eats a variety of animal life, including fishes, immature aquatic insects, crayfish, fingernail clams, and freshwater mussels.[149] Some fish are eaten by blue catfish as small as 4 inches in length, but the bulk of the diet of smaller individuals is composed of small invertebrates. Those larger than 8 to 13 inches eat mostly fish and larger invertebrates.

The blue catfish spawns in Louisiana in April and May,[148] and in the Mississippi River near Keokuk in June.[22] The nesting habits are similar to those of the channel catfish.[89]

In Lake Texoma, Oklahoma, the blue catfish reaches a length of 5.7 inches at the end of its first year of life and averages 10, 13.8, 17.4, 21, 25.8, 30.3, 34.3, 40.4, 42.1 and 44 inches at the end of succeeding years.[150] A 55-inch specimen from the Osage River near Warsaw weighed 90 pounds and was about 21 years old. Their growth in Lake Texoma is more rapid than the channel catfish and is nearly equal to that of the flathead catfish.

Most early reports of enormous catfish caught along the Missouri and Mississippi rivers almost certainly referred to the blue catfish. Before 1900, specimens weighing upwards from 100 pounds were common in Missouri waters. P.R. Hoy, a naturalist who traveled across Missouri in 1854, reported that on May 14 of that year "A lad caught on hook and line to-day a catfish weighing 136 pounds," from Grand River near Chillicothe in Livingston County.[247] In November, 1879, the U.S. National Museum received a blue catfish weighing 150 pounds that was taken in the Mississippi River near St. Louis.[151] This fish was sent by Dr. J.G.W. Steedman, chairman of the Missouri Fish Commission, who purchased it in the St. Louis fish market. The following quote from a letter sent by Dr. Steedman to Prof. Spencer F. Baird, United States Commissioner of Fish and Fisheries, suggests that catfish of this size were not uncommon: "Your letter requesting the shipment to you of a large Mississippi Catfish was received this morning. Upon visiting our market this P.M. I luckily found two—one of 144 lbs., the other 150 lbs. The latter I ship to you by express." Captain William L. Heckman, in his book "Steamboating Sixty-five Years on Missouri's Rivers", mentions a blue catfish weighing 315 pounds caught in the Missouri River near Morrison, Gasconade County, "'just after the Civil War,'" and indicates that at that time "'it was common to catch catfish weighing from 125 to 200 pounds'" from the Missouri River. Although blue catfish of this size have not been reported from Missouri waters in recent years, individuals weighing near or slightly above 100 pounds are still taken occasionally. Since 1963, three blue catfish weighing 89, 90, and 117 pounds have been caught in the Osage River near Warsaw, and, according to reports of fishermen, catfish weighing up to 40 pounds are taken there rather frequently. The largest blue catfish reported from the Missouri section of the Missouri River in recent decades was caught near Malta Bend and weighed 79 pounds.[152]

IMPORTANCE AND ANGLING

Because of its large size and firm, well-flavored flesh, the blue catfish is a highly valued food fish. But it is now so rare in Missouri waters that it is of only limited commercial importance. The blue catfish is much sought after by the sport fishermen along the Osage, Missouri, and lower Mississippi rivers. Trot lines and jug lines baited with fish and other live or cut baits are the most popular gear for taking it. Gizzard shad and skipjack herring are preferred above all other baits by many experienced fishermen because these are said to release oil into the water that is very attractive to catfishes. Commercial fishermen sometimes make good catches of blue catfish during the winter months by floating trammel nets with the current. At this time of year the fish are very sluggish and are unable to avoid the net.

Tadpole Madtom

Noturus gyrinus (Mitchill)

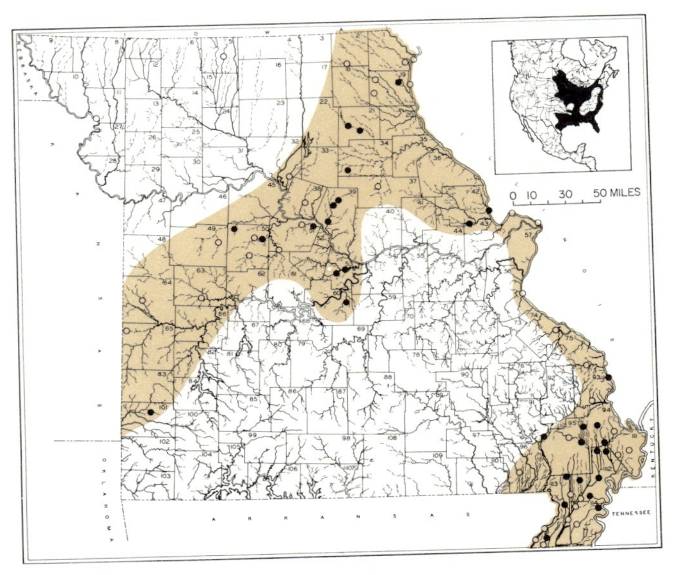

DESCRIPTION

Illustration: Page 205, 8b.

Characters: A small, chubby catfish with the rear margin of the tail fin broadly rounded, and the adipose fin forming a low, keel-like ridge rather than a free, flap-like lobe. Pectoral spine without saw-like teeth on rear margin. Midside usually with a prominent vein-like dark line that is not normally evident in other madtoms; body and fins otherwise plain, without definite dark blotches, bars, and speckles. Tooth pad on upper jaw without backward extensions.

Similar to freckled madtom, but with upper jaw not projecting beyond lower jaw, the two jaws nearly equal. Also, the underside of head and body are not sprinkled with dark speckles. Notch between adipose fin and tail fin closer to dorsal fin base than to tip of tail fin.

Life colors: Back and sides uniformly light tan or chocolate-brown with a narrow dark line along midside. Belly white or pale yellow. Fins similar in color to adjacent parts of body.

Size: Adults are commonly 1.9 to 3.4 inches long to a maximum of about 4 inches.

Scientific name: *Noturus,* Greek, meaning "back tail," in reference to the connection of the adipose fin and tail fin; *gyrinus,* Greek for "tadpole."

DISTRIBUTION AND HABITAT

The tadpole madtom occurs throughout the Lowland Faunal Region and in a broad northeastward-trending zone from Spring River in southwestern Missouri into tributaries of the Mississippi River in northeastern Missouri. In the Lowlands it is the commonest madtom.

It inhabits clear to moderately turbid waters having little current but with an abundance of cover, such as thick growths of submergent plants or accumulations of organic debris. In the Lowlands it is most abundant in ditches without noticeable current and along the vegetated margins of ditches having current. In the Prairie Region it inhabits quiet pools of sluggish creeks draining level uplands, and backwaters and overflow pools along the larger rivers.

HABITS AND LIFE HISTORY

Like all madtoms, this fish is secretive, spending the daylight hours lurking about heavy cover. A limited study of its food habits in Illinois suggests that it feeds primarily on insect larvae and small crustaceans that live on the bottom. Occasional small fish also are eaten.[24] The tadpole madtom spawns at this latitude in June or July.[93, 153] Egg clusters have been found in tin cans or beneath boards or crockery, guarded by one of the parent fish.[154] In central Missouri streams the tadpole madtom attains a length of about 1.3 to 2.2 inches by the end of its first summer of life. Most individuals probably mature during their second summer and few live beyond their third summer.

Freckled Madtom

Noturus nocturnus Jordon and Gilbert

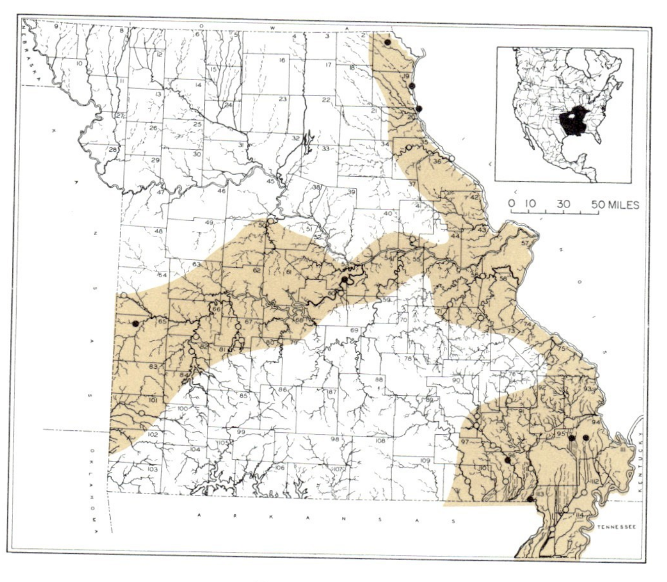

DESCRIPTION

Illustration: Page 206, 10b.

Characters: Similar to tadpole madtom, but with upper jaw projecting beyond lower jaw and with underside of head and body sprinkled with dark speckles. Midside without a prominent vein-like dark line. Notch between adipose fin and tail fin closer to tip of tail fin than to dorsal fin base.

Life colors: Like those of tadpole madtom, page 214, except as noted under *Characters*.

Size: Adults are commonly 2 to 3.5 inches long to a maximum of about 4.3 inches.

Scientific name: *Noturus,* Greek, meaning "back tail," in reference to the connection of the adipose fin and tail fin; *nocturnus,* Latin for "nocturnal," from its black color.

DISTRIBUTION AND HABITAT

The distribution of the freckled madtom in Missouri is much like that of the tadpole madtom but the two are seldom found together. The freckled madtom is not abundant at any location, but occurs commonly in the upper Mississippi and Osage rivers and in streams and ditches of the Lowlands.

This madtom inhabits clear to moderately turbid streams having permanent flow and low or moderate gradients. It occurs on riffles over a gravelly or rocky bottom.

HABITS AND LIFE HISTORY

Nothing has been published concerning the life history of the freckled madtom. Females with fully developed eggs were collected in southeast Missouri the last week of May, suggesting a spring or early summer spawning season.

Slender Madtom

Noturus exilis Nelson

DESCRIPTION

Illustration: Page 205, 8a.

Characters: A small, slender catfish with the rear margin of the tail fin rounded or squarish, and the adipose fin forming a low, keel-like ridge rather than a free, flap-like lobe. Pectoral spine with well-developed saw-like teeth along rear margin. Dorsal, tail, and anal fins prominently dark-edged or at least darkest along outer margins; body and fins otherwise nearly plain, without definite dark blotches, bars, or speckles. Upper jaw not projecting beyond lower jaw, the two nearly equal. Tooth pad on upper jaw without backward extensions. Notch between adipose fin and tail fin closer to tip of tail fin than to dorsal fin base.

Life colors: Back and sides yellowish-brown, often faintly mottled with darker brown. Underside of head and body white or pale yellow. Dorsal, tail, and anal fins with a definite black fringe, or at least darker on outer margins; fins otherwise yellowish or cream-white.

Size: Adults are commonly 3 to 5 inches long to a maximum of about 6 inches.

Scientific name: *Noturus*, Greek, meaning "back tail," in reference to the connection of the adipose fin and tail fin; *exilis*, Latin, meaning slim.

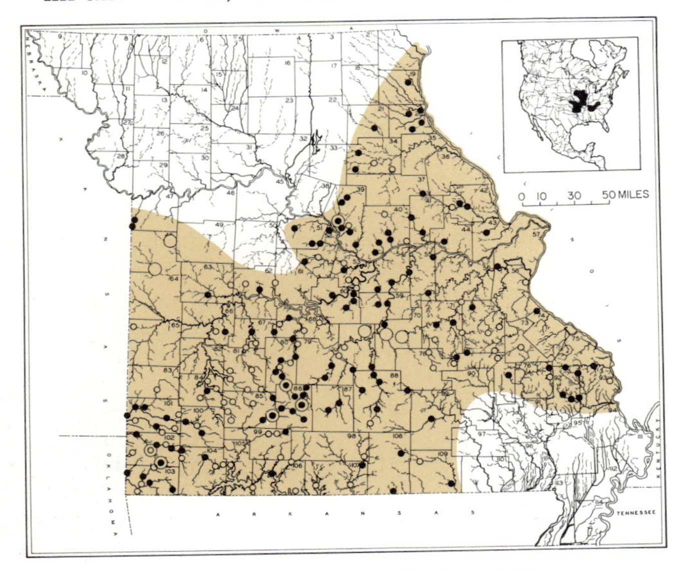

DISTRIBUTION AND HABITAT

The slender madtom is common over most of the Ozarks and in the clearer Prairie streams of northeastern Missouri. In the northern and western Ozarks it is the most abundant madtom in many small to medium-sized streams. It is scarce in the southern Ozarks, perhaps as a result of competition with the Ozark madtom, a species with similar habits.

The slender madtom is characteristic of small to medium-sized streams with rocky or gravelly bottoms, clear water, and permanent flow. It is usually found on riffles or in pools having enough current to keep the bottom free of silt.

HABITS AND LIFE HISTORY

The slender madtom hides beneath rocks during the daytime and forages actively over the bottom at night. Females with fully developed eggs have been collected in Ozark streams in April and early May, suggesting a spring spawning season. The spawning habits are not known but are probably like those of the closely related margined madtom, *Noturus insignis* (Richardson). This fish deposits a compact cluster of eggs in a shallow depression excavated beneath a flat rock.[155] The eggs and newly hatched young are guarded by one of the parent fish, presumably the male. The slender madtom adapts well to aquarium life and makes an attractive and interesting aquarium fish.

Stonecat

Noturus flavus Rafinesque

DESCRIPTION

Illustration: Page 206, 10a.

Characters: A moderately small, slender catfish with the rear margin of the tail fin squarish in outline and the adipose fin forming a low, keel-like ridge rather than a free, flap-like lobe. Pectoral spine nearly smooth, without saw-like teeth along rear margin. Body and fins nearly plain, without definite dark blotches, bars or speckles; fins not dark-edged. Upper jaw projecting beyond lower jaw. Tooth pad on upper jaw with a narrow, crescent-shaped extension on each side. Notch between adipose and tail fins closer to tip of tail fin than to dorsal fin base.

Life colors: Back and sides yellowish-brown, faintly mottled with darker brown. Underside of head and belly white or pale yellow. Tail fin dark centrally, the upper and lower margins whitish; other fins pale yellow or cream-white.

Size: Adults are commonly 3 to 5.5 inches long to a maximum of about 8 inches.

Scientific name: *Noturus*, Greek, meaning "back tail," in reference to the connection of the adipose fin and tail fin; *flavus*, Latin for "yellow," in reference to the color.

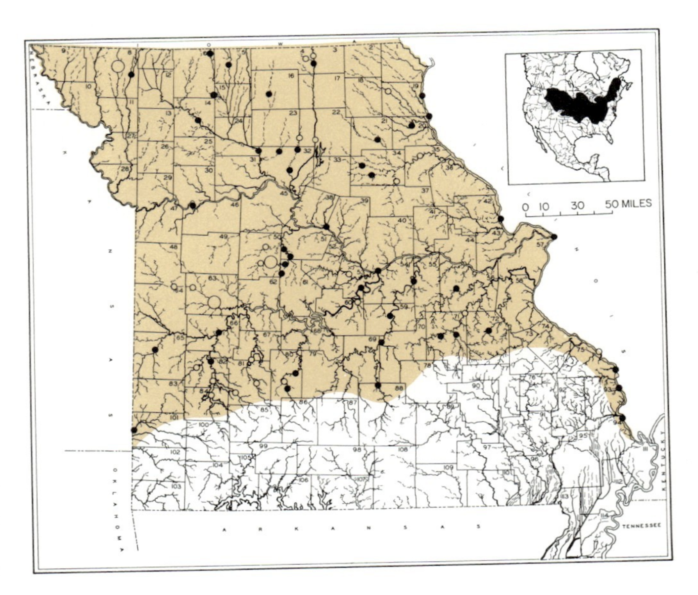

DISTRIBUTION AND HABITAT

The stonecat is the most abundant madtom in most large streams of the northern Ozarks and the Prairie Region. It also occurs commonly in the upper Mississippi River but is rare in the lower Mississippi and Missouri rivers. Stonecats from these streams differ from those elsewhere in the state in having very small eyes and a paler coloration. These differences were noted by Taylor,[156] who did not consider them to be of taxonomic significance.

The stonecat occurs in varied stream types but avoids those with intermittent flow or extremely high gradients. In stream systems where both occur, the stonecat is replaced towards the headwaters by the slender madtom. The stonecat is most often found on rocky riffles. In the Missouri River I have found it over sandy bottoms in areas with a swift current.

HABITS AND LIFE HISTORY

As is typical of madtoms, the stonecat is most active at night, hiding by day beneath large rocks or other cover. A limited study of the food habits by the writer indicates a diet consisting principally of the immature stages of various riffle-dwelling insects, supplemented with an occasional darter or other small fish. In Missouri the stonecat probably spawns in April or May. Young-of-the-year first appear in collections during June. The eggs are deposited in a compact cluster beneath flat stones and are attended by one of the parent fish.[157] In the Vermillion River, South Dakota, the stonecat averages 3.1 inches in length by the end of its first year of life and attains lengths of 3.9, 4.5, and 5.4 inches by the end of succeeding years.[158] The largest specimen examined in this study was 7.6 inches long and was in its seventh year of life.

Ozark Madtom

Noturus albater Taylor

DESCRIPTION

Illustration: Page 207, 11a.

Characters: A small, slender catfish with the tail fin squarish in outline and the adipose fin forming a low, keel-like ridge rather than a free, flap-like lobe. Pectoral spine with prominent saw-like teeth along rear margin. Body and fins rather distinctly mottled with dark blotches and bars. Upper jaw projecting beyond lower jaw. Tooth pad on upper jaw without backward extensions. Dark bar beneath adipose fin usually not reaching upward to margin of fin. No broad, dark bar across base of tail fin. Dorsal fin without a dark blotch towards outer margin. Head length going more than 3.5 times into standard length. Distance from tip of tail fin to notch between tail fin and adipose fin going more than 2 times into distance from notch forward to front of dorsal fin base.

Life colors: Back light brown with four indistinct dark cross-bars. Sides similarly colored, with faint dark mottlings. Belly pale yellow or cream-white. Fins pale yellowish-white with indistinct dark blotches and bars.

Size: Adults are commonly 2.5 to 4 inches long to a maximum of about 5 inches.

Scientific name: *Noturus*, Greek, meaning "back tail," in reference to the connection of the adipose fin and tail fin; *albater*, Latin, meaning "white and black," in reference to the contrasting light and dark colors.

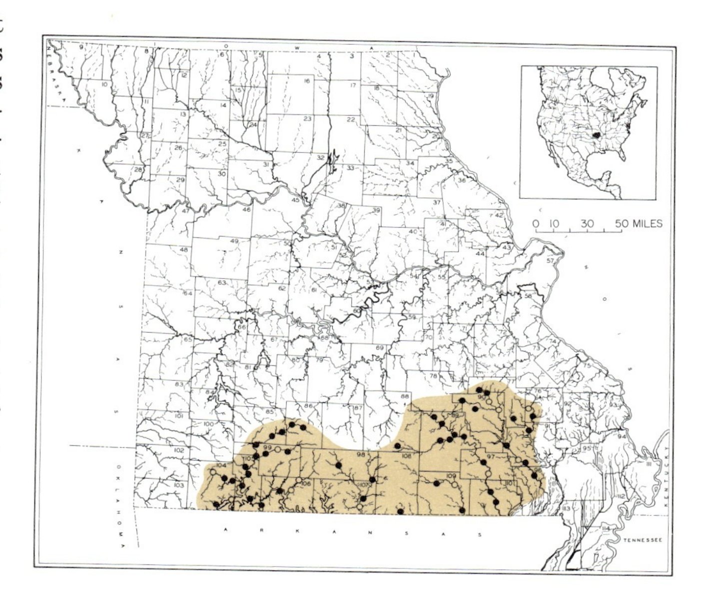

DISTRIBUTION AND HABITAT

The Ozark madtom has a highly localized distribution in the Ozark Region of southern Missouri and northern Arkansas. In the Missouri part of its range it is by far the most abundant madtom.

It inhabits the riffles and rocky pools of clear, high-gradient streams having permanent, strong flow.

HABITS AND LIFE HISTORY

The Ozark madtom hides beneath coarse gravel and rocks during the daytime, emerging at night to forage actively over the bottom in shallow riffles. An adult of this species was collected, along with a cluster of eggs, from a rocky riffle in late June, and females with fully developed eggs have been collected in late July. This suggests that spawning occurs in mid-summer. The Ozark madtom is about 1.3 to 1.9 inches in length by the end of its first summer of life. The maximum life span is 3 years or more.

Brindled Madtom

Noturus miurus Jordon

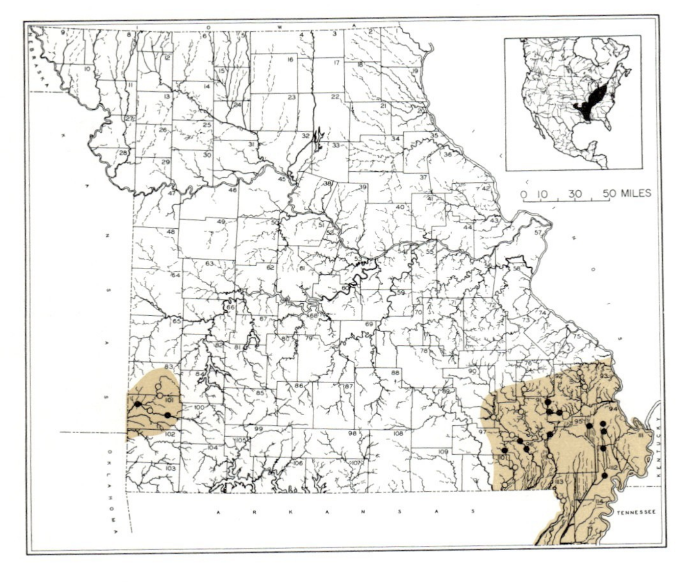

DESCRIPTION

Illustration: Page 208, 14b.
Characters: A small, moderately chubby catfish with the rear margin of the tail fin squarish or slightly rounded, and the adipose fin forming a low, keel-like ridge rather than a free, flap-like lobe. Pectoral spine with prominent, saw-like teeth along rear margin. Body and fins profusely mottled with dark blotches and bars. Upper jaw projecting beyond lower jaw. Tooth pad on upper jaw without backward extensions. No broad, black bar across base of tail fin. Dorsal fin with a dark blotch near outer margin; blotch extending only across first 4 fin rays. Head length going less than 3.5 times into standard length. Distance from tip of tail fin to notch between tail fin and adipose fin going less than 2 times into distance from notch forward to front of dorsal fin base.

Similar to Neosho madtom, page 219, but with dark bar beneath adipose fin reaching upward to or near fin margin, and with outer margins of dorsal and tail fins black-tipped. Also, the base of the tail fin often has a narrow dark line shaped like a question mark.

Life colors: Back and sides yellowish-brown with dusky mottlings. Back with 4 dark cross-bars. Belly pale yellowish-white. Fins marked by prominent blackish bands and blotches.

Size: Adults are commonly 2.2 to 3.5 inches long to a maximum of about 4 inches.

Scientific name: *Noturus,* Greek, meaning "back tail," in reference to the connection of the adipose fin and tail fin; *miurus,* Greek, meaning "curtailed."

DISTRIBUTION AND HABITAT

The brindled madtom occurs in two widely separate areas of Missouri. Its main area of occurrence is in the Lowlands of southeastern Missouri and adjacent parts of the Ozarks. In that area it is nearly as common as the tadpole madtom. The other area of occurrence is the Spring River system of southwestern Missouri, where it is rather rare.

The brindled madtom inhabits streams having low or moderate gradients and a permanent flow of warm, moderately clear water. It is usually found on riffles or in pools having noticeable current and gravelly or sandy bottoms. Often considerable quantities of detritus, such as sticks and leaves, are present.

HABITS AND LIFE HISTORY

The brindled madtom evidently spawns in Missouri during late spring and summer. Females full of eggs and others that had already spawned were collected in the Lowlands during late May. Taylor reported that this species spawns in Michigan during July and August.[156] He found males guarding clusters of eggs in sunken tin cans. The number of eggs or young guarded by each male was relatively small. For six broods that he counted, the number of eggs or young ranged from 28 to 46, averaging 36. The eggs were amber in color and adhered in an irregular mass, as is characteristic of catfish.

The food habits and growth of the brindled madtom have not been studied.

Mountain madtom

Noturus eleutherus Jordan

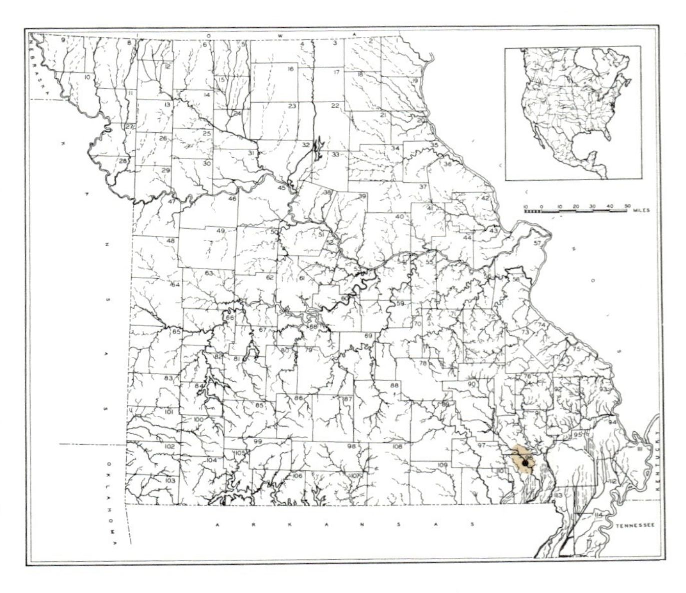

DESCRIPTION

Illustration: Page 208, 13b.

Characters: Similar to brindled madtom and Neosho madtom. Differs from brindled madtom in having the dark bar at base of adipose fin not reaching to near fin margin. Also, there is never a narrow, dark line shaped like a question mark along base of tail fin. Differs from Neosho madtom in not having a dark, crescent-shaped bar across middle of tail fin. Also, small saw-like teeth are well developed on front margin of pectoral fin spine.

Life colors: Similar to brindled madtom, but with dark markings brownish rather than blackish, and with bars and blotches less sharply defined.

Size: Adults are usually 2.2 to 3.5 inches long to a maximum of about 4 inches.

Scientific name: *Noturus,* Greek, meaning "back tail," in reference to the connection of the adipose fin and tail fin; *eleutherus,* Greek, meaning "free," in reference to the almost complete separation of the adipose fin and tail fin.

DISTRIBUTION AND HABITAT

The mountain madtom has been collected only once in Missouri. Eight small specimens were obtained from the Black River near Poplar Bluff in 1964. Other collections made not far upstream and downstream from this locality did not contain specimens, suggesting that this species is uncommon and localized in distribution.

The mountain madtom inhabits moderately large, clear upland streams. It occurs in rocky or gravelly riffles, sometimes in association with thick growths of aquatic vegetation.[156]

HABITS AND LIFE HISTORY

The life history of the mountain madtom has not been studied.

Neosho Madtom

Noturus placidus Taylor

DESCRIPTION

Illustration: Page 208, 13a.

Characters: Similar to brindled and mountain madtom. Differs from brindled madtom in having the dark bar beneath adipose fin not reaching upward to fin margin; also, there is never a narrow, dark line shaped like a question mark along base of tail fin. Differs from mountain madtom in having a dark crescent-shaped bar across middle of tail fin; also, small saw-like teeth are poorly developed on front margin of pectoral fin spine.

Life colors: Similar to brindled madtom, but with dark markings more brownish, rather than blackish, and with dark bars and blotches less sharply defined.

Size: The smallest Missouri catfish. Adults are commonly 1.8 to 2.7 inches long to a maximum of about 3 inches.

Scientific name: *Noturus,* Greek, meaning "back tail," in reference to the connection of the adipose fin and tail fin; *placidus,* Latin, meaning "mild," "quiet," or "gentle."

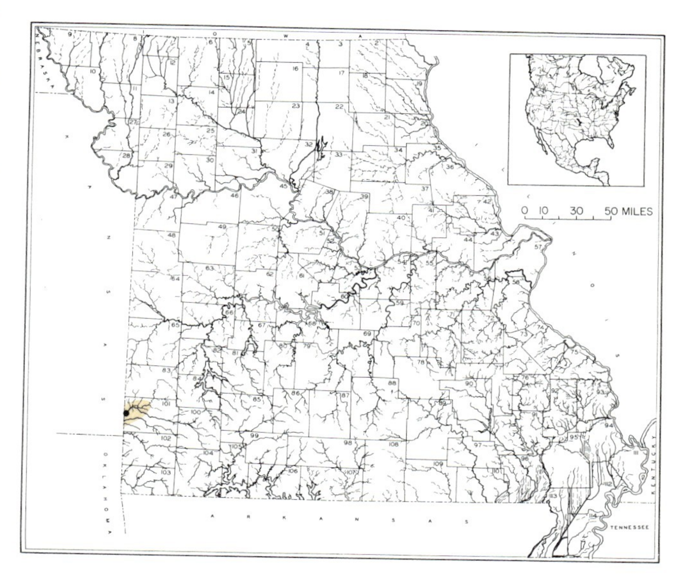

DISTRIBUTION AND HABITAT

The Neosho madtom has occurred in only a single collection from Missouri. This collection, from the Spring River just upstream from the Kansas state line, contained only two specimens, along with 83 stonecats and slender madtoms. Collections elsewhere in the Spring River system have yielded an abundance of other madtoms, but not the Neosho madtom.

This madtom inhabits the gravelly or rocky riffles of medium-sized to moderately large streams having moderate gradients, permanent flow, and fairly clear water.

HABITS AND LIFE HISTORY

Virtually nothing is known about the life history of this fish.

Checkered Madtom

Noturus flavater Taylor

DESCRIPTION

Illustration: Page 208, 14a; **41.**

Characters: A moderately small catfish with the

tail fin squarish or slightly rounded, and the adipose fin forming a low, keel-like ridge rather than a free, flap-like lobe. Pectoral spine with prominent, saw-like teeth along rear margin. Body and fins marked by prominent dark bars and blotches. Upper jaw projecting beyond lower jaw. Tooth pad on upper jaw without backward extensions. Dark bar beneath adipose fin reaching upward to fin margin. A broad, dark bar extends across base of tail fin. Dorsal fin with a dark blotch near outer margin; blotch extending across all fin rays except the last. Head length going less than 3.5 times into standard length. Distance from tip of tail fin to notch between tail fin and adipose fin going less than 2 times into distance from notch forward to front of dorsal fin base.

Life colors: Back yellowish with dusky mottlings and four prominent black cross-bars; bar at base of tail fin extending vertically downward and encircling the body. Sides yellowish with dusky mottlings. Belly pale yellowish-white. Fins marked by prominent black bands and blotches.

Size: Adults are commonly 4 to 6.7 inches long to a maximum of about 7.1 inches.

Scientific name: *Noturus,* Greek, meaning "back tail," in reference to the connection of the adipose fin and tail fin; *flavater,* Latin, meaning "yellow and black," in reference to the colors.

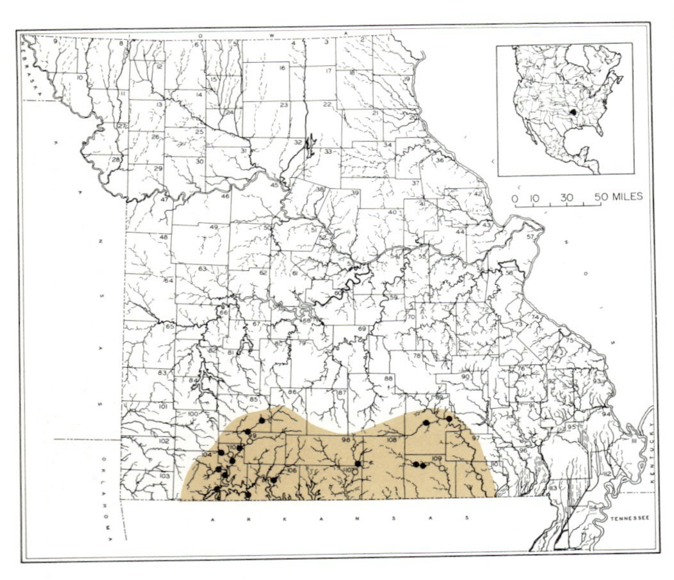

DISTRIBUTION AND HABITAT

The checkered madtom occurs in the southern Ozarks from the upper White River east to Current River. It is similar in distribution to the Ozark madtom but is generally less abundant. The principal difference in their distribution is the absence of the checkered madtom from the St. Francis and Black rivers.

This fish inhabits clear Ozark rivers having high gradients and permanent strong flow. It occurs in quiet pools or backwaters and along the margins of pools, often in association with thick deposits of leaves, sticks and other organic debris.

HABITS AND LIFE HISTORY

Virtually nothing is known of the habits and life history of this fish. Like other madtoms, it is nocturnal, ranging actively over the bottom at night in search of food.

Flathead Catfish

Pylodictis olivaris (Rafinesque)

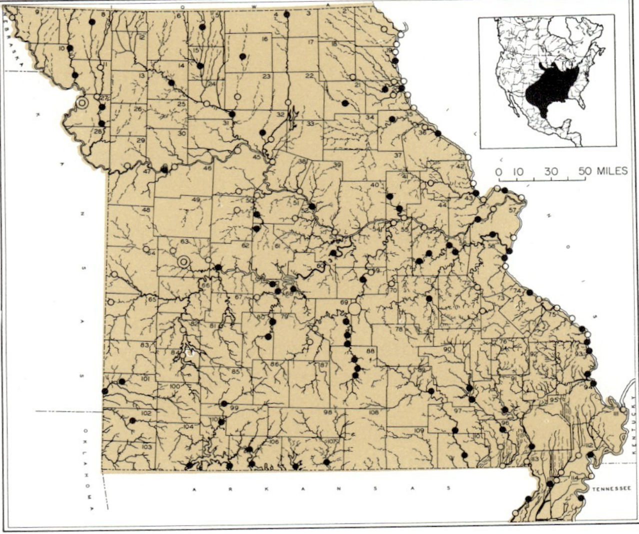

Other local names: Shovelhead cat, Yellow cat, Mud cat, Goujon, Appaluchion, Johnnie cat.

DESCRIPTION

Illustration: Page 203, 4a.

Characters: A slender catfish with a broadly flattened head and a projecting lower jaw. Rear margin of the tail fin slightly notched but not deeply forked; adipose fin forming a free, flap-like lobe. Tooth pad on upper jaw with a crescent-shaped backward extension on each side. Body often strongly mottled with brown or black. Upper lobe of tail fin lighter in color than remainder of fin (most evident in small specimens). Anal fin with 14 to 17 rays and with length of its base much less than head length.

Life colors: Back and sides pale yellow to light brown, mottled with dark brown or black (mottling often poorly developed in adults from turbid water). Belly pale yellow or cream-white. Tail fin dark brown or black except for upper lobe; other fins similar in color to adjacent parts of body.

Young darker colored and more boldly marked than adults.

Size: Adults are commonly 15 to 45 inches long and weigh 1 to 45 pounds. The present state record is a 94-pound specimen caught in the St. Francis River in 1971.

Scientific name: *Pylodictis,* Greek, meaning "mud fish"; *olivaris,* Latin, meaning "olive-colored."

DISTRIBUTION AND HABITAT

The flathead catfish occurs in most of the large streams of Missouri. It is one of the most abundant of the larger catfishes in the Missouri and Mississippi rivers, in their principal tributaries of the Prairie Region, and in the larger ditches of the Lowlands. In the Ozarks it is largely restricted to reservoirs and the downstream sections of the largest streams.

This catfish inhabits a variety of stream types but avoids those with high gradients or intermittent flow. The young are often found among rocks on riffles, occupying much the same habitat as the stonecat and other riffle-dwelling madtoms. Adults occur in pools, near submerged logs, piles of drift, or other cover.

HABITS AND LIFE HISTORY

The flathead catfish is a solitary species, and a single unit of cover such as a drift pile will usually yield only one, or at most two or three, adults. Each individual normally has a favorite resting place where it can be counted on to be each day unless disturbed. Adults move at night from deeper water or cover to riffles and the shallows of pools to feed. The young remain continuously on the riffles but are active only at night. Small flatheads, less than 4 inches in length, feed almost entirely on immature aquatic insects; larger flatheads subsist largely on fish and crayfish.[159] Unlike the channel catfish, the flathead is not a scavenger, rarely taking dead or decaying matter.

At this latitude the flathead catfish spawns in late June and July, somewhat later than the channel catfish.[159] The spawning habits, as observed in aquaria,[140, 160] are much like those of other large catfishes. A saucer-shaped depression is excavated in a natural cavity or near a large, submerged object by one or both parent fish. The eggs are laid in a compact, golden-yellow mass that may contain 100,000 eggs or more. The eggs are agitated continuously by fin movements of the parent fish during development to provide oxygen and flush away silt. After the young have hatched and begun to swim they remain for several days in a compact school near the nest, but soon disperse and take up a solitary life.

In Missouri's Salt River the flathead catfish is about 3 inches long by the end of its first year of life and averages 6.1, 9.1, 11.8, 13.7, 16.6, and 17.8 inches in length at the end of succeeding years.[126] Flatheads in the Missouri-Illinois section of the Mississippi River mature when 4 or 5 years old at a length of about 18 inches.[32] Among Missouri catfishes, only the blue catfish attains a larger size then the flathead.

IMPORTANCE AND ANGLING

The flathead catfish is an important commercial fish along the Missouri and Mississippi rivers and is commonly taken by sport fishermen in large streams and reservoirs over most of Missouri. More flatheads are taken on trot lines than by any other method, but many are caught by jugging or by still-fishing with rod and reel. Methods are similar to those for taking channel catfish except that only live or freshly killed baits are effective.

TROUT-PERCHES

Percopsidae

The trout-perches are peculiar little fishes that combine characters of both soft-rayed and spiny-rayed fishes. Only two species are known, of which one occurs in Missouri. Like the pirate perch, they seem to be the surviving remnants of a larger group that is now mostly extinct.

Trout-perch

Percopsis omiscomaycus (Walbaum)

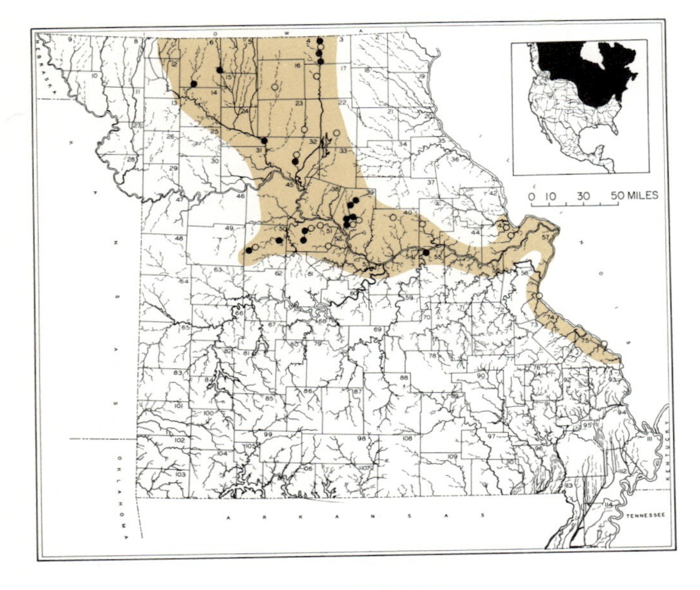

DESCRIPTION

Illustration: Page 24, 7a.

Characters: A thick-bodied, silvery fish with a single dorsal fin, an adipose fin, and ctenoid (rough edged) scales. Tail fin deeply forked. Mouth horizontal and small, the upper jaw not reaching front of eye. Undersurface of head distinctly flattened and with prominent internal tubular spaces (appearing externally as translucent or whitish lines). Lateral line present, containing 47 to 58 scales. Dorsal and anal fins each with 1 or more weak spines at front.

Life colors: Back and sides greenish-yellow or straw colored with silvery reflections and several longitudinal rows of dusky spots; belly white. Fins plain.

Size: Adults are commonly 3 to 5 inches long to a maximum of about 5.5 inches.

Scientific name: *Percopsis,* Greek, meaning "perch-like"; *omiscomaycus,* probably an Algonkian Indian name having "trout" as its root.

DISTRIBUTION AND HABITAT

The trout-perch is widespread in the Grand and Chariton stream systems and occurs eastward along the Missouri and Mississippi rivers to St. Charles and Perry counties. It is fairly common in parts of the Chariton, Lamine, Petite Saline, and Perche stream systems but is rare elsewhere in its Missouri range. Its distribution and abundance seem to have remained unchanged since the early 1940's.

This fish occurs most commonly in the deeper pools of prairie streams having permanent flow, moderately clear water, and bottoms consisting mostly of sand and gravel. Possibly the trout-perch was more widespread in northern and western Missouri before extensive channelization resulted in the destruction of pool-type habitats in many streams.

HABITS AND LIFE HISTORY

This nocturnal fish ranges actively over shallow bottoms in search of food at night, retiring to deeper water or hiding in accumulations of sticks, leaves or other detritus during daylight hours. Its diet consists mostly of aquatic insects and other small invertebrates taken from the bottom.[154]

At the latitude of Missouri the trout-perch spawns in early spring, perhaps in March.[24] In Minnesota spawning occurs over an extended period from May into August.[161] The breeding habits are not known in detail, but the eggs are probably deposited on rocky bottoms in a swift current.[162] Spawning of lake populations of trout-perch is preceded by movements of breeding adults into tributary streams.

In lower Red Lake, Minnesota, the trout-perch averages 2, 3.5, 4.2, and 4.5 inches by the end of its first through fourth growing seasons.[161] Females attain a larger size than males. The life span is 4 or 5 years.

IMPORTANCE

In some northern lakes the trout-perch is an important forage fish for burbot, northern pike, yellow perch, walleye, and freshwater drum. In Missouri it is too uncommon to be of much importance.

PIRATE PERCHES

Aphredoderidae

The pirate perch is the only living species of its family. Several related species are known as fossils. It, along with the cavefishes and several other groups, seems to be a holdover from an ancient fauna that occupied the present Mississippi Valley before the ancestors of most modern-day fishes had migrated into the region.

Pirate Perch

Aphredoderus sayanus (Gilliams)

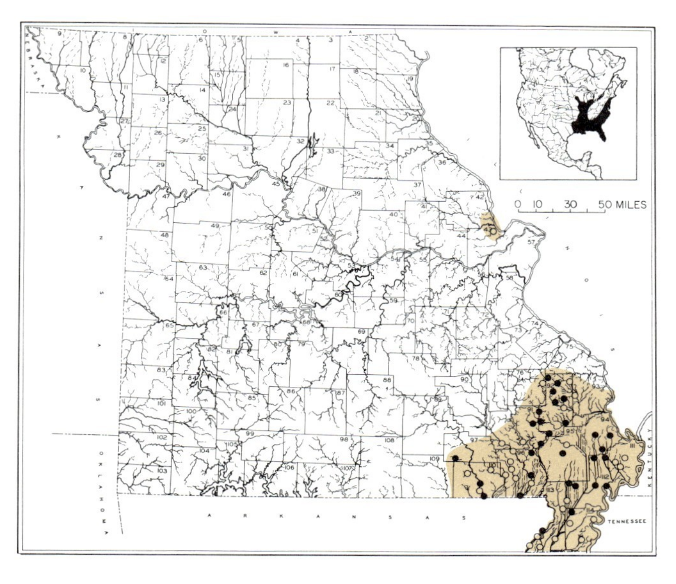

DESCRIPTION

Illustration: Page 25, 10a; **41.**

Characters: A stout, blackish fish with a single dorsal fin and with ctenoid (rough-edged) scales on the head and body. No adipose fin. Tail fin slightly notched, not deeply forked. Differs from all Missouri fishes except the cavefishes in having the anus far forward from front of anal fin—situated on throat in adults. Gill cover with a sharp spine; rear margin of preopercle (bone just ahead of gill cover) strongly serrate (saw-toothed). Dorsal and anal fins each with 2 or 3 weak spines at front. Lateral line absent or incomplete; scales along midside about 49 to 59.

Life colors: Body greyish, thickly speckled with black. A narrow, vertical dark bar present at base of tail fin; another bar often visible beneath eye. Fins dusky. Breeding adults tinged with purple or violet; males nearly black.

Size: Adults are commonly 2.5 to 4.5 inches long to a maximum of about 5 inches.

Scientific name: *Aphredoderus,* from the Greek *aphod,* meaning "excrement," and *dere,* meaning "throat," from the position of the anus; *sayanus,* named for Thomas Say, an entomologist.

DISTRIBUTION AND HABITAT

The pirate perch is widespread in the Lowlands and adjacent parts of the southeastern Ozarks. It is also known from Peruque Creek in St. Charles County and probably occurs elsewhere along the Mississippi River. In spite of its general occurrence in the Lowlands it is seldom abundant.

The pirate perch inhabits bottomland lakes, overflow ponds, and the quiet pools and backwaters of low-gradient streams. The habitats it occupies are characterized by clear, warm water, absence of current, and abundant cover in the form of aquatic plants or organic debris.

HABITS AND LIFE HISTORY

This solitary, secretive fish hides during the daylight hours about thick growths of aquatic plants or accumulations of organic debris, venturing forth to feed at night. Its food is entirely animal, consisting of immature aquatic insects, small crustaceans, and an occasional small fish.[24]

Spawning is said to occur at the latitude of Missouri in May.[24] The breeding habits are not known but it has been suggested that the pirate perch builds a nest that is guarded by both parents.[163] However, considering that the anus is situated on the throat, it seems more likely that the eggs are incubated in the gill cavities as has been demonstrated for some cavefishes where the anus is similarly situated.

An interesting feature of the early development of the pirate perch is that in the smallest young the anus is located just in front of the anal fin, but gradually moves forward to assume the adult position as the fish grows. In an Oklahoma lake the pirate perch grew to a length of about 2.4 inches by the end of its first year of life and attained lengths of 3.3, 4, and 4.5 inches in succeeding years.[164] Of the 82 specimens examined none were more than 4 years old.

CAVEFISHES

Amblyopsidae

This family includes five species confined to unglaciated regions of the eastern United States. Two species occur in Missouri. Both are rare and are seldom encountered unless a special effort is made to collect them. But because of their unusual appearance, the occasional specimens pumped from wells or seen near the entrances of caves and springs are sure to evoke interest in those unfamiliar with these little fishes.

ADDENDUM: After this book went to press, the spring cavefish, *Chologaster agassizi* Putnam, was collected from southeastern Missouri by Mr. Eugene McDonald. This significant discovery represents the first known occurrence of the spring cavefish from Missouri, or in fact from any locality west of the Mississippi River.

The spring cavefish differs in important respects from the other two species of cavefish found in Missouri. Most notably it has small, fully developed eyes and is well pigmented, whereas the other cavefish are without eyes and are nearly colorless. The spring cavefish is most often found in cave streams or about the mouths of springs, but occasionally has been reported from spring-fed swamps and small streams.

Key to the Cavefishes

1a. Sensory papillae on tail fin in 4 to 6 rows; dorsal fin rays usually 7, often 8.
Ozark cavefish
Amblyopsis rosae ..... **Page 225**

1b. Sensory papillae on tail fin in 2 rows; dorsal fin rays 8 or 9.
Southern cavefish
Typhlichthys subterraneus
.... **Page 225**

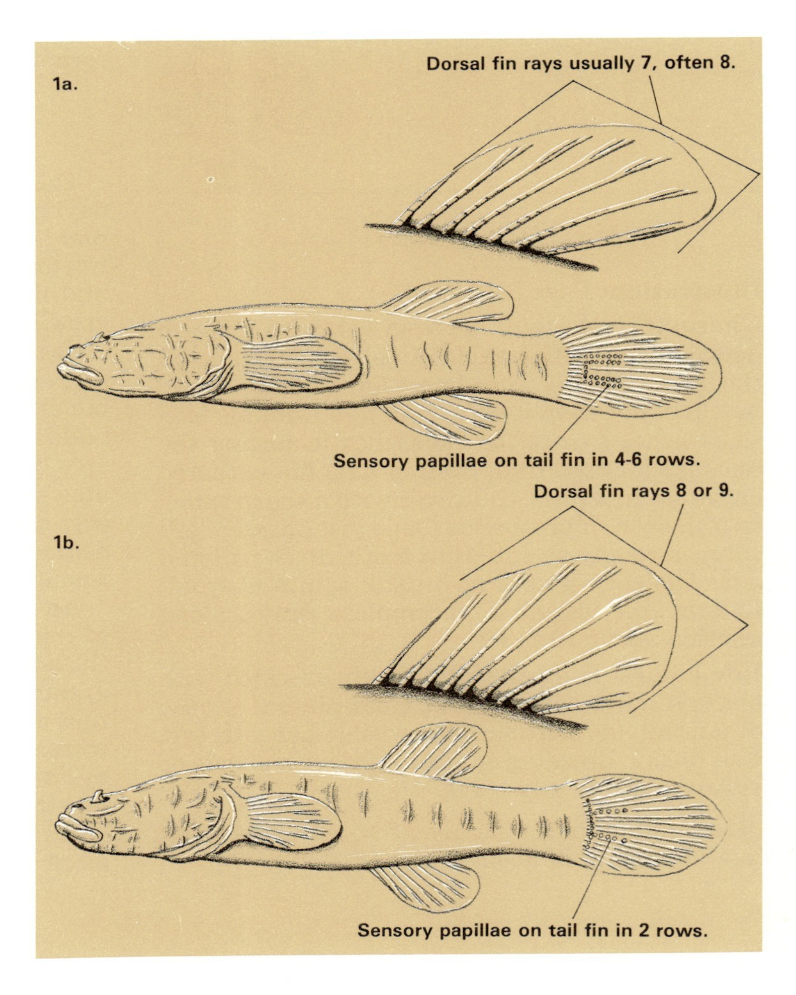
1a.
Dorsal fin rays usually 7, often 8.
Sensory papillae on tail fin in 4-6 rows.
1b.
Dorsal fin rays 8 or 9.
Sensory papillae on tail fin in 2 rows.

Ozark Cavefish

Amblyopsis rosae (Eigenmann)

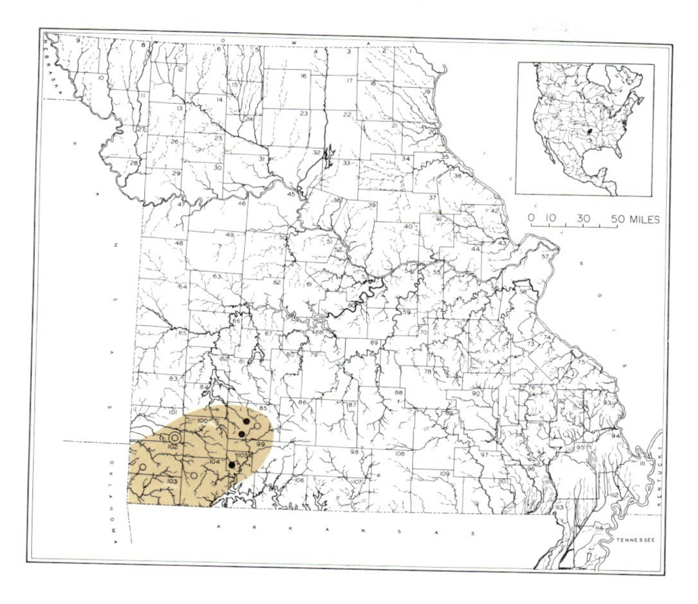

DESCRIPTION

Illustration: Page 224, 1a.

Characters: A small, white fish with a single dorsal fin, a broad, flattened head, and no eyes. Pelvic fins absent. Tail fin rounded. Scales small, the skin appearing naked. Anus far forward of anal fin, on throat in adults.

Very similar to southern cavefish but with sensory papillae on tail fin usually in 4 to 6 rows. Also, the dorsal fin has 8 (often 9) rays.

Life colors: Body nearly colorless except for a pinkish hue that results from blood vessels showing through the translucent skin and flesh. Undersurface of head and breast in region of gills and heart a deeper red.

Size: Not known to exceed 2.2 inches.

Scientific name: *Amblyopsis,* Greek, meaning "insensible vision"; *rosae,* named for Mrs. R. S. Eigenmann, a pioneer woman biologist.

DISTRIBUTION AND HABITAT

The Ozark cavefish is largely restricted to the Ozark Region of southwestern Missouri but has been recorded from one locality in northern Arkansas. It seems to be extremely rare. Less is known about the distribution and abundance of cavefish than of any other fishes found in Missouri. Future efforts directed at correcting this deficiency may reveal a more widespread distribution for this species and the southern cavefish.

The Ozark cavefish is confined to unglaciated uplands where the highly soluble limestone bedrocks are honeycombed by subsurface drainageways. This fish ventures rarely if ever into surface waters, having been collected only from caves, wells, and the outlets of springs. It occurs in quite small cave streams, most often over a rubble substrate.[165]

HABITS AND LIFE HISTORY

The external sense organs that occur abundantly over the head, body, and fins of the Ozark cavefish compensate very well for the absence of sight, permitting it to carry on its life functions in the eternal darkness of its underground home. Practically all of the activities of cavefish are dependent on touch (thigmotaxis). Their diet consists principally of small crustaceans called copepods, but small salamanders, crayfish, isopods, amphipods, and young of their own species are also eaten.[165]

The breeding habits of the Ozark cavefish are not known but are probably like those of the northern cavefish, *Amblyopsis spelaea* DeKay, a close relative occurring in caves of Kentucky and Indiana. In this fish the eggs, numbering about 70, are carried in the gill chamber of the female until they hatch. The young remain in the gill chamber until the yolk sac is absorbed, a period of 4 to 5 months.[165, 166] It is not known how the eggs become situated in the gill chamber, but perhaps they are first taken into the mouth. Cavefish kept in aquaria are able to recognize each other as individuals even without sight and there is much fighting among males. Breeding occurs during high water from February through April and the young appear in late summer or early fall.[165]

Southern Cavefish

Typhlichthys subterraneus Girard

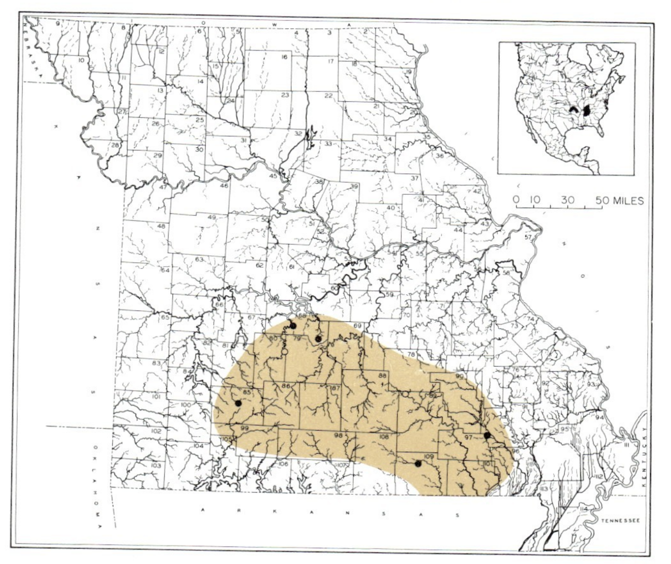

DESCRIPTION

Illustration: Page 224, 1b.

Characters: A small, white fish with a single dorsal fin, a broad, flattened head, and no eyes. Pelvic fins absent. Tail fin rounded. Scales small, the skin appearing naked. Anus far forward of anal fin, on throat in adults.

Very similar to Ozark cavefish, but usually with 2 rows of sensory papillae on tail fin (one row on upper half and one row on lower half). Also, the dorsal fin has 8 or 9 (occasionally 7 or 10) rays.

Life colors: Body nearly colorless, with a pinkish hue where blood vessels show through translucent skin and flesh. Individuals kept in light gradually assume a dusky coloration.

Size: Apparently a larger species than the Ozark cavefish. Largest Missouri specimen 3.4 inches in length.

Scientific name: *Typhlichthys,* Greek, meaning "blind fish"; *subterraneus,* Latin, meaning "under the earth."

DISTRIBUTION AND HABITAT

The southern cavefish inhabits underground waters of the central and southern Ozarks. It has not been found in the same caves as the Ozark cavefish, though both species are known from nearby caves in Greene County.

The habitat requirements of this species are much like those of the Ozark cavefish.

HABITS AND LIFE HISTORY

The diet of this species consists principally of small crustaceans called copepods, but is otherwise more diverse than that of the Ozark cavefish. Annulus formation, which marks the cessation of growth, occurs in the fall. As water levels rise growth is resumed and the eggs begin to enlarge. Breeding follows, and by June or July the females are spent and small to medium-sized young are abundant.[165]

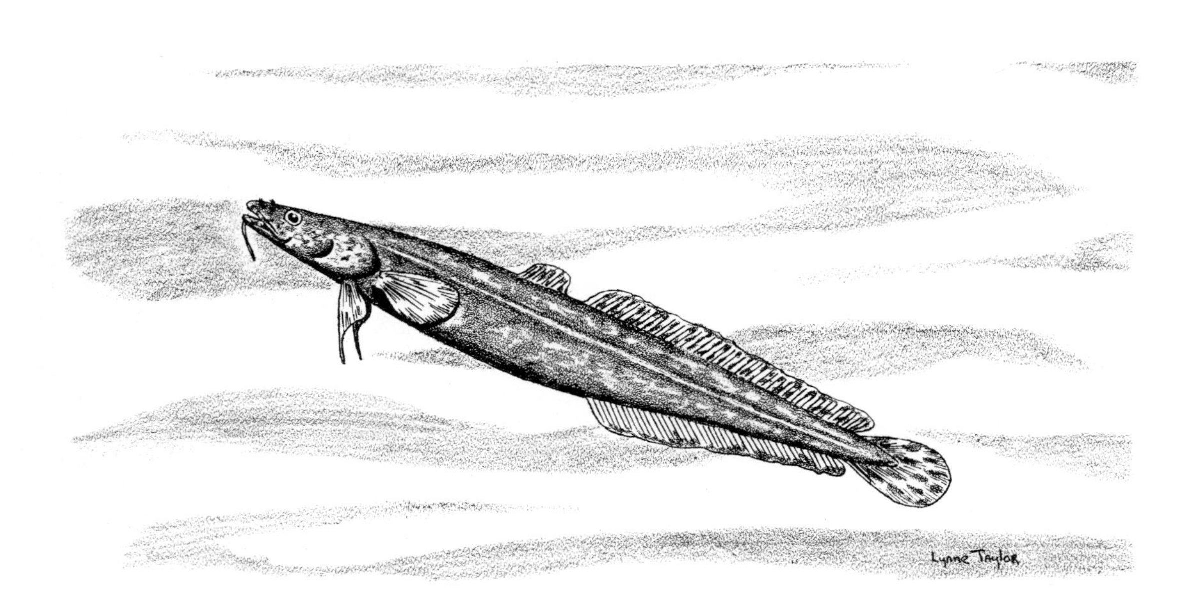

CODFISHES

Gadidae

This wide-ranging group of fishes is primarily marine in distribution. A single species, the burbot, occurs in freshwater. The burbot is a northern fish, occuring as far south as Missouri only as occasional stray individuals. Because of its rarity in our waters and unusual appearance, the occasional burbot taken by Missouri fishermen always attracts attention.

Burbot

Lota lota (Linnaeus)

Other local names: Freshwater codfish, Eelpout, Spineless catfish.

DESCRIPTION

Illustration: Page 30, 20a.
Characters: A slender, smooth-skinned fish with a large barbel in the middle of the chin and two dorsal fins. First dorsal fin short and without stiff spines; second dorsal very long—nearly half length of head and body. Anal fin nearly as long as second dorsal. Tail fin rounded and separate from dorsal and anal fins. Pelvic fins present, their point of attachment slightly ahead of pectoral fins. Scales present but so small that skin appears naked.
Life colors: Back and sides dark olive or brown, mottled and blotched with darker brown or black. Belly white or pale yellow. Fins similar in color to adjacent parts of body.
Size: The largest burbot reported from Missouri waters was 22.5 inches long and weighed 3.8 pounds. Elsewhere, weights of 12 pounds or more have been reported.
Scientific name: *Lota,* from *"la Lotte,"* French for codfish.

DISTRIBUTION AND HABITAT

Most records of the burbot in Missouri are based on single specimens, usually adults, taken from the Missouri and Mississippi rivers by commercial fishermen. Some years there are many reports; other years no burbots are reported. Probably there are no self-sustaining populations of this fish in Missouri and the occasional specimens reported are strays that have invaded our waters from farther north.

I have examined a burbot reportedly taken at Duck Creek Refuge, Bollinger County, on May 11, 1964, by Dr. Leonard Durham and his students from Eastern Illinois University. Durham told me that the specimen, a small individual, was not noticed at the time the collection was made, but was later found when the collection was being sorted. This record is in need of substantiation since it is far south of any previous Missouri locality and is the only report outside of the mainstream of the Missouri and Mississippi rivers. The specimen is much smaller than any burbot previously taken in Missouri, measuring only 1.9 inches long.

HABITS AND LIFE HISTORY

The burbot seems to be quite similar in habit to the eel. It is a secretive fish, spending the daylight hours hiding about piles of rocks, submerged logs, undermined bridge supports, and beds of aquatic vegetation.[167] At night it forages actively over the bottom, exploring holes and crevices in search of food. Young burbots feed primarily on mayfly nymphs and other insects; adults subsist largely on fish and crayfish.

The burbot spawns in winter. An interesting description of its breeding habits was given by Cahn.[168] He found a group spawning at night beneath the ice when the air temperature was -28°F. The spawning fish formed a slithering, writhing ball in which the individuals continually weaved in and out. The eggs are scattered over the bottom, requiring about 3 or 4 weeks to complete their development.

IMPORTANCE

The burbot is too rare in Missouri waters to be more than a curiosity. In more northern regions it is sometimes caught on hook-and-line and is reported to be a good food fish by those who are not repelled by its snake-like appearance.

KILLIFISHES

Cyprinodontidae

The killifishes or topminnows are a large group of interesting fishes that are most abundant and diverse in tropical regions. Seven species of this wide-ranging family are found in Missouri. All are small—none exceed 7 inches in length.

They are a close-knit group, sharing many features that readily separate them from minnows and other small fishes in Missouri waters. The most unusual features are related to their way of life. The "topminnows" are so named for their habit of skimming along just beneath the surface of the water, feeding on insects and other small invertebrates found there. As adaptations for this habit the top of the head and forward part of the back are broad and flat, and the mouth is tilted upward so that it opens at the upper surface of the head. A deep groove separates the upper jaw from the snout, allowing a considerable extension of the jaws.

The name "cyprinodont" that is sometimes applied to these fish literally translates to mean "toothed carp", in reference to the many small teeth on the jaws. The body is more or less cigar-shaped and is covered with cycloid (smooth-edged) scales. Scales are also present on the top and sides of the head. The lateral line is absent. The dorsal fin is single and is located far back over the anal fin. The tail fin is rounded. No spines are present in the fins.

Sex differences are often well marked in the topminnows. These differences are greatest during the spawning season but are more or less evident throughout the year. The fins are longer and more pointed in males and the color pattern is sometimes quite different in the two sexes. In most species the males develop "contact organs" during the spawning season. These small spine-like structures are present on the scales and fin rays. Females of most species have a fleshy sheath around the front of the anal fin.

An interesting feature of the coloration of topminnows is the presence in many species of iridescent golden or silvery marks on the upper surface of the head or back. The number, size, and shape of these marks are characteristic of the species. Since the marks are readily seen when the fish is in the water they provide excellent field marks for an observer who is familiar with the differences. The significance of these marks to the fish is not definitely known but they may serve as "disruptive" marks to confuse birds or other predators that attack from above.

Topminnows probably serve as food for game fishes and in some areas they are of importance as biological controls for the aquatic stages of mosquitoes. They adapt readily to aquarium life and make attractive and interesting aquarium fishes.

Key to the Killifishes

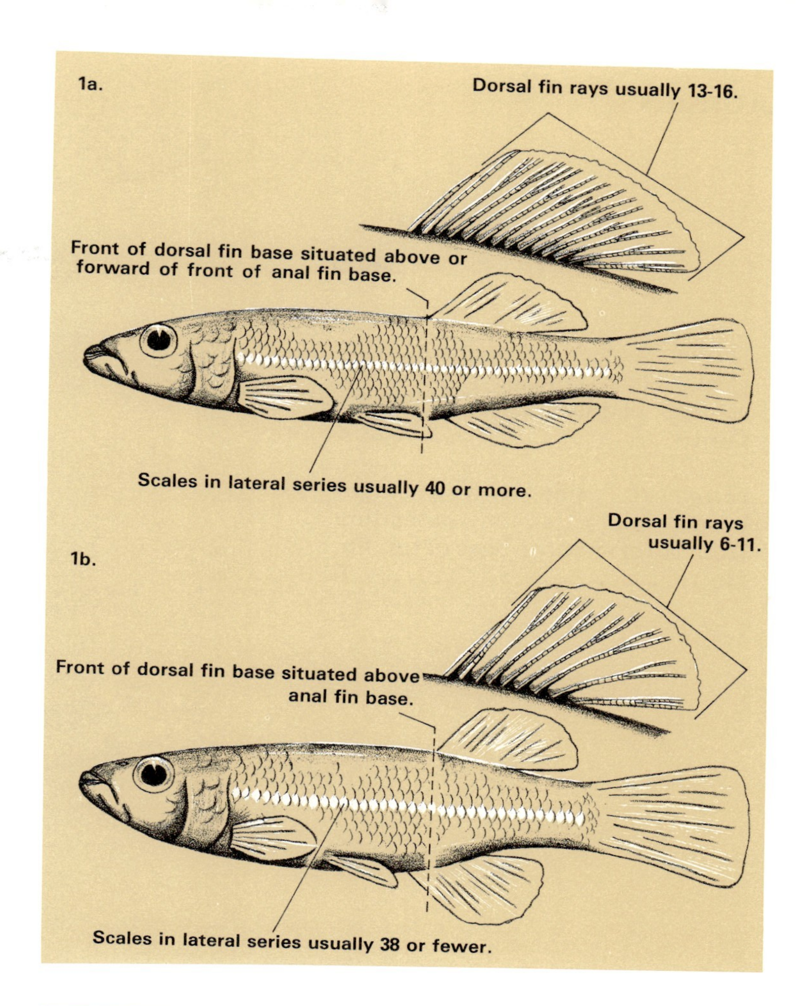
1a.
Dorsal fin rays usually 13-16.
Front of dorsal fin base situated above or forward of front of anal fin base.
Scales in lateral series usually 40 or more.
1b.
Dorsal fin rays usually 6-11.
Front of dorsal fin base situated above anal fin base.
Scales in lateral series usually 38 or fewer.

1a. Front of dorsal fin base situated above or forward of front of anal fin base; dorsal fin rays usually 13 to 16; scales in lateral series usually 40 or more.
Go to 2

1b. Front of dorsal fin base situated above anal fin base; dorsal fin rays usually 6 to 11; scales in lateral series usually 38 or fewer.
Go to 3

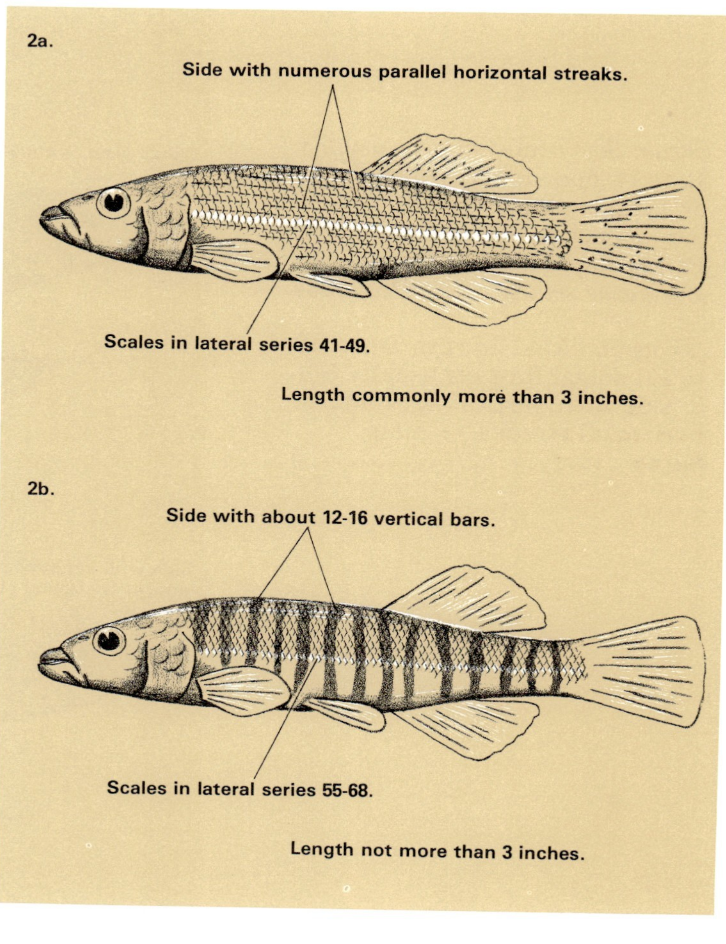
2a.
Side with numerous parallel horizontal streaks.
Scales in lateral series 41-49.
Length commonly more than 3 inches.
2b.
Side with about 12-16 vertical bars.
Scales in lateral series 55-68.
Length not more than 3 inches.

2a. *(From 1a.)* Side with numerous parallel horizontal streaks; scales in lateral series 41 to 49; length commonly more than 3 inches.
Northern studfish
Fundulus catenatus .. **Page 232**

2b. *(From 1a.)* Side with about 12 to 16 vertical bars, narrower in females than in males; scales in lateral series 55 to 68; length not more than 3 inches.
Plains killifish
Fundulus kansae ..... **Page 232**

3a.

Side marked with vertical bars and/or horizontal streaks, or plain.

3b.

Side with a single broad, black stripe extending from tip of snout to base of tail fin.

3a. *(From 1b.)* Side marked with vertical bars and/or horizontal streaks, or plain.
Go to **4**

3b. *(From 1b.)* Side with a single broad, black stripe extending from tip of snout to base of tail fin.
Go to **6**

4a. *(From 3a.)* Anal fin rays usually 12 to 14; dorsal fin rays usually 10 or 11; side plain, without vertical bars or horizontal streaks.
Plains topminnow
Fundulus sciadicus ... **Page 234**

4b. *(From 3a.)* Anal fin rays usually 8 to 11; dorsal fin rays usually 6 to 9; side with vertical bars and/or horizontal streaks, or plain.
Go to **5**

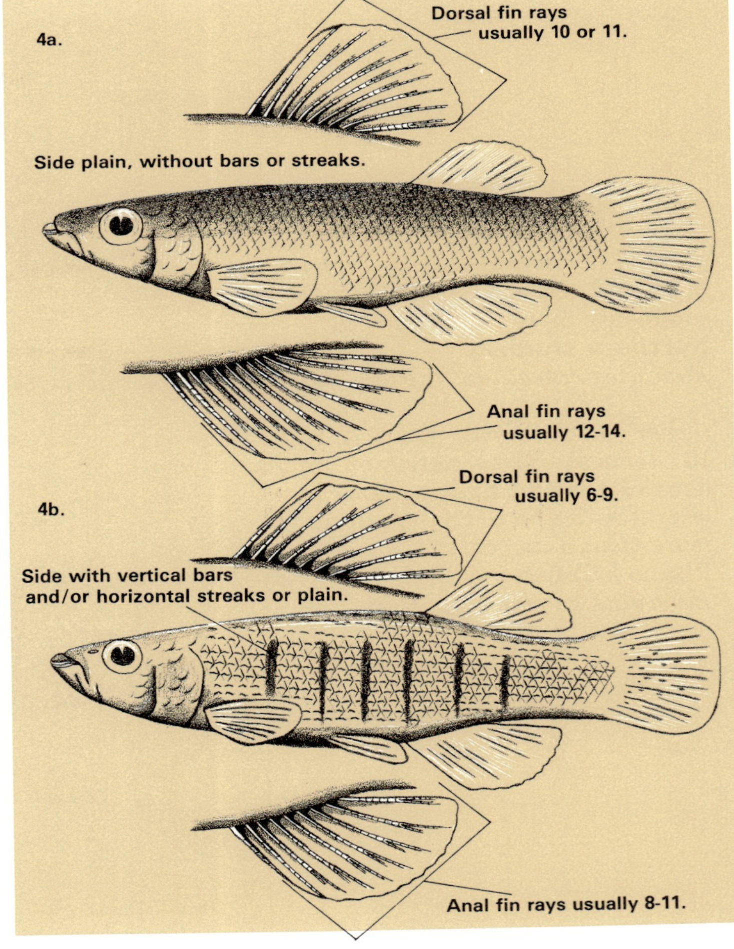
4a.
Dorsal fin rays usually 10 or 11.
Side plain, without bars or streaks.
Anal fin rays usually 12-14.
4b.
Dorsal fin rays usually 6-9.
Side with vertical bars and/or horizontal streaks or plain.
Anal fin rays usually 8-11.

5a. *(From 4b.)* A dark vertical bar beneath eye; side of females with prominent horizontal streaks, males with faint horizontal streaks and prominent vertical bars.
Starhead topminnow
Fundulus notti .... **Page 235**

5b. *(From 4b.)* No dark vertical bar beneath eye; side of both sexes without horizontal streaks but with vertical bars or plain.
Golden topminnow
Fundulus chrysotus .. **Page 233**

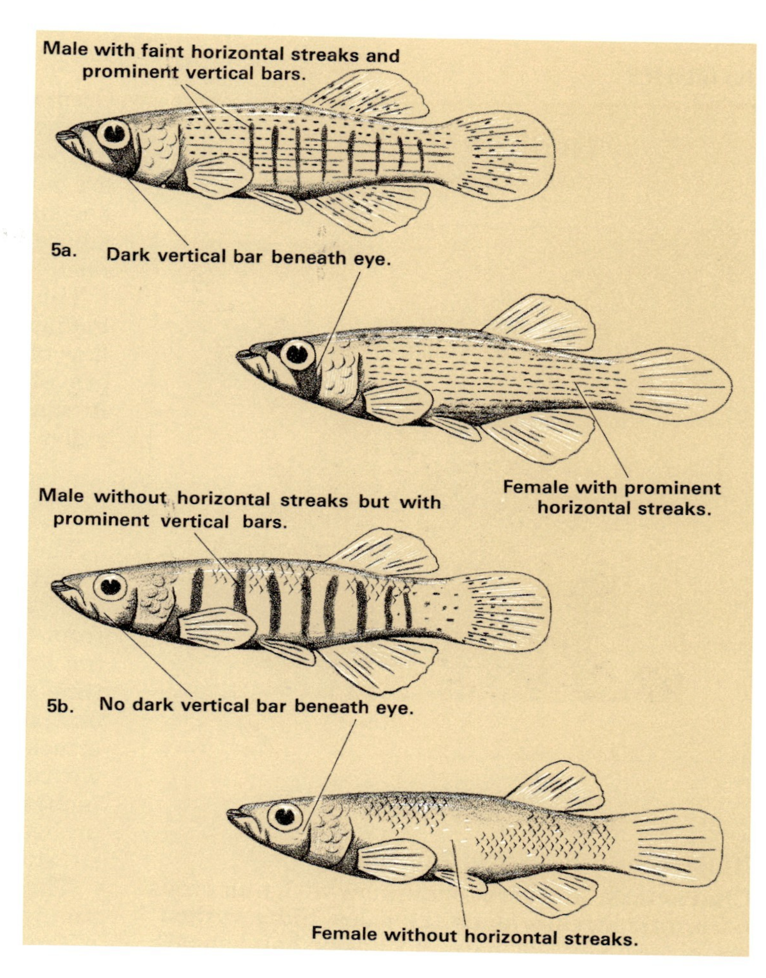

Male with faint horizontal streaks and prominent vertical bars.
5a.
Dark vertical bar beneath eye.
Female with prominent horizontal streaks.
Male without horizontal streaks but with prominent vertical bars.
5b.
No dark vertical bar beneath eye.
Female without horizontal streaks.

6a. *(From 3b.)* Upper side with few to many black spots that are regular in outline and about as dark as stripe along midside; scales in lateral series usually 34 to 36; dorsal fin rays usually 9 or 10.
Blackspotted topminnow
Fundulus olivaceus ... **Page 235**

6b. *(From 3b.)* Upper side without black spots or with spots that are irregular in outline and not as dark as stripe along midside; scales in lateral series usually 31 to 34; dorsal fin rays usually 9, often 8 or 10.
Blackstripe topminnow
Fundulus notatus .... **Page 236**

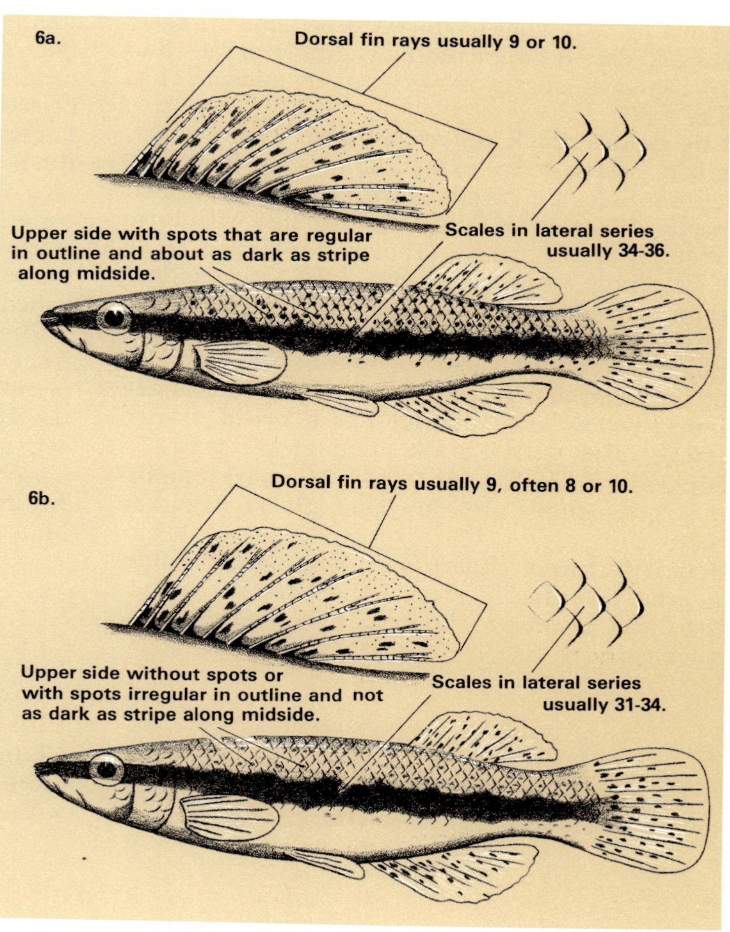

6a.
Dorsal fin rays usually 9 or 10.
Upper side with spots that are regular in outline and about as dark as stripe along midside.
Scales in lateral series usually 34-36.
6b.
Dorsal fin rays usually 9, often 8 or 10.
Upper side without spots or with spots irregular in outline and not as dark as stripe along midside.
Scales in lateral series usually 31-34.

Northern Studfish

Fundulus catenatus (Storer)

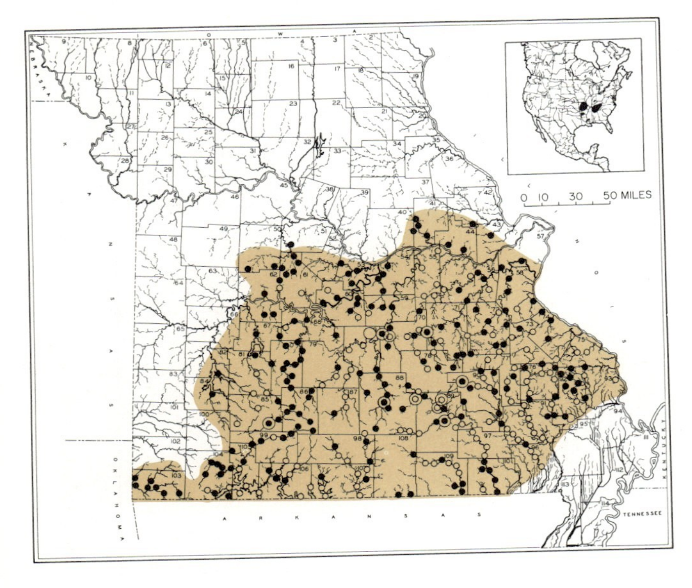

DESCRIPTION

Illustration: Page 229, 2a.

Characters: A silvery topminnow with numerous horizontal streaks along the sides. Sides without prominent vertical bars; no dusky bar beneath eye. Front of dorsal fin base situated directly above or only slightly forward of anal fin base. Rays in dorsal fin, including rudimentaries, 13 to 16. Scales in lengthwise series along midside 41 to 49.

Life colors: Back yellowish-brown with a short, broad, golden stripe extending forward from dorsal fin. Sides bluish-silver with numerous brown horizontal streaks. Dorsal and tail fins with rows of small brown specks; other fins plain.

Breeding males are more brilliantly colored than any other Missouri topminnow. The sides are bright blue with reddish-brown streaks, and numerous reddish spots are present over the sides of the head and in the fins. The paired fins are lemon-yellow. The tail fin has a broad orange fringe, often with a black submarginal band.

Size: The studfish is the largest Missouri topminnow, occasionally attaining a length of 6 inches or more.

Scientific name: *Fundulus*, from the Latin name *Fundus* meaning "bottom," the habitat; *catenatus*, Latin, meaning "chained," in reference to the color pattern.

DISTRIBUTION AND HABITAT

The northern studfish is one of the most common and widely distributed Ozark stream fishes. Occurrence of the studfish in Elk River of extreme southwestern Missouri seems to be the result of introduction at a fairly recent date. All records are based on specimens taken since 1960, and Hall has suggested that occurrence of the studfish in adjacent streams of northeastern Oklahoma is the result of introduction.[169]

This topminnow inhabits streams of all sizes having moderate or high gradients, permanent flow of clear water, and bottoms of silt-free sand, gravel and rock. The studfish is most often found in shallow water along the margins of pools and riffles where there is little current.

HABITS AND LIFE HISTORY

The studfish lives in small groups that cruise slowly along the shoreline or remain for considerable periods of time in protected inlets. It escapes from bass and other large predatory fish by staying in water only a few inches deep much of the time and depends mostly on speed and agility to escape from birds and other land predators. When attacked it often throws itself clear of the water with a quick flip of its tail and comes down several inches away, where it hovers quietly with body arched, waiting expectantly for the next move by its attacker.

The studfish seems to feed more from the bottom than some other topminnows. The stomachs of four specimens collected from Big Piney River in August contained a surprising variety of bottom life, consisting mostly of kinds that live in or near riffles. Included were the immature stages of caddisflies, mayflies, dragonflies, "true" flies, and beetles, along with adult riffle beetles, snails, fingernail clams and small crayfish. The only food items that might have been taken from the surface were adults of a few "true" flies. Studfish collected during high water are often stuffed with worms washed in from surrounding areas. These observations are in agreement with those of published studies.[170]

The studfish breeds over an extended period from mid-May to early August. No nest is prepared but the males establish and guard small territories in shallow, quiet water near shore. The eggs are deposited on clean gravel. I once observed a pair of studfish spawn on a longear sunfish nest. No information is available on age and growth. Males reach a larger size than females.

Plains Killifish

Fundulus kansae Garman

DESCRIPTION

Illustration: Page 229, 2b.

Characters: A silvery topminnow with 12 or more narrow, vertical bars along the side. Sides without horizontal streaks; no dusky bar beneath eye. Front of dorsal fin base situated forward of front of anal fin base. Rays in dorsal fin, including rudimentaries, 13 to 16. Scales in lengthwise series along midside 55 to 68.

Life colors: Back olive-brown, fading to silvery-white on sides and belly. Sides with numerous dusky bars (bars narrower and more numerous in females than in males). Fins plain or yellowish in females and immature individuals, bright yellowish-orange in breeding males.

Size: Adults are commonly 1.5 to 3 inches long to a maximum of about 3.5 inches.

Scientific name: *Fundulus,* from the Latin name *Fundus* meaning "bottom," the habitat; *kansae,* "from Kansas."

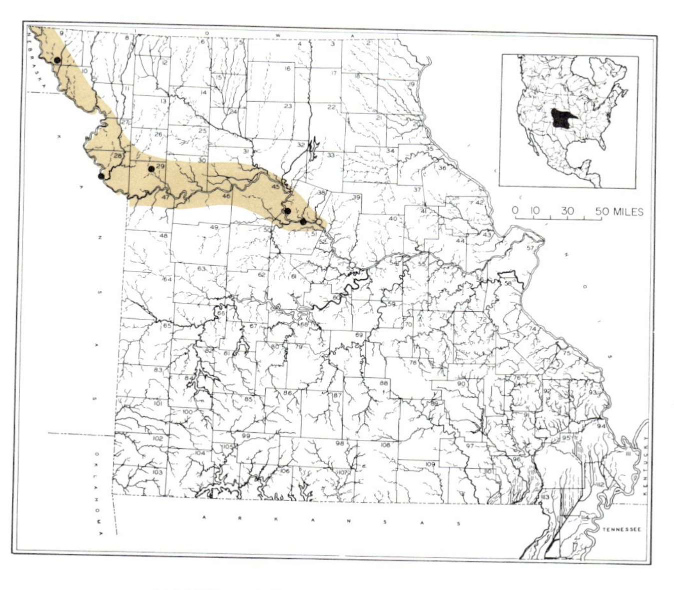

DISTRIBUTION AND HABITAT

The plains killifish has occurred abundantly only in Salt Creek below Boone's Lick Spring, Howard County, and in Clear Creek, Clay County. In Salt Creek it is the most abundant fish. Fisher collected this species from the Missouri River as far downstream as Franklin County in 1945.[41] But none have been collected downstream from Howard County in recent years.

The plains killifish normally inhabits streams with alkaline or saline waters and few other kinds of fish. Perhaps its distribution is limited by a requirement for high salinity or by inability to compete in the more diverse fish populations found in typical stream situations. Boone's Lick Spring has a salt concentration approximately 31% that of sea water,[171] and this has a marked effect on the chemical composition of Salt Creek below the confluence of the spring and the stream. The plains killifish is the only species of fish occurring in Salt Creek near the spring during periods of low stream flow, although several other species are found there at other times. It occurs in all types of habitats, from pools and backwaters to shallow sandy areas with considerable current.

HABITS AND LIFE HISTORY

Except as otherwise noted, the following information is from a study of the Salt Creek population of plains killifish by Bonham.[171] This species lives in small, loosely organized schools. During periods of inactivity it often lies buried in the sand with only its head showing. Its food habits are very generalized, including a variety of plant and animal life. In Salt Creek insects and other aquatic invertebrates are preferred, but diatoms and other plant material are eaten when invertebrates are scarce. Large quantities of sand are consumed incidental to feeding on the diatoms that grow as a layer over the sandy bottom.

The plains killifish spawns in central Missouri from early June to early August and there may be three or more separate periods of spawning activity during the spawning season. In Salt Creek each spawning period follows a moderate or heavy rain, suggesting that spawning activity is stimulated by a sudden freshening of the water or a change in water temperature. Males do not establish territories but become very aggressive towards each other while spawning and compete vigorously for the attentions of the females.[172] Mating occurs during a brief pairing of a single male and female; the eggs are buried in the sand.

In Salt Creek the plains killifish reaches a length of about 1.2 to 1.8 inches at the end of its first year of life and averages about 2.1 to 2.5 inches at the end of 2 years. Individuals hatched early in the summer become sexually mature the following year at a length of about 1.4 inches; others hatched late in the summer do not mature until they are 2 years old.

Golden Topminnow

Fundulus chrysotus (Günther)

DESCRIPTION

Illustration: Page 231, 5b.

Characters: An olive-green topminnow of rather uniform coloration (females and immatures) or with sides marked by 6 to 10 vertical bars (males). No dusky bar beneath eye. Front of dorsal fin base situated above anal fin base. Rays in dorsal fin, including rudimentaries, 7 to 9, and in anal fin 9 to 11. Scales in lengthwise series along midside 31 to 33.

Life colors: Back and sides yellowish-green with a small golden spot near each nostril and a short golden stripe in front of dorsal fin. Females and immatures have many pearl-blue spots on sides; males have red spots and several faint dusky bars. Fins in males yellowish with reddish-brown spots.

Size: Adults are commonly 1.8 to 2.7 inches long to a maximum of about 3 inches.

Scientific name: *Fundulus,* from the Latin name *Fundus* meaning "bottom," the habitat; *chrysotus,* Greek, meaning "gilded" or "golden."

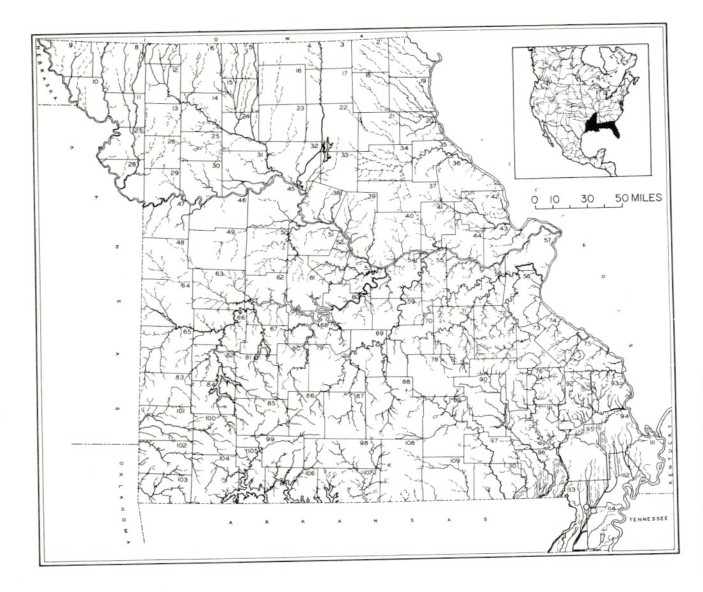

DISTRIBUTION AND HABITAT

This Lowland species is known in Missouri only from five specimens collected at two localities more than 25 years ago. Recent attempts to obtain the golden topminnow at these localities were unsuccessful and this species may no longer occur in the state.

The golden topminnow inhabits clear, quiet pools and backwaters where submerged aquatic plants are abundant.

HABITS AND LIFE HISTORY

A Florida study indicates that the golden topminnow feeds on insects at the water's surface.[173] In the aquarium the golden topminnow has been observed depositing its eggs on submerged plants, stones, and the side of the aquarium.[174] The eggs are laid a few at a time over a period of a week or more. This topminnow is somewhat more aggressive than the starhead but makes an interesting and attractive aquarium fish.

Plains Topminnow

Fundulus sciadicus Cope

DESCRIPTION

Illustration: Page 230, 4a; **41.**

Characters: An olive-brown topminnow without prominent bars, streaks, or stripes on the side of the head or body. Front of dorsal fin base situated above anal fin base. Rays in dorsal fin, including rudimentaries, 10 or 11, and in anal fin 12 to 14. Scales in lengthwise series along midside 33 to 37.

Life colors: Back and sides olive-brown with bronze reflections and faint blue-green crosshatching. A narrow golden stripe extends forward along midline of back from front of dorsal fin to a point about halfway to tip of snout. Fins yellowish or plain in females and immature individuals; orange-red in breeding males.

Size: Adults are commonly 1.5 to 2.5 inches long to a maximum of about 2.8 inches.

Scientific name: *Fundulus,* from the Latin name *Fundus* meaning "bottom," the habitat; *sciadicus,* a Greek name for some species of dusky fish.

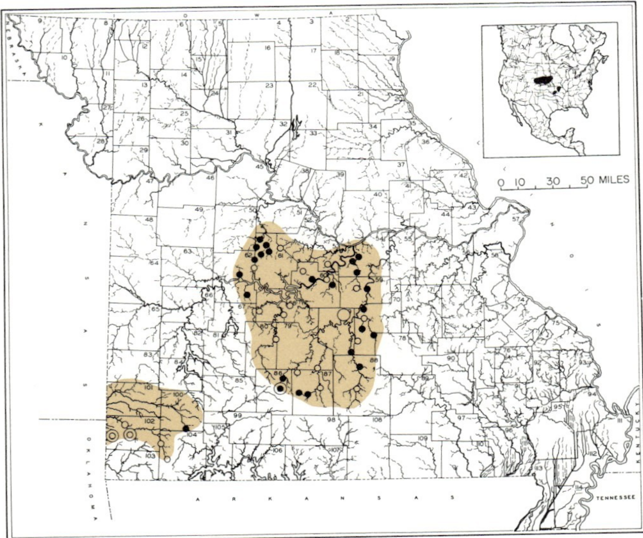

DISTRIBUTION AND HABITAT

The plains topminnow occurs along the northwestern margin of the Ozarks from Shoal Creek northeastward to the lower Osage and Gasconade rivers. It is not presently known from tributaries of the upper Osage, and populations in southwestern Missouri are widely separated from those in the northern Ozarks. This topminnow has apparently disappeared from the Shoal Creek and Niangua River drainages since the early 1940's. Because of its specialized requirements the plains topminnow tends to occur as isolated colonies but is rather common in its preferred habitat.

It inhabits quiet pools of small creeks, and backwaters and overflow pools of larger streams. It is invariably found where the water is clear and without noticeable current, often in or adjacent to beds of submergent vegetation. Its distribution in Missouri is much like that of the least darter, a fish with similar requirements.

HABITS AND LIFE HISTORY

The plains topminnow occurs singly or in small groups near the surface of the water. Nothing is known of its food habits. Spawning occurs in May and June in Missouri. The eggs are deposited on aquatic plants or algae where they hatch in 8 or 10 days at a temperature of about 70° F.[175]

This species makes a hardy and attractive aquarium fish but is difficult to keep with other species because of its aggressive disposition.

Starhead Topminnow

Fundulus notti (Agassiz)

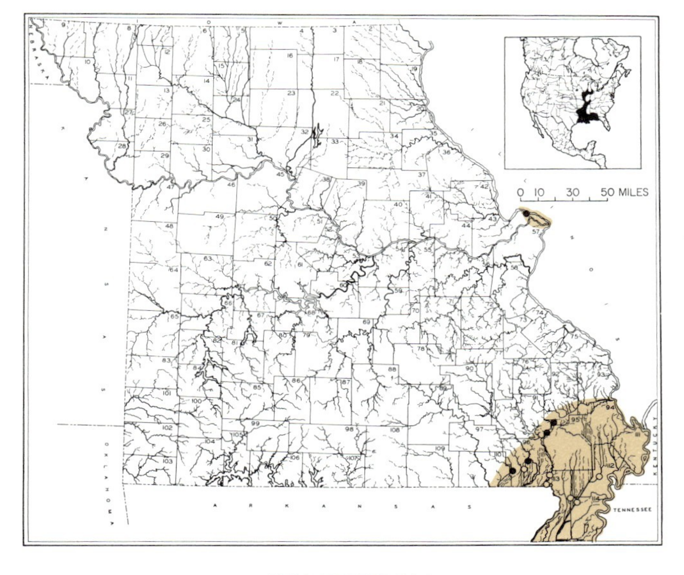

DESCRIPTION

Illustration: Page 231, 5a.

Characters: A pale-colored topminnow with the sides marked by prominent horizontal streaks (females and immatures) or by faint streaks and about 10 dark vertical bars (males). In adults a prominent wedge-shaped dusky bar extends down from eye. Front of dorsal fin base situated above anal fin base. Rays in dorsal fin, including rudimentaries, 6 or 7, and in anal fin 8 or 9. Scales in lengthwise series along midside 30 to 34.

Life colors: Back greenish-yellow with a large golden spot on top of head and a similar but smaller spot at front of dorsal fin. Sides silvery with narrow brownish streaks (females and immatures) or with rows of reddish dots and several dark green vertical bars (males). Adults have a dusky or black bar beneath eye. Males have red spots in the dorsal, anal, and tail fins.

Size: Adults are commonly 1.8 to 3 inches long to a maximum of about 3.2 inches.

Scientific name: *Fundulus,* from the Latin name *Fundus* meaning "bottom," the habitat; *notti,* named for Dr. Nott, its discoverer.

DISTRIBUTION AND HABITAT

The starhead topminnow is known only from the Lowlands and a single locality in St. Charles County. Though limited and localized in distribution, this topminnow is common at most localities where it occurs. The starhead topminnow appears to have disappeared from several localities in the Lowlands since the early 1940's.

This species is characteristic of quiet backwaters and cut-off ponds and lakes having clear water and an abundance of submerged aquatic plants. Many of the habitats where it occurs are connected with flowing waters only during floods.

HABITS AND LIFE HISTORY

The starhead topminnow normally occurs singly or in pairs. It skims along just beneath the surface of the water and will not dive even when pursued. It sometimes jumps onto the bank when pursued by a bass or other predator and remains there for several minutes until the predator has gone. Experiments with individuals displaced to unfamiliar surroundings suggest that the starhead topminnow orients with the sun as a compass to find its way back into the water.[176] The food of this topminnow consists primarily of insects, about half of which are terrestrial kinds that have fallen into the water.[24] Nothing is known of its breeding habits except that spawning probably occurs in May.

This attractive topminnow has a gentle disposition and makes an excellent aquarium fish.

Blackspotted Topminnow

Fundulus olivaceus (Storer)

DESCRIPTION

Illustration: Page 231, 6a.

Characters: A light brown topminnow with a broad, black horizontal stripe along the midside. No dusky vertical bar beneath eye. Front of dorsal fin base situated above anal fin base.

Very similar to blackstripe topminnow, page 236, but upper sides with few to many black spots that are regular in outline and about as dark as stripe along midside. Also, there are usually 34 to 36 scales in a lengthwise series along the midside, and 9 or 10 rays, including rudimentaries, in dorsal fin.

Life colors: Light brown above and white below, the two areas separated by a broad, black lengthwise stripe. Margins of stripe nearly straight in females and immatures but uneven in males. Upper surface of body and unpaired fins with small black spots; tail fin yellow in breeding males.

Size: Adults are commonly 2 to 3.5 inches long to a maximum of about 3.8 inches.

Scientific name: *Fundulus,* from the Latin name *Fundus* meaning "bottom," the habitat; *olivaceus,* Latin, meaning "olive-colored."

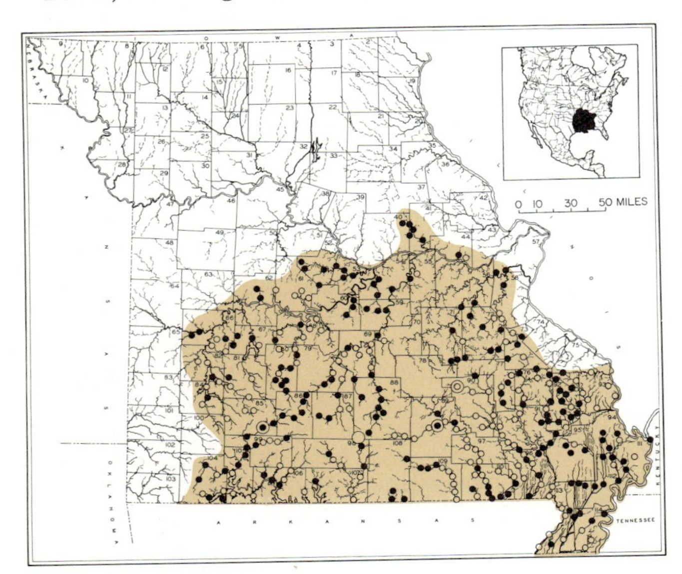

DISTRIBUTION AND HABITAT

The blackspotted topminnow is widespread and abundant in the Ozark and Lowland faunal regions. In the Lowlands it is the most abundant and widely distributed topminnow and in the Ozarks it is second in abundance only to the studfish. In the Ozarks this species occurs in all stream systems not occupied by the closely related blackstripe topminnow. The blackspotted topminnow inhabits clear, permanent-flowing streams where it is generally found in quiet water along the margins of pools, near thick stands of water willow or other emergent aquatic plants.

HABITS AND LIFE HISTORY

The blackspotted topminnow is often observed cruising along the shoreline in pairs or small groups. In Reelfoot Lake, Tennessee, it feeds primarily on small crustaceans and insects taken at the water surface.[177] Considerable plant material (diatoms and duckweed) also occurs in stomachs, but may be consumed accidentally since much of it passes through undigested. The breeding habits are probably like those of the blackstripe topminnow. Adults of the blackspotted topminnow in breeding condition have been taken in Missouri during May.

Blackstripe Topminnow

Fundulus notatus (Rafinesque)

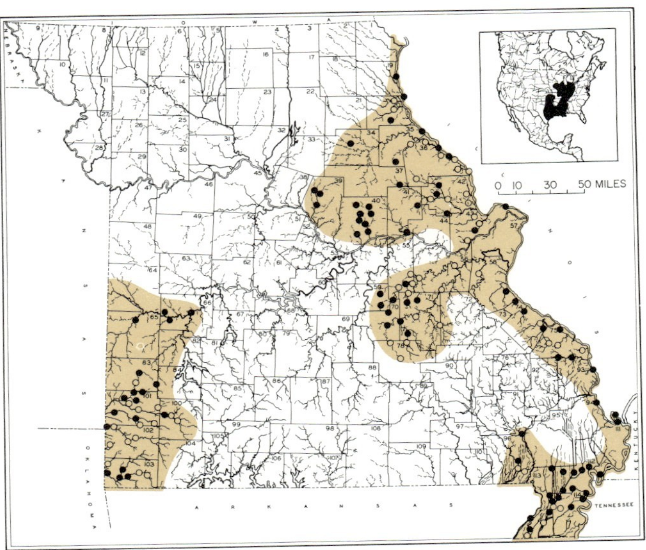

DESCRIPTION

Illustration: Page 231, 6b.

Characters: A light brown topminnow with a broad, black horizontal stripe along the midside. No dusky vertical bar beneath eye. Front of dorsal fin base situated above anal fin base.

Very similar to blackspotted topminnow, page 235, but without prominent black spots on upper sides or, if present, spots are lighter in color than black stripe along midside and are irregular in outline. Also, there are usually 31 to 34 scales in a lengthwise series along the midside, and 9 (often 8 or 10) rays, including rudimentaries, in dorsal fin.

Life colors: Like those of blackspotted topminnow, page 235, except as noted above under *Characters.*

Size: Adults are commonly 2 to 3.5 inches long with a maximum of about 3.8 inches.

Scientific name: *Fundulus,* from the Latin name *Fundus* meaning "bottom," the habitat; *notatus,* Latin, meaning "spotted."

DISTRIBUTION AND HABITAT

The blackstripe topminnow is the most abundant and widespread topminnow in the southwestern Ozarks and the northeastern Ozark border. It is also common in the Lowlands of southeastern Missouri but is less abundant at most localities than the blackspotted topminnow. The presence of this fish in the Auxvasse and Perche drainages of central Missouri is the result of introduction within the last three decades. The blackstripe topminnow and its close relative, the blackspotted topminnow, rarely occur at the same locality. Perhaps intense competition between them is an important factor in determining their distribution. The requirements of these two species seem similar but apparently are sufficiently different so that, at any given locality, one species is more successful than the other and eliminates its competitor.

The blackstripe topminnow seems to prefer slightly warmer and more turbid waters than the blackspotted topminnow, but otherwise their habitats are not notably different. The blackstripe topminnow is most often found along large lowland rivers and in the pools of streams draining undissected uplands.

HABITS AND LIFE HISTORY

The general behavior of this fish is similar to that of the blackspotted topminnow. The blackstripe topminnow feeds most intensely in the morning and again in the late afternoon and evening.[178] Terrestrial insects comprise nearly 50% of its diet with the remainder divided between aquatic insects, crustaceans, snails, and algae. The algae passes through the gut undigested. The breeding habits of the blackstripe topminnow were described by Carranza and Winn.[179] During the prolonged summer spawning season this fish usually travels in pairs consisting of a male and a female. Each pair limits its activities to an area along the shore which they tend to defend against others of their own species. The eggs are deposited singly on algae or other submergent vegetation as the male and female lie side by side. Spawning is accompanied by rapid vibrations and ends with a flip of the tail fin, usually by the male, which throws the egg into the vegetation. The female deposits 20 or 30 eggs over a short period of time, repeating the performance several days later when another batch of eggs ripens. Males of the blackstripe topminnow grow larger than females, as is also the case for the blackspotted topminnow.

LIVEBEARERS

Poeciliidae

Many species of livebearers are found from Mexico southward into Central and South America, but only one species, the mosquitofish, occurs as far north as Missouri. The mosquitofish has the distinction of being the only Missouri fish that gives birth to living young. Fertilization is therefore internal. Males are much smaller than females and have the anal fin modified into a long, slender structure for transfer of the sperm.

In habit and structure the mosquitofish has much in common with the topminnows and in most respects the general description given for topminnows, page 228, will serve for both. The mosquitofish differs mainly in having fewer scales along the midside, in the relative positions of the dorsal and anal fins, in the structure of the sensory canal on the side of the head, and in the shape of the anal fin of males. These differences are described under *Characters* in the species account.

The mosquitofish has been widely stocked for mosquito control but is probably little more effective in this regard than the native fishes it often replaces. Introduction of this aggressive fish into isolated waters of the desert southwest has brought to extinction certain rare and highly localized fishes that were unable to compete.

Mosquitofish

Gambusia affinis (Baird and Girard)

DESCRIPTION

Illustration: Page 30, 19b.

Characters: A small, stout fish with a terminal, strongly upturned mouth, a rounded tail fin, and scales on the head. Sides plain, without stripes, bars, or streaks; usually a V-shaped dusky bar is present beneath the eye. Base of anal fin situated entirely ahead (males) or almost entirely ahead (females and immature individuals) of dorsal fin. Scales in lengthwise series along midside usually 27 to 30. Sensory canal on side of head an open groove, without pore-like openings. Third ray of anal fin, including rudimentaries, unbranched. First few rays of anal fin greatly prolonged in adult males.

Life colors: Back and sides yellowish-brown, the dark edgings on scales forming a characteristic pattern of cross-hatchings. A dusky bar of variable intensity is present beneath eye. Fins mostly plain, the dorsal and tail fins with 2 or 3 rows of faint dark specks.

Size: Maximum length of females about 2.8 inches. Males are smaller, seldom exceeding 1.2 inches.

Scientific name: *Gambusia,* derived from a provincial Cuban word, *Gambusino; affinis,* Latin, meaning "related."

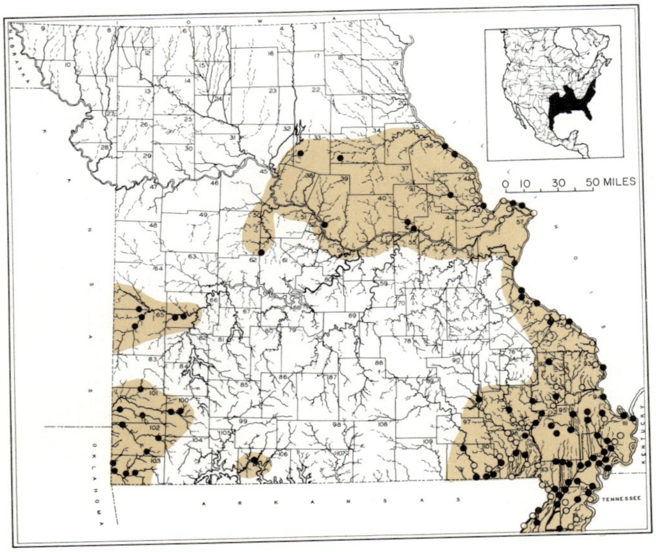

DISTRIBUTION AND HABITAT

The mosquitofish seems to be more widespread and abundant in Missouri now than it was 30 years ago. Collections made in the 1940's suggest that this fish was formerly restricted to the Lowlands of southeastern Missouri and waters immediately adjacent to the Mississippi River northward to Pike County. In recent collections it has occurred abundantly at scattered localities in central Missouri and at many localities in the upper Osage and Spring River systems of the southwest. These range extensions have almost certainly resulted from widespread stocking for mosquito control. The mosquitofish is one of the most abundant and widespread fishes in the Lowland Faunal Region.

Backwaters and adjacent oxbows of warm, sluggish, Lowland streams are the favorite habitat of the mosquitofish. In such situations the mosquitofish occurs most abundantly in shallow, marginal areas where the water is warm and there is considerable aquatic vegetation or other cover.

HABITS AND LIFE HISTORY

The mosquitofish remains most of the time near the surface in water only a few inches deep, cruising about singly or in small groups. Its food habits are diverse, including both plant and animal material.[180] Animal food includes insects, spiders, small crustaceans, rotifers, and snails. Duckweed and other plants are less important than animal life and may be eaten accidentally along with the animals.

At the latitude of Missouri the mosquitofish reproduces over a period of 10 or 15 weeks during the summer and a single female may produce three or four broods.[181] Males pursue and court females more or less continuously during the breeding season. Fertilization is internal, sperm transfer being accomplished by means of a groove along the modified anal fin. Special muscles permit the male to direct the anal fin forward and to the side during courtship. The sperm are retained in a living state within a special pouch possessed by the female and several successive broods of eggs may be fertilized by the sperm from a single mating. Eggs hatch 21 to 28 days after fertilization. The number of young in a single brood may vary from a few to several hundred.

Growth is rapid and mosquitofish born early in the year commonly mature and reproduce during their first summer of life. Females mature at a length of about one inch and attain a much larger size than males. Males mature at a length of less than an inch. Mosquitofish usually die during the summer in which they mature and few survive beyond their second summer. Males are not as long-lived as females.

SILVERSIDES

Atherinidae

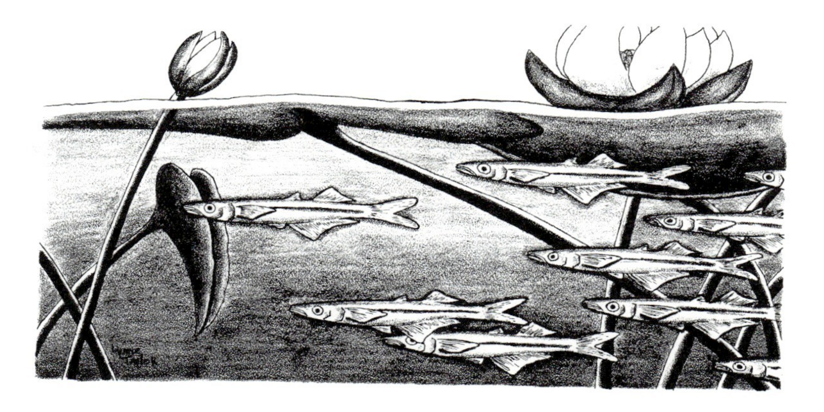

The silversides is a wide-ranging marine group with a few species that live in fresh water. Two of these occur in Missouri. They are small fish, superficially resembling minnows.

Silversides can be recognized by their pencil-thin body; pointed, rather beak-like snout; and long, sickle-shaped anal fin. Two widely separate dorsal fins are present, but the first dorsal is so small that it is easily overlooked. This fin is over or slightly forward from the front of the anal fin and contains three to five weak, flexible spines. The pectoral fin is farther up on the side than in most fishes, its point of attachment being near the upper end of the gill opening. The mouth is directed obliquely upward and can be extended because of a deep groove separating the upper jaw and the snout. The family name comes from the bright, silvery stripe extending lengthwise along the side.

The brook silverside and the Mississippi silverside are often abundant in waters inhabited by game fishes and are important as forage. In Ozark reservoirs the largemouth bass, white bass, and the crappies feed extensively on them.

Key to the Silversides

1a. Jaws not forming a beak; snout length (A) equal to or less than diameter of eye (B); anal fin rays usually 15 to 20. Scales large, usually 38 to 46 in lateral series.
Mississippi silverside
Menidia audens ...... **Page 241**

1b. Jaws forming a beak; snout length (A) much greater than diameter of eye (B); anal fin rays usually 22 to 25; scales small, usually 74 to 87 in lateral series.
Brook silverside
Labidesthes sicculus .. **Page 240**

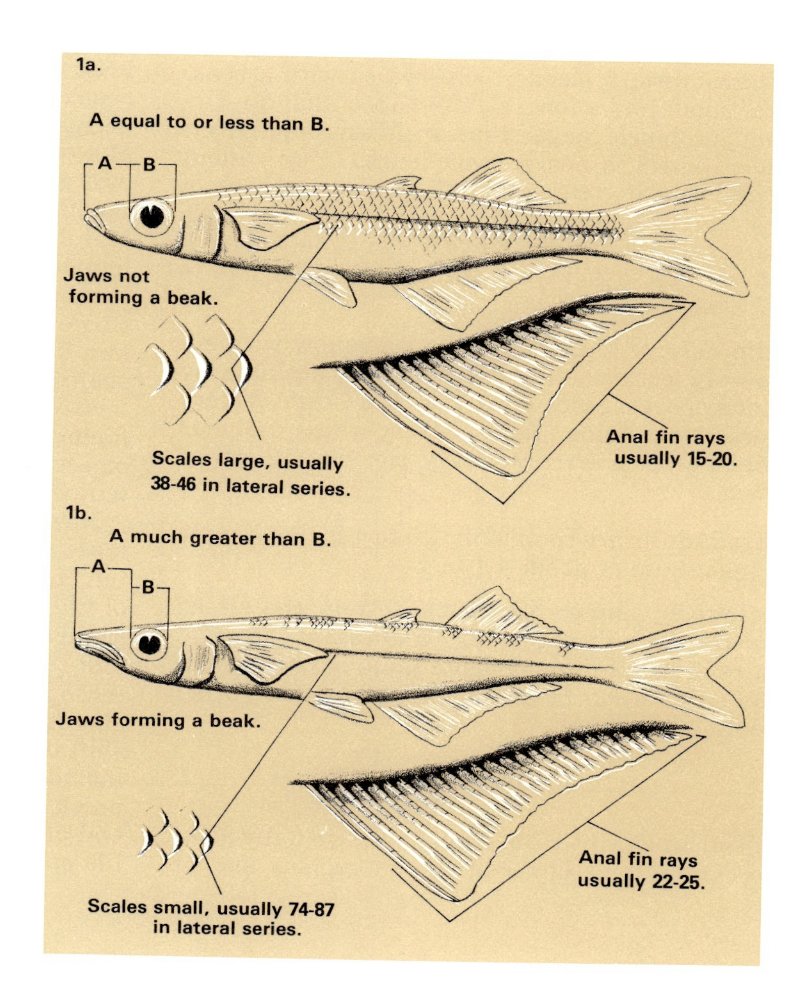

Brook Silverside

Labidesthes sicculus (Cope)

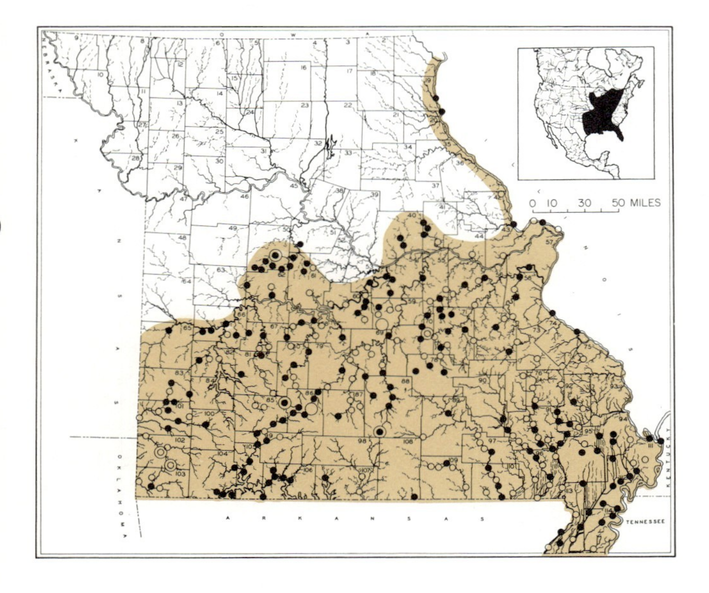

Other local names: Needlenose, Stick minnow, Skipjack.

DESCRIPTION

Illustration: Page 239, 1b.

Characters: A slender, silvery fish with a beak-like snout and a long, sickle-shaped anal fin. Upper jaw much longer than in Mississippi silverside, its length nearly twice length of eye. Snout length much greater than distance from back of eye to rear margin of gill cover. Front of spinous dorsal almost directly above front of anal fin. Anal fin with 22 to 25 rays. Scales small, usually 74 to 87 along midside.

Life colors: Back pale greenish-yellow with silvery reflections, the scales faintly outlined by black specks. Sides silvery with a bright silvery horizontal stripe. Belly silvery-white. Spinous dorsal with a narrow dusky tip; fins otherwise plain.

Size: Adults are commonly 2.5 to 4 inches long to a maximum of about 4.4 inches.

Scientific name: *Ladidesthes,* from the Greek *labidos,* "a pair of forceps," and *esthio,* "to eat," in reference to the elongate jaws; *sicculus,* from the Latin *siccus* meaning "dried," found in dried pools.

DISTRIBUTION AND HABITAT

The brook silverside occurs over virtually all of the Ozark and Lowland faunal regions and at scattered localities northward along the Mississippi River. It is common in preferred habitats of Ozark streams and is the most abundant small fish in large Ozark reservoirs.

The brook silverside is characteristic of clear, warm waters having no noticeable current. In the Ozarks it is common in the large pools of upland creeks receiving little spring flow and the warm backwaters and overflow pools of large streams. In lakes and reservoirs the brook silverside is most abundant in coves and along the shore.

HABITS AND LIFE HISTORY

The brook silverside remains most of the time within inches of the water's surface and never descends to depths greater than a few feet. The flattened head and up-turned mouth are adaptations for a surface-dwelling life. This species has a definite daily cycle of activity that seems to be regulated primarily by light intensity.[182] In the daytime it is intensely active, darting about continuously and frequently leaping out of the water. It is also active on moon-lit nights, but lies motionless at the surface if the night is dark. When a beam of light is directed at the surface, silversides are attracted and concentrate in the circle of illumination.

The brook silverside spawns in Indiana from at least mid-June to early August.[183] Young have been collected in Table Rock Lake as early as May 22, indicating that spawning is earlier in southern Missouri than in Indiana. The eggs are deposited over gravelly shoals or beds of submerged vegetation.[182, 184] Males begin following the females several days before spawning begins. Pursuit of the females becomes more intense as the spawning season advances. Often several males pursue a single female, but only one actually pairs with her. The eggs are released and fertilized as the spawning pair glide at an angle from the surface towards the bottom. Each egg has a long adhesive filament by which it becomes attached to the first object it encounters. Eggs hatch in 8 days at a temperature of 77°F.[182]

Newly hatched young form compact schools and move from shore into deeper and more open water. Here they remain for most of the first summer of life, feeding on cladocera, copepods, and other small crustaceans. Late in the summer they spend more and more time close to shore and by the second summer remain continuously along the shoreline. With this change in habitat there is a shift in the diet from microcrustaceans to insects, including both aquatic and terrestrial kinds. The brook silverside matures, spawns, and dies by the end of its second summer of life. The maximum life span thus is only about 17 months.[182, 184]

Mississippi Silverside

Menidia audens Hay

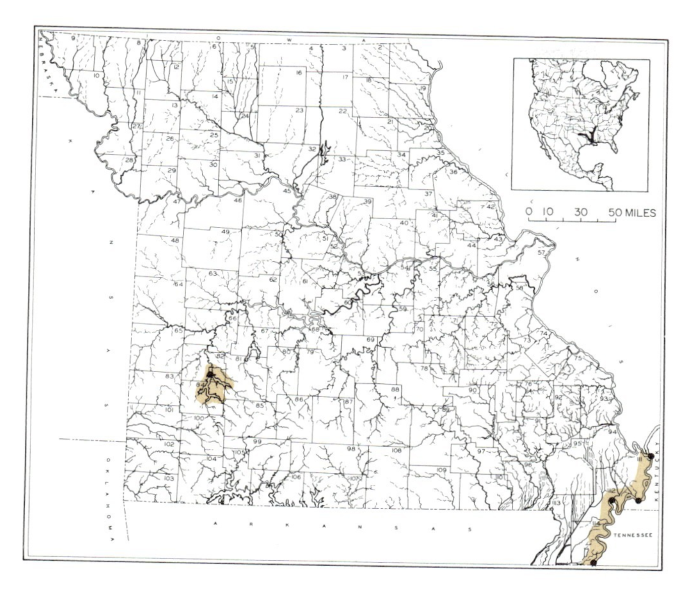

DESCRIPTION

Illustration: Page 239, 1a.

Characters: A slender, silvery fish with a beak-like snout and a long, sickle-shaped anal fin. Upper jaw shorter than in brook silverside, its length about equal to length of eye. Snout length less than distance from back of eye to rear margin of gill cover. Front of spinous dorsal well ahead of front of anal fin. Anal fin with 15 to 20 rays. Scales large, usually 38 to 46 along midside.

Life colors: As in brook silverside, page 240, but paler and more yellowish. Spinous dorsal without a dusky tip.

Size: Adults are commonly 2.5 to 4 inches long to a maximum of about 4.8 inches.

Scientific name: *Menidia,* an ancient Greek name for some small, silvery fish; *audens,* Latin, meaning "daring," having gone far from the sea.

DISTRIBUTION AND HABITAT

The Mississippi silverside occurs commonly in the Mississippi River from the mouth of the Ohio River southward. It was first collected in Missouri in 1963, but may have been present but unnoticed prior to that time. It was introduced into Stockton Reservoir in 1970 and has maintained itself through natural reproduction since that time. Presently it makes up about 20 percent of the silverside population in the reservoir.

This fish inhabits the surface waters of large, moderately clear streams and reservoirs. It moves inshore during the hours of darkness, returning to deeper water in the daytime.

HABITS AND LIFE HISTORY

Information about the life history of the Mississippi silverside results primarily from studies in Lake Texoma, Oklahoma.[185, 186] The food habits of this fish are similar to those of the brook silverside except that the latter species feeds more frequently at the surface. The Mississippi silverside spawns in Lake Texoma from late March or early April to about mid-July. The eggs have been found in algae growth on the stems of emergent bushes. Adults disappear from the population in July of the year following hatching, indicating a normal life span of about 16 months. However, some females may live 2 years. Females grow more rapidly than males. The Mississippi silverside attains a length of about 1 to 3 inches by September of its first summer of life.

SCULPINS

Cottidae

Like the silversides, this family is primarily marine with several species that occur in freshwater. Two species are found in Missouri.

Sculpins may be recognized by the broad, flattened head, tapering abruptly into the rather slender body. Scales are absent, but small prickles are often present on the head and body. The dorsal fin is divided into two distinct parts; the forward part contains spines, but these are soft and flexible, superficially resembling soft rays. The pectoral fins are large and fan-shaped. The pelvic fins each contain one stiff spine and three or four soft rays. The rear margin of the tail fin is rounded.

1a. Lateral line incomplete, ending beneath base of soft dorsal; dark vertical bar crossing body at base of tail fin narrow and indistinct.
Mottled sculpin
Cottus bairdi .... **Page 242**

1b. Lateral line usually complete, ending near base of tail fin; dark vertical bar crossing body at base of tail fin broad and distinct.
Banded sculpin
Cottus carolinae ...... **Page 243**

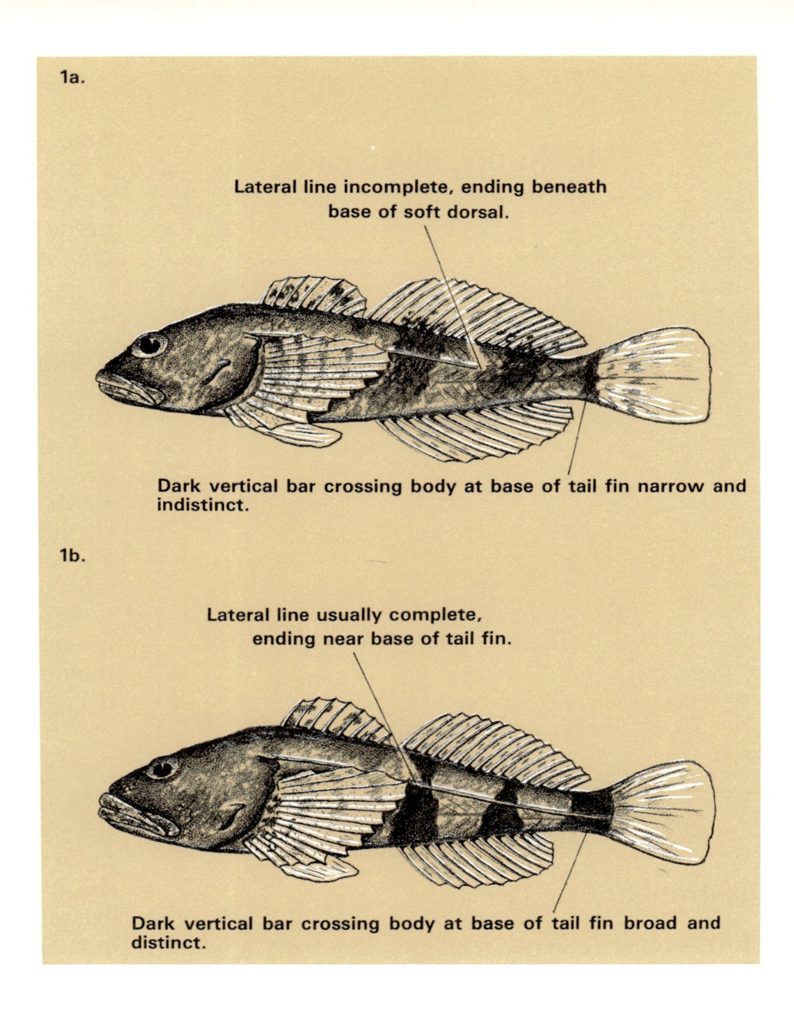
1a.
Lateral line incomplete, ending beneath base of soft dorsal.
Dark vertical bar crossing body at base of tail fin narrow and indistinct.
1b.
Lateral line usually complete, ending near base of tail fin.
Dark vertical bar crossing body at base of tail fin broad and distinct.

Mottled Sculpin

Cottus bairdi Girard

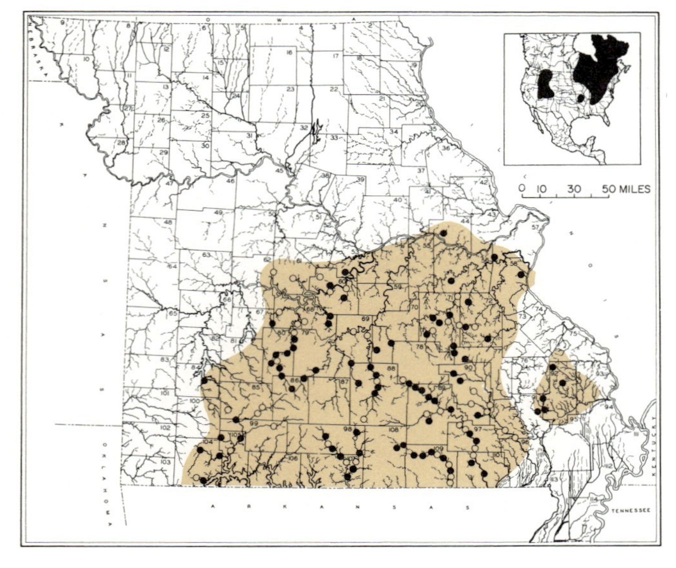
0 10 30 50 MILES
TENNESSEE

DESCRIPTION

Illustration: Page 242, 1a; **50.**

Characters: An olive-brown, strongly mottled sculpin without definite dark cross-bars on the back, or with cross-bars that are quite indistinct. Lateral line incomplete, ending beneath soft dorsal. Dorsal fins always somewhat connected.

Life colors: Back and sides olive-brown splotched with darker brown and with 4 indistinct saddle bars. Usually an indistinct crescent-shaped or bilobed dark bar is present across base of tail fin. Belly and underside of head white with faint to obvious dusting of brown specks. Spinous dorsal splotched with dark brown or black; other fins (except pelvics) faintly banded with brown lines; pelvic fins white. Breeding males are darker, sometimes almost black above, and have the underparts blue-green. Spinous dorsal black at base, the outer 1/3 of fin bright orange.

Size: Adults are commonly 2.4 to 3.6 inches long to a maximum of about 4.5 inches.

Scientific name: *Cottus,* Greek, an old name for the European miller's thumb; *bairdi,* named for S.F. Baird, first United States Fish Commissioner.

DISTRIBUTION AND HABITAT

The mottled sculpin is common and widespread

in the Ozarks, occurring in most of the principal stream systems. It is absent from southwestern drainages—Spring and Elk rivers—and has not occurred in collections from the St. Francis River system, though it is found in the adjacent Black and Castor stream systems. North of the Missouri River it is known only from Lost Creek in Warren County. Because of its specialized habitat it tends to occur as isolated colonies but in higher population densities than the banded sculpin.

The mottled sculpin inhabits spring branches and streams kept cool by spring flow. It is found in riffles as well as pools, over bottom types ranging from silt to gravel and rock. Generally it is most abundant about cover such as coarse rock or thick growths of water cress.

HABITS AND LIFE HISTORY

The mottled sculpin lives on the bottom, spending considerable time lying motionless in one spot and moving in short, quick dashes in a manner similar to darters. Many fishes can modify their colors to match their background, and this ability is developed to a high degree in the mottled sculpin. This ability probably helps the mottled sculpin to escape detection by its enemies and may also be useful in capturing prey from ambush. Its diet consists largely of larval aquatic insects supplemented by other aquatic invertebrates and an occasional small fish.[187] This species is somewhat cannibalistic. Apparently sculpins do not feed to any great extent on eggs and young of trout, as is sometimes charged.

Eggs thought to be those of the mottled sculpin have been found in Ozark streams from early November to late February and males guarding eggs have been found during February. This fish deposits its eggs in clusters of about 200 on the undersides of stones.[188] The nest cavity is cleaned by the male who remains with it until the fry disperse. The incubation period is 3 to 4 weeks.[189]

In the Ozarks the mottled sculpin is about 1.1 to 1.4 inches long when a year old. It probably does not mature until its third or fourth summer of life.

Banded Sculpin

Cottus carolinae (Gill)

DESCRIPTION

Illustration: Page 242, 1b.

Characters: A reddish-brown sculpin without strong mottling but with well defined dark bars across back and sides. Lateral line complete, extending to base of tail fin. Dorsal fins usually not connected.

Life colors: Back and sides a rather uniform reddish-brown with 4 or 5 saddle bars. Posterior three bars prominent, extending obliquely forward onto sides. Belly yellowish-white sprinkled with faint to obvious dusting of brown specks. Spinous dorsal splotched with dark-brown; other fins, except pelvics, usually faintly banded with dark brown lines; pelvic fins white.

Size: Adults are commonly 2.5 to 5 inches long to a maximum of 7.2 inches or more.

Scientific name: *Cottus,* Greek, an old name for the European miller's thumb; *carolinae,* "from Carolina."

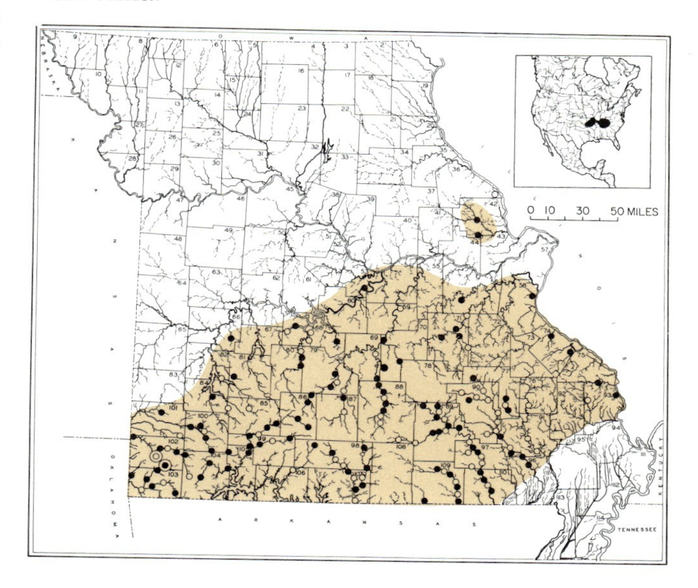

DISTRIBUTION AND HABITAT

The banded sculpin occurs in most of the principal stream systems of the Ozarks and in the Cuivre River drainage north of the Missouri River. It is more widespread in Missouri than the mottled sculpin.

The requirements of the two species of sculpins are much alike and they are often found together. However, the banded sculpin seems tolerant of higher temperatures than the mottled sculpin and is the more abundant of the two species in the larger and warmer Ozark streams. Because the habitat of the banded sculpin is more continuous than that of the mottled sculpin, it tends to occur less as isolated colonies.

HABITS AND LIFE HISTORY

The habits of this species are not known in detail but are probably much like those of the mottled sculpin. An egg mass thought to have been of the banded sculpin was found beneath a rock on Current River the third week of May. This suggests a much later spawning season than for the mottled sculpin. The nest was located in a swift riffle; the water temperature was 75°F.

SEA BASSES

Percichthyidae

As their name implies, the sea basses are primarily marine in distribution, but a few species occur in fresh water. Two of these, the white bass and yellow bass, are native to Missouri. A third species, the striped bass, has recently been introduced on an experimental basis in some Ozark reservoirs. The sea basses are sometimes referred to as the "true" basses to distinguish them from fishes such as the smallmouth bass, spotted bass, largemouth bass, and rock bass, which are members of the sunfish family.

The sea basses are moderately deep and slab-sided fishes with two entirely separate or only slightly connected dorsal fins, the first containing nine stiff spines, and rough-edged (ctenoid) scales on the head and body. A characteristic feature of all Missouri species is the prominent horizontal dark streaks along the upper sides. Three spiny rays are present at the front of the anal fin and a short, triangular spine is present on the gill cover near its rear margin. The free margin of the preopercle (bone just ahead of gill cover) is strongly serrate.

Key to the Sea Basses

1a. Spinous dorsal and soft dorsal slightly connected; soft rays in anal fin 9; second spine of anal fin about same length as third spine; stripes along side usually sharply broken and offset above front of anal fin; back of tongue without teeth.
Yellow bass
Morone mississippiensis
.... **Page 248**

1b. Spinous dorsal and soft dorsal entirely separate; soft rays in anal fin 11 to 13; second spine of anal fin distinctly shorter than third spine; stripes along side usually continuous, not sharply broken and offset above front of anal fin; back of tongue with teeth.
Go to **2**

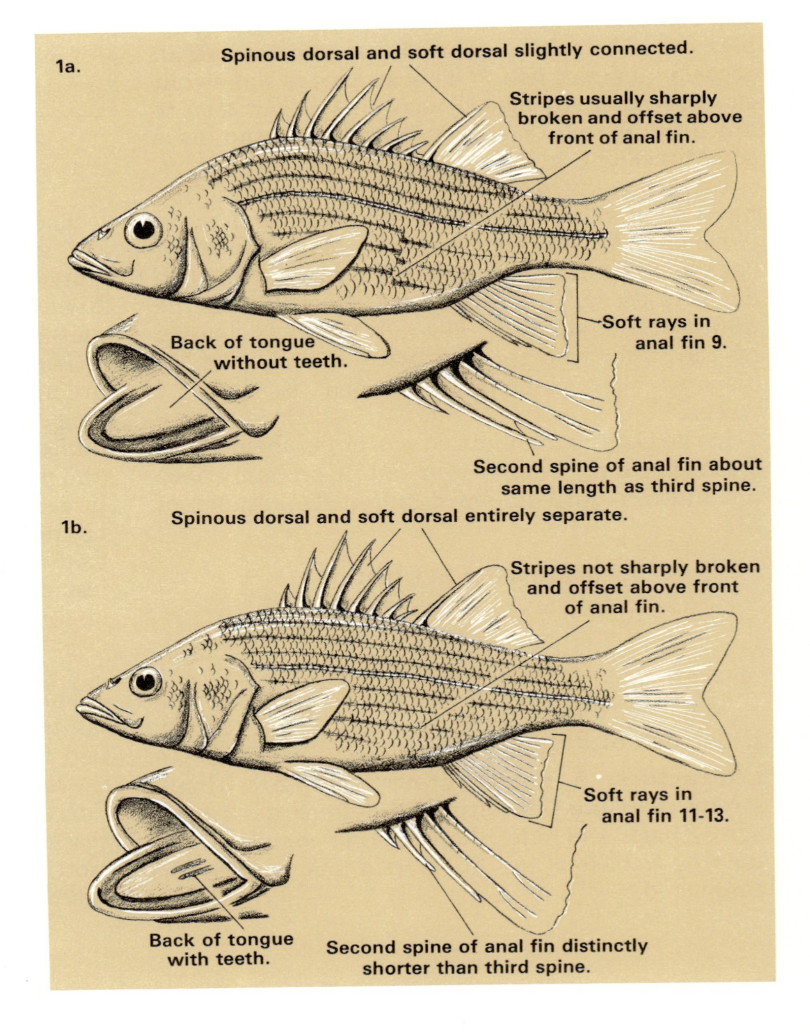
1a.
Spinous dorsal and soft dorsal slightly connected.
Stripes usually sharply broken and offset above front of anal fin.
Soft rays in anal fin 9.
Back of tongue without teeth.
Second spine of anal fin about same length as third spine.
1b.
Spinous dorsal and soft dorsal entirely separate.
Stripes not sharply broken and offset above front of anal fin.
Soft rays in anal fin 11-13.
Back of tongue with teeth.
Second spine of anal fin distinctly shorter than third spine.

2a. *(From 1b.)* Body deeper, its depth (A) usually going less than 3 times into standard length (B); teeth on back of tongue in a single patch.
White bass
Morone chrysops ..... **Page 245**

2b. *(From 1b.)* Body more slender, its depth (A) usually going more than 3 times into standard length (B); teeth on back of tongue in 2 parallel patches.
Striped bass
Morone saxatilis ..... **Page 246**

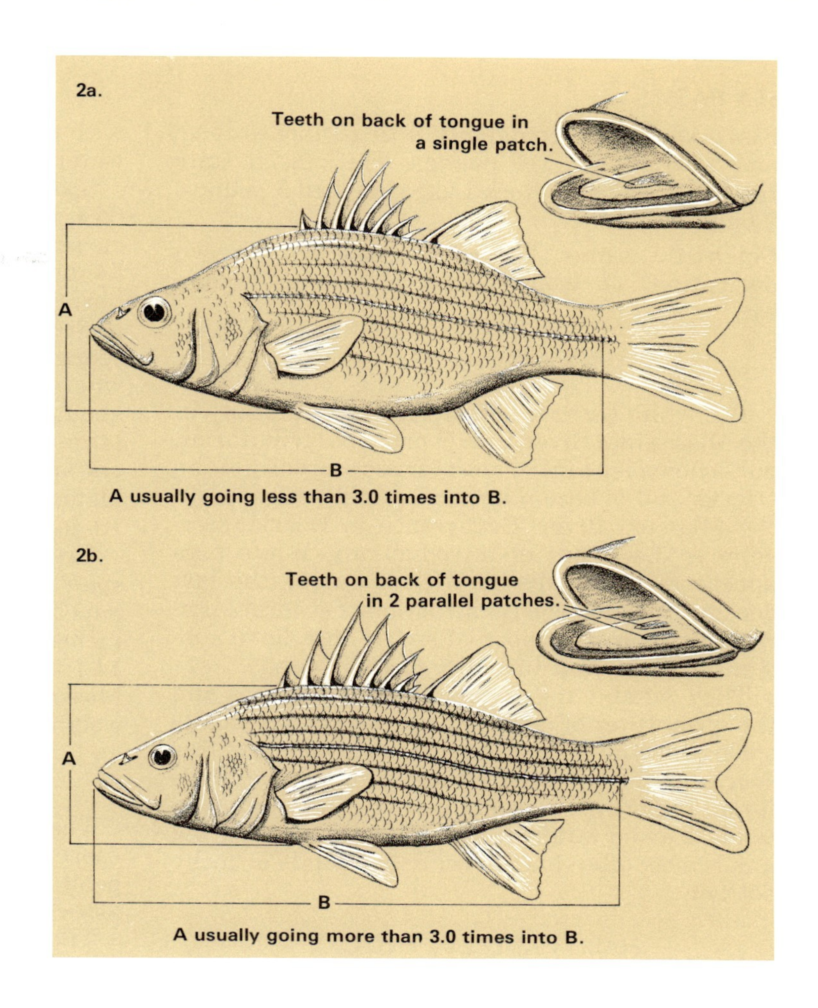

White Bass

Morone chrysops (Rafinesque)

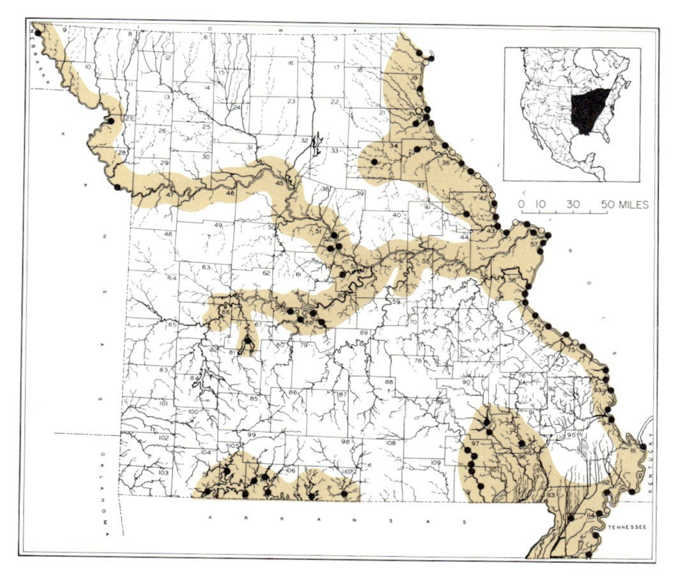

Other local names: Striped bass, Striper, Streaker, Silver bass.

DESCRIPTION

Illustration: Page 245, 2a.

Characters: A silvery, spiny-rayed fish with several dark, horizontal streaks along sides. Streaks often discontinuous, but not sharply broken or offset above anal fin as in yellow bass. Spinous and soft parts of dorsal fin entirely separate. Spines at front of anal fin graduated in length, the first shorter than the second, and the second shorter than the third. Lower jaw projects beyond upper jaw. Anal fin rays 11 to 13.

Similar to the recently introduced striped bass but with the following differences: body deeper, its depth usually going less than 3 times into standard length; back more strongly arched, the profile of the top of head and forward part of back concave (rounded inward); teeth on upper surface of tongue in a single patch; not attaining nearly so large a size as striped bass.

Life colors: Back blue-gray with silvery reflections. Sides silvery with a faint blue-green tinge and several horizontal olive-gray streaks. Dorsal, tail, and anal fins pale slate; pelvic fins opaque-white; pectoral fins clear.

Size: Adults are commonly 9 to 15 inches long, and weigh 1/4 to 1 1/4 pounds. The official state record, from Table Rock Lake, weighed 5 pounds, 2 ounces.

Scientific name: *Morone,* a name of unknown derivation; *chrysops,* Greek, meaning "golden eye."

DISTRIBUTION AND HABITAT

The white bass was formerly abundant only in the Mississippi River and its principal tributaries, but is now plentiful in most large reservoirs of the Ozarks and is becoming increasingly common in the Missouri River. Occurrence in Ozark reservoirs is the result of introductions. White bass appeared in the Missouri River during the last decade following the construction of several large reservoirs on the upper Missouri that have substantially reduced turbidity of the river.

They inhabit the deeper pools of streams and the open water of lakes and reservoirs. During its spring spawning migrations large numbers of this species enter tributary streams and are the basis for an important seasonal fishery. The white bass tends to avoid waters that are continuously turbid and is most often found over a firm sandy or rocky bottom.

HABITS AND LIFE HISTORY

The white bass is an active, schooling fish, appearing in large numbers where food is abundant and moving on when the supply is exhausted. It feeds most actively in early morning and late evening, often very near the surface where forage fish, small crustaceans, and the emerging stages of aquatic insects tend to concentrate. The feeding activities are sometimes quite spectacular. Large, compact schools move rapidly about in pursuit of small fishes, often driving them to the surface where they may leap from the water in a vain effort to evade capture. Small crustaceans and insects are the most important items in the diet of young white bass; adults generally consume a larger volume of fish than any other food item.[190] In large Ozark reservoirs the gizzard shad is a staple food item, and abundance of the white bass fluctuates drastically in response to changes in abundance of this forage fish.

The white bass is an early spring spawner and spawning is commonly preceded by runs of mature adults into tributary streams. In Missouri, they enter tributaries in March and remain until the middle or latter part of April. Notable spawning runs occur out of the Mississippi River into the Salt and Cuivre rivers and out of Lake Norfork into North Fork River. Males become mature and move to the spawning grounds about a month before the females. At that time the mature adults occur in schools composed of only one sex, with the schools of females being found in deeper water not far from the spawning grounds.

Spawning occurs in midwater or near the surface, over a gravelly or rocky bottom, often in a current, and without preparation of a nest. A female indicates her readiness to spawn by rising towards the surface, at which time several males rush in and crowd around her as the eggs and sperm are released. The eggs settle to the bottom where they become attached to rocks and hatch in about 2 days. The eggs are very small and a single large female may produce nearly a million eggs in one spawning season. Spawning is generally completed at any given locality over a period of 5 to 10 days.[191]

Growth of the white bass is rapid and the life span is seldom more than 4 years. In Lake Wappapello, this fish reaches a length of about 7.3 inches its first year, and averages 11.9, 13.3, and 14.1 inches by the end of succeeding years.[192] In Missouri, few white bass attain a length and weight of more than 17.5 inches and 2 3/4 pounds.

IMPORTANCE AND ANGLING

The white bass is one of the most important sport fishes in impounded waters. During years of peak abundance it makes up 40% or more of the fish creeled in some Ozark reservoirs.

The best fishing for white bass is during their spring spawning migrations or when large schools are feeding near the surface in mid-summer. At such times a fish will often be taken on nearly every cast. Minnows are the best live bait. Small plugs, spoons, and fly and spinner combinations in a variety of patterns and colors will take this fish. White lures seem to be more effective than others, perhaps because they most nearly resemble the small fish on which adult white bass feed.

Striped Bass

Morone saxatilis (Walbaum)

DESCRIPTION

Illustration: Page 245, 2b.

Characters: A silvery, spiny-rayed fish with several dark, horizontal streaks along the sides. Streaks not sharply broken or offset above anal fin. Spinous and soft parts of dorsal fin entirely separate. Spines at front of anal fin graduated in length, the first shorter than the second, and the second shorter than the third. Lower jaw projects beyond upper jaw. Anal fin rays usually 11.

Similar to white bass, but with the following differences: body more slender, its depth usually going more than 3 times into standard length; back less strongly arched, the profile of the top of head and forward part of back convex (rounded outward); teeth on upper surface of tongue in two parallel patches; size larger, the weight commonly exceeding 5 pounds.

Life colors: Back olive-green, grading to silver on sides and white on belly. Sides with about seven blackish horizontal streaks; these more prominent and continuous than in white bass. Dorsal, tail, and anal fins pale slate; pelvic fins opaque white; pectoral fins clear.

Size: Adults commonly weigh 5 to 20 pounds with weights of over 100 pounds reported from salt water.

Scientific name: *Morone*, a name of unknown derivation; *saxatilis*, Latin, meaning "dwelling among rocks."

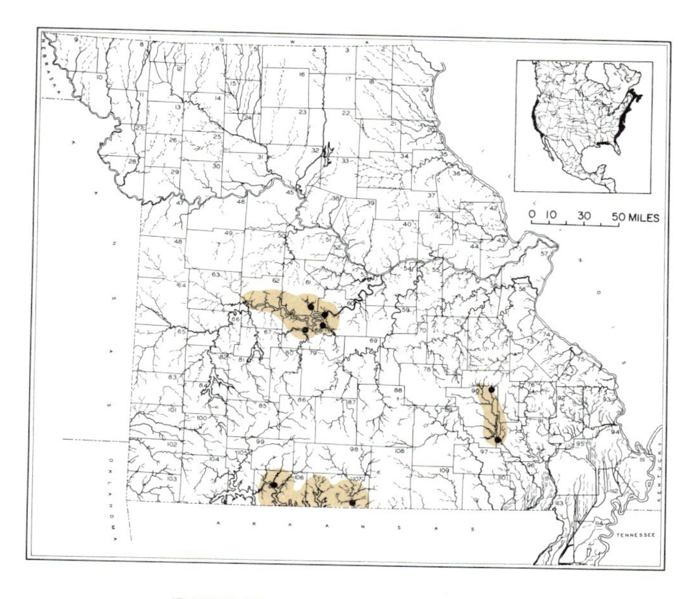

DISTRIBUTION AND HABITAT

The striped bass is a recent addition to the Missouri fish fauna. The first introductions were made in 1966 when fry were stocked in Taum Sauk Reservoir, a small pump-back power facility operated by Union Electric Company on the East Fork of Black River, Reynolds County. The Department of Conservation began stocking striped bass in Lake of the Ozarks in 1967 and has stocked them annually since. Norfork and Bull Shoals reservoirs have been stocked by the Arkansas Game and Fish Department. Survival from all of these stockings appears to have been good, as indicated by their occurrence in the creel. Many have been caught from Lake of the Ozarks and from the Osage River below Bagnell Dam. Some of those stocked in Taum Sauk Reservoir escaped over the dam and have been caught more than 30 miles downstream, below Clearwater Dam. There are also reports of striped bass caught in the St. Francis and Mississippi rivers, but the source of these fish is uncertain.

The striped bass inhabits a variety of habitats. In marine waters it occurs along shores, bays, and estuaries of both the Atlantic and Pacific Coasts. These populations ascend coastal streams to spawn, sometimes going as far as 100 miles inland. A land-locked population that completes its entire life cycle in freshwater occurs in the Santee-Cooper Reservoirs of North Carolina. Present evidence suggests that this population descended from a distinct "race" of striped bass that was already land-locked in the Santee-Cooper River system before these reservoirs were built. Offspring of this population have been used to stock reservoirs elsewhere in the United States, including Missouri.

HABITS AND LIFE HISTORY

The land-locked populations of striped bass in Santee-Cooper Reservoir have been the subject of intensive studies.[193, 194, 195]

They live in large, continuously-moving schools, much as does the white bass. In Santee-Cooper Reservoir the food of the striped bass consists principally of fish, but mayfly nymphs are the dominant food item in spring. Four members of the herring family—gizzard shad, threadfin shad, alewife and glut herring—comprise the bulk of the fish eaten. Striped bass introduced into Missouri reservoirs will probably feed principally on gizzard shad.

The spawning requirements of the striped bass are very exacting, a major factor limiting the establishment of self-sustaining populations. Spawning is successful only where they have access to a large river with sufficient current to maintain the semi-bouyant eggs in suspension until they hatch. In the absence of current the eggs settle to the bottom where they become silted over and die. Because the hatching time is 36 to 75 hours, a considerable stretch of flowing water is required. In Missouri, only the Osage River above Lake of the Ozarks appears to fulfill these requirements. However, the striped bass is readily propagated in hatcheries and populations can be maintained by periodic stocking in reservoirs not having tributaries suitable for spawning.

Spawning occurs in the spring when the water temperature exceeds 58°F. It takes place in areas characterized by rapids and strong currents. The spawning act is accompanied by much splashing as a group of about 5 to 50 individuals rolls and splashes at the water surface. Such a group usually consists of a single large female accompanied by the smaller males. On the east coast the striped bass is commonly called "rock fish" and this activity is referred to as "rock fights".

Growth is quite variable and is more rapid in females than in males. In Santee-Cooper Reservoir a length of about 7.8 inches is reached at one year of age and lengths averaging 15.1, 20.3, 24.1, 26, 27.8, and 30.1 inches are achieved in succeeding years. Scale samples thus far obtained indicate comparable growth in Missouri reservoirs. Four striped bass stocked in Lake of the Ozarks in 1970 ranged from 18 to 22 inches long and 3¾ to 5½ pounds in weight when caught by fishermen in early summer, 1973. A specimen from Taum Sauk Reservoir was 28 inches long and weighed 13¼ pounds when 7 years old. In Santee-Cooper Reservoir some male striped bass are sexually mature when 10 inches in length and one year old, but most do not mature until their second year. Most females are mature when 24 inches long and 4 years old, but some do not mature until their fifth or sixth year.

IMPORTANCE

The striped bass is a highly valued sport fish wherever it occurs, in fresh and salt water. Its appeal results from the large size attained, its fighting qualities, and the firm, well-flavored flesh. In the Santee-Cooper Reservoirs, 727,470 fishermen are reported to have caught more than 1,500,000 striped bass over a 7-year period.

They are being stocked in Missouri reservoirs not only as a contribution to the fishery, but also to provide a large predator capable of utilizing gizzard shad that have grown too large to be effectively taken by white bass and other already established predatory fishes.

ANGLING

Striped bass can be caught with the same techniques employed for white bass, but heavier tackle should be used. Schools feeding on shad and other forage fish can be located on calm days by watching for disturbances of the water surface. It is important to move in quickly to get a lure into the school before it sounds or moves on. The most effective lures are those that imitate a small fish, such as a silver spoon or a white feathered jig. Trolling with deep-running lures, including spoons, plugs and lead-head jigs, is an effective method for taking striped bass when they are not feeding at the surface. They are also taken by still-fishing with bait minnows or cut shad.

Yellow Bass

Morone mississippiensis Jordan and Eigenmann

DESCRIPTION

Illustration: Page 244, 1a.

Characters: A silvery-yellow, spiny-rayed fish with several dark, horizontal streaks along the sides. Streaks darker and broader than in white bass, and sharply broken and offset above front of anal fin. Spinous and soft parts of dorsal fin slightly connected. Spines at front of anal fin not graduated in length, the second and third spines nearly equal, and much longer than first spine. Lower jaw not projecting beyond upper jaw. Anal fin rays 9. No teeth on upper surface of tongue.

Life colors: Like those of white bass, page 245, but with sides golden-yellow rather than silvery.

Size: A smaller fish than the white bass, seldom exceeding a length of 12 inches or a weight of a pound.

Scientific name: *Morone,* a name of unknown derivation; *mississippiensis,* named for the Mississippi River.

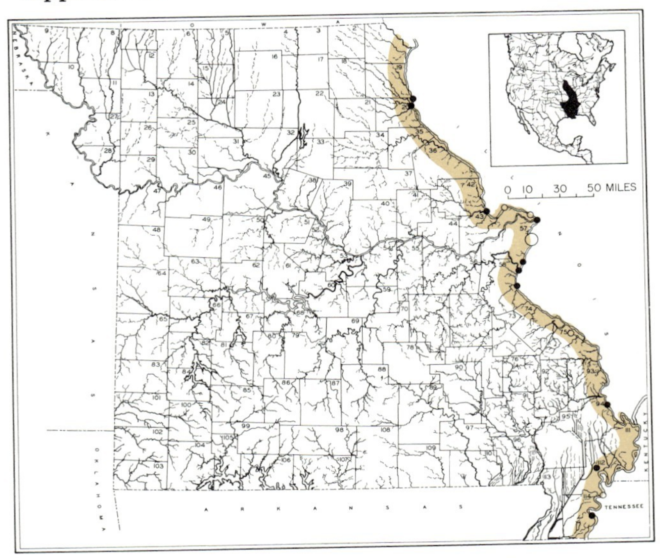

DISTRIBUTION AND HABITAT

The yellow bass occurs only in the Mississippi River and its overflow waters. In the river channel it is nowhere abundant, but is more common above the mouth of the Missouri than below.

Like the white bass, this species is typically an inhabitant of the quiet pools and backwaters of large streams and of reservoirs and natural lakes.

HABITS AND LIFE HISTORY

The yellow bass lives in schools and feeds in midwater or near the surface. When young it feeds primarily on small crustaceans and insects; adults consume significant quantities of fish, including their own young.[196, 197]

This species spawns in April or May with the peak of spawning between April 15 and May 15.[198] Like the white bass, the yellow bass commonly moves into tributary streams to spawn. The eggs are deposited over gravelly bottoms in water 2 or 3 feet deep. A male and a female temporarily pair off during the spawning act, releasing the eggs and sperm as they swim slowly along or stop for a few seconds. The eggs, which are even smaller than those of the white bass, sink slowly to the bottom where they hatch in 4 to 6 days at a temperature of 70° F.

In Reelfoot Lake, Tennessee, the yellow bass reaches a length of about 7.7 inches by its second year of life and is 8.7, 9.5, and 10.7 inches long by the end of succeeding years.[199] The maximum life span is about 6 years.

IMPORTANCE AND ANGLING

The yellow bass is too rare in Missouri waters to be of much importance as a sport fish. Elsewhere in its range it is of considerable importance, but is held in less esteem than the white bass because of its smaller size and tendency to stunt.

Angling methods are similar to those for the white bass.

SUNFISHES

Centrarchidae

Of the 30 species in this strictly North American fish family, 17 are found in Missouri. Included are many of the most popular game and pan fishes.

Members of the sunfish family are characterized by deep, laterally compressed bodies and spiny-rayed fins. The dorsal fin consists of a forward spiny-rayed part and a soft-rayed rear part that are broadly connected in most species. The attachment of the pelvic fins is far forward, nearly beneath the pectoral fins. There are three or more spines at the front of the anal fin. In all species except the pygmy sunfish the scales are ctenoid (rough-edged). Fish superficially resembling the sunfishes occur in the sea bass, perch, and drum families, but none of these agree in all respects with the description given above.

The habits and life history of all sunfishes are basically alike, differing only in detail. Most are rather sedentary fish, remaining much of the time near submerged cover or hovering quietly in the shade of a tree or other object hanging over the water. They do not form schools except for a brief period when very young, but often occur in loose aggregations having little obvious social organization. Individuals of most species show a definite attachment to a particular pool or stretch of shoreline to which they will return after being displaced or after voluntary absences. Often the same fish may be found at about the same spot a year or more after its initial capture and may spend its entire life within a rather restricted area.

Feeding is primarily by sight and generally only moving objects are attractive. Insects, crustaceans, and small fish are the most important foods. Feeding occurs at the surface as well as on the bottom and food may be obtained by active foraging or by ambush from a place of hiding. Suction created when the rather large mouth is suddenly opened aids in capturing the prey. Commonly, there is a peak of feeding activity in early morning and again in late evening, accompanied by movement into shallow water.

Sunfishes spawn in late spring or early summer. With rare exceptions, all species construct a nest, typically consisting of a saucer-shaped depression with a diameter about twice the length of the nest-building fish. Only males participate in this activity. Nests are fanned out by violent sweeping motions of the tail fin that sweep away the silt and other fine sediments, leaving a clean bed for attachment of the eggs. Females visit the nest only when ready to spawn, entering voluntarily or under escort of the male. When on the nest the female commonly has the dark markings characteristic of the species very prominently developed and she is readily distinguishable from the male, even in species such as the smallmouth bass in which the coloration of the sexes is otherwise much alike. This color change is under nervous control and the female rapidly reassumes her original coloration upon leaving the nest. Males of some sunfish are very colorfully marked during the spawning season, but these colors are controlled by hormones and are not subject to rapid change.

During spawning, which may require a period of 20 minutes to several hours for completion, the spawning pair circle more or less continuously over the nest, pausing briefly as the eggs are deposited and fertilized. During the spawning act the female assumes a nearly horizontal position on her side while the male remains upright. Several females may spawn in a single nest and one female may spawn in two or more nests with different males. The male remains more or less continuously with the nest until the eggs hatch. In a few species he guards the fry for a time after they have left the nest. Would-be predators are vigorously driven from the area if they attempt to enter the nest, but certain species of minnows that habitually spawn over sunfish nests are tolerated.

Key to the Sunfishes

1a. Tail fin without a notch; spinous dorsal usually with 4 or 5 spines; anal fin usually with 5 or 6 soft rays; lateral line absent; size small, length 2 inches or less.
Banded pygmy sunfish
Elassoma zonatum ... **Page 275**

1b. Tail fin with a definite notch; spinous dorsal usually with 6 or more spines; anal fin usually with 8 or more soft rays; lateral line present; size larger, length often much more than 2 inches.
Go to 2

1a.
Spinous dorsal usually with 4 or 5 spines.
Lateral line absent.
Tail fin without a notch.
Size small, length 2.0 inches or less.
Anal fin usually with 5 or 6 soft rays.

1b.
Spinous dorsal usually with 6 or more spines.
Lateral line present.
Tail fin with a definite notch.
Size larger, length often much more than 2.0 inches.
Anal fin usually with 8 or more soft rays.

2a. *(From 1b.)* Anal fin spines usually 3, rarely 2 or 4.
Go to 3

2b. *(From 1b.)* Anal fin spines usually 5 to 8.
Go to 14

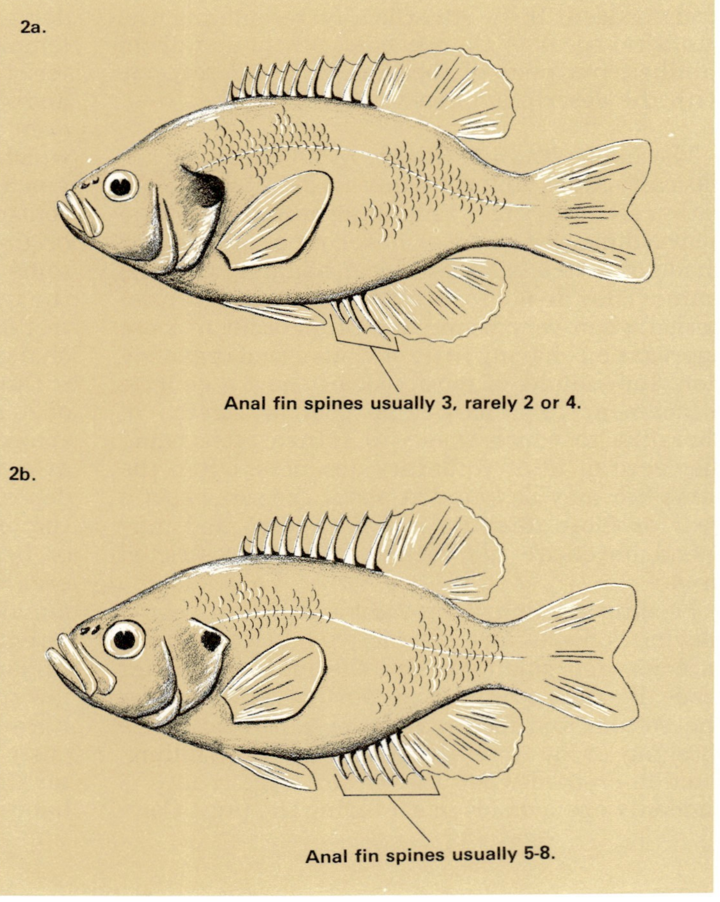
2a.
Anal fin spines usually 3, rarely 2 or 4.
2b.
Anal fin spines usually 5-8.

3a. *(From 2a.)* Body more slender, its depth (A) going 3 times or more into standard length (B) except in largest adults; mouth larger, upper jaw extending to or behind middle of eye; scales small, with 55 or more in lateral line.
Black basses, *Micropterus*
Go to **4**

3b. *(From 2a.)* Body deeper, its depth (A) going less than 3 times into standard length (B); mouth smaller, upper jaw not extending behind middle of eye except in adults of a few species; scales larger, with fewer than 55 in lateral line.
Sunfishes, *Lepomis*
Go to **6**

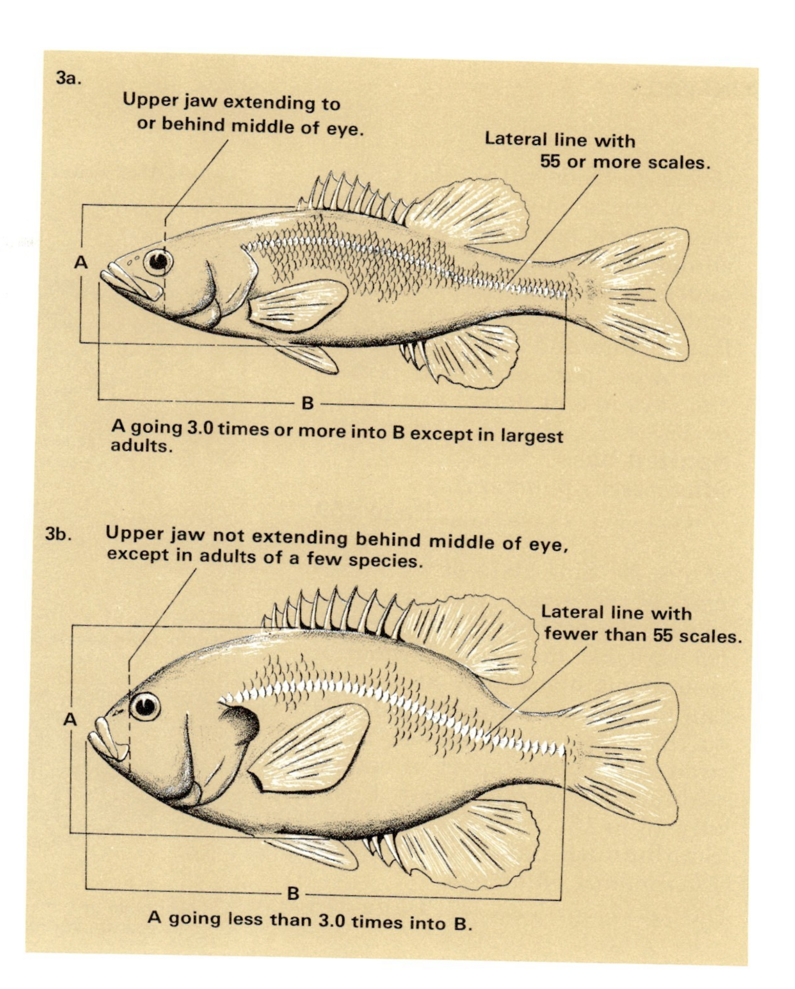
3a.
Upper jaw extending to or behind middle of eye.
Lateral line with 55 or more scales.
A
B
A going 3.0 times or more into B except in largest adults.
3b.
Upper jaw not extending behind middle of eye, except in adults of a few species.
Lateral line with fewer than 55 scales.
A
B
A going less than 3.0 times into B.

4a. *(From 3a.)* Mouth large, upper jaw extending far behind back of eye in fish more than 6 inches in length; spinous dorsal and soft dorsal nearly separate; margin of spinous dorsal strongly convex, the length of shortest spine near notch (A) less than half the length of longest spine (B); midside with a dark horizontal stripe; tail fin of young 2-colored rather than 3-colored, the rear part of fin darker than base.
Largemouth bass
Micropterus salmoides
.... **Page 260**

4b. *(From 3a.)* Mouth smaller, upper jaw not extending much behind back of eye; spinous dorsal and soft dorsal well connected; margin of spinous dorsal gently rounded, the length of shortest spine near notch (A) more than half the length of longest spine (B); midside with or without a dark horizontal stripe; tail fin of young distinctly 3-colored with a prominent, dark vertical bar separating yellow or orange base from white fringe on rear margin of fin.

Go to **5**

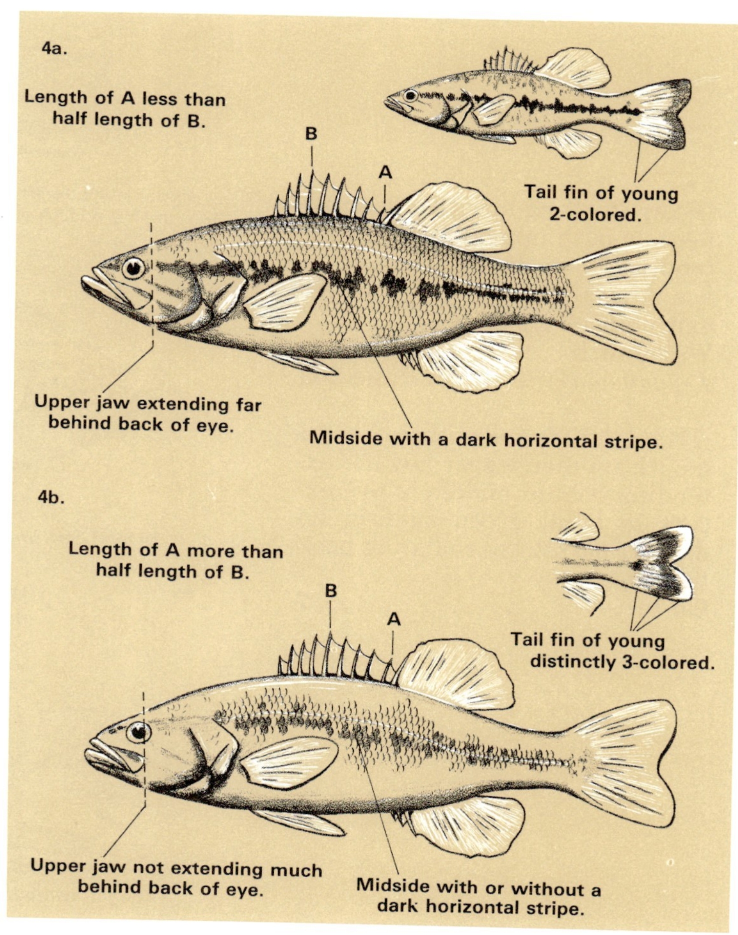
4a.
Length of A less than half length of B.
B
A
Tail fin of young 2-colored.
Upper jaw extending far behind back of eye.
Midside with a dark horizontal stripe.
4b.
Length of A more than half length of B.
B
A
Tail fin of young distinctly 3-colored.
Upper jaw not extending much behind back of eye.
Midside with or without a dark horizontal stripe.

5a. *(From 4b.)* Side with a dark horizontal stripe; lower side with a series of dark horizontal streaks in adults; juveniles with a prominent black spot at base of tail fin; scales larger, usually 59 to 65 in lateral line and 23 to 26 around narrowest part of caudal peduncle; rays in soft dorsal usually 12 or 13.
Spotted bass
Micropterus punctulatus
.... **Page 259**

5b. *(From 4b.)* Side plain or with a series of separate vertical bars; lower side without dark horizontal streaks; juveniles without a prominent black spot at base of tail fin; scales smaller, usually 68 to 76 in lateral line and 29 to 31 around narrowest part of caudal peduncle; rays in soft dorsal usually 13 to 15.
Smallmouth bass
Micropterus dolomieui
.... **Page 258**

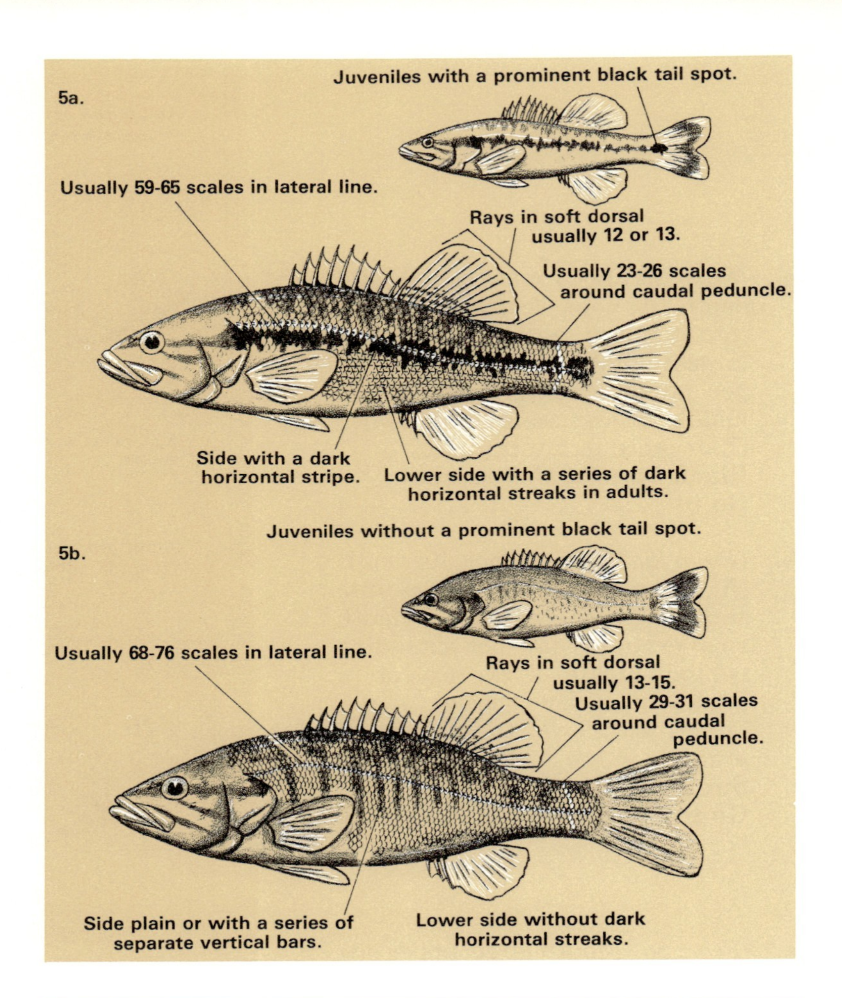
5a.
Juveniles with a prominent black tail spot.
Usually 59-65 scales in lateral line.
Rays in soft dorsal usually 12 or 13.
Usually 23-26 scales around caudal peduncle.
Side with a dark horizontal stripe.
Lower side with a series of dark horizontal streaks in adults.
5b.
Juveniles without a prominent black tail spot.
Usually 68-76 scales in lateral line.
Rays in soft dorsal usually 13-15.
Usually 29-31 scales around caudal peduncle.
Side plain or with a series of separate vertical bars.
Lower side without dark horizontal streaks.

6a. *(From 3b.)* Tongue with a patch of teeth; mouth large, upper jaw extending to or behind middle of eye; several distinct dark lines radiating back from eye.
Warmouth
Lepomis gulosus ..... **Page 262**

6b. *(From 3b.)* Tongue without teeth; mouth smaller, upper jaw not extending behind middle of eye except in adult green sunfish; no distinct dark lines radiating back from eye.
Go to **7**

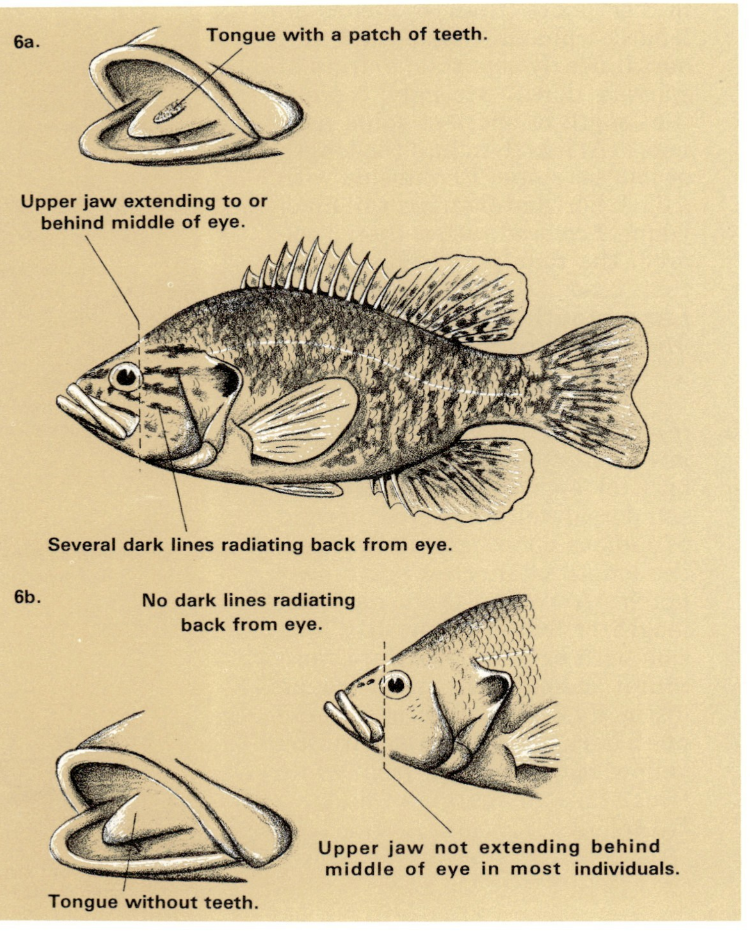
6a.
Tongue with a patch of teeth.
Upper jaw extending to or behind middle of eye.
Several dark lines radiating back from eye.
6b.
No dark lines radiating back from eye.
Upper jaw not extending behind middle of eye in most individuals.
Tongue without teeth.

7a. *(From 6b.)* Pectoral fin shorter and more rounded, usually not extending beyond front of eye when bent forward towards eye; mouth larger, upper jaw extending to beneath pupil of eye except in small young.
Go to **8**

7b. *(From 6b.)* Pectoral fin longer and more pointed, usually extending far beyond front of eye when bent forward toward eye; mouth smaller, upper jaw not extending to beneath pupil of eye.
Go to **12**

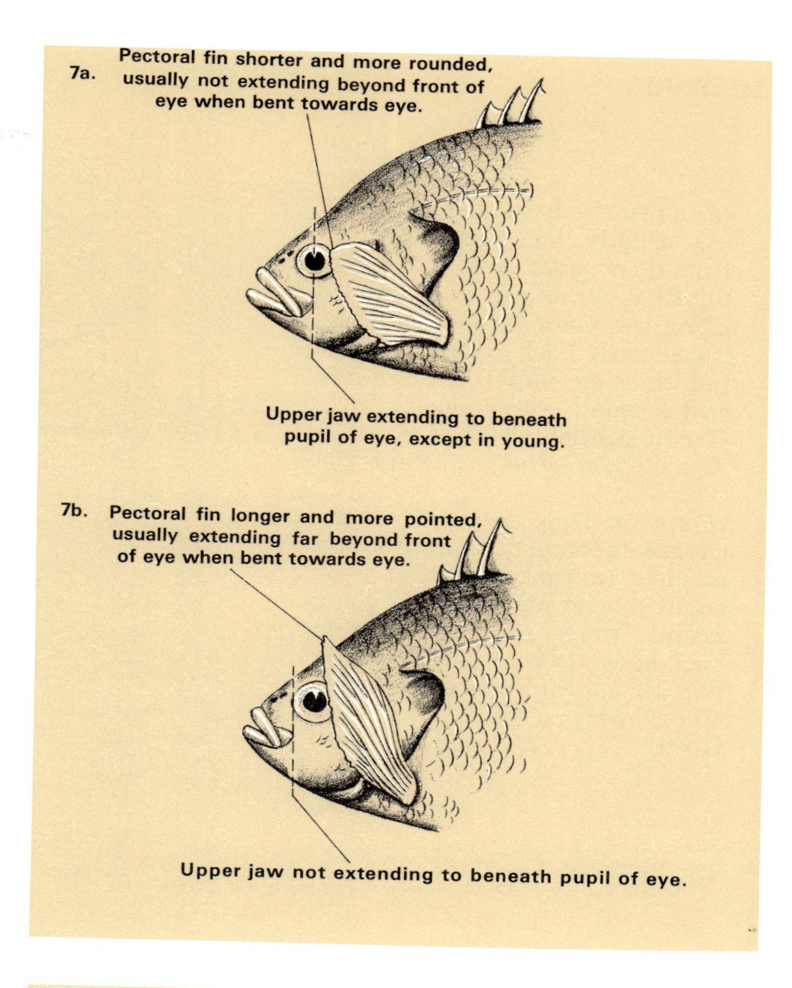

8a. *(From 7a.)* Rear margin of gill cover (lying within base of, but not including membranous ear flap) stiff; membranous ear flap not greatly elongated.
Go to **9**

8b. *(From 7a.)* Rear margin of gill cover thin and flexible; membranous ear flap elongated in adults, especially males.
Go to **11**

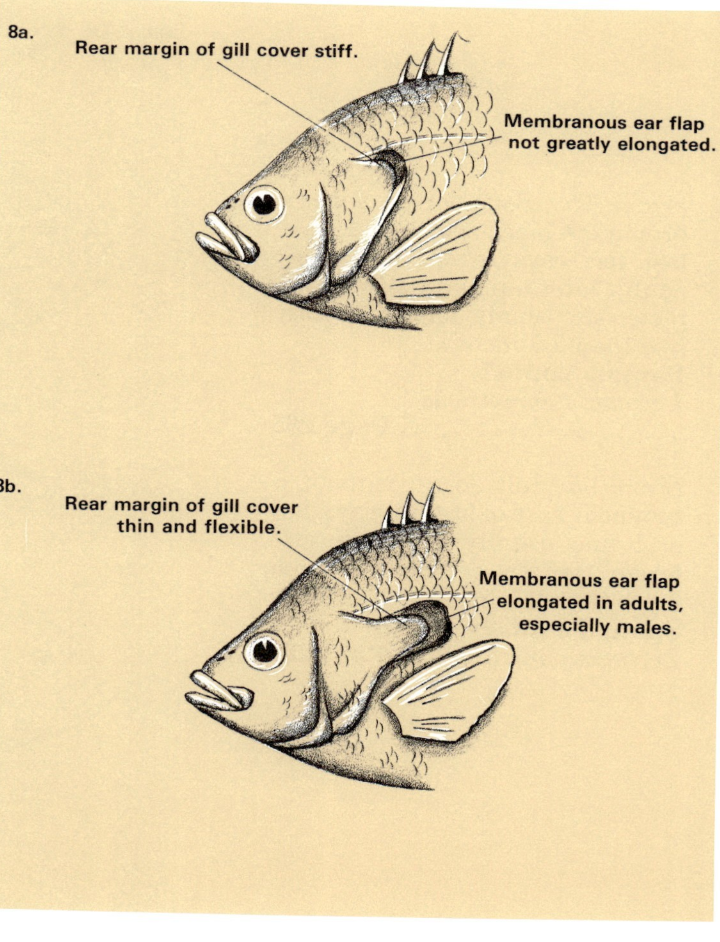

9a. *(From 8a.)* Body slender, its depth (A) usually less than distance from tip of snout to front of dorsal fin (B); snout longer, its length (C) going less than 2 times into distance from back of eye to rear margin of ear flap (D); lateral line scales usually 41 or more.
Green sunfish
Lepomis cyanellus .... **Page 263**

9b. *(From 8a.)* Body deeper, its depth (A) greater than distance from tip of snout to front of dorsal fin (B); snout shorter, its length (C) going about 2 times into distance from back of eye to rear margin of ear flap (D); lateral line scales usually 40 or fewer.
Go to **10**

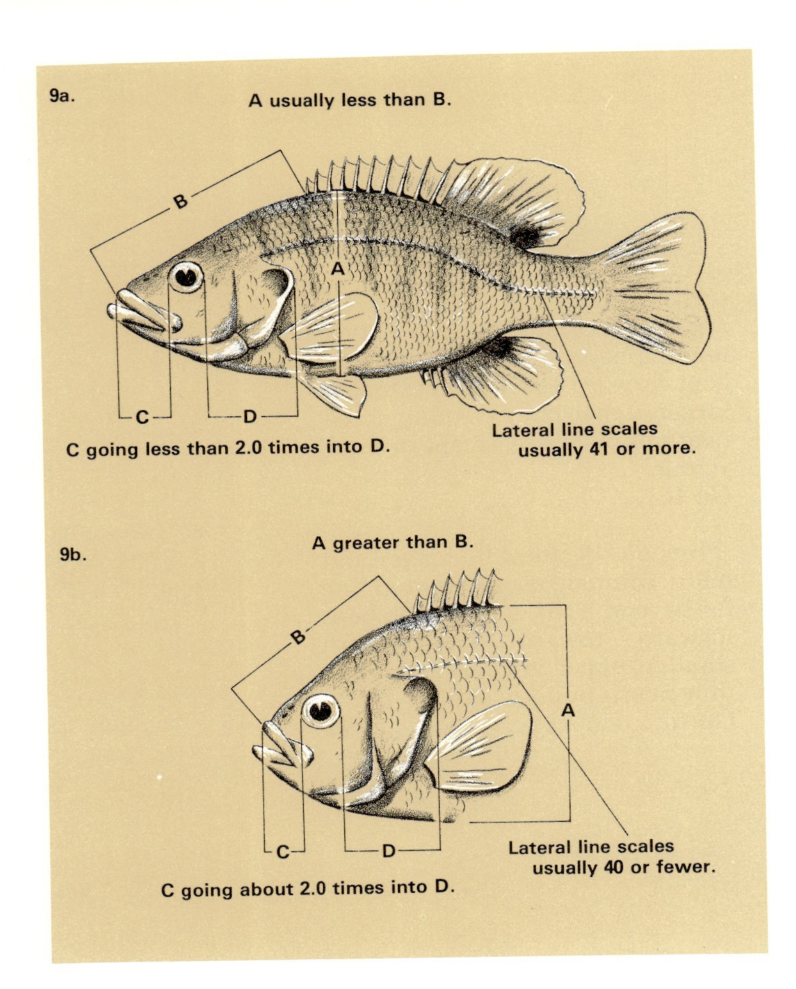
9a.
A usually less than B.
B
A
C
D
C going less than 2.0 times into D.
Lateral line scales
usually 41 or more.
9b.
A greater than B.
B
A
C
D
Lateral line scales
usually 40 or fewer.
C going about 2.0 times into D.

10a. *(From 9b.)* Soft dorsal with a prominent black spot near base of last few rays except in largest adults; lateral line usually incomplete; size small, length usually less than 2.5 inches.
Bantam sunfish
Lepomis symmetricus
.... **Page 265**

10b. *(From 9b.)* Soft dorsal without a spot near base of last few rays; lateral line usually complete; size larger, length commonly much more than 2.5 inches.
Spotted sunfish
Lepomis punctatus ... **Page 264**

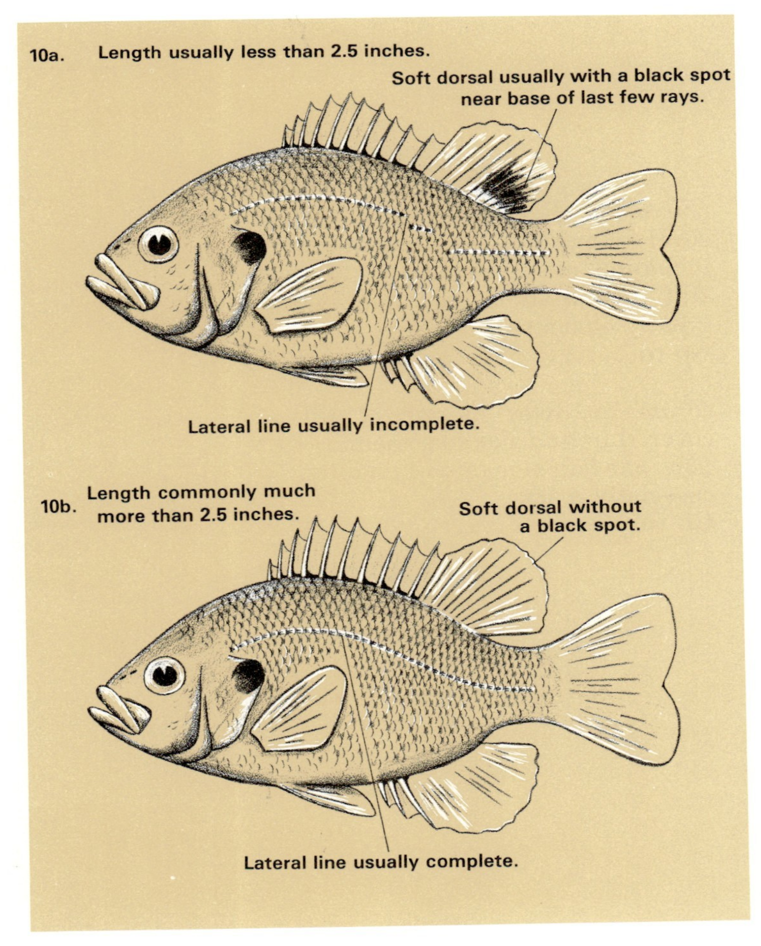
10a.
Length usually less than 2.5 inches.
Soft dorsal usually with a black spot
near base of last few rays.
Lateral line usually incomplete.
10b.
Length commonly much
more than 2.5 inches.
Soft dorsal without
a black spot.
Lateral line usually complete.

11a. *(From 8b.)* Gill rakers on first arch moderately long and thin, their length more than twice their width; two pit-like depressions in skull between eyes large, their width (A) about equal to distance between them (B).
Orangespotted sunfish
Lepomis humilis ..... **Page 267**

11b. *(From 8b.)* Gill rakers on first arch short and thick, their length less than twice their width; two pit-like depressions in skull between eyes small, their width (A) much less than distance between them (B).
Longear sunfish
Lepomis megalotis .... **Page 268**

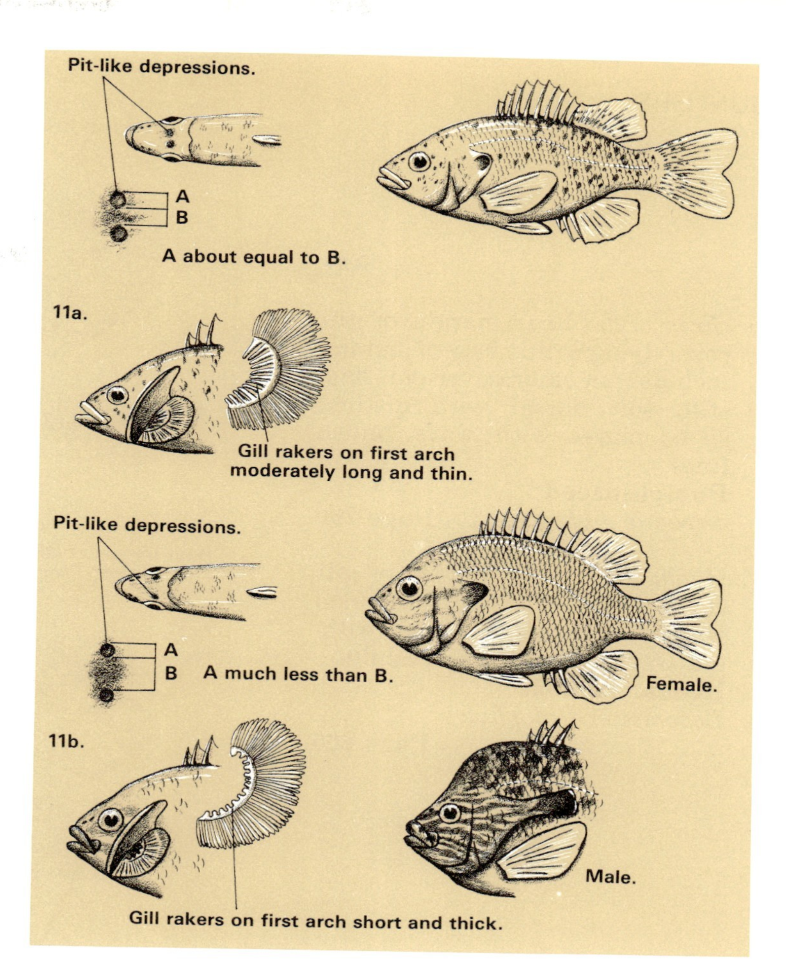
Pit-like depressions.
A
B
A about equal to B.
11a.
Gill rakers on first arch
moderately long and thin.
Pit-like depressions.
A
B
A much less than B.
Female.
11b.
Male.
Gill rakers on first arch short and thick.

12a. *(From 7b.)* Soft dorsal with a distinct black blotch near base of last few rays; gill rakers on first arch long and thin, their length more than twice their width; ear flap dark to its margin, without a light-colored border; ear flap without a red or orange spot.
Bluegill
Lepomis macrochirus . **Page 269**

12b. *(From 7b.)* Soft dorsal without a blotch near base of last few rays; gill rakers on first arch short and thick, their length less than twice their width; ear flap not dark to its margin, with a light-colored border; ear flap with a prominent red or orange spot in adults.
Go to **13**

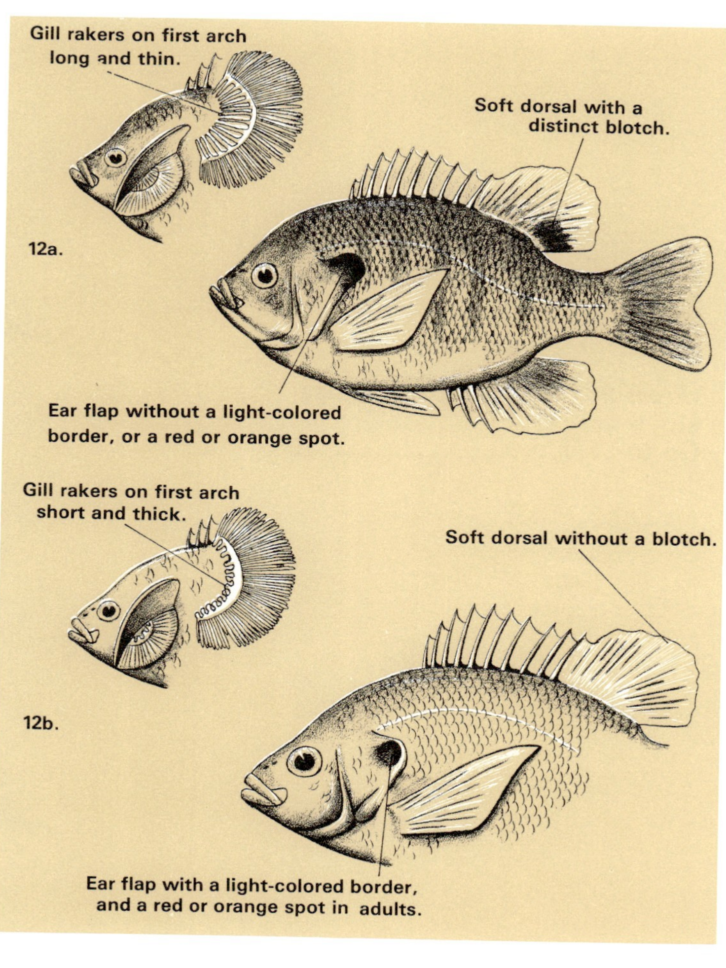
Gill rakers on first arch
long and thin.
Soft dorsal with a
distinct blotch.
12a.
Ear flap without a light-colored
border, or a red or orange spot.
Gill rakers on first arch
short and thick.
Soft dorsal without a blotch.
12b.
Ear flap with a light-colored border,
and a red or orange spot in adults.

Rear margin of gill cover (within base of flap) stiff.
Soft dorsal with distinct spots.
13a.
Wavy bluish lines in adults.
Rear margin of gill cover thin and flexible.
Soft dorsal without distinct spots.
13b.
Without wavy bluish lines.

13a. *(From 12b.)* Rear margin of gill cover (lying within base of, but not including membranous ear flap) stiff; soft dorsal with distinct spots; cheek with wavy bluish lines.
Pumpkinseed
Lepomis gibbosus ..... **Page 266**

13b. *(From 12b.)* Rear margin of gill cover thin and flexible; soft dorsal without distinct spots; cheek without wavy bluish lines in adults.
Redear sunfish
Lepomis microlophus
.... **Page 265**

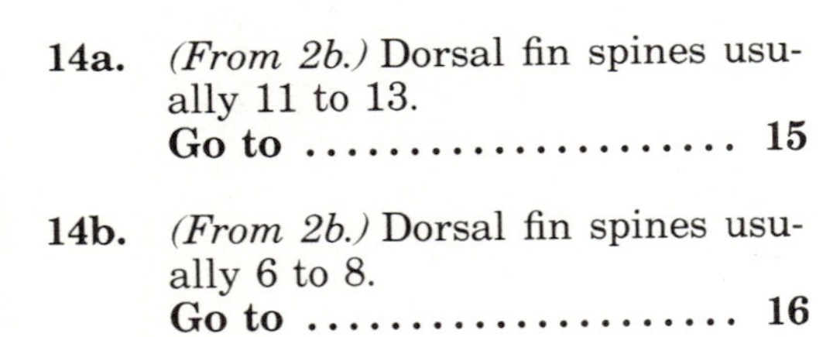

14a. *(From 2b.)* Dorsal fin spines usually 11 to 13.
Go to **15**

14b. *(From 2b.)* Dorsal fin spines usually 6 to 8.
Go to **16**

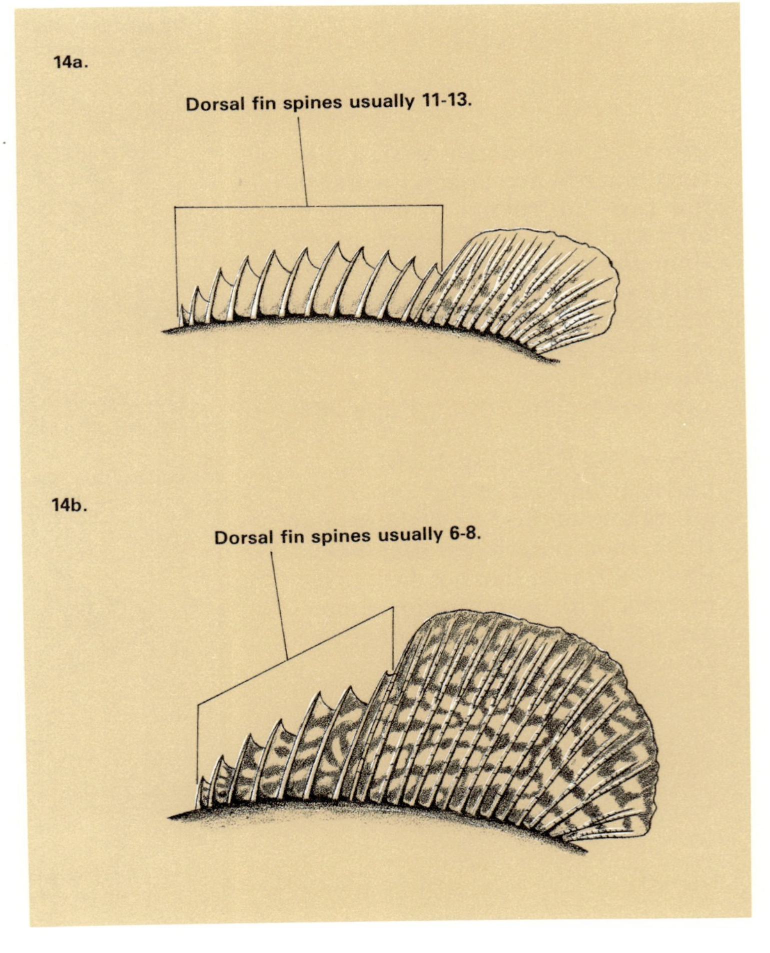

14a.
Dorsal fin spines usually 11-13.
14b.
Dorsal fin spines usually 6-8.

15a. *(From 14a.)* Anal fin much smaller than dorsal fin, with 6 spines and 10 or 11 rays; body depth (A) less than half the standard length (B).
Rock bass
Amploplites rupestris . **Page 270**

15b. *(From 14a.)* Anal fin nearly as large as dorsal fin, with 7 or 8 spines and 13 to 15 rays; body depth (A) about half the standard length (B).
Flier
Centrarchus macropterus
.... **Page 274**

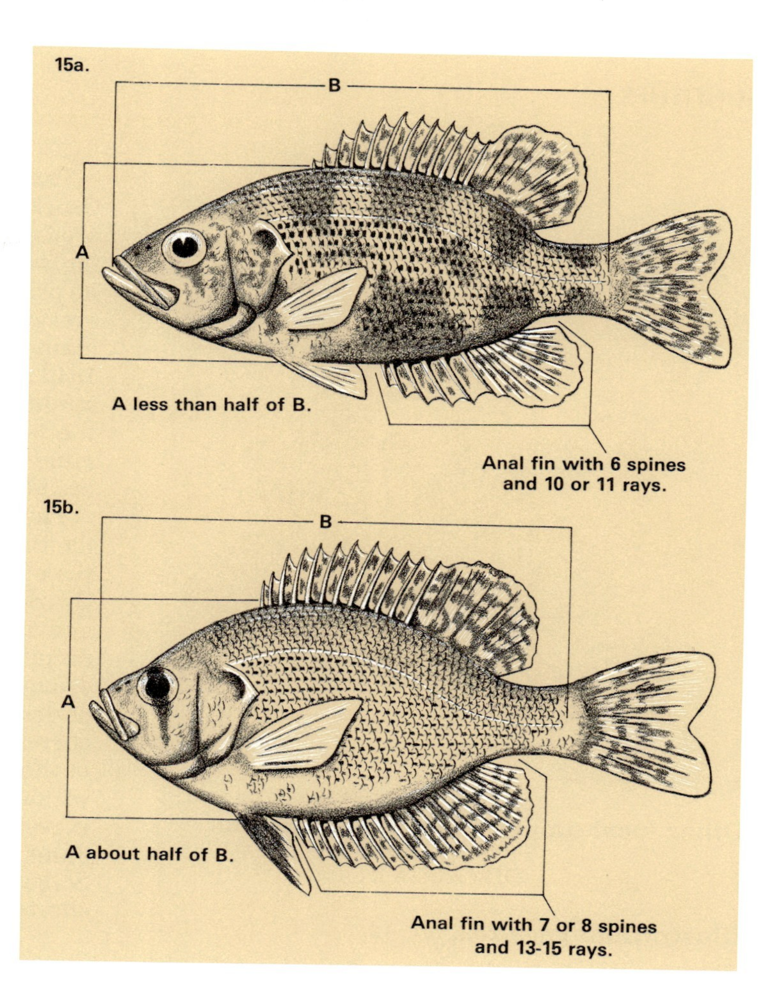
15a.
B
A
A less than half of B.
Anal fin with 6 spines and 10 or 11 rays.
15b.
B
A
A about half of B.
Anal fin with 7 or 8 spines and 13-15 rays.

16a. *(From 14b.)* Dorsal fin spines usually 7 or 8; dark markings on sides consisting of irregularly arranged speckles and blotches.
Black crappie
Pomoxis nigromaculatus
.... **Page 273**

16b. *(From 14b.)* Dorsal fin spines usually 6; dark markings on sides consisting of regularly arranged vertical bars.
White crappie
Pomoxis annularis ... **Page 272**

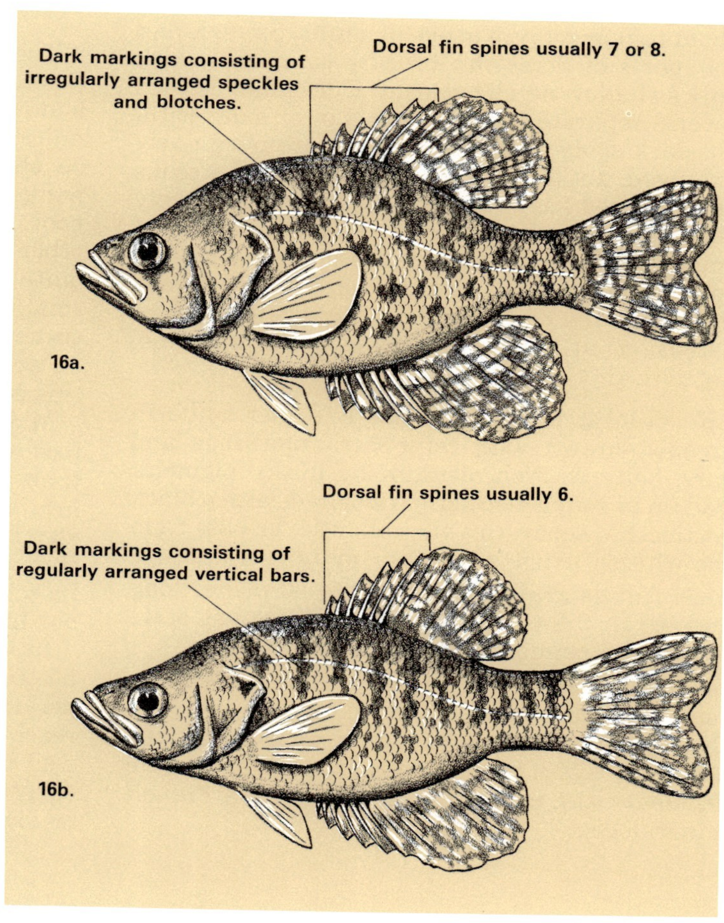
Dark markings consisting of irregularly arranged speckles and blotches.
Dorsal fin spines usually 7 or 8.
16a.
Dorsal fin spines usually 6.
Dark markings consisting of regularly arranged vertical bars.
16b.

Smallmouth Bass

Micropterus dolomieui Lacépède

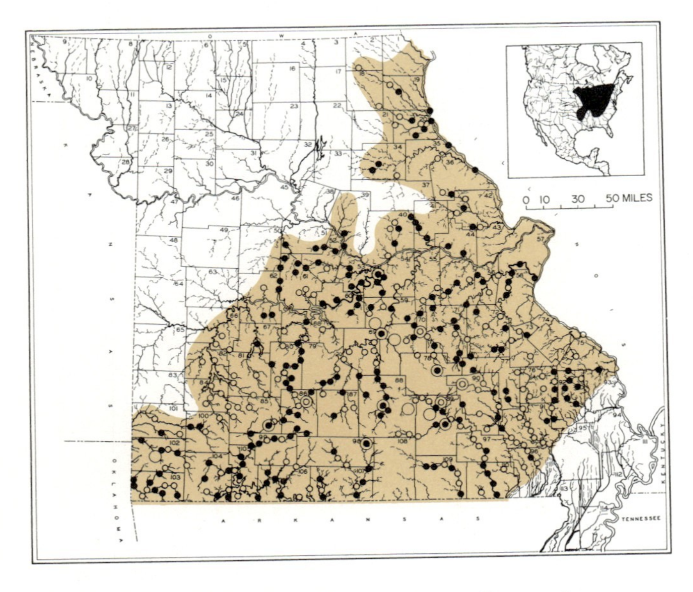

Other local names: Brown bass, Brownie

DESCRIPTION

Illustration: Page 252, 5b; **42.**

Characters: A slender, streamlined sunfish with a moderately large mouth, the upper jaw reaching about to rear margin of eye in adults. Spinous and soft parts of dorsal fin broadly connected, with only a shallow notch between. Sides plain or with several separate vertical bars. Lower sides without dark spots or with spots that are irregularly arranged, not forming definite horizontal streaks as in spotted bass. Margin of spinous dorsal only slightly rounded outward (convex), the shortest spine in fin more than half the length of longest spine. Anal fin with 3 (rarely 2 or 4) spines. Scales in lateral line 68 to 76. Pyloric caeca (finger-like extensions at junction of stomach and intestine) not forked.

Life colors: Back and sides a rather uniform greenish-brown with faint dark mottlings and bars; belly whitish overlain by dusky pigment. Tail fin in young distinctly tricolored, with a black vertical bar separating the yellowish fin base from the whitish fringe along rear margin of fin.

Size: Adults are commonly 10 to 20 inches long and weigh 0.5 to 4.2 pounds. The present state record is 6 pounds, 7 ounces.

Scientific name: *Micropterus,* Greek, meaning "small fin," the name resulting from an injury to the type specimen that made it appear that the posterior rays of the soft dorsal formed a separate fin; *dolomieui,* named for M. Dolomieu, a French mineralogist.

DISTRIBUTION AND HABITAT

The smallmouth bass occurs throughout the Ozarks where it is the dominant species of large, predatory fish in most streams. It also occurs sparingly in the upper Mississippi River and most of its principal prairie tributaries. Although the general distribution of the smallmouth bass has remained essentially unchanged since the early 1940's, it has declined in abundance in many streams, particularly along the Ozark border and the northeastern prairies. Occurrence in the Lamine River drainage results from an introduction in 1952.

The smallmouth is the ecological replacement for the spotted bass and the largemouth bass in the clear, cool, permanent-flowing streams of the Ozarks. It exhibits little tolerance for siltation and turbidity and occurs only in streams that maintain flow except during the most severe droughts. It generally is found over a silt-free rock or gravel bottom, near riffles, but not in the main current. Adults are most abundant around cover in the form of boulders, rootwads, or beds of water willow *(Justicia).* In the upper Mississippi River it is restricted to the rocky shoals below navigation dams where stream-like conditions still prevail. Some are also found along the wind-swept, rocky shores of large Ozark reservoirs.

HABITS AND LIFE HISTORY

The smallmouth normally restricts its activities to a single stream pool, but occasionally its home range includes several pools as much as 0.5 miles apart.[200] During the daylight hours it may be observed lying almost motionless near submerged cover or cruising slowly about its home pool. When actively foraging for minnows and other prey it commonly prowls the shoreline in quite shallow water. An interesting habit of the smallmouth bass is to follow a large turtle or sucker as it digs or roots in the bottom, pouncing on any insects or crayfish that are disturbed by this activity.

Midge larvae and microcrustaceans are the first food of smallmouth fry in Ozark streams. Fry less than an inch in length are already eating small fish, and fish remain an important part of their diet throughout life. Crayfish and fish occur in about equal amounts in the diet of adult bass. Insects are taken frequently, but are of only minor importance.

In Ozark streams the smallmouth bass begins nesting in early or mid-April when the water temperature exceeds 60° F. Nesting activity usually reaches its peak in May, but sometimes continues well into June or even July. Renesting occurs if early nests are unsuccessful because of high water or low temperatures, and may occur even if the first nests are successful. Nests are located in quiet water near shore or downstream from a boulder or other obstruction that breaks the force of the current. Typically, nests are located where there is no perceptible current, not far from cover or deeper water to which the male retreats when frightened.

Smallmouth bass eggs are golden yellow and about 0.1 inch in diameter. They are distinguished from those of the spotted bass and largemouth bass by their larger size. Nests contain about 2,500 eggs on the average, but occasionally as many as 10,000 eggs are present. They hatch in 2 or 3 days. After hatching, the light-colored fry drop down into the gravel where they remain for about 6 more days. By the ninth or tenth day after spawning the fry have worked their way out of the gravel and are very black. A few days later they are swimming in a dense cloud over the nest, and soon thereafter they begin to disperse. The male continues to guard the fry for a day or so as they spread away from the nest. Fry begin feeding at about the time they leave the nest. As many as 80,000 bass fry are produced in a single mile of Ozark stream, but these may be reduced to less than 100 by early September of the first year of life.[201]

In Missouri streams the smallmouth bass averages 3.5 inches long when one year of age, and attains lengths of about 6.7, 9.6, 11.4, 13.5, and 14.6 inches in succeeding years.[52] As is commonly the case with fishes, growth is more rapid in larger streams than in headwater creeks. A 10-inch Missouri smallmouth will weigh about half a pound, and a 14-inch specimen will weigh about 1 pound, 6 ounces. They seldom exceed a length of 22 inches or a weight of 5½ pounds. Missouri smallmouth become mature during their third or fourth summer of life and occasionally live 10 or 12 years.

IMPORTANCE AND ANGLING

The smallmouth bass is the most sought-after sport fish in the clear, cool streams of the central Ozarks. In recent years it has become increasingly abundant and important in the sport fishery of Table Rock Reservoir.

Minnows, crayfish, and hellgrammites are the most effective live baits for taking the smallmouth. Spinning and casting with the same types of lures used for taking the largemouth bass are also effective. Fly fishing with surface lures, such as dry flies, rubber bugs, and poppers, is considered by some fishermen to be the ultimate sporting method for catching smallmouth bass.

Spotted Bass

Micropterus punctulatus (Rafinesque)

Other local names: Kentucky bass

DESCRIPTION

Illustration: Page 252, 5a; **43.**

Characters: A slender, streamlined sunfish with a large mouth, the upper jaw reaching to or slightly beyond the rear margin of the eye in adults. Midside with a broad, continuous stripe—sometimes indistinct in large adults and individuals from turbid water—but margins of stripe more broken and uneven than in largemouth bass. Lower sides with dark spots that are arranged in rows, forming a series of prominent horizontal streaks that are characteristic of this species. Margin of spinous dorsal less strongly rounded outward (convex) than in largemouth bass, the shortest spine in fin more than half the length of longest spine. Anal fin with 3 (rarely 2 or 4) spines. Scales in lateral line 59 to 65. Pyloric caeca (finger-like extensions at junction of stomach and intestine) not forked.

Life colors: Upper parts greenish with darker mottlings and golden reflections, lower sides and belly whitish. Midside with a broad blackish stripe having wavy margins. Lower side with prominent dark streaks. Tail fin in young bass with a black vertical bar that separates the yellowish-orange fin base from a whitish fringe along rear margin of fin.

Size: Adults are commonly 10 to 17 inches in length and weigh 0.6 to 3.5 pounds. Individuals weighing more than 4 pounds are rare. The present state record is 7.5 pounds from Table Rock Lake.

Scientific name: *Micropterus*, Greek, meaning "small fin," the name resulting from an injury to the type specimen that made it appear that the posterior rays of the soft dorsal formed a separate fin; *punctulatus*, Latin, meaning "dotted," in reference to the rows of dark spots along the lower sides.

DISTRIBUTION AND HABITAT

The spotted bass has two distribution centers in Missouri: 1) Lowland ditches and the larger streams of the southeastern Ozarks; 2) the western periphery of the Ozarks, including parts of the White, Spring, and Missouri systems. In the Lowlands it is the most abundant species of black bass in flowing waters; elsewhere in its Missouri range it is the most abundant black bass in the larger streams. It is more abundant than the smallmouth bass in large Ozark reservoirs.

Presence of the spotted bass in the Missouri River system seems to be the result of introduction into the Osage drainage at a relatively recent date. This introduction is undocumented, but occurred sometime prior to 1940. By the early 1940's the spotted bass was well established in the upper Osage system, but it was not until sometime in the late 1950's that it invaded the Moreau River, which empties into the Missouri River not far upstream from the mouth of the Osage River. It is now quite common in the Moreau where it hybridizes extensively with the native smallmouth bass. I have not seen spotted bass from Moniteau Creek, the next tributary of the Missouri River westward, but several hybrids have been taken there since 1962.

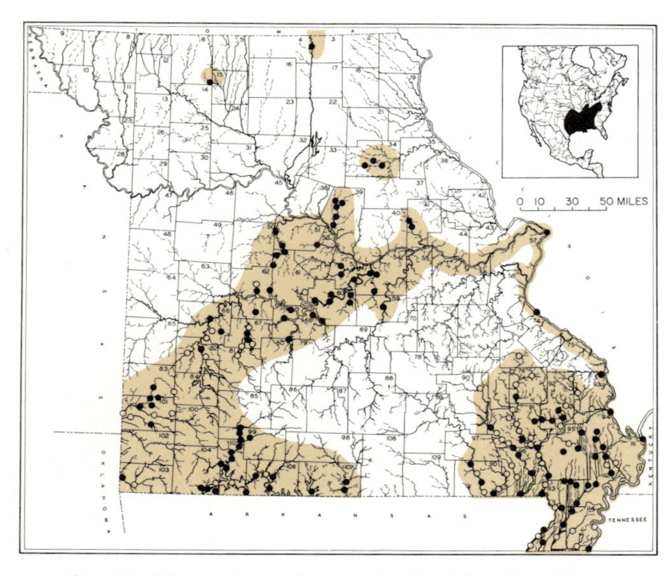

Spotted bass have been stocked by the Department of Conservation in the Lamine, Grand, Chariton, Perche, Loutre, and Salt stream systems since 1962. Reproduction has occurred in all of these and the spotted bass is well established in the Lamine, Perche and Loutre stream systems. A single juvenile was seined at the junction of the Missouri and Mississippi rivers in 1969, and several more were subsequently taken from Isle du Bois Creek, Jefferson County. Two specimens were collected from the Gasconade River in 1974, indicating that the spotted bass is now well established in that stream system.It is likely that they will eventually become established in all suitable streams of central Missouri.

The spotted bass generally inhabits permanent-flowing waters that are warmer and slightly more turbid than those where the smallmouth bass occurs. In the main channels of large rivers within its area of occurrence the spotted bass occurs almost to the exclusion of other black basses. It is largely replaced by the smallmouth bass in cool, spring-fed streams, and by the largemouth bass in standing waters. In large Ozark reservoirs it generally is found at depths greater than those occupied by other black basses.

HABITS AND LIFE HISTORY

The habits of the spotted bass are much like those of the smallmouth, but it is a more active fish. There is some indication of an annual movement between larger rivers and reservoirs and their tributaries. Spotted bass appear in the smaller streams after high water in the spring, returning to larger waters in the fall. A study of the food habits in the Wabash River, Illinois, revealed that immature stages of aquatic insects were the principal food item in the diet of bass of all sizes. In bass less than 3 inches long, insects were supplemented by small crustaceans, and in larger bass by crayfish and fish.[202]

At any given locality the spotted bass generally begins nesting a few days later than the smallmouth bass. In Missouri, nesting activity of the spotted bass is most intense from mid-April to early June. The nests are similar to those of the smallmouth bass and both species sometimes nest simultaneously in the same stream pools. Spotted bass eggs are quite small, less than one-third the size of smallmouth eggs. Development of eggs and fry is comparable to that of the smallmouth at the same temperature. Fry of the spotted bass disperse from the nest 8 or 9 days after spawning if the water temperature is in the upper 60s or 70s. The fry are pale green or translucent, not black as in the smallmouth bass, and as a consequence are difficult to observe. The male spotted bass is a less attentive parent than the smallmouth. Once the eggs hatch he moves off the nest but remains in the vicinity and deserts the fry about the time they leave the nest.

Growth of spotted bass in Missouri streams is slightly faster than that of the smallmouth for the first 4 years of life but is slower thereafter. A length of about 3.4 inches is attained the first year and lengths of about 7.2, 10, 11.5, 12.7, and 13.9 inches are reached in succeeding years.[52] Studies in Lake Wappapello indicated more rapid growth than in streams,[192] and the same is probably true of other large Missouri reservoirs. Few spotted bass live longer than 6 years or attain a weight much greater than 3 pounds.

IMPORTANCE AND ANGLING

The spotted bass is an important game fish in large streams and reservoirs of the Ozarks. However, it is less important in Missouri waters than the smallmouth and largemouth basses because of its more restricted distribution.

Fishing methods for this species are not notably different from those for taking the other basses.

Largemouth Bass

Micropterus salmoides (Lacépède)

Other local names: Lineside bass

DESCRIPTION

Illustration: Page 251, 4a.

Characters: A slender, streamlined sunfish with a very large mouth, the upper jaw reaching far beyond rear margin of eye (except in small young). Spinous and soft parts of dorsal fin almost completely separated by a deep notch. Midside with a broad, continuous stripe—sometimes indistinct in large adults and individuals from turbid water. Lower side without dark spots or with dark spots that are irregularly arranged, not forming definite horizontal streaks as in spotted bass. Margin of spinous dorsal more strongly rounded outward (convex) than in spotted bass and smallmouth bass, the shortest spine in fin less than half the length of longest spine. Anal fin with 3 (rarely 2 or 4) spines. Scales in lateral line 59 to 68. Pyloric caeca (finger-like extensions at junction of stomach and intestine) forked.

Life Colors: Upper parts greenish with a silvery or brassy luster; lower sides and belly white. Midside with a broad, blackish stripe. Tail fin in young distinctly bicolored (not tricolored as in smallmouth bass and spotted bass), the rear part of fin much darker than basal part.

Size: Adults are commonly 10 to 20 inches long and weigh 0.5 to 4.5 pounds. Individuals weighing up to 8 pounds are not uncommon and the present state record is 13 pounds, 14 ounces.

Scientific name: *Micropterus,* Greek, meaning "small fin," the name resulting from an injury to the type specimen that made it appear that the posterior rays of the soft dorsal formed a separate fin; *salmoides,* from *Salmo,* the trout—this species is often called "trout" in southern states.

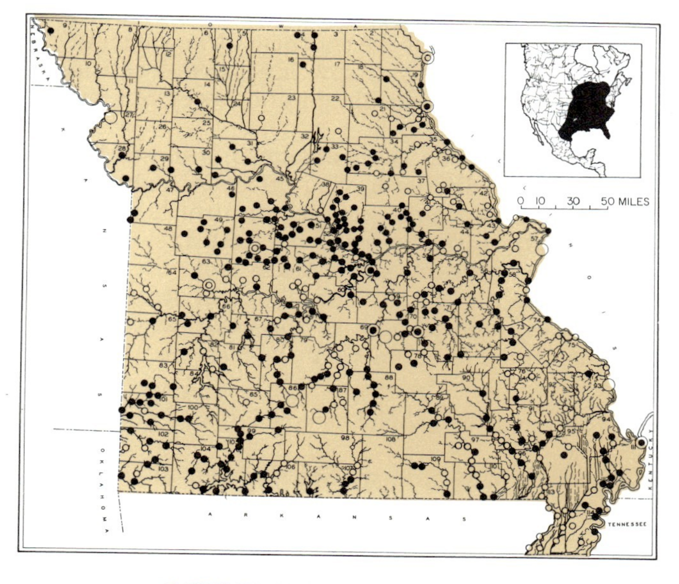

DISTRIBUTION AND HABITAT

The largemouth bass is more widely distributed in Missouri than the smallmouth and spotted basses. It is the most abundant species of black bass in standing-water habitats over all of Missouri. It is particularly characteristic of natural Lowland lakes, man-made impoundments of all sizes, the permanent pools of small streams with low or intermittent flow, and the quiet backwaters of large rivers. Despite continuous escapement from ponds and lakes where it is stocked, the largemouth bass is rare or absent in many streams of northwest Missouri.

The largemouth tolerates varied conditions but is more characteristic of standing than of flowing waters. It is intolerant of excessive turbidity and siltation; it is largely replaced by one of the other basses in streams with continuous strong flow. The largemouth thrives in warm, moderately clear waters having no noticeable current.

HABITS AND LIFE HISTORY

The largemouth bass commonly spends the day in deeper water or lurking about logs, drift piles and other cover, moving into the shallows in the evening to feed. The first food of young largemouth consists mostly of water fleas and other small crustaceans, but these are supplemented by insects and their larvae as the young bass increases in size. Adults feed principally on fish, crayfish and large insects, along with an occasional frog, mouse, or almost any other animal that swims or falls into the water. In large reservoirs the largemouth bass depends heavily on gizzard shad as food and there is a definite correlation between the trends in abundance of the largemouth and those of its principal prey species.

In Missouri the largemouth bass begins spawning about mid-April and continues into late May or June. Rocky or gravelly bottoms are preferred for nest construction, but almost any type of bottom may be used as long as a firm, silt-free bed can be created. Sometimes the eggs are deposited on the finely divided rootlets or leaves of submerged vegetation, with little nest preparation. Water depth over nests may vary from a foot or less to 15 feet or more, being deepest in the clear waters of large impoundments. The largemouth bass virtually never nests where there is any current or wave action. In reservoirs the nests are commonly located in inlets; in streams they are located in sloughs or the deeper and quieter parts of pools.

Eggs are about the size of spotted bass eggs and are much smaller than those of the smallmouth. They hatch in 3 or 4 days and the fry rise from the nest and begin to feed 5 to 8 days after hatching.[203] The fry form a tight school that remains over the nest for 4 or 5 more days and then moves about the nursery area. Schools break up 26 to 31 days after hatching. By this time the young bass are slightly over an inch long. The male largemouth is a more attentive parent than any of the other sunfishes, remaining with the schooling young for some time after they leave the nest.

Growth of the largemouth bass is extremely variable, depending on local conditions. In Lake Wappapello a length of about 5.4 inches is attained the first year and lengths of 10.9, 13.3, 16.1, 18.1, and 19.6 inches are reached in succeeding years.[192] Comparable or higher growth rates are achieved in new, well-managed ponds, but highly turbid or overpopulated ponds may contain bass 4 years or more in age that are still less than 10 inches long. Under average conditions a 12-inch bass will weigh about three-fourths of a pound and a 22-inch bass will weigh about 6 pounds.

IMPORTANCE AND ANGLING

Because of its widespread distribution and sporting qualities, the largemouth bass ranks as one of the most important North American warm-water sport fishes. Along with the crappies and white bass, it forms the backbone of the sport fishery in many large Missouri reservoirs and is stocked as the principal predatory fish in farm ponds.

A variety of natural and artificial baits are effective for taking largemouth bass. Among natural baits minnows, crayfish, worms, hellgrammites, and frogs are commonly used. Artificial lures made to imitate any of the above are effective, along with flies, popping bugs, plugs, and spoons in a variety of shapes and colors. Both surface lures and underwater types are used. A favorite method for taking lunker-sized bass is to attach a large plastic worm or eel to a weedless hook and fish it slowly over the bottom about submerged trees or other heavy cover.

Warmouth

Lepomis gulosus (Cuvier)

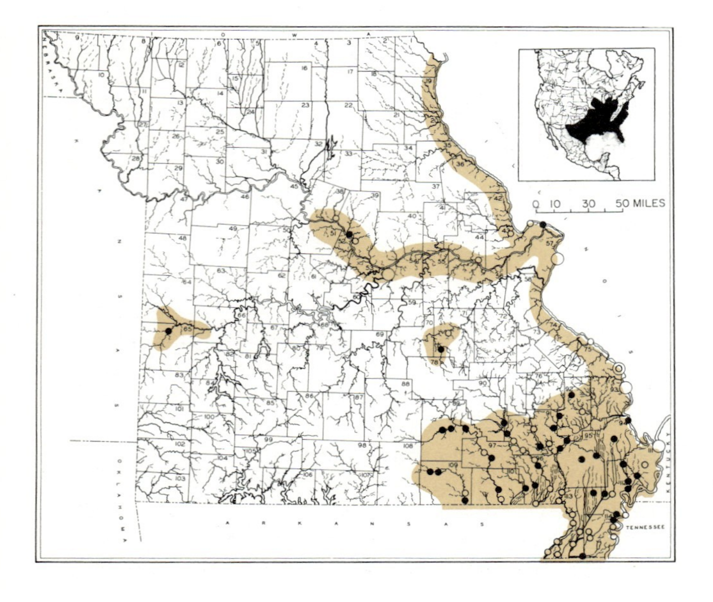

Other local names: Goggle-eye

DESCRIPTION

Illustration: Page 252, 6a.

Characters: The presence of a small patch of teeth on the tongue, detected by rubbing forefinger over upper surface of tongue, and the dark streaks radiating back from eye are useful characters for identifying this thick-bodied sunfish. Mouth large, the upper jaw reaching to or beyond middle of eye. Spinous dorsal with 10 (very rarely 9 or 11) spines, and broadly connected to soft dorsal. Often confused with the rock bass, but with 3 instead of 6 spines at front of anal fin. Lateral line scales 36 to 44.

Life colors: Back and sides rich olive-brown with numerous dark brown mottlings, fading to light yellow on belly. A characteristic feature is the 4 or 5 reddish-brown streaks radiating from eye across side of head. Iris of eye red. Fins strongly spotted and banded with dark brown, the bands most prominent on soft dorsal and anal.

Size: Maximum length and weight known for Missouri is 8.2 inches and 8 ounces; the maximum weight reported is about a pound.

Scientific name: *Lepomis,* Greek, meaning "scaled gill cover"; *gulosus,* Latin, meaning "large-mouthed."

DISTRIBUTION AND HABITAT

The main area of occurrence for the warmouth in Missouri is the Lowlands of the southeast and the downstream sections of adjacent Ozark streams. In the Lowlands it is one of the common sunfishes. Outside of the southeast the warmouth is known from only a few scattered localities, mostly along the Mississippi and lower Missouri rivers.

In the Lowlands the warmouth is most abundant in weedy ditches having little noticeable current, and in swamps, sloughs, natural lakes and borrow pits. Elsewhere in the state it is almost invariably found in oxbow lakes and other overflow waters along the flood plains of streams. It exhibits a definite affinity for clear water and thick growths of submergent vegetation.

HABITS AND LIFE HISTORY

The following information is from an Illinois study.[204] The warmouth is a sedentary and secretive fish, seeking the cover of weed masses, stumps, or rocky banks, and avoiding intense light. It occurs in schools only as newly hatched fry, but adults form loose aggregations about weed beds and other cover. The first food of warmouth fry consists mostly of waterfleas and other small crustaceans. Adults feed primarily on crayfish, aquatic sowbugs (isopods), immature aquatic insects, and small fishes.

The nesting season at the latitude of Missouri extends from mid-May into July and August, but reaches its peak in early June. Nests are usually located near a stump, rock, clump of vegetation, or other large object. Various bottom types are used, but rubble lightly covered with silt and detritus is preferred. Nests are guarded vigorously by the male until the fry depart. Males approach intruders with gill covers widespread and mouth open; at that time the eyes become blood red and the body takes on a bright yellow color. Eggs hatch in about 34½ hours, and the fry are swimming actively over the nest by the end of the fifth day after hatching.

In Illinois the warmouth attains a length of about 1.6 inches its first year and 3.4, 4.9, 6.4, 7.4, 8, 8.5, and 8.6 inches in succeeding years.

IMPORTANCE

Because of its small size and limited distribution, the warmouth is of only minor importance as a pan fish in Missouri. Significant numbers occur in the creel only in Clearwater Lake, Lake Wappapello, and the sloughs, streams, and ditches of the Lowlands.

Green Sunfish

Lepomis cyanellus Rafinesque

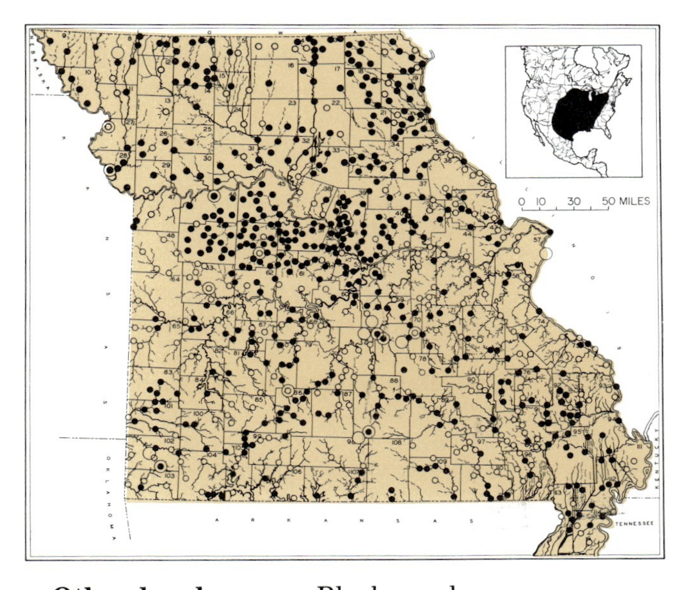

Other local names: Black perch

DESCRIPTION

Illustration: Page 254, 9a.

Characters: A thick-bodied sunfish with a larger mouth than most other sunfishes, the upper jaw reaching about to middle of eye in adults. Spinous dorsal with 10 (rarely 9 or 11) spines, and broadly connected to soft dorsal. Pectoral fin short and rounded, not reaching past front of eye when bent forward across eye. Ear flap never greatly prolonged. Rear margin of bony gill cover (lying within base of membranous ear flap) hard and inflexible. Rakers on front of first gill arch long and slender. Anal fin spines 3. Lateral line scales 41 to 52.

Life colors: Back and sides bluish-green with emerald and yellow reflections, grading to pale yellow or white on belly. Several blackish vertical bars sometimes evident on sides. Emerald mottlings and streaks present on side of head; ear flap black with a whitish or yellowish-orange margin. Black blotch usually present near bases of last few fin-rays of dorsal fin and anal fin. Fins otherwise plain except in breeding males which have a broad whitish or orange fringe on dorsal, tail, and anal fins.

Size: Rarely exceeding a length of 10 inches or a weight of a pound. Largest specimen reported from Missouri weighed 2 pounds, 2 ounces.

Scientific name: *Lepomis,* Greek, meaning "scaled gill cover"; *cyanellus,* Greek, meaning "blue."

DISTRIBUTION AND HABITAT

The green sunfish is without question the most widely distributed Missouri fish, occurring at least as strays in virtually every stream in the state capable of supporting fish life. It is the most abundant sunfish in many streams of the Prairie Region. In the Ozarks and Lowlands the green sunfish is largely replaced by other sunfishes, especially the longear. It occurs only as strays in the Missouri and Mississippi rivers, but is sometimes abundant in muddy sloughs and ditches of their flood plains.

This sunfish tolerates a wide range of conditions, but it does best where few other sunfishes occur. It tolerates extremes of turbidity, dissolved oxygen, temperature, and flow, and is well suited for survival in the fluctuating environment of small Prairie streams. By late summer and fall these small streams often consist of series of isolated, stagnant pools. In this habitat green sunfish are often abundant, along with other fishes with similar tolerances, including the creek chub, fathead minnow, and black bullhead. These hardy pioneers are among the first fishes to repopulate Prairie streams that dry entirely during droughts.

HABITS AND LIFE HISTORY

The green sunfish is decidedly a homebody; marked individuals have been found in the same stream pool a year or more after their initial capture. Insects, small fish, and crayfish are the principal items in its diet. Because of its large mouth the green sunfish has the capacity to ingest larger food items than most other typical sunfishes.

Nesting begins in Missouri during the middle or latter part of May when the water temperature rises above 70° F. Nesting activity reaches a peak in June, but often continues into August. The nesting season in Prairie and Ozark border streams is usually somewhat advanced over that in the cool, spring-fed streams of the central Ozarks. Nests are constructed by the male in typical sunfish fashion, in backwaters or protected areas along shore, frequently in water a foot or less in depth. Gravelly or rocky bottoms are preferred, but nests are occasionally fanned out on water-soaked tree leaves and twigs. Nests may be fairly close together if suitable nest sites are at a premium, but the green sunfish is not colonial in its nesting habits. Females assume a pattern of prominent dark vertical bars while spawning. Several females may spawn in a single nest. Males remain with the nest for 6 or 7 days after the eggs are deposited, about the time required for the fry to become free-swimming.[211] Hybrids between the green sunfish and the bluegill, presumably the result of cross-mating, are very common. In central Missouri the redfin, red, and Topeka shiners spawn over or around the periphery of green sunfish nests.

In the headwaters of Salt River, the green sunfish attains lengths of about 1.7, 3.2, 4.7, 5.9, and 7.6 inches at an age of 1 through 5 years respectively.[126] This is more rapid growth than in some Ozark streams of comparable size, but slower than in larger Ozark streams such as the lower Meramec River. A 6-inch green sunfish weighs about 3 ounces; the occasional individual that achieves a length of 12 inches may weigh 2 pounds. Few individuals exceed a length of 9 inches or a weight of three-fourths of a pound.

IMPORTANCE AND ANGLING

Because of its widespread distribution the green sunfish is known to fishermen throughout Missouri. However, its greatest contribution is to the fishery of small intermittent creeks that are incapable of supporting most other kinds of hook-and-line fish. Such creeks often yield large stringers of pan-sized green sunfish.

Still-fishing with a cane pole and bobber using worms, grubs, or grasshoppers as bait is about as effective as any method for catching them. A small popping bug or rubber spider fished with a light fly rod can also be counted on to get a response from any green sunfish in the vicinity. In fact, just about any method that is effective for other members of the sunfish family will take green sunfish.

Spotted Sunfish

Lepomis punctatus (Valenciennes)

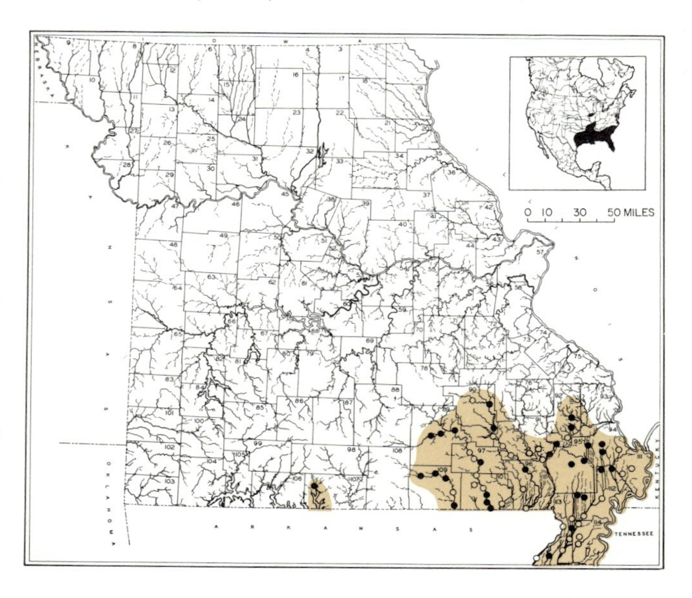

DESCRIPTION

Illustration: Page 254, 10b; **44.**

Characters: A deep and slab-sided sunfish with a moderate-sized mouth, the upper jaw reaching past front of eye. Spinous dorsal with 10 (rarely 9 or 11) spines and broadly connected to soft dorsal. Pectoral fin short and rounded, not reaching past front of eye when bent forward across eye. Ear flap never greatly elongated. Rear margin of bony gill cover (lying within base of membranous ear flap) not flexible. Rakers on front of first gill arch long and slender. Anal fin spines 3. Lateral line scales 34 to 39.

Similar in appearance to bantam sunfish, but never with a black spot near base of last few dorsal fin rays. Lateral line complete.

Life colors: Back and sides dark blue with a yellowish hue; belly yellowish or dusky white. Scales of side marked by yellowish-orange (females) or red (males) spots, forming lengthwise rows. Spots absent in young individuals. Ear flap black, sometimes narrowly edged with white or pale yellow. Fins dusky or plain, without definite markings.

Size: Larger than bantam sunfish, page 265, attaining a length and weight of about 8 inches and 7 ounces.

Scientific name: *Lepomis,* Greek, meaning "scaled gill cover"; *punctatus,* Latin, meaning "spotted."

DISTRIBUTION AND HABITAT

The spotted sunfish is common in the Lowlands, and penetrates far into the southeastern Ozarks along major streams that enter the Lowlands.

In the Lowlands the spotted sunfish occurs most abundantly in the more sluggish ditches where submerged aquatic plants are present; in Ozark streams it occurs in quiet pools near boulders and submerged logs, and in clear, heavily vegetated backwaters.

HABITS AND LIFE HISTORY

Spotted sunfish spawn in Illinois during May.[24] In Jack's Fork, Shannon County, nesting activity has been observed in early July. Nests were in water only a few inches in depth among the stems of water willow, over a bottom of sand and gravel. The spotted sunfish is usually a solitary nester, but sometimes two or more males build nests so close together that they become confluent. The courtship, spawning, and nest defense are typical of sunfishes.[205] Males possess striking black pelvic fins which are boldly extended during defense of the nest and are opened and closed almost constantly during courtship. The eggs hatch in about 48 to 52 hours at a temperature of 68 to 75° F., and the fry rise from the nest and begin feeding by the tenth day after hatching.

IMPORTANCE

The spotted sunfish occurs occasionally in the catch of fishermen in southeastern Missouri but is usually taken incidentally while fishing for other species. Because of its small size and limited distribution, the spotted sunfish is of little direct importance to man.

Bantam Sunfish

Lepomis symmetricus Forbes

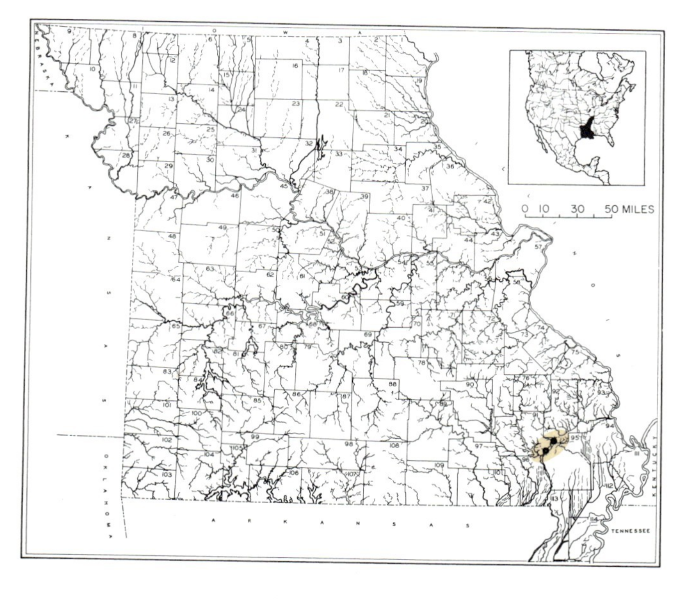

DESCRIPTION

Illustration: Page 254, 10a.

Characters: A small, deep and slab-sided sunfish with a moderate-sized mouth, the upper jaw reaching past front of eye. Spinous dorsal with 10 (rarely 9 or 11) spines and broadly connected to soft dorsal. Pectoral fin short and rounded, not reaching past front of eye when bent forward across eye. Ear flap never greatly prolonged. Rear margin of bony gill cover (lying within base of membranous ear flap) not flexible. Rakers on front of first gill arch long and slender. Anal fin spines 3. Lateral line scales 32 to 37.

Similar in appearance to spotted sunfish, but with a prominent black spot present near base of last few dorsal fin rays (spot sometimes undeveloped in large adults). Lateral line incomplete, not reaching to near base of tail fin.

Life colors: Back and sides olive-blue, fading to pale yellow on belly. Sides often marked by lengthwise rows of dark spots and faint dusky vertical bars. Fins dusky or plain, except for prominent black spot near back of dorsal fin.

Size: The smallest of the true sunfishes, *Lepomis,* seldom exceeding a length of 2 inches.

Scientific name: *Lepomis,* Greek, meaning "scaled gill cover"; *symmetricus,* from symmetrical, in reference to the even contours of the body.

DISTRIBUTION AND HABITAT

The bantam sunfish has been collected in the state only from Duck Creek Wildlife Area and the adjacent Mingo National Wildlife Refuge in Bollinger and Wayne counties. Perhaps it was more common and widely distributed in the Lowlands before the swamps were ditched and drained.

This fish inhabits clear, quiet waters which have considerable quantities of submerged aquatic vegetation and standing timber.

HABITS AND LIFE HISTORY

Little is known of the habits of this diminutive sunfish. The general behavior and feeding of bantam sunfish kept in aquaria were similar to other sunfishes. At Mingo Swamp the bantam seldom exceeds 2 inches in length, but individuals stocked in a pond near Columbia achieved a length of 4 inches or more.

Redear Sunfish

Lepomis microlophus (Günther)

DESCRIPTION

Illustration: Page 256, 13b.

Characters: A deep and slab-sided sunfish with a rather small mouth, the upper jaw not reaching past front of eye. Spinous dorsal with 10 (rarely 9 or 11) spines and broadly connected to soft dorsal.

Pectoral fin long and pointed, reaching well past front of eye when bent forward across eye. Ear flap never greatly prolonged, with a light-colored border. Rakers on front of first gill arch short and stout. Anal fin spines 3. Lateral line scales 39 to 44.

Very similar to pumpkinseed, but differing in the following respects: soft dorsal and anal fins uniform in color, without rows of dark spots; no wavy blue lines on cheek; rear margin of bony gill cover (lying within base of membranous ear flap) thin and flexible.

Life colors: Back and sides golden or light olive-green, belly yellow or orange-yellow. Sides often marked by a series of blackish vertical bars (most prominent in small individuals). Ear flap black with a whitish border and (in adults) a prominent orange or red spot. Fins greenish-olive, without definite spots. Colors brighter in males than in females.

Size: Occasionally reaching a length of 10.5 inches and a weight of a pound, but seldom exceeding 8.9 inches and 6.5 ounces. A 1 pound, 6 ounce redear was caught in Prairie Lake, Jackson County, in 1971.

Scientific name: *Lepomis,* Greek, meaning "scaled gill cover"; *microlophus,* Greek, meaning "small nape."

DISTRIBUTION AND HABITAT

In natural waters the redear is confined to the southern half of the state where it is rare. However, the redear has been widely stocked in small reservoirs and ponds elsewhere in the state. Self-sustaining populations have resulted from many of these stockings.

The redear does best in warm, clear waters with no noticeable current and an abundance of aquatic plants. In streams it is more often found in protected bays and overflow pools than in the main stream channel.

HABITS AND LIFE HISTORY

The food of the redear consists primarily of snails,[206] and this has earned it the common name "shellcracker." The pavement-like throat teeth of the redear, with their broad, flattened surfaces, are well suited for crushing the shells of molluscs. In Missouri the redear nests in May or June. In some Missouri ponds a second nesting has been observed in August. The nests are saucer-shaped depressions, fanned out in silt if no gravel is present. The redear tends to nest in colonies, with the rims of the nests often almost touching. This sunfish grows more rapidly and attains a larger size than bluegill from the same waters. In Reelfoot Lake, Tennessee, the redear sunfish averages 4.3 inches in length in its second summer of life, and attains lengths of about 6, 6.9, 7.5, and 8.1 inches during succeeding summers.[207] Maturity is often reached during the second summer of life, and few redears live more than six summers.

IMPORTANCE AND ANGLING

The redear is an excellent panfish and contributes significantly to the creel in impounded waters where it has been introduced. Most redear are caught from spawning "beds" in early summer. They may be taken on artificial lures, but natural baits, such as earthworms and grubs, are most effective.

Pumpkinseed

Lepomis gibbosus (Linnaeus)

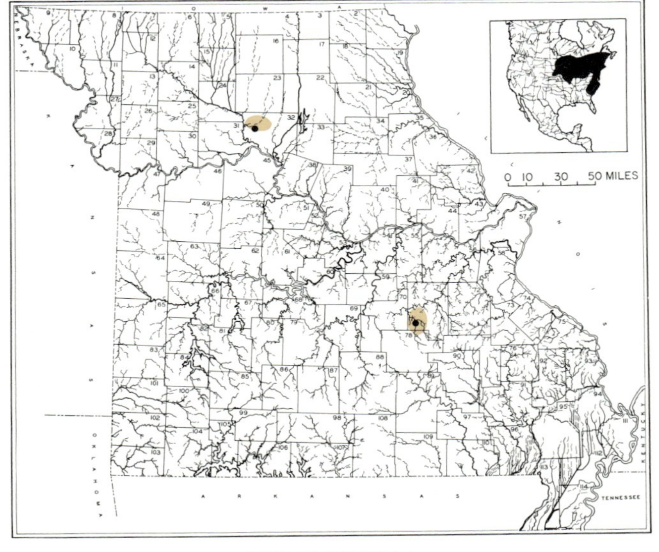

DESCRIPTION

Illustration: Page 256, 13a.

Characters: A deep and slab-sided sunfish with a rather small mouth, the upper jaw not reaching past front of eye. Spinous dorsal with 10 (rarely 9 or 11) spines and broadly connected to soft dorsal. Pectoral fin long and pointed, reaching well past front of eye when bent forward across eye. Ear flap never greatly prolonged, with a light-colored border. Rakers on first gill arch short and stout. Anal fin spines 3. Lateral line scales 39 to 44.

Very similar to redear sunfish, but with the following differences: soft dorsal and anal fins with rows of faint dark spots; cheek with wavy blue lines; rear margin of gill cover (lying within base of membranous ear flap) thick and inflexible.

Life colors: Like those of redear, page 265, but more strongly mottled and spotted.

Size: Similar to the redear.

Scientific name: *Lepomis,* Greek, meaning "scaled gill cover"; *gibbosus,* Greek, meaning "wide margin."

DISTRIBUTION AND HABITAT

The pumpkinseed has been recorded only twice from natural waters of Missouri. A single sub-adult was collected in 1963 from an overflow pool along the Meramec River in Crawford County, and five sub-adults were taken in 1967 from Salt Creek, a small tributary of Grand River in Chariton County. Perhaps these records result from escapement of pumpkinseeds that had been stocked in ponds of these watersheds, but there is no evidence of this. The pumpkinseed does occur in the Grand River system of Iowa. Thus, its occurrence in the Missouri part of that drainage is to be expected.

Elsewhere in its range the pumpkinseed inhabits clear, quiet waters with much aquatic vegetation; this is the habitat in which it was found along the Meramec River. However, Salt Creek is a small, turbid prairie stream with a silty bottom and no aquatic vegetation. Perhaps the pumpkinseeds collected in Salt Creek were strays from nearby Swan Lake or other natural lakes along the Grand River.

HABITS AND LIFE HISTORY

The pumpkinseed is the northern counterpart of the redear sunfish and in most respects their habits and life history are similar. Like the redear, this sunfish depends heavily on snails and other small molluscs as food, but also eats aquatic insects and small fish. Nesting occurs at about the same time as the bluegill and is like that of other small sunfishes.

IMPORTANCE

The pumpkinseed is too rare in Missouri waters to be of any importance, although it may have some potential as a pond fish. In northern states where it is more abundant it is an important panfish.

Orangespotted Sunfish

Lepomis humilis (Girard)

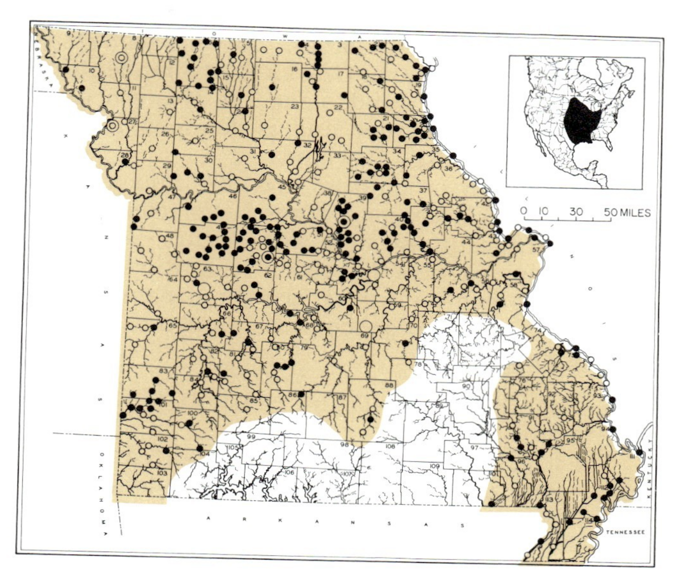

Illustration: Page 255, 11a; **44.**

Characters: A moderately deep and slab-sided sunfish with a rather large mouth, the upper jaw reaching past front of eye. Spinous dorsal with 10 (rarely 9 or 11) spines and broadly connected to soft dorsal. Pectoral fin rounded and moderately short, usually not reaching past front of eye when bent forward across eye. Ear flap considerably elongated in adults, especially males. Rear margin of bony gill cover (lying within base of membranous ear flap) thin and flexible. Rakers on front of first gill arch long and slender. Sensory pits (two depressions in skull between eyes) larger than in any other sunfish *(Lepomis),* the width of each pit about equal to distance between the pits. Anal fin spines 3. Lateral line scales 32 to 39.

Life colors: Back and sides greenish with silver-blue reflections, belly white or yellow. Lower sides marked by numerous reddish-brown spots. Ear flap black with a broad whitish margin. Fins plain, without prominent spots or blotches. Breeding males are among the most brilliantly colored of Missouri fishes: the spots on the lower sides are red or reddish-orange; the belly and fins are mostly reddish-orange; and the pelvic and anal fins are fringed with black. Small orangespotted sunfish often have rather distinct vertical bars and lack brownish spots on the sides.

Size: A small sunfish with a maximum length of about 4 inches.

Scientific name: *Lepomis,* Greek, meaning "scaled gill cover"; *humilis,* Latin, meaning "humble."

DISTRIBUTION AND HABITAT

The orangespotted sunfish is distributed over much of Missouri but occurs only at scattered localities in the central Ozarks. It is abundant in the Prairie Region and along the western and northern Ozark border and is common in the siltier ditches of the Lowlands.

It is tolerant of siltation and continuous high turbidity and is commonly found in streams with low or intermittent flow, but occurs less frequently in extreme headwater situations than does the green sunfish. It avoids streams with high gradient, clear or cool water, and continuous strong flow.

HABITS AND LIFE HISTORY

The food of this small sunfish is reported to consist principally of small crustaceans, along with larval aquatic insects and an occasional small fish.[208] In Missouri the orangespotted sunfish nests from late May into August. The nests are similar to those of the green sunfish but are smaller. The male sunfish remains with the nest until the eggs hatch, about five days after spawning.[208] The red shiner and redfin shiner have been observed spawning over nests of the orangespotted sunfish in central Missouri. Young orangespots are about an inch long by the end of their first year of life, and attain lengths of 1.4, 1.8, and 2.3 inches in succeeding years.[208] Some orangespotted sunfish mature and spawn during their second summer of life, but most do not mature until their third summer.

IMPORTANCE

The orangespotted sunfish is occasionally taken on hook-and-line but is too small to be of much value as a panfish.

Longear Sunfish

Lepomis megalotis (Rafinesque)

Other local names: Pumpkinseed, Creek perch

DESCRIPTION

Illustration: Page 255, 11b; **45.**

Characters: A deep and slab-sided sunfish with a moderate-sized mouth, the upper jaw nearly reaching front of eye. Spinous dorsal with 10 (rarely 9 or 11) spines and broadly connected to soft dorsal. Pectoral fin rounded and short, not reaching past front of eye when bent forward across eye. Ear flap considerably elongated in adults, especially males. Rear margin of bony gill cover (lying within base of membranous ear flap) thin and flexible. Rakers on front of first gill arch very short and thick, their length less than twice their width. Anal fin spines 3. Lateral line scales 35 to 41.

Life colors: Back and sides blue-green speckled with yellow and emerald; belly yellow or orange. Side of head olive or light orange with emerald-blue vermiculations. Ear flap black, often with a narrow white border. Fins without prominent spots or blotches. Breeding males have all colors more intense, with the undersurface of head and belly bright orange-red. Males from central and southwestern Missouri have a prominent reddish nape, but this is only slightly developed in populations from elsewhere in the state.

Size: The maximum length and weight in Missouri streams is about 7 inches and 4.5 ounces.

Scientific name: *Lepomis,* Greek, meaning "scaled gill cover"; *megalotis,* Greek, meaning "great ear," in reference to the prominent ear tab.

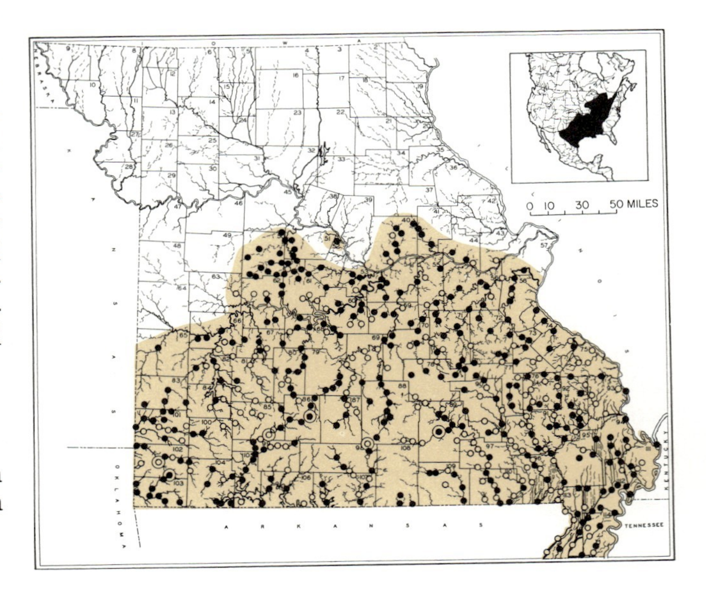

DISTRIBUTION AND HABITAT

The longear is by far the most abundant and generally distributed sunfish over the southern half of Missouri. The northern and northwestern limit of its range corresponds closely to the boundary of the Ozarks. But unlike many characteristic Ozark stream fishes, its distribution continues uninterruptedly into the Lowlands. North of the Missouri River the longear occurs only in short, direct tributaries of the Missouri River from Callaway County eastward.

This sunfish is characteristic of clear, permanent-flowing streams having sandy or rocky bottoms. It is often found in association with aquatic vegetation, but this is not an essential requirement. The longear occurs in streams of all sizes but is more abundant in creeks than in large rivers.

Like most sunfishes it avoids strong currents, occurring most commonly in pools, inlets, and overflow waters adjacent to the stream channel. The longear sunfish occurs in abundance along the shoreline of most large Ozark reservoirs.

HABITS AND LIFE HISTORY

The habits of the longear are much like those of the green sunfish. Insects and other small invertebrates, with an occasional small fish, make up the bulk of its diet. Like the smallmouth bass, it follows turtles and large suckers about as they forage over the bottom, feeding on insect larvae and small crayfish exposed by this activity. Longears commonly gather about the nests of smallmouth bass and other sunfishes (including their own species), rushing in to feed greedily on eggs or fry if the guardian male is momentarily distracted or frightened away.

In Ozark streams this colonial nester spawns from mid-May into late July or early August. The nests are nearly always fanned out over small chert gravel and are more evenly rounded in outline than those of the green sunfish. The male longear seems to prefer the company of other nesting males; often the nests are so close together that their rims nearly touch. Courtship, spawning, and nest defense are much like that of other small sunfishes.[209, 210]

Male longears are larger than the females with which they spawn. When a female approaches the nest the male rushes out to meet her, swimming rapidly about and above her, tilting his body in such a way as to display his bright, orange-red belly. All of the male's colors appear more brilliant during this display and the subsequent spawning. The female assumes a strongly barred appearance as she swims onto the nest. Spawning occurs as the pair of fish circle rapidly in the nest, pausing momentarily to deposit and fertilize the eggs a few at a time. This continues for a period of several minutes, after which the male unceremoniously chases the female from the nest. The female may return to spawn again with this or another male. The male may break off from spawning at any time to chase away intruders. He continues to guard the nest for a week or more until the young have completed their early development and dispersed.

In Missouri streams the longear sunfish attains a length of about 1.3 inches its first year and 2.5, 3.6, 4.3, 4.8, and 5.0 inches in succeeding years.[52]

IMPORTANCE AND ANGLING

In spite of its small size, the longear sunfish is of considerable importance as a panfish in Ozark streams. This is because of its abundance and its willingness to bite. Worms, grasshoppers, and small minnows are good natural baits for taking them. Small spinners, popping bugs, flies, and fly and spinner combinations are also effective. When taken on light tackle the longear can provide some real sport.

Bluegill

Lepomis macrochirus Rafinesque

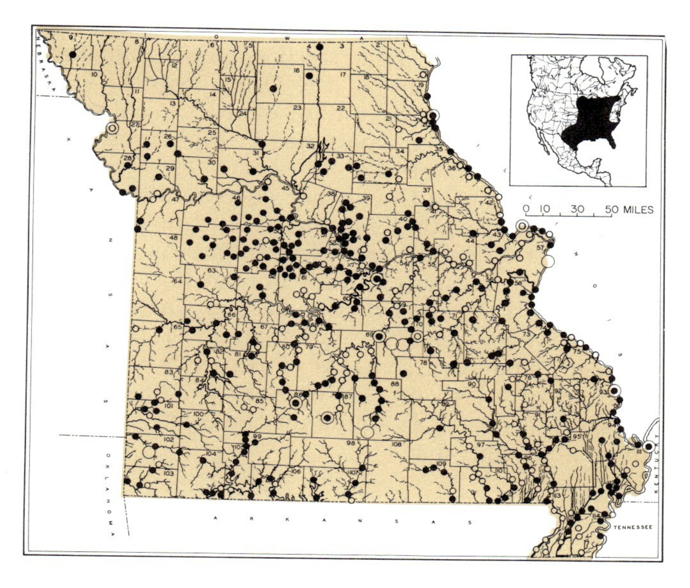

Other local names: Bream, Pond perch

DESCRIPTION

Illustration: Page 255, 12a; **46.**

Characters: A deep and slab-sided sunfish with a rather small mouth, the upper jaw not reaching past front of eye. Spinous dorsal with 10 (rarely 9 or 11) spines and broadly connected to soft dorsal. Pectoral fin pointed and long, reaching well past front of eye when bent forward across eye. Often with a characteristic black blotch near bases of last few rays in soft dorsal. Ear flap moderately prolonged in adults, especially males. Rear margin of bony gill cover (lying within base of membranous ear flap) thin and flexible. Rakers on front of first gill arch long and slender. Anal fin spines 3. Lateral line scales 39 to 44.

Life colors: Back and sides dark olive-green with emerald and brassy reflections, breast and belly yellow or reddish-orange. Sides often marked by dusky vertical bars, these best developed in small individuals. Chin and lower part of gill cover blue; ear flap entirely black. Except for black blotch in back part of soft dorsal the fins are without prominent markings. All colors are more intense in breeding males. Young are more silvery than adults.

Size: The bluegill commonly reaches a length of 9.5 inches and a weight of 12 ounces. The largest specimen from Missouri weighed 3 pounds.

Scientific name: *Lepomis,* Greek, meaning "scaled gill cover"; *macrochirus,* Greek, meaning "large hand," perhaps in reference to the body shape.

DISTRIBUTION AND HABITAT

The bluegill occurs in natural waters over most of the state, but only as strays in many Prairie streams of northwestern Missouri. It reaches its greatest abundance along the flood plains of major rivers and in streams of the Ozark border. The bluegill is the most abundant of the typical sunfishes *(Lepomis)* in man-made impoundments throughout the state.

It is common in the deeper pools and backwaters of streams, but is most abundant in overflow ponds, oxbow lakes, and impoundments created by man. It is intolerant of continuous high turbidity and siltation and thrives best in warm, clear waters where aquatic plants or other cover is present. The requirements of this fish are very similar to those of the largemouth bass, and where one species is abundant the other is likely to be abundant also.

HABITS AND LIFE HISTORY

The bluegill is quite gregarious, often moving about in loose aggregations of as many as 20 or 30 individuals. During midday it remains in deeper water or loafs about in the shade of an overhanging tree or boat dock. In early morning and again in the evening it moves into the shallows to feed. Feeding is primarily by sight and occurs at all levels. When mayflies and other aquatic insects are emerging the bluegill feeds at the surface. It has a rather small mouth and this limits, to some extent, the kinds of food that it can eat. Bluegill fry feed primarily on small crustaceans. Insects are the staple food item for adults, but small fish, crayfish, and snails are also eaten. Algae and other vegetation is eaten when animal food is scarce.

Bluegill begin nesting in late May, somewhat later than the largemouth bass, and continue into late July or August. Usually the spawning peak is in June. Almost any type of bottom may be used for nesting, but gravel is preferred. Nests are usually in water a foot or two in depth and consist of roundish depressions with a diameter about twice the length of the male that builds it. Usually many nests are located close together in a limited area. Several females often spawn in the same nest and a female may deposit her eggs in more than one nest. The male guards the nest vigorously until the eggs hatch, but does not guard the fry once they leave the nest.

Growth of the bluegill varies considerably from one body of water to another (Table 1). Growth is most rapid in new ponds and reservoirs and slowest in turbid or overpopulated ponds. Stunting commonly occurs in the latter situation. In most Missouri waters the bluegill reaches a length of 6 inches and a weight of about 2.5 ounces by the end of its third or fourth summer of life. An 8.5-inch individual weighs about 8 ounces. The largest bluegill on record is a 4 pound, 12 ounce fish caught in Alabama.

Table 1 Average length in inches of bluegills at the end of each year of life in selected Missouri waters.

Type of Water	Age Group				
	1	2	3	4	5
New reservoir [250]	2.8	4.2	5.6	6.6	
Older reservoir [192]	1.7	3.0	4.4	5.6	6.8
Missouri ponds [212]	2.2	4.6	5.7	6.2	6.4
Missouri streams [52]	1.5	3.1	4.4	5.4	6.2

IMPORTANCE AND ANGLING

The bluegill is one of the most widely distributed and popular panfishes in North America. It provides fishing opportunities in many types of natural waters, and is almost universally stocked in man-made ponds as forage for largemouth bass. The prolific bluegill serves well in this capacity, but tends to stunt in ponds where predation is reduced because of too much cover or overharvest of bass.

The bluegill bites readily on a variety of small baits, both natural and artificial. Crickets, grasshoppers, or worms still-fished with cane pole and bobber provide a popular and effective means for catching bluegill. Fly fishing with wet flies, dry flies or popping bugs is also effective, especially near dusk on warm summer evenings when bluegill move into the shallows to feed. The bluegill puts up a vigorous fight and provides considerable sport when taken on light tackle. Its flesh is generally firm, flaky, and well flavored.

Rock Bass

Ambloplites rupestris (Rafinesque)

Other local names: Goggle-eye

DESCRIPTION

Illustration: Page 257, 15a; **46.**

Characters: A heavy-bodied sunfish with a large mouth, the upper jaw extending past middle of eye. Spinous and soft parts of dorsal fin broadly connected, without a notch between. Anal fin distinctly shorter and smaller than dorsal fin. A combination of 6 anal fin spines and 12 dorsal fin spines readily separates the rock bass from all other similar species. The similar-appearing warmouth and other typical sunfishes have only 3 anal fin spines.

Life colors: Color variable. Typically, the back and sides are greenish-olive with brassy reflections and prominent dark brown mottlings; the breast and belly are dusky white. Lower sides commonly marked by dark spots that form prominent horizontal lines. Dorsal, tail, and anal fins faintly banded and mottled with dark brown.

Size: Commonly attaining a length and weight of up to 11 inches and one pound. The largest authenticated specimen from Missouri was 17 inches long and weighed 2 pounds, 12 ounces.

Scientific name: *Ambloplites,* Greek, meaning "blunt armature"; *rupestris,* Latin, meaning "living among the rocks."

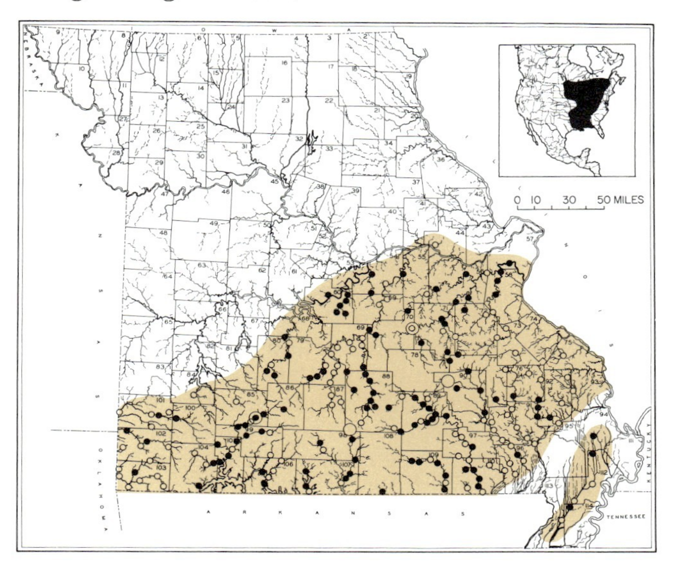

DISTRIBUTION AND HABITAT

The rock bass is one of the most widely distributed and characteristic sunfishes in the Ozarks. The total poundage of rock bass in Ozark streams often equals or exceeds that of all other small sunfishes combined. Some ditches of the Lowlands support small populations, but it does not occur widely in that area. North of the Missouri River the rock bass is known only from Lost Creek in Warren County. Occurrence in the Osage and Gasconade systems may be the result of introduction. There are no early records for rock bass in these streams and at present they do not occur in all tributaries of the Osage River that appear to provide suitable habitat.

In Missouri the rock bass is decidedly a stream fish, occurring only rarely in large Ozark reservoirs. Permanent flow, low turbidity, abundant cover, and silt-free bottoms are its basic requirements. In Ozark streams it is most abundant around boulders, submerged logs, and dense beds of water willow *(Justicia),* where there is a slight to moderate current. A deep rocky pool immediately below a riffle is a favored spot. In the Lowlands the rock bass is found in the clearer ditches where flow is strong and dense beds of submerged aquatic vegetation exist.

HABITS AND LIFE HISTORY

The rock bass is a sedentary and secretive fish, spending much of its time lying in the shadows about a boulder or submerged log. It is the "chameleon" of the sunfish family and can undergo rapid and dramatic color changes to match its surroundings. Individuals caught in dark, shadowy places may be nearly black, but soon fade to brassy-yellow when placed on a stringer in full sunlight. It will take a bait at any hour of the day or night, but it forages most actively at dusk and at night. Adult and immature aquatic insects make up the bulk of its diet, supplemented in larger rock bass by generous quantities of small minnows and crayfish.

In Ozark streams the nesting season coincides with that of the smallmouth bass and precedes those of the longear and green sunfish. Nests have been observed as early as the first week of April and as late as early June, but in any given year the season seldom lasts more than a month. Nesting activity is triggered by stream temperatures of 55 to 60° F. In typical sunfish fashion, the male rock bass fans out a saucer-shaped depression about 8 to 10 inches in diameter over a bottom of coarse sand or gravel. Nests are located in water ranging in depth from one to 5 feet, usually near a boulder or other large object, and often where there is a slight current. Unlike the longear, which nests in colonies, the rock bass is a solitary nester. The female visits the nest only when ready to deposit her eggs, but the male remains until the fry have dispersed.

In Ozark streams rock bass average 1.6 inches in length by the end of their first year of life and attain lengths of 3.4, 5.5, 7, 8, and 8.5 inches in succeeding years.[52] Those caught by fishermen average about 7 inches long and weigh about 5 ounces. Few rock bass live more than 5 or 6 years, but occasional individuals attain an age of 10 years or more.

IMPORTANCE AND ANGLING

The rock bass is the mainstay of the fishery in many Ozark streams and is exceeded in popularity only by the smallmouth bass. It attains a larger size than other stream sunfishes *(Lepomis)* and can be caught by a variety of methods. It puts up a vigorous fight when first hooked, providing much sport when taken on light tackle.

The same methods and baits that take the smallmouth bass will also take this species, though in general the baits should be somewhat smaller. Live baits such as minnows, worms, grubs, or grasshoppers fished near the bottom in rocky places having a slight current and plenty of cover often produce good catches. Small spinners, wet flies, or fly and spinner combinations fished slow and deep through the same areas will produce similar results. Dry flies and small popping bugs are most effective near dusk when the rock bass is feeding at the surface on adult and emerging insects. In winter excellent catches of rock bass are sometimes made with minnows or worms fished in the outlets of large springs.

White Crappie

Pomoxis annularis Rafinesque

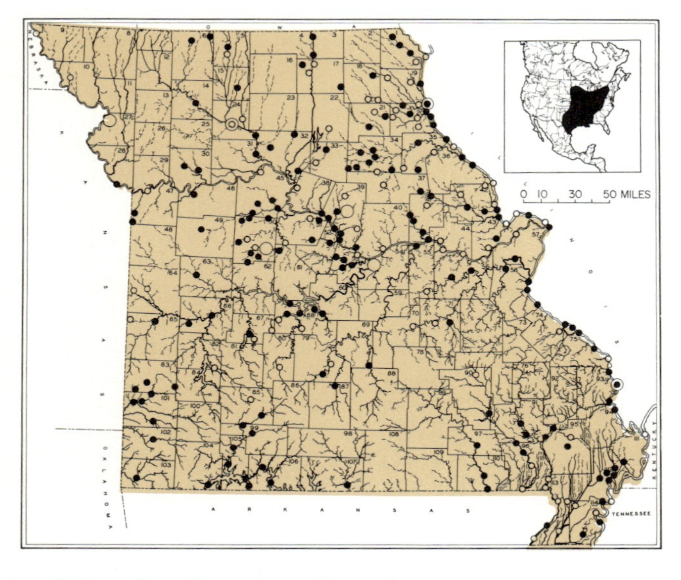

Other local names: Crappie

DESCRIPTION

Illustration: Page 257, 16b; **46.**

Characters: A silvery, deep and slab-sided sunfish with a large mouth, the upper jaw reaching well past the middle of the eye. Spinous dorsal and soft dorsal fins broadly connected, without a notch between. Anal fin nearly as long and as large as dorsal fin, and with 6 spines. Upper surface of head and forward part of back strongly concave.

Very similar to black crappie, but with the following differences: dorsal fin with 6 spines, the length of its base much less than distance from front of dorsal fin forward to eye; color pattern of sides consisting principally of faint, vertical bars rather than irregularly arranged speckles and blotches.

Life colors: Back dark olive with emerald and purple reflections, fading to silver-white on sides and belly. Sides mottled with brown or black, these markings tending to form narrow vertical bars. Dorsal, tail, and anal fins banded and mottled with black. Dark markings variably developed, but on the whole a lighter colored species than the black crappie. Breeding males are much darker and more boldly marked than other adults.

Size: Seldom exceeding a length of 15.5 inches or a weight of 2 pounds. The largest authenticated specimen from Missouri weighed 3 pounds, 12 ounces.

Scientific name: *Pomoxis,* Greek, meaning "opercle sharp," in reference to the spines on the gill cover; *annularis,* Latin, meaning "having rings," in reference to the dark bands extending around the body.

DISTRIBUTION AND HABITAT

The white crappie is more abundant and widespread in Missouri than the black crappie. It is nearly statewide in distribution, but is rare or absent from many streams of the central Ozarks and northwestern part of the Prairie Region. The white crappie attains its greatest abundance in natural Lowland lakes, navigation pools of the upper Mississippi River, and large man-made impoundments throughout the state.

In reservoirs the white crappie frequents areas having standing timber or other cover. During the spring spawning season, adults are found in relatively shallow water near the upper ends of coves; later they move to deeper water, commonly occurring at depths of 15 feet or more. Young crappie are often found over open water of considerable depth. In streams, the white crappie is most abundant in the deeper pools or in overflow ponds and lakes away from the stream channel. It avoids streams that are excessively turbid and those kept continuously cool by spring flow.

HABITS AND LIFE HISTORY

The white crappie does not school but congregates in loose aggregations about submerged trees, boat docks, and other suitable cover. It feeds principally on small fishes, aquatic insects, and microcrustaceans, with the proportions of these three staples varying with locality, season, and age of the crappie. Young crappie subsist mainly on microcrustaceans; adults depend more heavily on fish. Small gizzard shad and threadfin shad are the staple food item for adult crappie in many reservoirs.

According to observations by biologist Fred Vasey, white crappie nest in Table Rock Reservoir from the second or third week of April to early June. Nesting activity is initiated when the water temperature rises to about 56° F. Nests are invariably located in coves that are protected from wave action, and many nests are sometimes concentrated in the same cove. Males fan out nests on a variety of silt-free substrates in water ranging from a few inches to 20 feet in depth. Most nests in Table Rock Lake are in 10 to 14 feet of water. The most favored nest sites are near a log or other large object, on a substrate consisting of fine gravel or finely divided plant roots for attachment of the eggs. Often there is little nest preparation except for fanning away any loose material. The location of the nest is indicated only by the presence of the male. Eggs hatch in about 3 days and the fry remain attached to the substrate by an adhesive substance from the egg for several more days. A few hours before leaving the nest the young crappie free themselves by vigorous swimming motions. Fry leave the nest only at night, according to observations by Vasey. The fry do not school.

In Lake Wappapello the white crappie attains a length of about 3.9 inches its first year and averages 7, 10.2, 11.7, 12.6, 13.3, and 13.9 inches in succeeding years.[192] Slightly more rapid growth has been reported from other Missouri reservoirs. In Missouri streams a 3-year-old white crappie averages about 8.1 inches in length.[52] An 8-inch crappie weighs about 4 ounces, and an 11 inch specimen weighs close to a pound. Few white crappie live more than 3 or 4 years, but occasional individuals live as long as 8 years. Maturity is reached during the second or third summer of life.

IMPORTANCE AND ANGLING

In large Missouri impoundments and natural lakes the white crappie is one of the most important fishes in the creel. Because it reaches a fairly large size and is readily caught, it ranks as one of the most popular panfishes.

Still-fishing or slow trolling with small minnows near submerged trees or other cover is one of the most effective methods for catching white crappie. Small plugs, spoons, streamers, and fly and spinner combinations are also effective. These should be fished slow and at considerable depths. Dry flies and other surface lures are usually effective only in late evening.

Black Crappie

Pomoxis nigromaculatus (Lesueur)

Other local names: Crappie

DESCRIPTION

Illustration: Page 257, 16a.

Characters: A silvery, black speckled, deep and slab-sided sunfish with a large mouth, the upper jaw reaching well past middle of eye. Spinous dorsal and soft dorsal broadly connected, without a notch between. Anal fin nearly as long and as large as dorsal fin, and with 6 spines. Upper surface of head and forward part of back strongly concave.

Very similar to white crappie but with the following differences: dorsal fin with 7 or 8 spines, the length of its base about equal to distance from front of dorsal fin forward to eye; color pattern of sides consisting principally of irregularly arranged speckles and blotches, rather than vertical bars.

Life colors: Dark olive with emerald and purple reflections above, silvery or white on sides and belly. Sides boldly and rather evenly mottled with dark green or black. Often with a broad dark brown stripe extending along midline of back from front of dorsal fin forward to tip of lower jaw, and backward along undersurface of head to throat. Dorsal, tail, and anal fins strongly reticulated with black, giving the appearance of a dark-colored fin with many whitish spots.

Size: Seldom exceeding a length of 14.5 inches or a weight of 1 pound, 12 ounces. The largest authenticated specimen from Missouri weighed 4 pounds, 8 ounces.

Scientific name: *Pomoxis,* Greek, meaning "opercle sharp," in reference to the spines on the gill cover; *nigromaculatus,* Latin, meaning "black spotted."

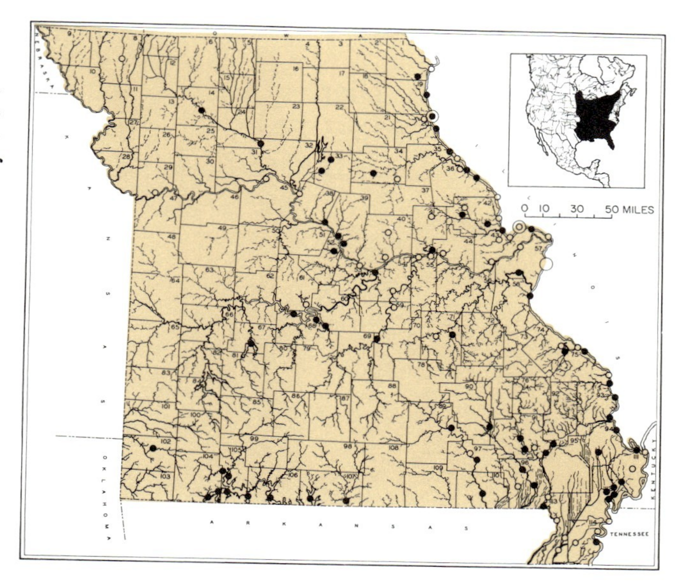

DISTRIBUTION AND HABITAT

The black crappie is widespread but sporadic in distribution in Missouri. It is most prevalent in large Ozark reservoirs, navigation pools of the upper Mississippi River, and natural lakes and borrow pits of the Lowlands. It is less abundant at most localities than the white crappie.

The habitat requirements of this fish are like those of the white crappie except that the black crappie is less tolerant of turbidity and siltation. In reservoirs the black crappie is noticeably more abundant in the arms fed by the clearer streams. Clear water, absence of noticeable current, and abundant cover in the form of submerged timber or aquatic vegetation are the principal requirements of the black crappie.

HABITS AND LIFE HISTORY

The biology of the black crappie is, in most respects, so similar to that of the white crappie that a detailed description is unnecessary. Growth in length of the black crappie is generally less than that of white crappie in the same waters. However, the black crappie is heavier at any given length than the white crappie, so that if growth is compared in terms of weight, there is little growth difference between the two species.

IMPORTANCE AND ANGLING

The black crappie has the same excellent qualities as a panfish as the white crappie but is less important in most waters because it is generally not as abundant. However, in the Little North Fork Arm of Bull Shoals Reservoir the black crappie occurs almost to the exclusion of the white crappie and makes up over one-fourth of all the fish creeled.[213]

Angling methods are the same as for the white crappie.

Flier

Centrarchus macropterus (Lacépède)

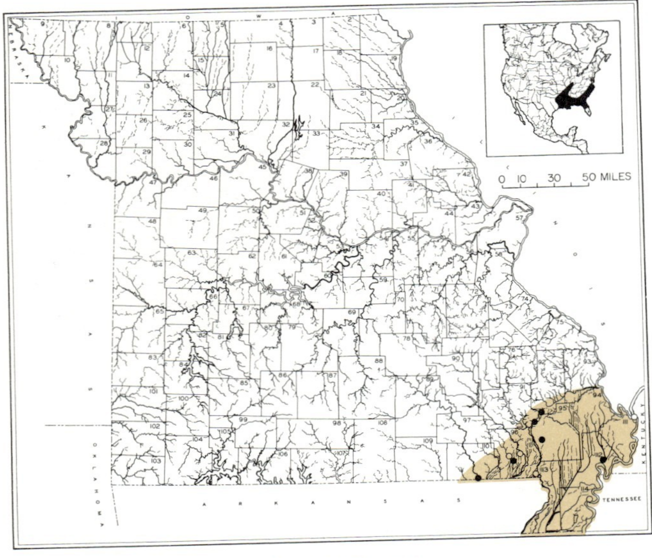

DESCRIPTION

Illustration: Page 257, 15b; **46.**

Characters: A deep and slab-sided sunfish with a moderately large mouth, the upper jaw reaching nearly to middle of eye. Spinous dorsal and soft dorsal broadly connected, without a notch between. Anal fin nearly as long and as large as dorsal fin. Most nearly resembling the crappies but with 7 or 8 (occasionally 6) spines in anal fin and 11 or 12 (rarely 13) spines in dorsal fin. As in the crappies, the free margin of the preopercle (bone just ahead of gill cover) is distinctly saw-toothed (serrate).

Life colors: Olive-green (darker above than below) with rows of brown spots on sides forming a series of horizontal lines similar to those characteristic of the rock bass. Usually a wedge-shaped dusky bar is present beneath eye. Fins banded or barred with dark brown. Small fliers have a prominent and characteristic black spot surrounded by orange near back of soft dorsal fin.

Size: A small fish, seldom exceeding a length of 7 inches. Maximum length and weight about 8 inches and 6.5 ounces.

Scientific name: *Centrarchus,* from the Greek, *kentron,* meaning "spine," and *archos,* meaning "anus," in reference to the development of the anal spines; *macropterus,* Greek, meaning "long fin."

DISTRIBUTION AND HABITAT

The flier is confined to the Lowlands where it is uncommon and sporadic in distribution. Its preferred habitat is clear, heavily vegetated waters without noticeable current. Considering these requirements, it is likely that the flier was much more common before the Lowland swamps were ditched and drained than is now the case. At present the largest populations are at Duck Creek Wildlife Area and nearby Mingo National Wildlife Refuge where extensive areas of standing-water habitat remain.

HABITS AND LIFE HISTORY

The following remarks concerning the biology of the flier are from a study made in southeastern Missouri.[214] The food of the flier varies considerably with size. Those less than an inch long feed exclusively on copepod crustaceans. Small crustaceans continue to comprise the bulk of the diet of larger fliers (up to 7 inches in length), but aquatic insects are of increasing importance. Fliers over 7 inches in length feed primarily on insects, with fish and crustaceans each making up about 7% by weight of the diet. Young bluegills are the principal fish eaten by fliers.

The flier spawns in southeastern Missouri in April, with the spawning period lasting about 10 to 14 days. The nesting habits are not known in detail but apparently are like those of other small sunfishes. Sexual maturity is reached at a length of about 2.8 inches and an age of one year.

In southeastern Missouri the flier attains a length of about 2.2 inches by the end of its first year of life and averages 3.9, 5.2, 6.2, 7.1, 7.6, and 7.8 inches in succeeding years. Females live longer and attain a larger size than males.

IMPORTANCE AND ANGLING

Because of its localized distribution and limited abundance the flier is of little importance as a sport fish in Missouri. Since all except the largest adults feed almost exclusively on small crustaceans, only occasional individuals are ever taken on hook-and-line

The same methods that are effective for taking bluegill and other small panfish will also take the flier.

Banded Pygmy Sunfish

Elassoma zonatum Jordan

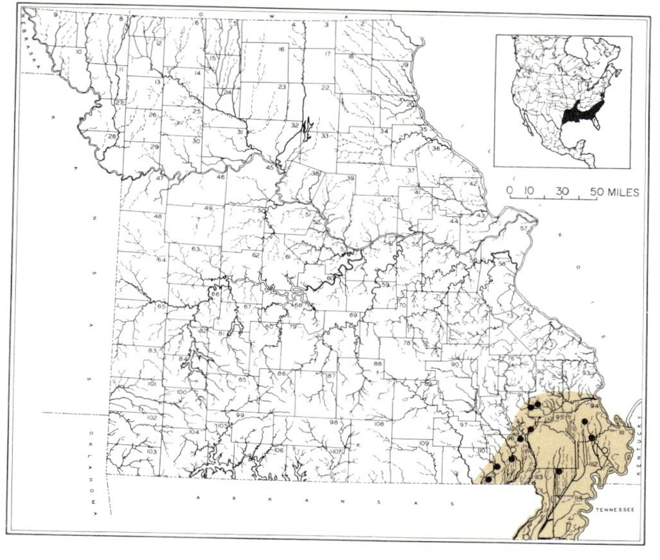

DESCRIPTION

Illustration: Page 250, 1a.

Characters: A small blackish fish, readily separated from all other sunfish by the presence of only 4 or 5 spines at front of dorsal fin and the absence of a lateral line. Anal fin usually with 8 spines and 5 or 6 soft rays. Scales smooth-edged (cycloid). Tail fin rounded in outline.

Life colors: Dark olive-green heavily stippled with black. Sides marked by a series of blackish vertical bars and a large black spot below front of dorsal fin. Tail fin and soft parts of dorsal and anal fins banded with black.

Size: True to its name, this fish is the smallest of the Missouri sunfishes. Maximum length about 1.5 inches.

Scientific name: *Elassoma,* Greek, meaning "small"; *zonatum,* Latin, meaning "banded."

DISTRIBUTION AND HABITAT

The pygmy sunfish is restricted to Lowlands in the southeastern part of the state. It is not widespread but is sometimes locally abundant. Like the flier, it inhabits clear, quiet waters having thick growths of submerged vegetation. The pygmy sunfish was probably more abundant before the Lowland swamps were ditched and drained.

HABITS AND LIFE HISTORY

This diminutive sunfish is very secretive, remaining motionless for hours in the shadows among the stems and leaves of submerged plants. It is a solitary fish, exhibiting no tendency to form schools or aggregations as do some other members of its family. It feeds principally by sight and is attracted only to living prey. Objects are pounced upon only when some movement is evident. A Louisiana study reveals that small crustaceans are the principal food, with larvae and pupae of midges being next in importance.[215]

In northern Louisiana the spawning season extends from about the middle of March to the first of May. This is probably several weeks earlier than in Missouri. No nest is prepared. Spawning occurs in midwater, with the eggs becoming scattered over the bottom and covered with debris. A female of average size (about an inch) will lay about 300 eggs that are dropped at intervals of several days in lots of 40 to 60. The incubation period at 65° F. is about 7 days. Sexual maturity is reached at one year of age and the maximum life span is 3 years.[215]

PERCHES

Percidae

The perch family is one of the largest groups of North American freshwater fishes, including about 100 named species. Among them are three popular game fishes—walleye, sauger, and yellow perch—and a host of small, lesser-known fishes collectively referred to as darters. The walleye, sauger, and yellow perch are represented by the same or closely related species in Europe; darters are native only to North America east of the Rocky Mountains. Thirty-seven members of the perch family have been recorded from Missouri waters.

The perches are slender, more or less cylindrical fishes with spiny-rayed fins and rough-edged (ctenoid) scales. The dorsal fin is divided into two separate parts, with 6 or more stiff spines in the forward part and fewer than 23 rays in the second part. One or two spines are present at the front of the anal fin; the second spine (if present) is never more than half again as long as the first spine. The pelvic fins are attached far forward, nearly beneath the pectoral fins, and each has a spine and 5 soft rays. Superficially similar fishes that depart in one or more respects from the description given above are found in the sculpin, sea bass, sunfish and drum families.

Darters are not well known to most people. Fishermen sometimes capture them while seining for bait and think they are young walleyes or saugers. Perhaps the best way to tell a darter from young of their better-known relatives is that the walleye and sauger have large, prominent canine teeth on the jaws and roof of the mouth, while darters have teeth that are small and inconspicuous. Also, the pectoral fins of most darters are large and fan-shaped; those of the walleye and sauger are of a size and shape more typical of fish in general. Many species of darters do not exceed a length of 3 inches and the largest species, the logperch, rarely exceeds 7 inches. The appropriately named least darter is one of the smallest spiny-rayed fishes, with a maximum length of about 1.8 inches.

The yellow perch is so rare in Missouri waters as to scarcely qualify as a native fish, while the walleye and sauger are widespread in large streams and reservoirs. Most parts of Missouri have one or more species of darters, but none occur in the northwestern section of the Prairie Region. Some darters have a very restricted distribution. A few occur only in Missouri. The Missouri saddled darter is found only in the northern Ozarks, and the Niangua darter is known only from a few tributaries of the Osage River.

Darters are adapted for life in the swift-flowing sections of clear, rocky streams. To keep from being swept downstream, they have lost the gas-filled swim bladder found in most fishes. They sink immediately to the bottom when they stop swimming, and the press of the current against their enlarged pectoral fins tends to hold them in place. Darters remain much of the time beneath or between rocks and are thus afforded some measure of protection from the direct action of the current. When moving from place to place darters proceed by a series of short, quick dashes, and it is this characteristic form of locomotion that has earned them the name "darter."

Not all darters are found in swift currents. The sand darters inhabit the sandy stretches of sluggish streams. Here they hide much of the time beneath the sand with only their eyes showing. The least darter lives in quiet pools where it clambers about over the leaves and stems of submerged plants.

So far as is known, all perches spawn in spring or early summer. The walleye and sauger spawn early (March or April), scattering their eggs over the rocky shoals of streams. The males of many darters occupy small territories during the spawning season and possess brilliant colors that serve to advertise their presence to other fish of their own species. Most do not practice parental care, abandoning the territory once spawning has been completed. The johnny darter and fantail darter are exceptions. They spawn on the underside of rocks or other submerged objects and the male remains with the eggs until they hatch.

Key to the Perches

1a. Rear margin of preopercle (bone just ahead of gill cover) distinctly saw-toothed (serrate); mouth larger, upper jaw extending beyond middle of eye; branchiostegal rays (slender bones in membrane along lower margin of gill cover) usually 7, rarely 8; size larger, length commonly more than 10 inches.
Go to 2

1b. Rear margin of preopercle smooth or very weakly saw-toothed; mouth smaller, upper jaw usually not extending past middle of eye; branchiostegal rays usually 6 (7 in one species); size smaller, length rarely more than 7 inches.
Darters
Go to 4

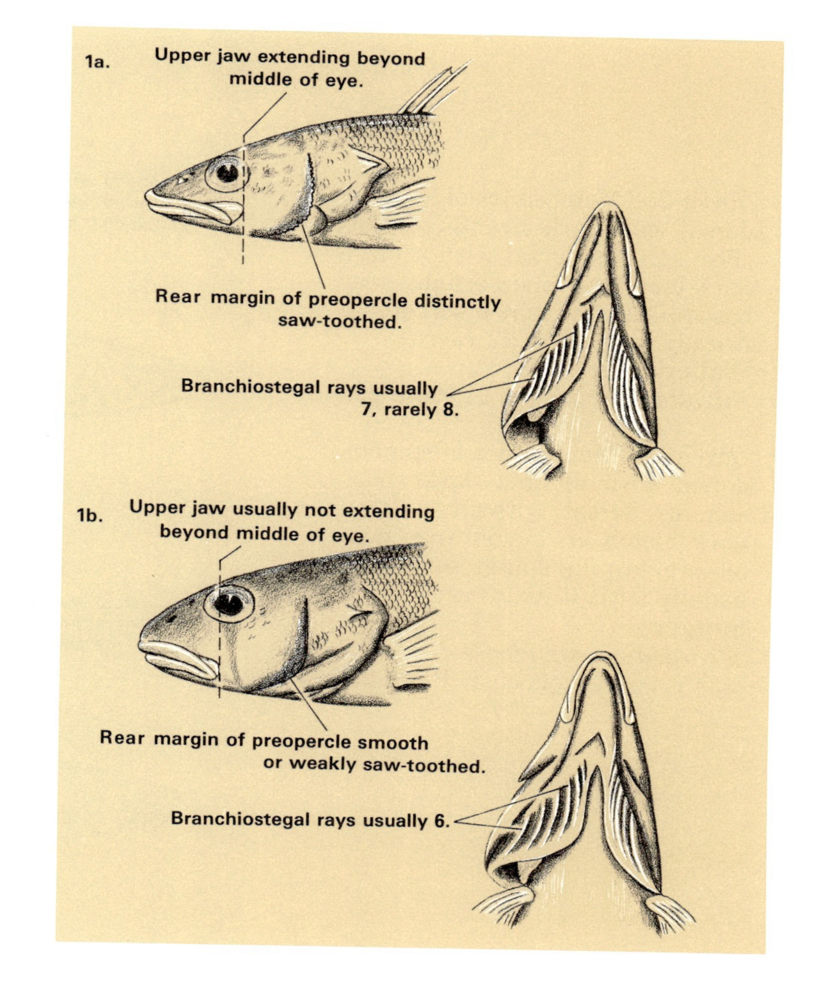
1a.
Upper jaw extending beyond middle of eye.
Rear margin of preopercle distinctly saw-toothed.
Branchiostegal rays usually 7, rarely 8.
1b.
Upper jaw usually not extending beyond middle of eye.
Rear margin of preopercle smooth or weakly saw-toothed.
Branchiostegal rays usually 6.

2a. *(From 1a.)* Jaws and roof of mouth without large, prominent teeth; back and sides crossed by several vertical bars that are regular in size and shape; anal fin with 6 to 8 soft rays.
Yellow perch
Perca flavescens ...... **Page 297**

2b. *(From 1a.)* Jaws and roof of mouth with large, prominent teeth; back and sides without bars or crossed by several oblique bars that are irregular in size and shape; anal fin with 11 to 14 soft rays.
Go to **3**

2a.
Jaws and roof of mouth without prominent teeth.
Back and sides with several vertical bars.
Anal fin with 6-8 soft rays.

2b.
Jaws and roof of mouth with prominent teeth.
Back and sides without bars or with oblique bars.
Anal fin with 11-14 soft rays.

3a. *(From 2b.)* Membranes of spinous dorsal with dark streaks or blotches; spinous dorsal with a large dark blotch on membranes near bases of last few spines; soft dorsal usually with 19 to 22 rays.
Walleye
Stizostedion vitreum .. **Page 295**

3b. *(From 2b.)* Membranes of spinous dorsal with distinct dark spots; spinous dorsal without a large dark blotch on membranes near bases of last few spines; soft dorsal usually with 17 to 20 rays.
Sauger
Stizostedion canadense
.... **Page 297**

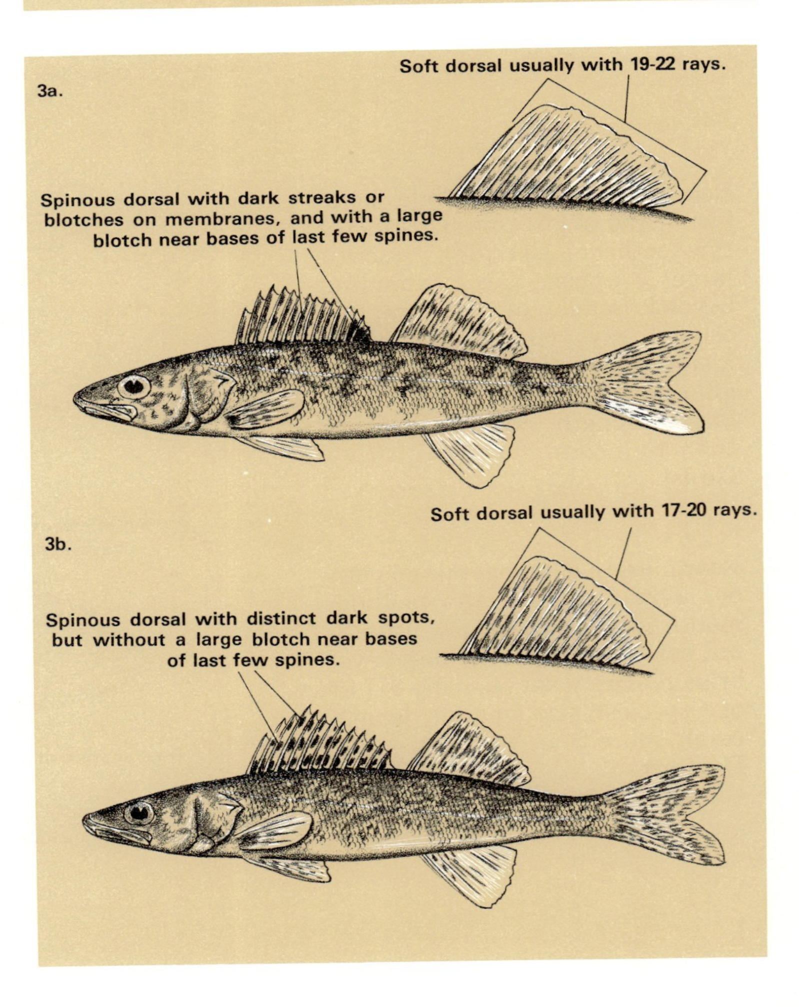
3a.
Soft dorsal usually with 19-22 rays.
Spinous dorsal with dark streaks or blotches on membranes, and with a large blotch near bases of last few spines.
3b.
Soft dorsal usually with 17-20 rays.
Spinous dorsal with distinct dark spots, but without a large blotch near bases of last few spines.

4a. *(From 1b.)* Body very slender, its depth (A) usually going 7 times or more into standard length (B); anal fin with 1 spine; belly without scales.
Go to 5

4b. *(From 1b.)* Body deeper, its depth (A) going less than 7 times into standard length (B); anal fin usually with 2 spines (1 in two species); belly usually with at least a few scales.
Go to 7

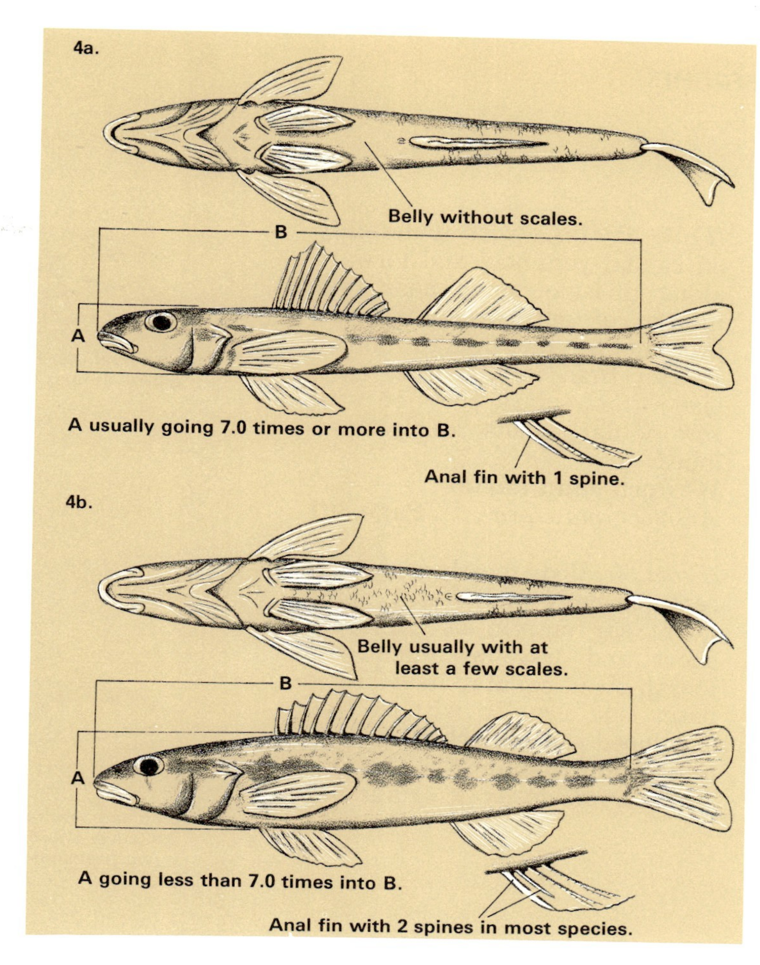
4a.
Belly without scales.
B
A
A usually going 7.0 times or more into B.
Anal fin with 1 spine.
4b.
Belly usually with at least a few scales.
B
A
A going less than 7.0 times into B.
Anal fin with 2 spines in most species.

5a. *(From 4a.)* Back with about 4 dark cross-bars that extend obliquely forward onto upper sides; upper lip joined to snout at middle by a bridge of skin (frenum); anal fin with 12 to 14 soft rays; soft dorsal usually with 12 to 16 rays; lateral line scales more than 80.
Crystal darter
Ammocrypta asprella **. Page 306**

5b. *(From 4a.)* Back with a series of dark spots that do not extend onto sides; upper lip separated from snout at middle by a groove; anal fin with 8 to 10 soft rays; soft dorsal usually with 9 to 11 rays; lateral line scales fewer than 80.
Go to 6

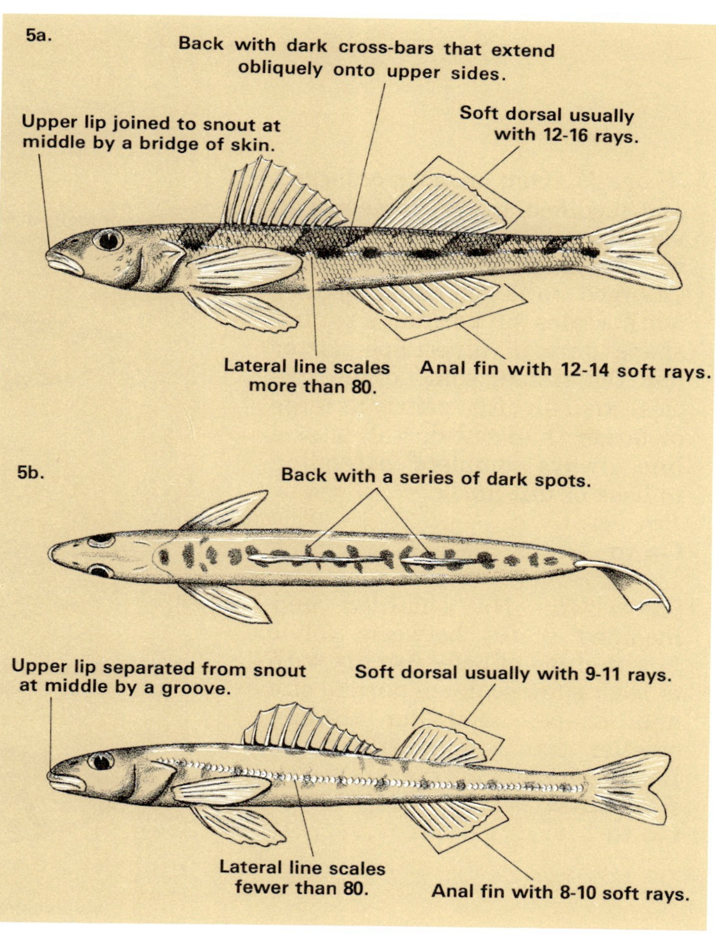
5a.
Back with dark cross-bars that extend obliquely onto upper sides.
Upper lip joined to snout at middle by a bridge of skin.
Soft dorsal usually with 12-16 rays.
Lateral line scales more than 80.
Anal fin with 12-14 soft rays.
5b.
Back with a series of dark spots.
Upper lip separated from snout at middle by a groove.
Soft dorsal usually with 9-11 rays.
Lateral line scales fewer than 80.
Anal fin with 8-10 soft rays.

6a. *(From 5b.)* Body with scales only on caudal peduncle and forward along midside; spine near rear margin of gill cover long and prominent, its length much greater than its width at base; side without dark spots or with row of dark spots poorly developed.
Western sand darter
Ammocrypta clara .... **Page 307**

6b. *(From 5b.)* Body mostly scaled except for belly and breast; spine near rear margin of gill cover short and less prominent, its length about equal to its width at base; side usually with a well developed row of dark spots.
Scaly sand darter
Ammocrypta vivax ... **Page 307**

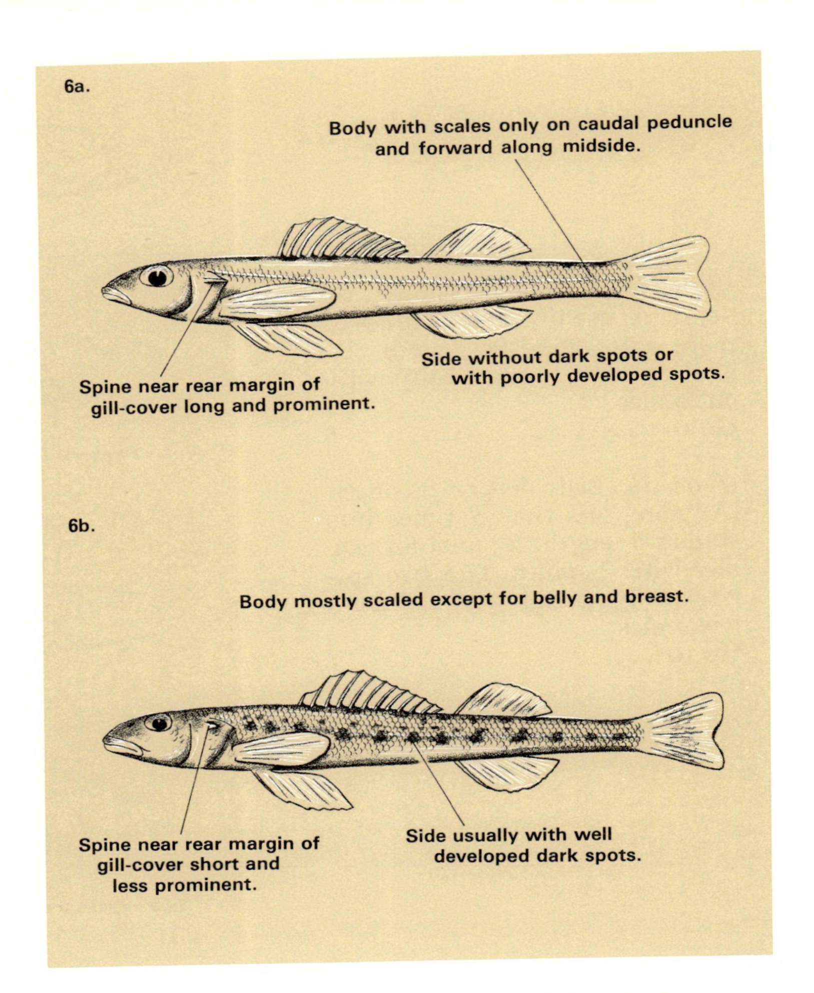
6a.
Body with scales only on caudal peduncle and forward along midside.
Spine near rear margin of gill-cover long and prominent.
Side without dark spots or with poorly developed spots.
6b.
Body mostly scaled except for belly and breast.
Spine near rear margin of gill-cover short and less prominent.
Side usually with well developed dark spots.

7a. *(From 4b.)* One or more enlarged and modified scales between pelvic fins; midline of belly usually without scales or with a series of enlarged and modified scales (with scales of normal size and shape only in bluestripe darter and females of some other species); anal fin often nearly as large or larger than soft dorsal; lateral line always complete, extending to base of tail fin.
Percina
Go to 8

7b. *(From 4b.)* No enlarged and modified scales between pelvic fins; midline of belly usually with at least a few scales of normal size and shape; anal fin usually smaller than soft dorsal; lateral line incomplete in several species.
Etheostoma
Go to 17

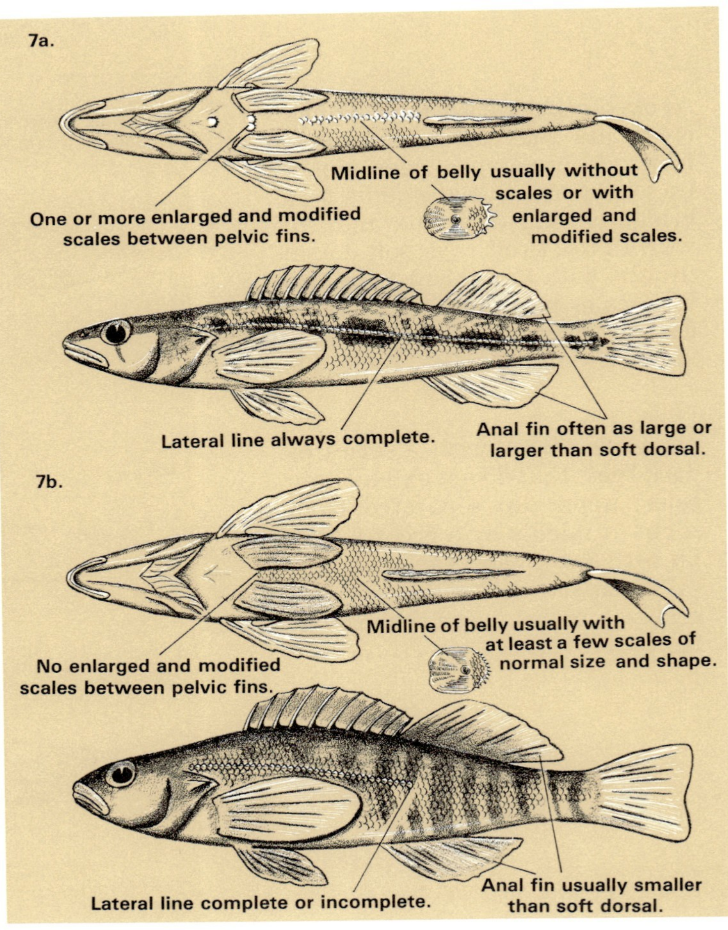
7a.
Midline of belly usually without scales or with enlarged and modified scales.
One or more enlarged and modified scales between pelvic fins.
Lateral line always complete.
Anal fin often as large or larger than soft dorsal.
7b.
Midline of belly usually with at least a few scales of normal size and shape.
No enlarged and modified scales between pelvic fins.
Lateral line complete or incomplete.
Anal fin usually smaller than soft dorsal.

8a. *(From 7a.)* Mouth overhung by distinctly conical snout; color pattern consisting of about 15 to 20 narrow, vertical brownish bars that are continuous across back.
Logperch
Percina caprodes ..... **Page 302**

8b. *(From 7a.)* Mouth not overhung by snout; color pattern consisting of a series of blackish blotches, or of fewer than 15 vertical bars.
Go to **9**

8a.
Sides with 15-20 narrow, vertical brownish bars.
Mouth overhung by distinctly conical snout.

8b.
Mouth not overhung by snout.
Sides with a series of blackish blotches, or fewer than 15 vertical bars.

9a. *(From 8b.)* Distance from front of upper lip to junction of gill covers (A) equal to or greater than distance from junction of gill covers to back of pelvic fin base (B).
Go to **10**

9b. *(From 8b.)* Distance from front of upper lip to junction of gill covers (A) much less than distance from junction of gill covers to back of pelvic fin base (B).
Go to **11**

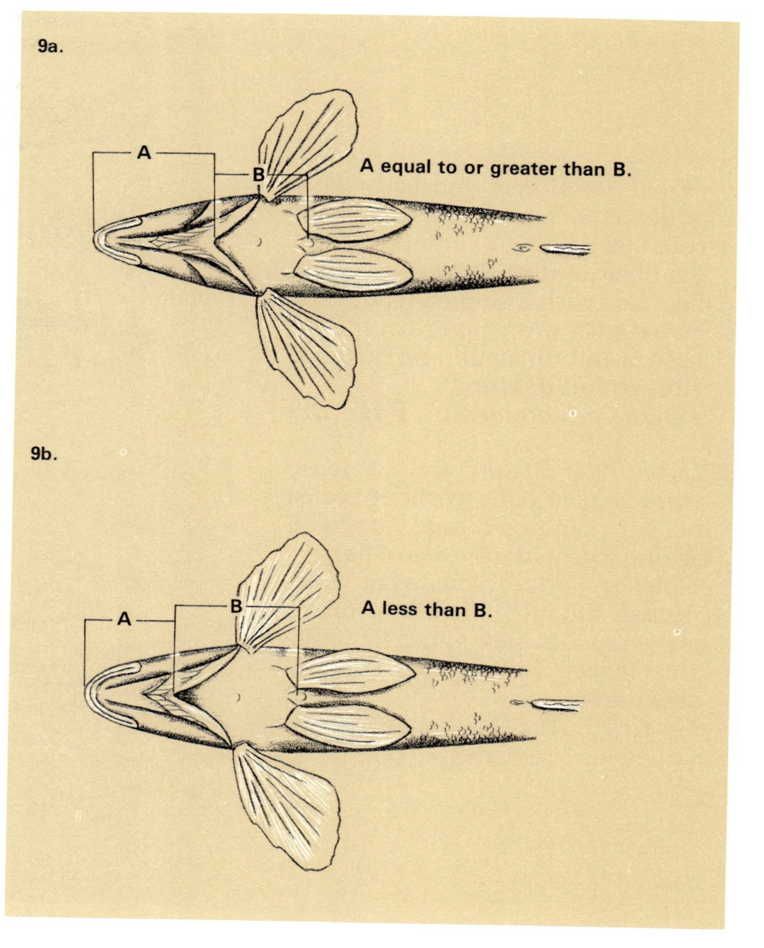

10a. *(From 9a.)* Snout shorter, its length (A) about equal to distance from back of eye to rear margin of preopercle (B); branchiostegal rays 6.
Slenderhead darter
Percina phoxocephala
.... **Page 301**

10b. *(From 9a.)* Snout longer, its length (A) much greater than distance from back of eye to rear margin of preopercle (B); branchiostegal rays usually 7.
Longnose darter
Percina nasuta .... **Page 302**

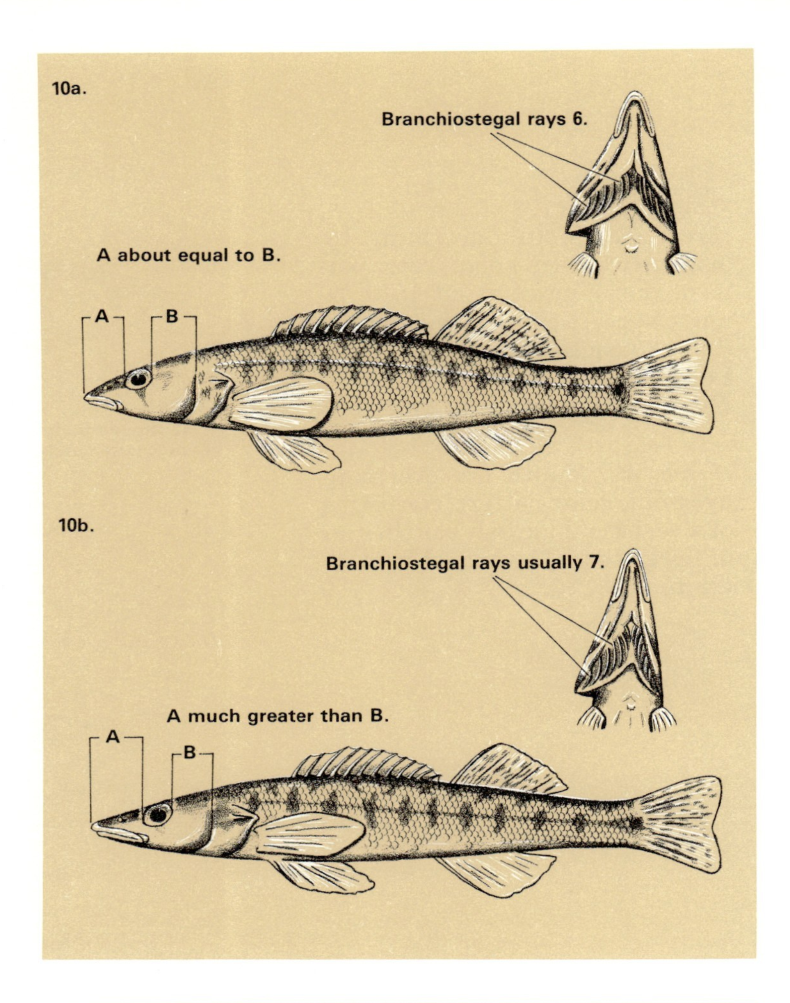
10a.
Branchiostegal rays 6.
A about equal to B.
A
B
10b.
Branchiostegal rays usually 7.
A much greater than B.
A
B

11a. *(From 9b.)* Breast and belly with scales of normal size and shape except for 1 to 3 enlarged and modified scales between pelvic fins; side with a single broad, dark stripe with wavy margins; spot at base of tail fin small and distinct.
Bluestripe darter
Percina cymatotaenia . **Page 298**

11b. *(From 9b.)* Breast and at least front half of belly without scales or with enlarged and modified scales; side with a series of bars or blotches, often somewhat connected, but not forming a broad stripe; spot at base of tail fin indistinct (except in juveniles of blackside darter).
Go to **12**

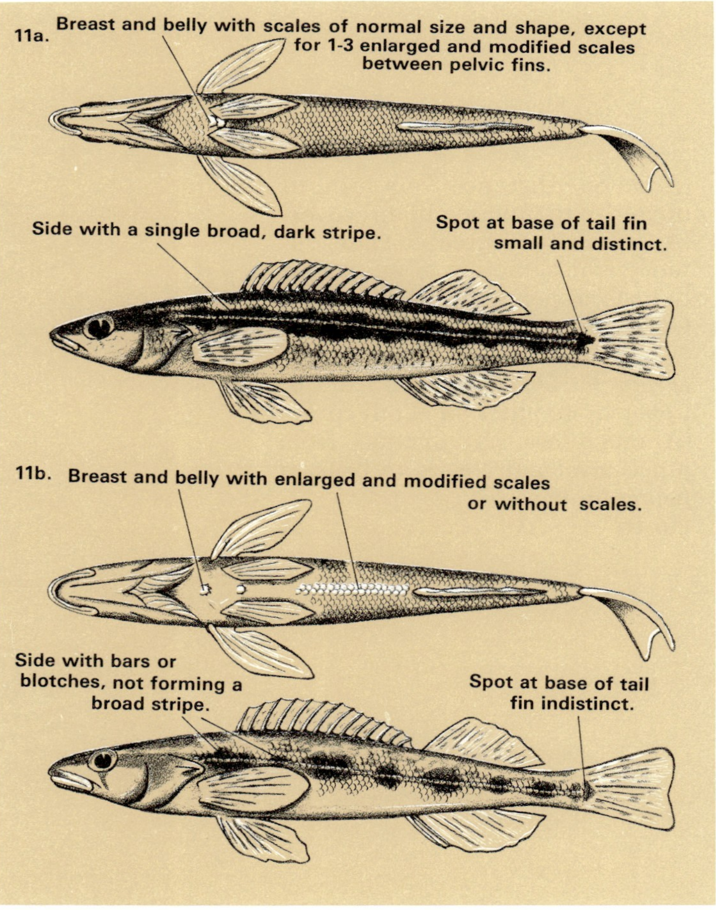
11a.
Breast and belly with scales of normal size and shape, except for 1-3 enlarged and modified scales between pelvic fins.
Side with a single broad, dark stripe.
Spot at base of tail fin small and distinct.
11b.
Breast and belly with enlarged and modified scales or without scales.
Side with bars or blotches, not forming a broad stripe.
Spot at base of tail fin indistinct.

12a. *(From 11b.)* Upper lip separated from snout at midline by a continuous deep groove; anal fin usually with 8 or 9 soft rays.
Channel darter
Percina copelandi .... **Page 305**

12b. *(From 11b.)* Upper lip joined to snout at midline by a bridge of skin (frenum), only rarely crossed by a shallow groove; anal fin usually with 10 to 12 soft rays.
Go to **13**

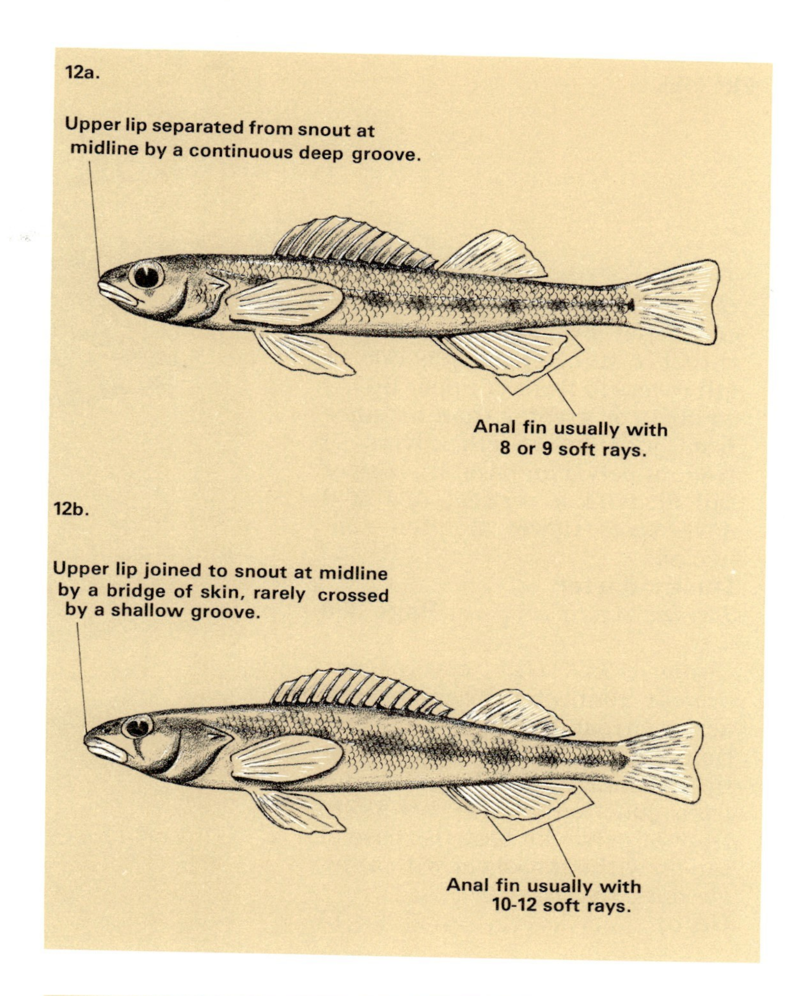
12a.
Upper lip separated from snout at midline by a continuous deep groove.
Anal fin usually with 8 or 9 soft rays.
12b.
Upper lip joined to snout at midline by a bridge of skin, rarely crossed by a shallow groove.
Anal fin usually with 10-12 soft rays.

13a. *(From 12b.)* Lateral line scales usually 59 to 78; spinous dorsal usually with 12 to 15 (occasionally 11) spines; anal fin of male similar in size to that of female.
Go to **14**

13b. *(From 12b.)* Lateral line scales usually 47 to 58; spinous dorsal usually with 9 or 10 (occasionally 11) spines; anal fin of adult male greatly enlarged, extending nearly to tail fin.
Go to **16**

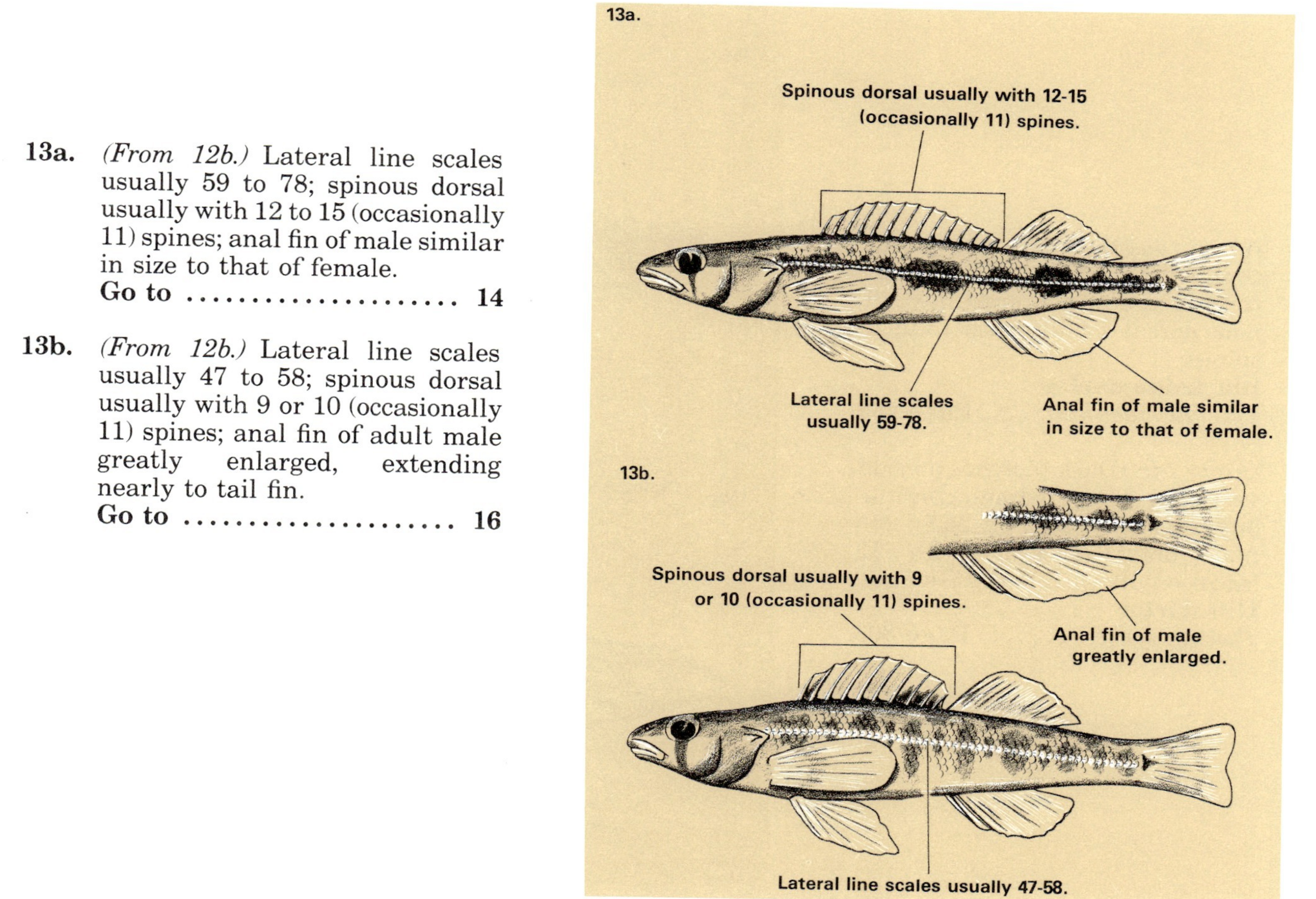
13a.
Spinous dorsal usually with 12-15 (occasionally 11) spines.
Lateral line scales usually 59-78.
Anal fin of male similar in size to that of female.
13b.
Spinous dorsal usually with 9 or 10 (occasionally 11) spines.
Anal fin of male greatly enlarged.
Lateral line scales usually 47-58.

14a. *(From 13a.)* Gill covers broadly connected by membrane across throat, distance from junction of gill covers to front of upper lip (A) equal to or greater than distance from junction of gill covers to front of pelvic fin base (B); base of tail fin with a vertical row of 3 dark spots (lower 2 often connected).
Dusky darter
Percina sciera .... **Page 300**

14b. *(From 13a.)* Gill covers not broadly connected by membrane across throat, distance from junction of gill covers to front of upper lip (A) much less than distance from junction of gill covers to front of pelvic fin base (B); base of tail fin without spots or with a single dark spot.
Go to **15**

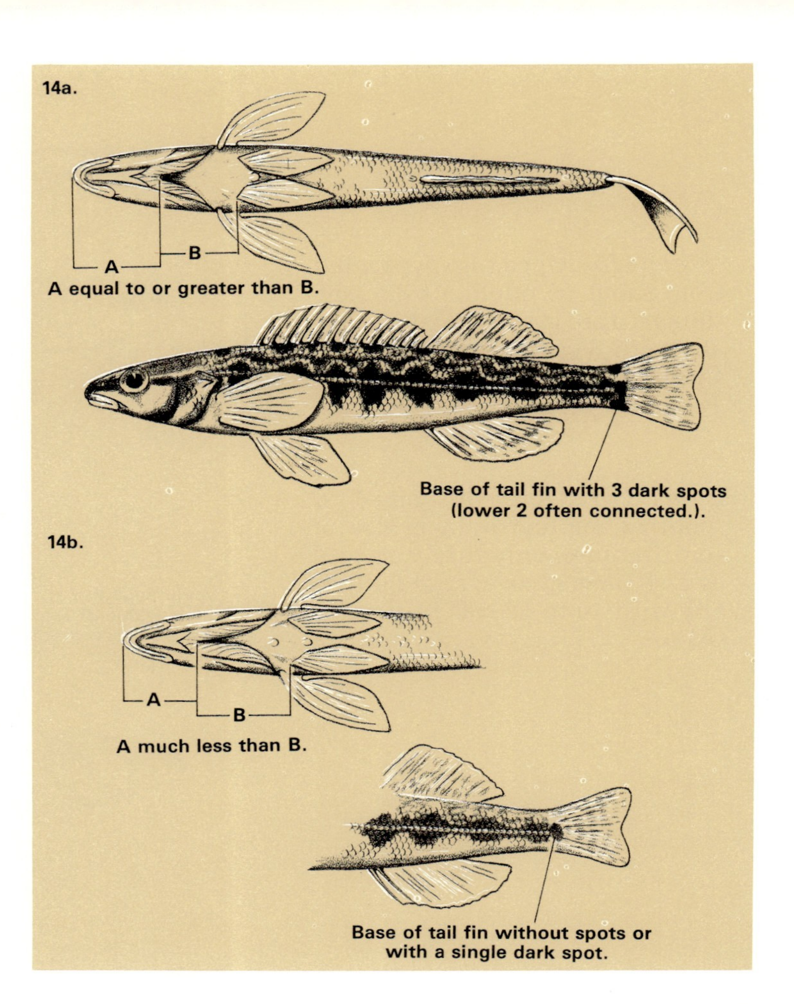
14a.
A
B
A equal to or greater than B.
Base of tail fin with 3 dark spots (lower 2 often connected.).
14b.
A
B
A much less than B.
Base of tail fin without spots or with a single dark spot.

15a. *(From 14b.)* Dark blotches on side confined to midside and somewhat connected along lateral line; spinous dorsal usually with 13 to 15 spines.
Blackside darter
Percina maculata .... **Page 299**

15b. *(From 14b.)* Dark blotches on side vertically elongated and continuous with cross-bars on back; spinous dorsal usually with 12 (occasionally with 11 or 13) spines.
Gilt darter
Percina evides .... **Page 303**

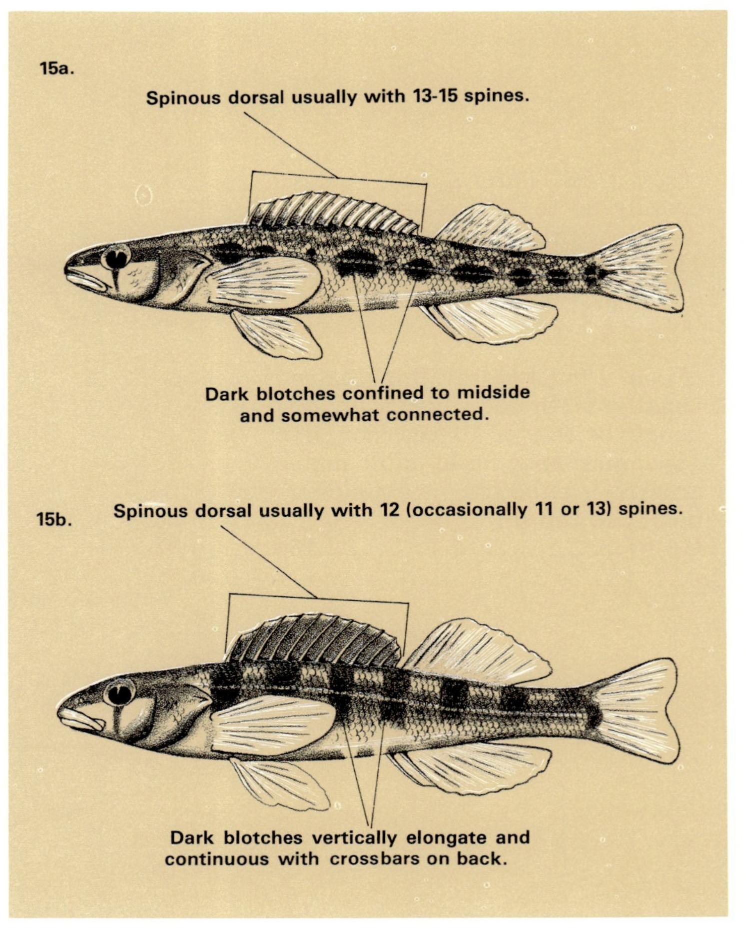
15a.
Spinous dorsal usually with 13-15 spines.
Dark blotches confined to midside and somewhat connected.
15b.
Spinous dorsal usually with 12 (occasionally 11 or 13) spines.
Dark blotches vertically elongate and continuous with crossbars on back.

16a. *(From 13b.)* Spinous dorsal with a distinct black blotch at base of first membrane and another at bases of last three membranes; nape (upper surface of body in front of dorsal fin) with only a few scattered scales; cheek fully scaled.
River darter
Percina shumardi .... **Page 304**

16b. *(From 13b.)* Spinous dorsal without distinct black blotches; nape fully scaled; cheek without scales or with a few scattered scales.
Stargazing darter
Percina uranidea ..... **Page 305**

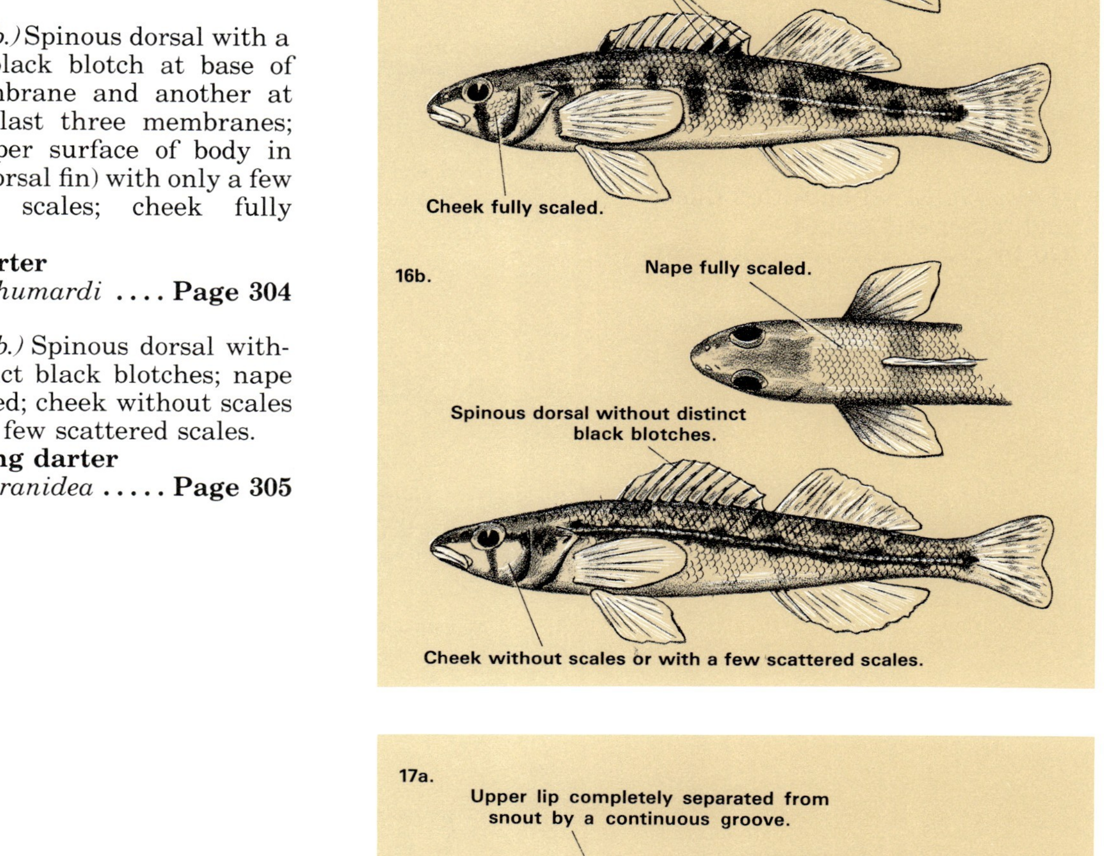
16a.
Nape with only a few scattered scales.
Spinous dorsal with distinct black blotches.
Cheek fully scaled.
16b.
Nape fully scaled.
Spinous dorsal without distinct black blotches.
Cheek without scales or with a few scattered scales.

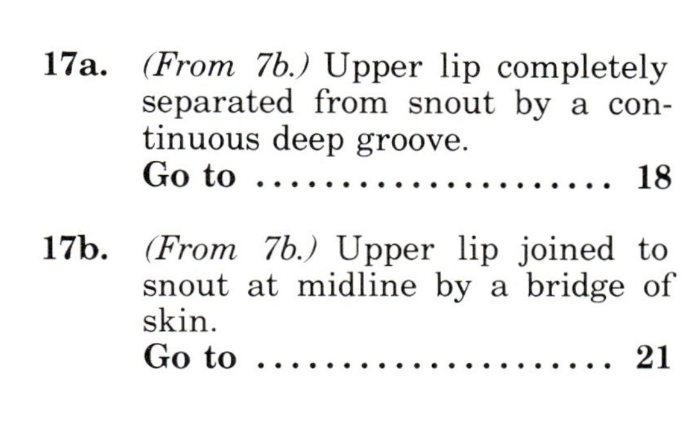

17a. *(From 7b.)* Upper lip completely separated from snout by a continuous deep groove.
Go to **18**

17b. *(From 7b.)* Upper lip joined to snout at midline by a bridge of skin.
Go to **21**

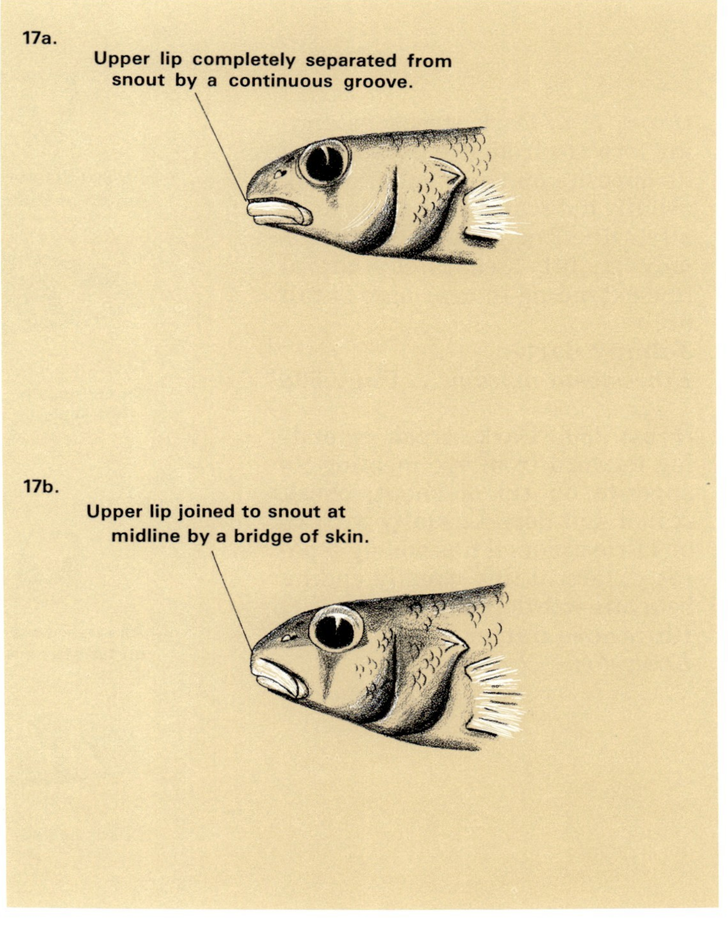
17a.
Upper lip completely separated from snout by a continuous groove.
17b.
Upper lip joined to snout at midline by a bridge of skin.

18a. *(From 17a.)* Anal fin with 1 thin and flexible spine.
Go to 19

18b. *(From 17a.)* Anal fin with 2 thick and rather stiff spines.
Go to 20

18a.

Anal fin with 1 thin and flexible spine.

18b.

Anal fin with 2 thick and rather stiff spines.

19a. *(From 18a.)* Dark streak extending forward from eye not meeting its opposite on tip of snout; cheek usually not scaled; soft dorsal usually with 12 or 13 rays; dorsal fins only slightly separated; lateral line extending to near base of tail fin.
Johnny darter
Etheostoma nigrum **.. Page 308**

19b. *(From 18a.)* Dark streak extending forward from eye meeting its opposite on tip of snout; cheek scaled; soft dorsal usually with 10 or 11 rays; dorsal fins widely separated; lateral line usually ending beneath soft dorsal.
Bluntnose darter
Etheostoma chlorosomum
.... Page 309

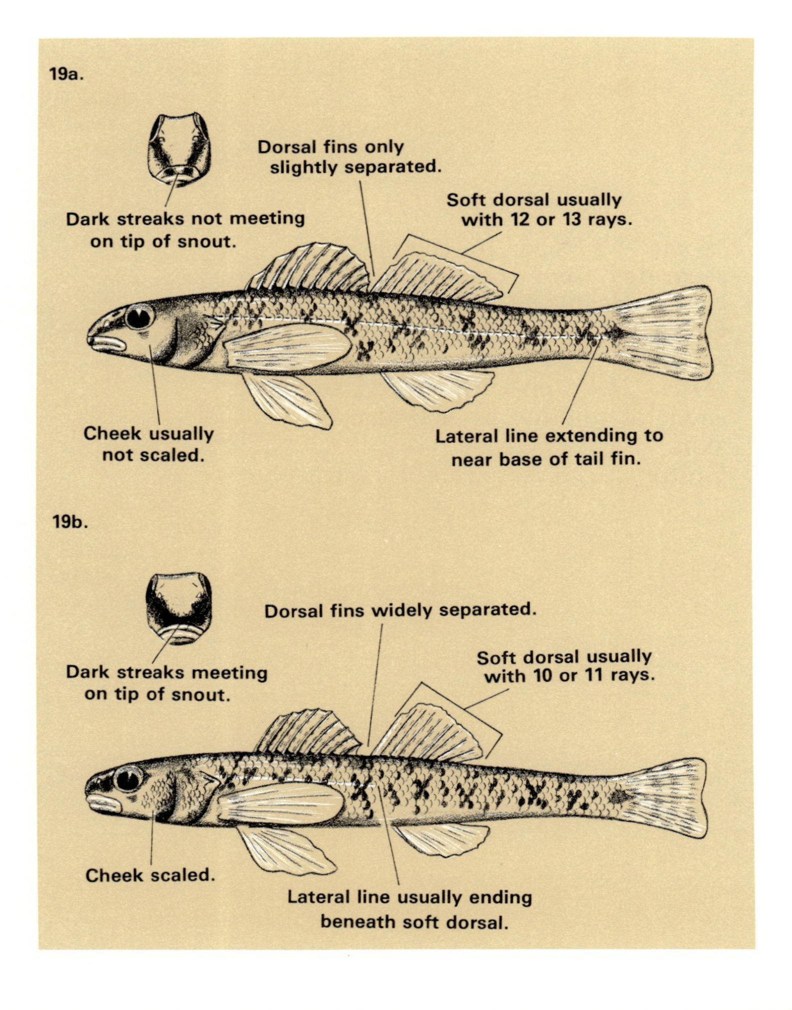
19a.
Dorsal fins only slightly separated.
Soft dorsal usually with 12 or 13 rays.
Dark streaks not meeting on tip of snout.
Cheek usually not scaled.
Lateral line extending to near base of tail fin.
19b.
Dorsal fins widely separated.
Soft dorsal usually with 10 or 11 rays.
Dark streaks meeting on tip of snout.
Cheek scaled.
Lateral line usually ending beneath soft dorsal.

20a. *(From 18b.)* Mouth not overhung by snout; upper lip without a nipple-like projection at middle; gill covers only slightly connected by membrane across throat; lateral line incomplete, with about 43 to 53 scales in lateral series.
Speckled darter
Etheostoma stigmaeum
.... **Page 309**

20b. *(From 18b.)* Mouth overhung by blunt, rounded snout; upper lip with a nipple-like projection at middle (poorly developed in small specimens); gill covers broadly connected by membrane across throat; lateral line complete and with about 57 to 78 scales.
Greenside darter
Etheostoma blennioides **Page 313**

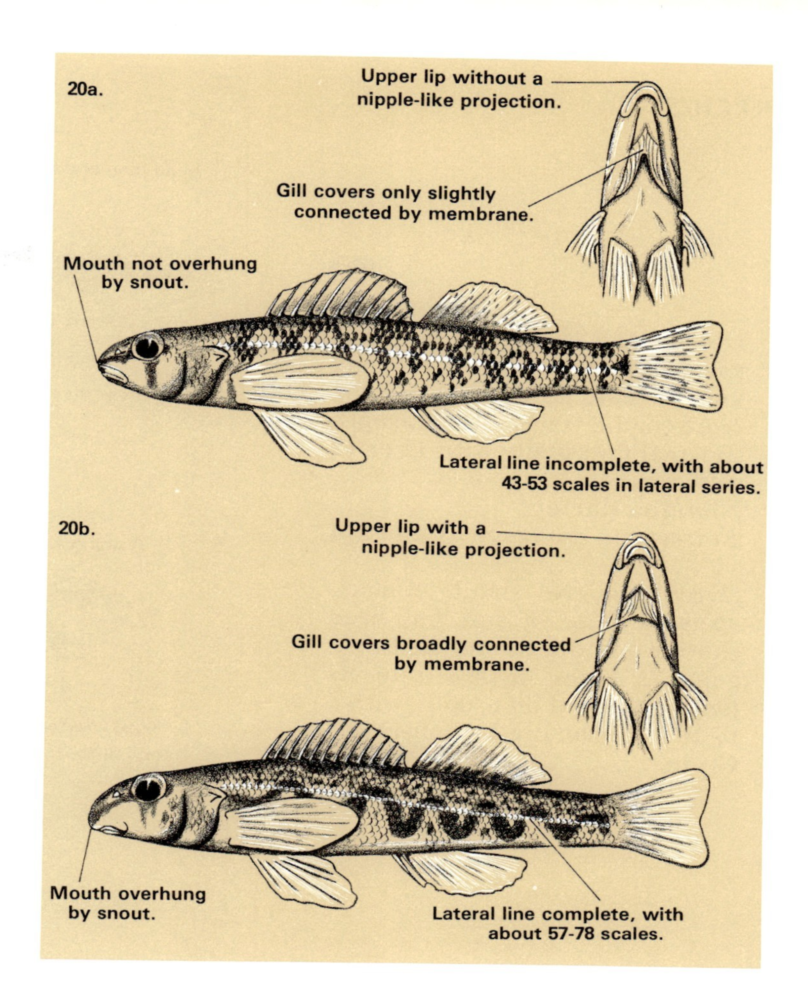
20a.
Upper lip without a nipple-like projection.
Gill covers only slightly connected by membrane.
Mouth not overhung by snout.
Lateral line incomplete, with about 43-53 scales in lateral series.
20b.
Upper lip with a nipple-like projection.
Gill covers broadly connected by membrane.
Mouth overhung by snout.
Lateral line complete, with about 57-78 scales.

21a. *(From 17b.)* Lateral line always with more than 8 pored scales; scales in lateral series more than 40; length commonly more than 1.8 inches.
Go to **22**

21b. *(From 17b.)* Lateral line absent, or with fewer than 8 pored scales; scales in lateral series 38 or fewer; length seldom more than 1.8 inches.
Go to **36**

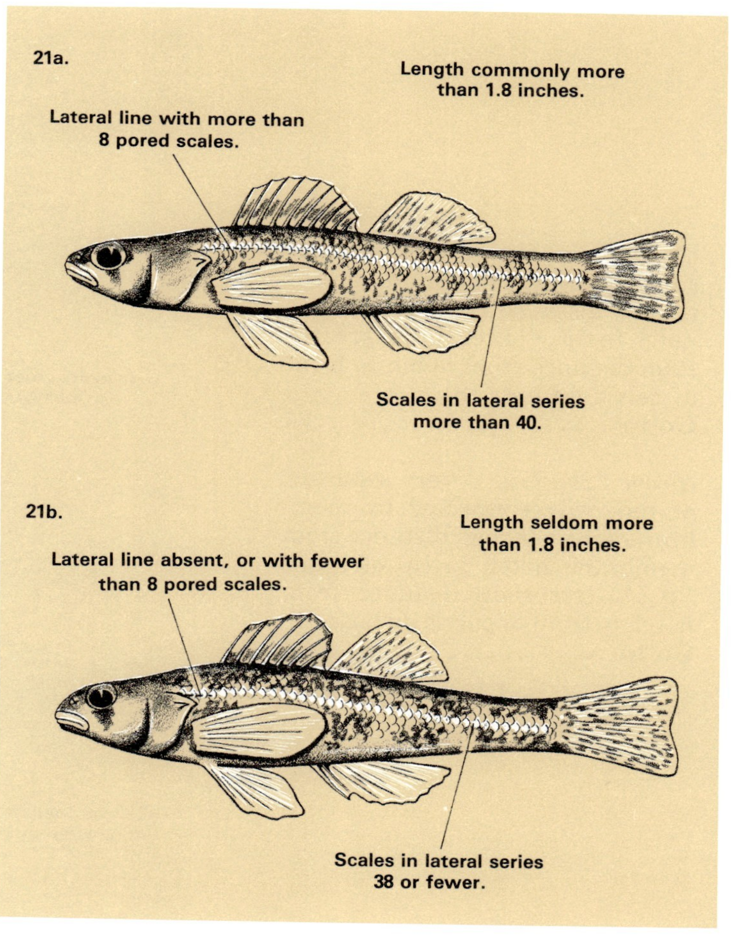
21a.
Length commonly more than 1.8 inches.
Lateral line with more than 8 pored scales.
Scales in lateral series more than 40.
21b.
Length seldom more than 1.8 inches.
Lateral line absent, or with fewer than 8 pored scales.
Scales in lateral series 38 or fewer.

22a. *(From 21a.)* Two small jet-black spots at base of tail fin; head long and slender, its depth (A) going more than 2 times into its length (B); anal fin usually with 11 or 12 soft rays.
Niangua darter
Etheostoma nianguae . **Page 314**

22b. *(From 21a.)* No small jet-black spots at base of tail fin; head shorter and deeper, its depth (A) going 2 times or less into its length (B); anal fin usually with 5 to 10 (occasionally 11) soft rays.
Go to 23

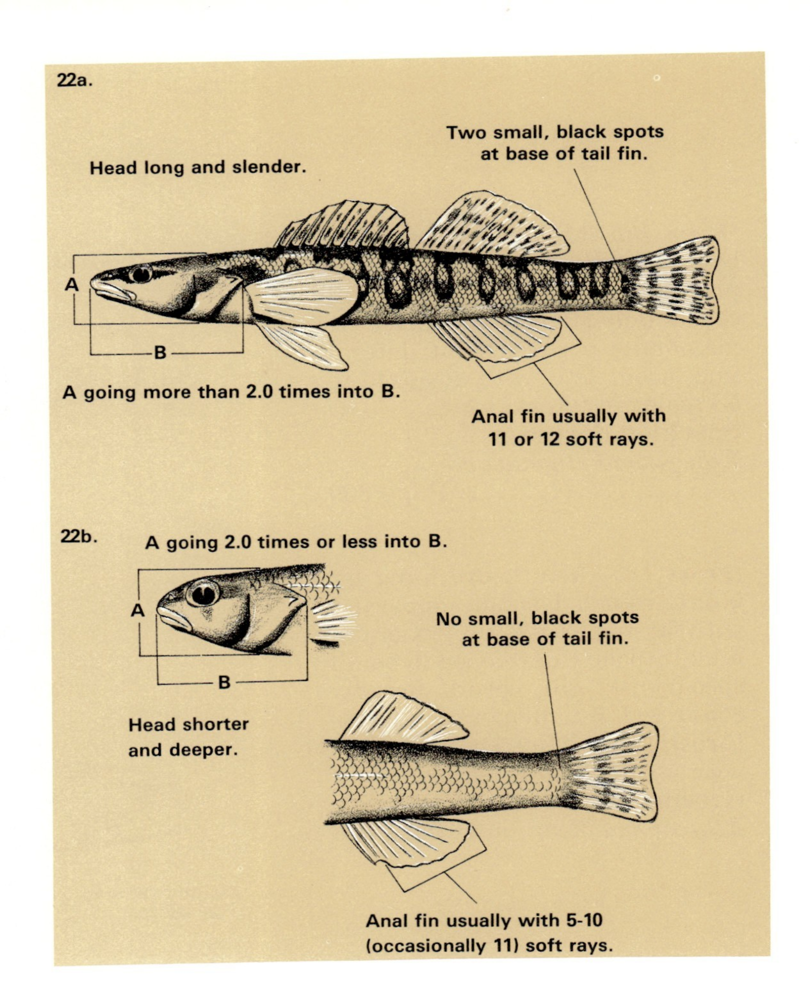
22a.
Head long and slender.
Two small, black spots at base of tail fin.
A
B
A going more than 2.0 times into B.
Anal fin usually with 11 or 12 soft rays.
22b.
A going 2.0 times or less into B.
A
B
No small, black spots at base of tail fin.
Head shorter and deeper.
Anal fin usually with 5-10 (occasionally 11) soft rays.

23a. *(From 22b.)* Gill covers broadly connected by membrane across throat; distance from membrane notch to tip of lower lip (A) greater than distance from notch to front of pelvic fin base (B).
Go to 24

23b. *(From 22b.)* Gill covers separate or narrowly connected by membrane across throat; distance from membrane notch to tip of lower lip (A) less than distance from notch to front of pelvic fin base (B).
Go to 31

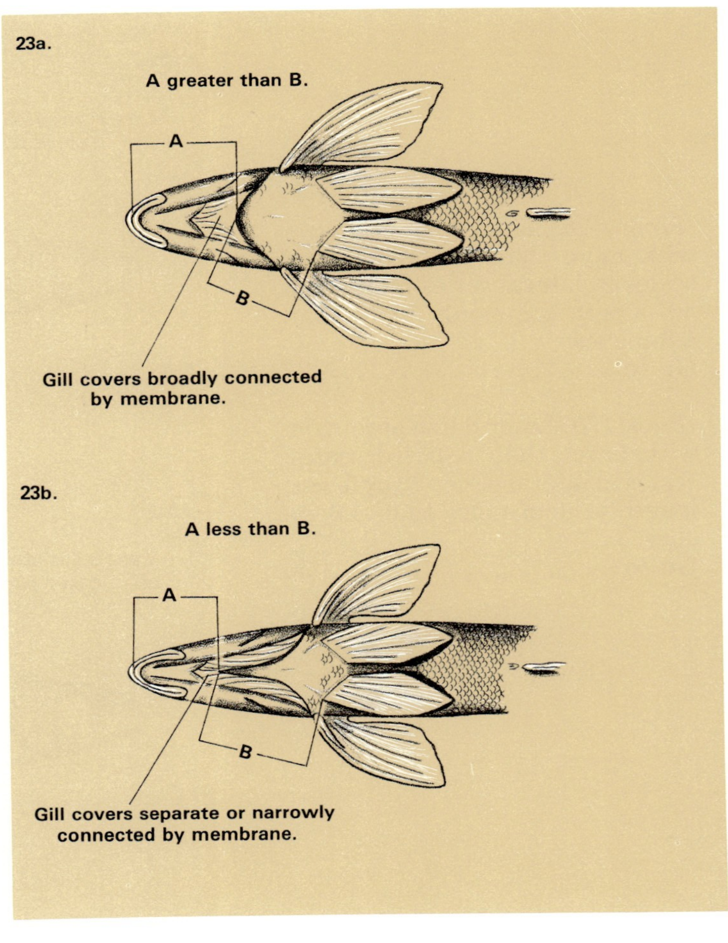
23a.
A greater than B.
A
B
Gill covers broadly connected by membrane.
23b.
A less than B.
A
B
Gill covers separate or narrowly connected by membrane.

24a. *(From 23a.)* Back crossed by 1 to 4 prominent dark bars.
Go to 25

24b. *(From 23a.)* Back not crossed by bars or crossed by more than 4 indistinct bars.
Go to 27

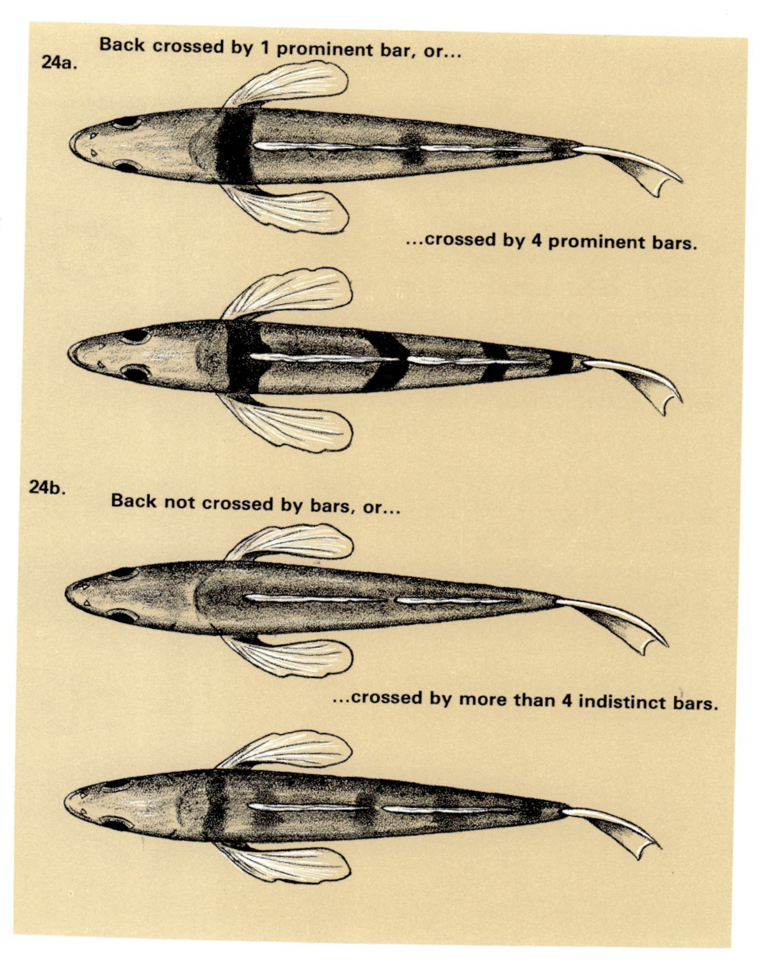
24a.
Back crossed by 1 prominent bar, or...
...crossed by 4 prominent bars.
24b.
Back not crossed by bars, or...
...crossed by more than 4 indistinct bars.

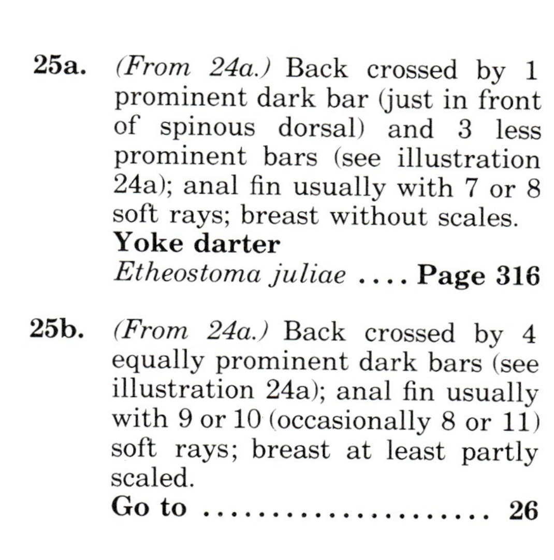

25a. *(From 24a.)* Back crossed by 1 prominent dark bar (just in front of spinous dorsal) and 3 less prominent bars (see illustration 24a); anal fin usually with 7 or 8 soft rays; breast without scales.
Yoke darter
Etheostoma juliae .... **Page 316**

25b. *(From 24a.)* Back crossed by 4 equally prominent dark bars (see illustration 24a); anal fin usually with 9 or 10 (occasionally 8 or 11) soft rays; breast at least partly scaled.
Go to 26

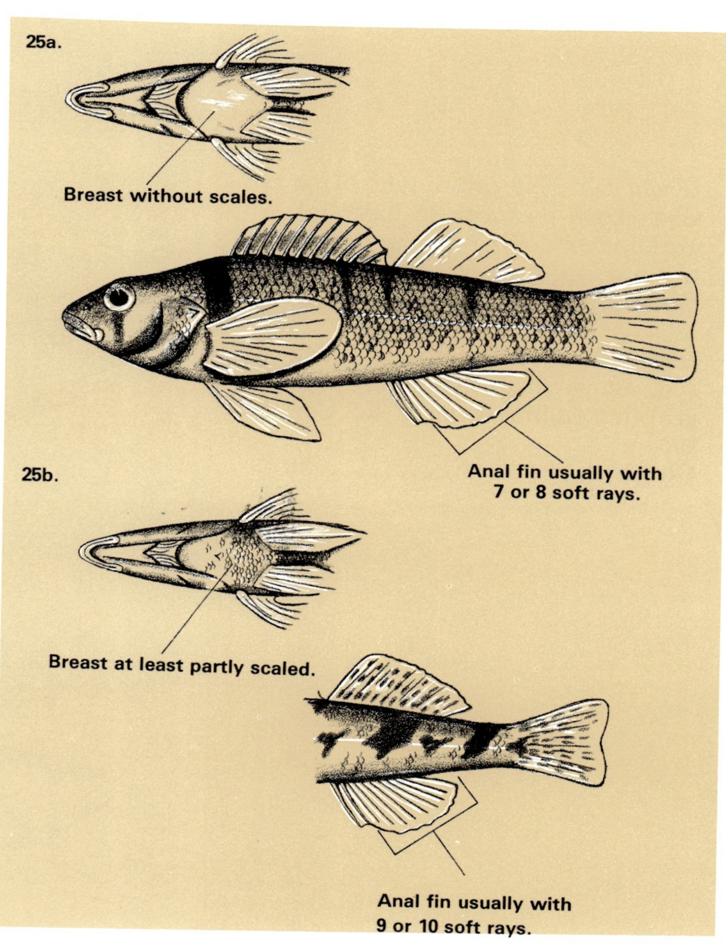
25a.
Breast without scales.
Anal fin usually with
7 or 8 soft rays.
25b.
Breast at least partly scaled.
Anal fin usually with
9 or 10 soft rays.

26a. *(From 25b.)* Lateral line scales fewer than 58; scales above lateral line usually 5 or 6.
Missouri saddled darter
Etheostoma tetrazonum
.... **Page 310**

26b. *(From 25b.)* Lateral line scales usually 60 or more; scales above lateral line usually 7 or 8.
Arkansas saddled darter
Etheostoma euzonum . **Page 311**

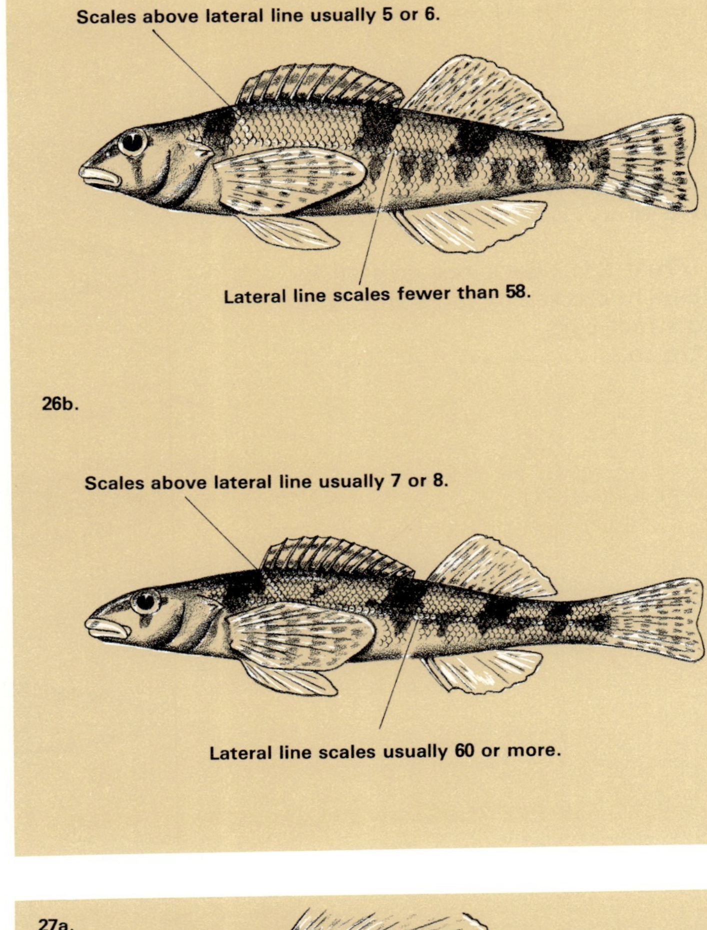
26a.
Scales above lateral line usually 5 or 6.
Lateral line scales fewer than 58.
26b.
Scales above lateral line usually 7 or 8.
Lateral line scales usually 60 or more.

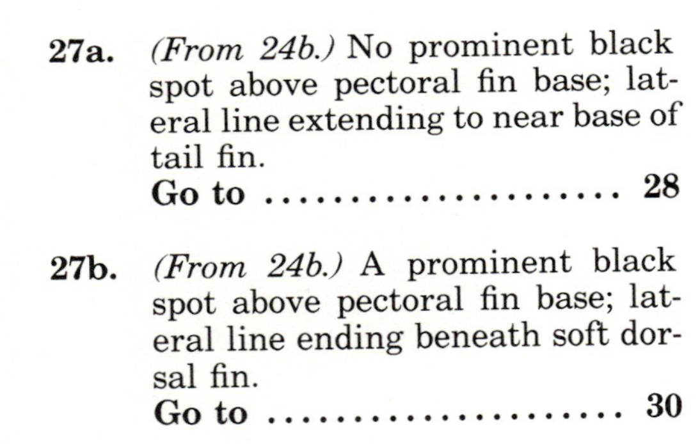

27a. *(From 24b.)* No prominent black spot above pectoral fin base; lateral line extending to near base of tail fin.
Go to **28**

27b. *(From 24b.)* A prominent black spot above pectoral fin base; lateral line ending beneath soft dorsal fin.
Go to **30**

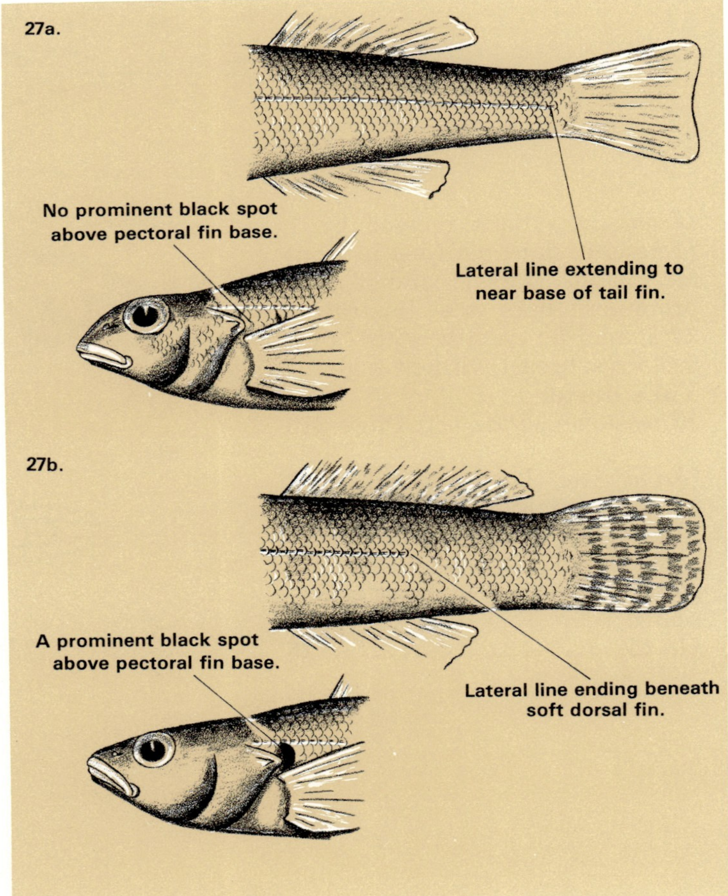
27a.
No prominent black spot above pectoral fin base.
Lateral line extending to near base of tail fin.
27b.
A prominent black spot above pectoral fin base.
Lateral line ending beneath soft dorsal fin.

28a. *(From 27a.)* Pectoral fin short and rounded, its length (A) much less than length of head (B); pectoral fin not prominently banded; lateral line scales often without dark pigment adjacent to pores, producing a pale stripe along midside.
Goldstripe darter
Etheostoma parvipinne
.... **Page 318**

28b. *(From 27a.)* Pectoral fin longer and more pointed, its length (A) usually greater than length of head (B); pectoral fin usually prominently banded; lateral line scales uniformly pigmented, not producing a pale stripe along midside.
Go to 29

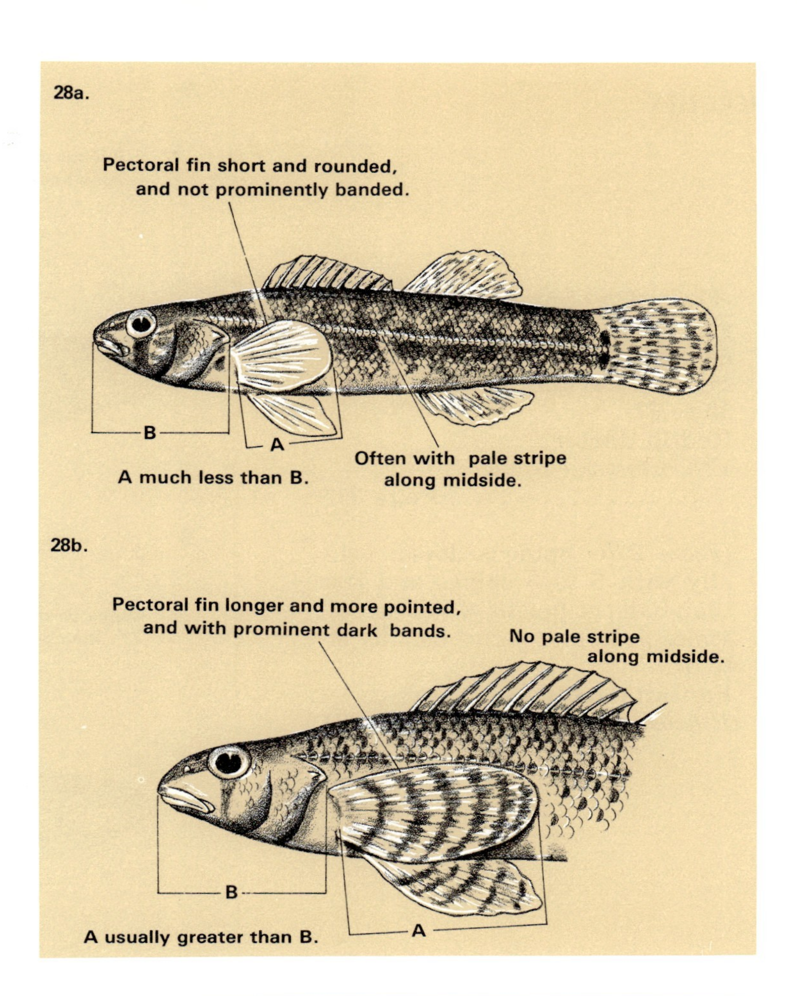
28a.
Pectoral fin short and rounded, and not prominently banded.
B
A
A much less than B.
Often with pale stripe along midside.
28b.
Pectoral fin longer and more pointed, and with prominent dark bands.
No pale stripe along midside.
B
A usually greater than B.
A

29a. *(From 28b.)* Cheek, gill cover, and front half of belly without scales; spinous dorsal usually with 9 (occasionally 10) spines; pectoral fin longer, extending backward far beyond tip of pelvic fin.
Harlequin darter
Etheostoma histrio ... **Page 312**

29b. *(From 28b.)* Cheek, gill cover, and belly entirely scaled; spinous dorsal usually with 11 or 12 (occasionally 10) spines; pectoral fin shorter, extending backward to or only slightly beyond tip of pelvic fin.
Banded darter
Etheostoma zonale ... **Page 311**

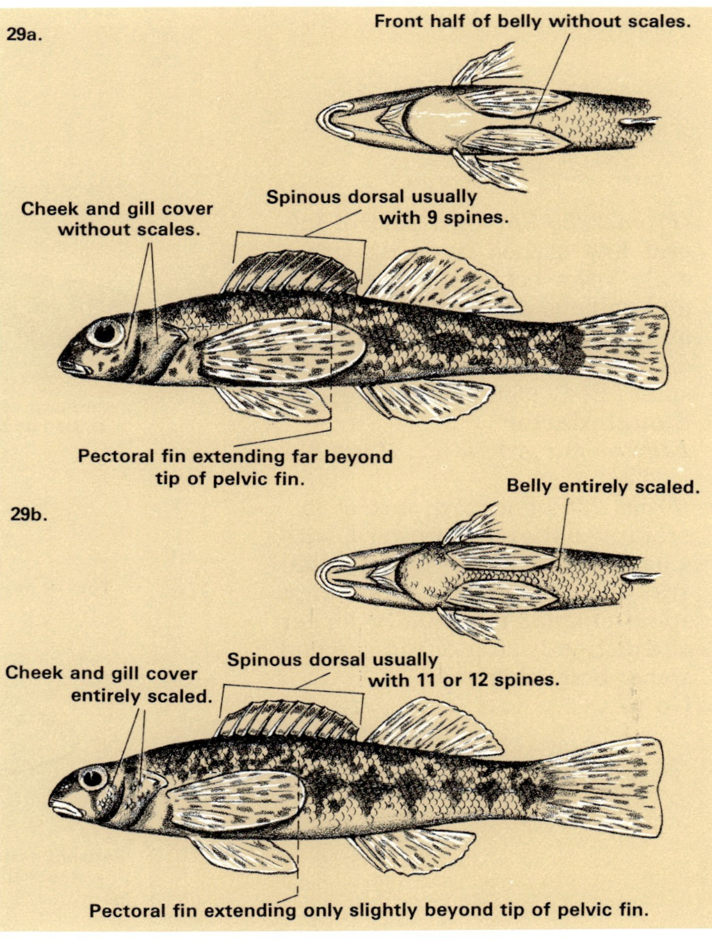
29a.
Front half of belly without scales.
Cheek and gill cover without scales.
Spinous dorsal usually with 9 spines.
Pectoral fin extending far beyond tip of pelvic fin.
29b.
Belly entirely scaled.
Cheek and gill cover entirely scaled.
Spinous dorsal usually with 11 or 12 spines.
Pectoral fin extending only slightly beyond tip of pelvic fin.

30a. *(From 27b.)* Spinous dorsal usually with 11 or 12 spines and nearly equal in height to soft dorsal; scales in lateral series usually 59 to 67.
Redfin darter
Etheostoma whipplei
.... **Page 315**

30b. *(From 27b.)* Spinous dorsal usually with 6 to 8 spines and less than half the height of soft dorsal; scales in lateral series usually 40 to 57.
Fantail darter
Etheostoma flabellare . **Page 321**

30a.
Spinous dorsal usually with 11 or 12 spines, and nearly equal in height to soft dorsal.
Scales in lateral series usually 59-67.

30b.
Spinous dorsal usually with 6-8 spines, and less than half the height of soft dorsal.
Scales in lateral series usually 40-57.

31a. *(From 23b.)* Forward part of lateral line arched upward, with 3 scale rows between lateral line and spinous dorsal; first spine of anal fin usually shorter and not distinctly stouter than second spine. Body slender.
Slough darter
Etheostoma gracile ... **Page 322**

31b. *(From 23b.)* Forward part of lateral line not arched upward, with 4 or more scale rows between lateral line and spinous dorsal; first spine of anal fin usually longer and distinctly stouter than second spine. Body stouter.
Go to **32**

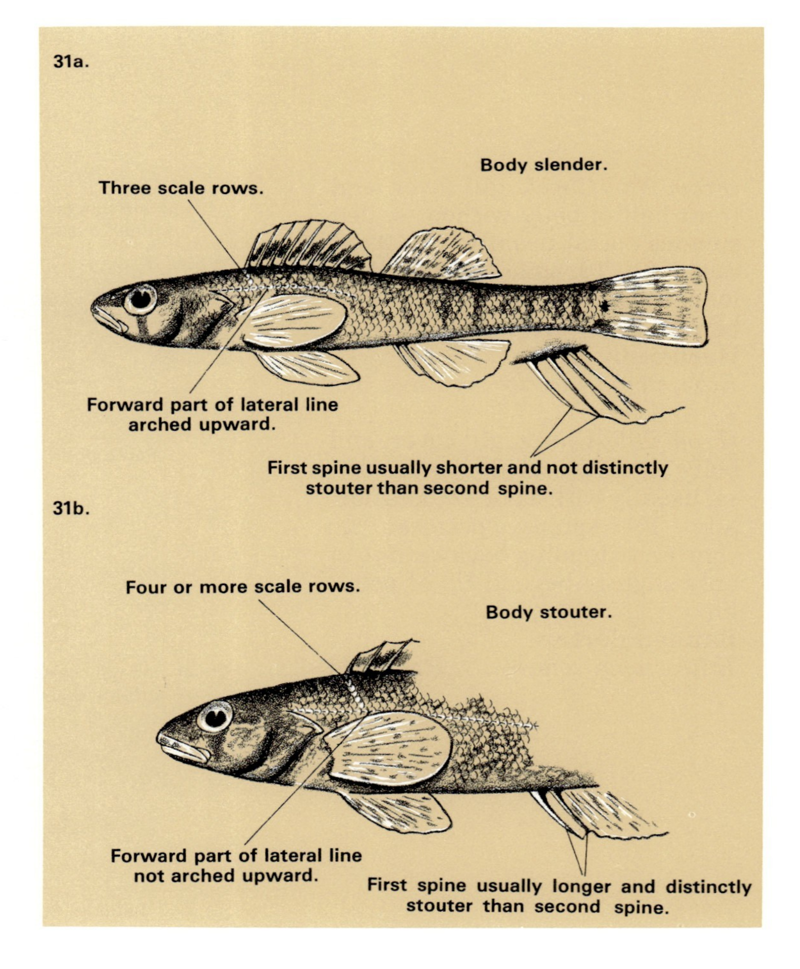
31a.
Body slender.
Three scale rows.
Forward part of lateral line arched upward.
First spine usually shorter and not distinctly stouter than second spine.
31b.
Four or more scale rows.
Body stouter.
Forward part of lateral line not arched upward.
First spine usually longer and distinctly stouter than second spine.

32a. *(From 31b.)* Scales in lateral series usually 58 to 80; soft dorsal usually with 14 or 15 rays.
Stippled darter
Etheostoma punctulatum
.... **Page 318**

32b. *(From 31b.)* Scales in lateral series usually 40 to 55; soft dorsal usually with 11 to 13 (occasionally 14) rays.
Go to **33**

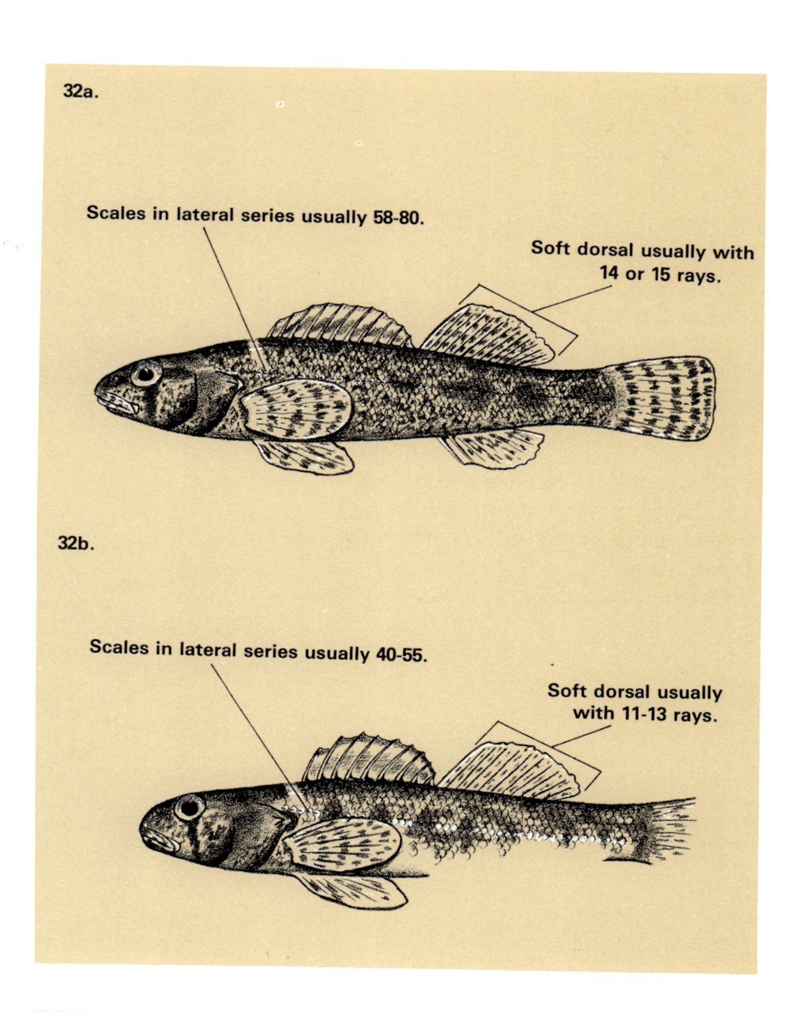
32a.
Scales in lateral series usually 58-80.
Soft dorsal usually with 14 or 15 rays.
32b.
Scales in lateral series usually 40-55.
Soft dorsal usually with 11-13 rays.

33a. *(From 32b.)* Lateral line usually ending beneath spinous dorsal and with fewer than 20 pored scales; spinous dorsal usually with 9 or 10 spines; gill cover without scales.
Arkansas darter
Etheostoma cragini ... **Page 317**

33b. *(From 32b.)* Lateral line usually extending beyond spinous dorsal and with 20 or more pored scales; spinous dorsal usually with 10 or 11 (rarely 9) spines; gill cover usually at least partly scaled.
Go to **34**

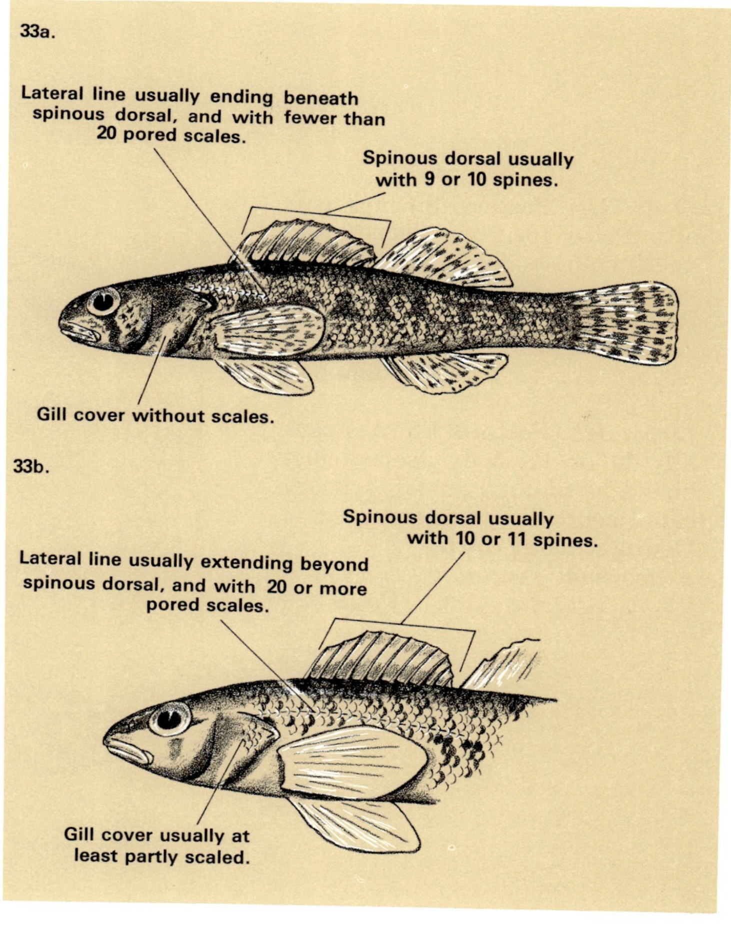
33a.
Lateral line usually ending beneath spinous dorsal, and with fewer than 20 pored scales.
Spinous dorsal usually with 9 or 10 spines.
Gill cover without scales.
33b.
Spinous dorsal usually with 10 or 11 spines.
Lateral line usually extending beyond spinous dorsal, and with 20 or more pored scales.
Gill cover usually at least partly scaled.

34a. *(From 33b.)* Cheek fully scaled; anal fin usually with 8 or more soft rays.
Mud darter
Etheostoma asprigene
.... **Page 316**

34b. *(From 33b.)* Cheek without scales or with a few small scales near eye; anal fin usually with 6 or 7 soft rays.
Go to **35**

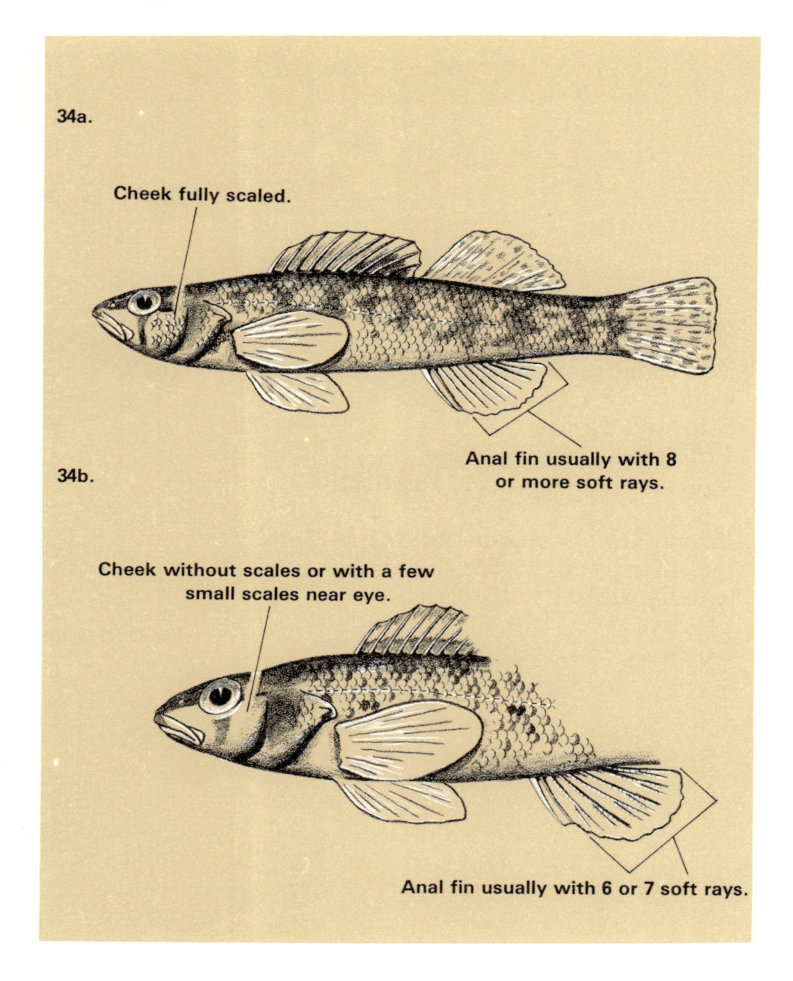
34a.
Cheek fully scaled.
Anal fin usually with 8 or more soft rays.
34b.
Cheek without scales or with a few small scales near eye.
Anal fin usually with 6 or 7 soft rays.

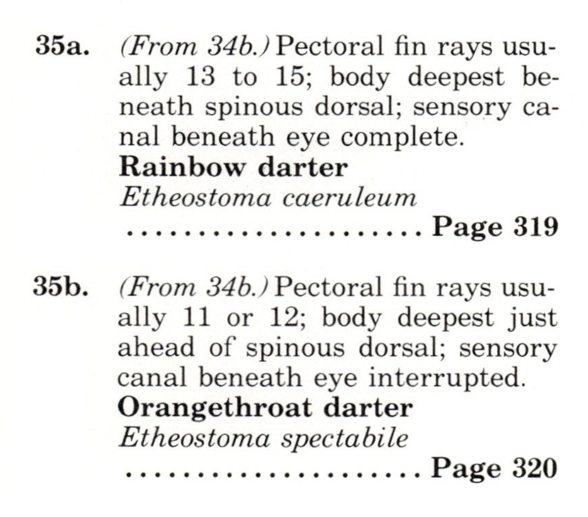

35a. *(From 34b.)* Pectoral fin rays usually 13 to 15; body deepest beneath spinous dorsal; sensory canal beneath eye complete.
Rainbow darter
Etheostoma caeruleum
.... **Page 319**

35b. *(From 34b.)* Pectoral fin rays usually 11 or 12; body deepest just ahead of spinous dorsal; sensory canal beneath eye interrupted.
Orangethroat darter
Etheostoma spectabile
.... **Page 320**

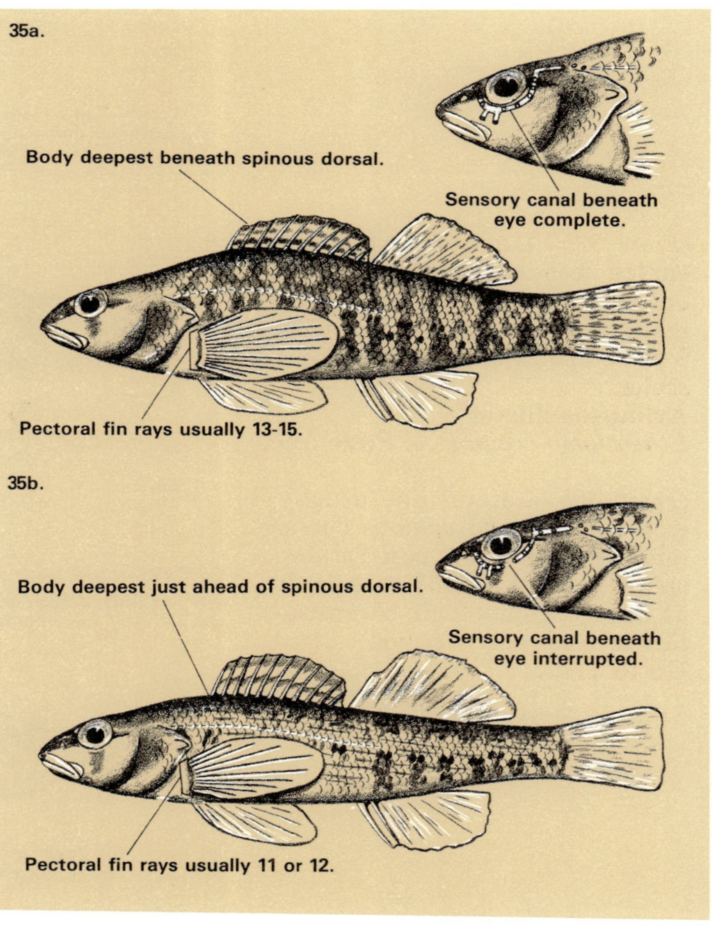
35a.
Body deepest beneath spinous dorsal.
Sensory canal beneath eye complete.
Pectoral fin rays usually 13-15.
35b.
Body deepest just ahead of spinous dorsal.
Sensory canal beneath eye interrupted.
Pectoral fin rays usually 11 or 12.

36a. *(From 21b.)* Cheek and gill cover with scales; lateral line usually represented by a few pored scales near head; upper jaw extending distinctly behind front of eye; anal fin often with only 1 spine.
Cypress darter
Etheostoma proeliare
.... **Page 324**

36b. *(From 21b.)* Cheek without scales, gill cover usually without scales or with a few scales; lateral line usually entirely absent; upper jaw extending only to or slightly behind front of eye; anal fin almost always with 2 spines.
Least darter
Etheostoma microperca
.... **Page 323**

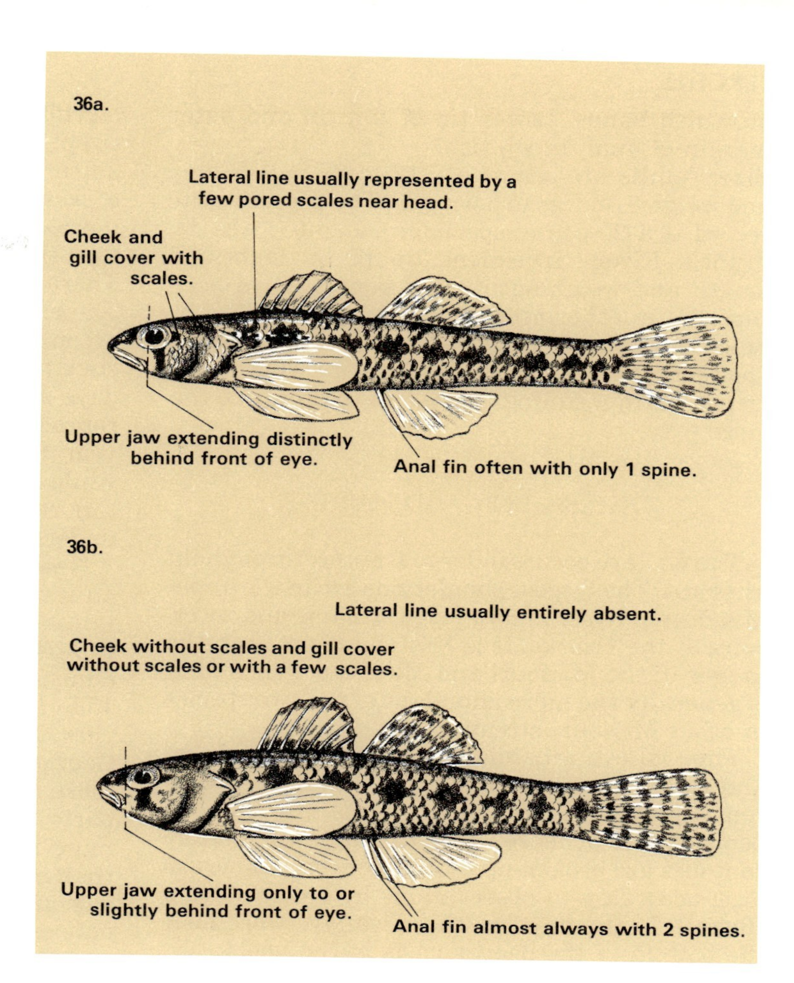
36a.
Lateral line usually represented by a few pored scales near head.
Cheek and gill cover with scales.
Upper jaw extending distinctly behind front of eye.
Anal fin often with only 1 spine.
36b.
Lateral line usually entirely absent.
Cheek without scales and gill cover without scales or with a few scales.
Upper jaw extending only to or slightly behind front of eye.
Anal fin almost always with 2 spines.

Walleye

Stizostedion vitreum (Mitchill)

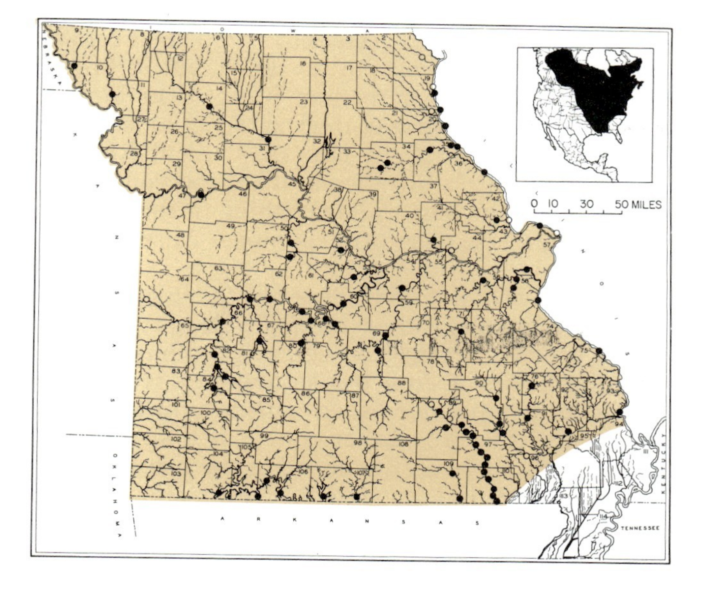
0 10 30 50 MILES
ARKANSAS
OKLAHOMA
TENNESSEE
KENTUCKY

Other local names: Jack salmon, Walleyed pike

DESCRIPTION

Illustration: Page 278, 3a.

Characters: A slender, spiny-rayed fish with two separate dorsal fins and a large mouth, the upper jaw extending about to rear margin of eye. Jaws and roof of mouth with prominent teeth. Rear margin of preopercle (bone just ahead of gill cover) strongly saw-toothed (serrate). Tail fin distinctly forked. Anal fin with 2 spines and 11 to 14 soft rays.

Very similar to sauger, page 297, but spinous dorsal with membranes (webbing) marked by streaks or blotches rather than spots; a large black blotch especially characteristic of the walleye normally occurs near bases of last few fin spines. Lower tip of tail fin lighter in color than remainder of fin. Soft dorsal usually with 19 to 22 rays. Pyloric caeca (finger-like extensions near junction of stomach and intestine) usually 3 in number and about as long as stomach.

Life colors: Back and sides yellowish or olive-brown with darker mottlings and blotches; belly white. Spinous dorsal streaked and blotched with black; soft dorsal and tail fin marked by narrow, brownish bands. Lower tip of tail fin and outer margin of anal fin whitish.

Size: Adults are commonly 12 to 28 inches long and weigh 8 ounces to 8 pounds. The present state record is a 20-pound specimen caught in the St. Francis River. Specimens up to 36 inches in length and weighing over 22 pounds have been reported in other areas.

Scientific name: *Stizostedion,* Greek, meaning "pungent throat," according to its author; *vitreum,* Latin meaning "glass," in reference to the large eyes.

DISTRIBUTION AND HABITAT

The walleye occurs in large streams throughout Missouri. The largest populations are in the upper Mississippi River and in large streams and reservoirs of the Ozarks. It is less abundant than the sauger in the Missouri and Mississippi rivers but is generally the more abundant of the two species in other Missouri streams.

The walleye inhabits the open water of lakes and reservoirs and the pools of streams. In Current River the largest populations are found in pools 12 feet or more in depth where the bottom contours are broken up by boulders or submerged logs, according to observations by biologist Tom Russell. In the daytime these walleye were near the bottom in the deeper parts of the pools.

HABITS AND LIFE HISTORY

The walleye generally occurs in loose aggregations of a few to many individuals. It ranges over a wide area rather than restricting its activities to a definite home range. It is decidedly nocturnal, moving to shoal areas to feed in late evening and returning to deeper water before daybreak. The opaque "walleyed" appearance of the eye results from its unique structure. Because of this structure the eye is very efficient at gathering the available light. Apparently the retreat of walleyes to deeper and darker water during daylight hours is in response to the dazzling effect of direct sunlight.

The food of walleye fry is small crustaceans and insects. Insects, particularly mayflies, are a significant food item throughout life, but fish are the principal food of adults.[216]

The spawning season sometimes begins as early as late February and extends into early April. The peak of spawning activity is generally in March. Spawning is commonly preceded by movements out of larger rivers and reservoirs into tributaries, with the males arriving at the spawning grounds ahead of the females. An extensive spawning run occurs each year out of Lake of the Ozarks into the upper Osage River. In streams spawning occurs on riffles, but in lakes and reservoirs, rocky wave-swept shorelines are often used. The presence of a firm silt-free substrate and a strong circulation of water are the principal requirements. Spawning occurs at night, sometimes in water so shallow that the backs of the spawning fish are exposed. There is no preparation of a nest or parental care. The eggs are scattered at random by the female, accompanied by several males. The adhesive eggs stick to the substrate. Hatching occurs in about 7 days at a temperature of 57° F.[217] Conditions for reproduction and survival are not ideal every year. Large year-classes are produced some years, while in others no young are produced. The factors responsible for these variations are not well understood.

Newly hatched walleye fry are only about half an inch in length, but under ideal conditions attain a length of 10 inches or more the first year. In Missouri's Current River the walleye averages 8 inches in length the first year and is about 12.5, 15.5, 17.3, 18.9, 20.7, 24.1, 25.5, 27.9, and 29.6 inches in succeeding years (unpublished data of George G. Fleener). Growth in Current River is more rapid than that reported for most other parts of the walleye's range.[216] Females grow more rapidly and attain a larger maximum size than males. The following are average weights for various lengths of the walleye: 10 inches–6 ounces; 15 inches–1 pound, 5 ounces; 20 inches–2 pounds, 14 ounces; 30 inches–11 pounds. The usual life span is 7 or 8 years, but individuals 13 or 14 years of age are not uncommon.

IMPORTANCE AND ANGLING

Because of its excellent sporting qualities, large size, and firm, well-flavored flesh, the walleye ranks as one of the most important freshwater game fishes in North America. It is fished commercially in some parts of its range, but in Missouri it is strictly a game fish. Most of the large reservoirs and streams of the Ozarks provide walleye fishing. Lake of the Ozarks, Current River, and Black River below Clearwater Reservoir provide some of the best walleye fishing in the state. Walleye are also caught in the upper Mississippi River.

It is likely that more walleye are taken by trolling than by any other method. Deep-running plugs, spoons, and fly and spinner combinations are all effective. A June bug spinner or a Number 3 Hildebrand spinner fished with a minnow are favorites with many fishermen. A bell sinker is attached about 18 inches ahead of the lure and it is trolled just fast enough to keep the spinner turning. The best fishing is in late evening or at night. Since walleye occur in aggregations, when one is caught others can be expected from the same area and depth.

Sauger

Stizostedion canadense (Smith)

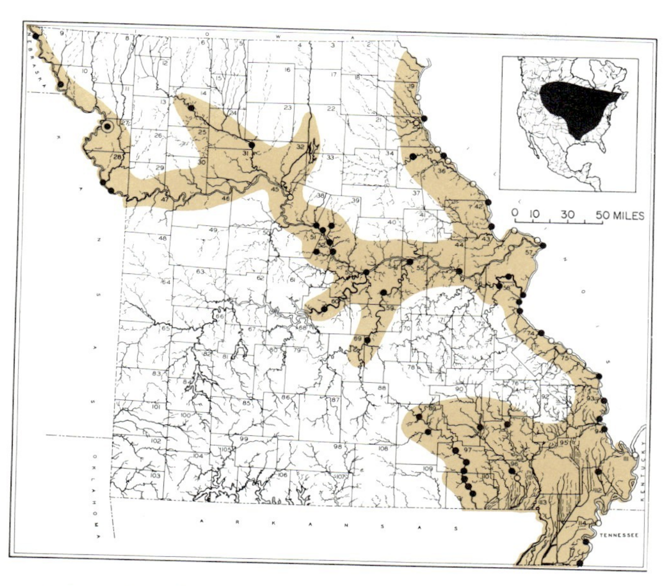

Other local names: Jack salmon, Spotted jack, Sand pike

DESCRIPTION

Illustration: Page 278, 3b.

Characters: A slender, spiny-rayed fish with two separate dorsal fins and a large mouth, the upper jaw extending about to rear margin of eye. Jaws and roof of mouth with prominent teeth. Rear margin of preopercle (bone just ahead of gill cover) strongly saw-toothed (serrate). Tail fin distinctly forked. Anal fin with 2 spines and 11 to 14 soft rays.

Very similar to walleye, page 295, but spinous dorsal with membranes (webbing) marked by rows of roundish black spots; no large black blotch present near bases of last few fin spines. Lower tip of tail fin similar in color to remainder of fin. Soft dorsal usually with 17 to 20 rays. Pyloric caeca (fingerlike extensions near junction of stomach and intestine) usually 5 to 8 in number and shorter than stomach.

Life colors: Back and sides brown, usually with about 4 darker brown bars extending obliquely forward onto sides. Belly white. Spinous dorsal marked by roundish black spots; soft dorsal and tail fin with narrow brownish bands.

Size: A smaller fish than the walleye, seldom exceeding a length of 18 inches or a weight of 2½ pounds.

Scientific name: *Stizostedion,* Greek, meaning "pungent throat", according to its author; *canadense,* "from Canada."

DISTRIBUTION AND HABITAT

The sauger is more restricted in distribution than the walleye, occurring principally in large, free-flowing streams. It is the most abundant of the two species in the Missouri and Mississippi rivers; elsewhere in Missouri the walleye generally predominates.

The habitat requirements of the sauger are much like those of the walleye, except that the sauger is more tolerant of high turbidity and is more often found in areas with strong current.

HABITS AND LIFE HISTORY

The life history of the sauger is, in most respects, like that of the walleye. Spawning may occur in Missouri in April, since females that had still not spawned have been taken from the Mississippi River in late March. The sauger grows more slowly and does not attain as large a size as the walleye. In the Iowa section of the Mississippi River the sauger reaches lengths of 5.7, 10.6, 14, 16.3, 17.7, 18.9, and 20.2 inches at the end of years one through seven respectively.[218] Females grow more rapidly than males after the third year of life and attain a larger maximum size. Average weights at various lengths for the sauger are: 11.7 inches–0.5 pound; 14.5 inches–1 pound; 17.4 inches–2 pounds; and 21.1 inches–4 pounds. Lengths and weights up to 30 inches and 8.2 pounds have been reported for the sauger elsewhere in its range,[219] but specimens weighing more than 3 pounds are uncommon in Missouri waters.

IMPORTANCE AND ANGLING

The sauger is an excellent sport fish but is less important than the walleye because of its smaller size and more restricted distribution. Though some sauger are caught in most large Missouri streams, the only significant fishery is in the upper Mississippi River. This stretch of river provides excellent sauger fishing from about Labor Day to freeze-up. Walleye also occur in the catch, but are outnumbered by the sauger in a ratio of about 9:1.

Sauger may be taken by the same methods as are effective for walleye. Most of the fishing on the upper Mississippi River is with minnows trolled slowly over the bottom in swift, rocky areas just below the navigation dams.

Yellow Perch

Perca flavescens (Mitchill)

DESCRIPTION

Illustration: Page 278, 2a.

PERCHES

Characters: A rather deep, slab-sided (nearly sunfish-shaped) fish with two separate dorsal fins and a moderately large mouth, the upper jaw extending about to middle of eye. Jaws and roof of mouth with teeth small and inconspicuous. Rear margin of preopercle (bone just ahead of gill cover) strongly saw-toothed (serrate). A characteristic feature is the 6 to 8 regularly spaced dark bars that cross the back and extend vertically onto sides. Anal fin with 2 spines and 6 to 8 soft rays.

Life colors: Back olive-green grading to golden-yellow on sides; belly white. Back and sides crossed by blackish or dark green vertical bars. Spinous dorsal dusky, usually with a prominent black blotch near back and a smaller blotch near front; other fins yellowish or white.

Size: Adults are commonly 6 to 12 inches long and weigh 4 ounces to 1 pound.

Scientific name: *Perca,* ancient Greek name for perch; *flavescens,* Latin, meaning "yellowish."

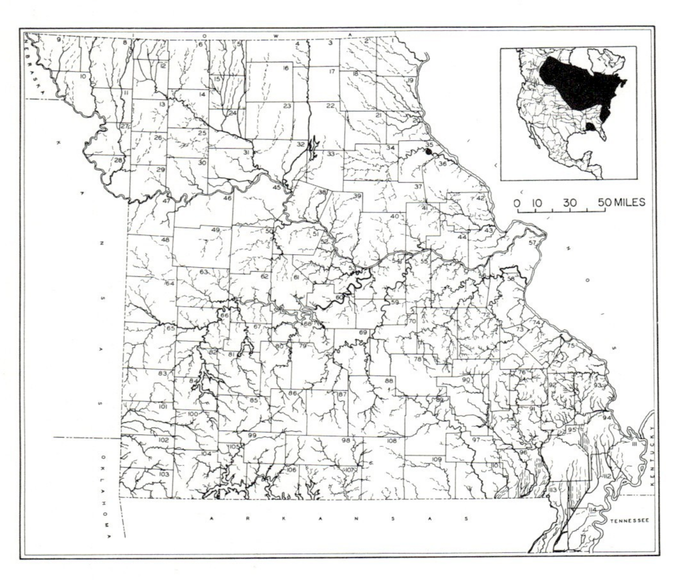

DISTRIBUTION AND HABITAT

In Missouri the yellow perch is so rare in natural waters that it seems certain that there are no self-sustaining populations. The only specimen known to me was caught in Salt River east of New London in Ralls County. Missouri is on the extreme southern edge of the range for the yellow perch and this specimen probably represents a straggler from farther north along the Mississippi River. Numerous yellow perch were stocked by the Missouri Fish and Game Commission throughout Missouri in the 1930's without noticeable success. Small self-sustaining populations are present in some artificial lakes, including Butler City Lake in Bates County and Blue Jay Lake in Pulaski County.

The yellow perch is primarily a lake fish and its rarity in Missouri waters is probably related in some measure to the scarcity of natural lakes. This species might thrive if introduced into the many large reservoirs constructed in recent years, but it might not be a worthwhile addition to the fishery.

HABITS AND LIFE HISTORY

The yellow perch lives in large schools. It spends the day in deep water, moving inshore to feed in late afternoon or evening. Small crustaceans, insects, and fish are the principal items in its diet. Spawning occurs in the spring, when the eggs are scattered over sandy or gravelly bottoms or on vegetation. The eggs are released in long, gelatinous strings that remain attached after deposition. Growth of the yellow perch is variable, depending on local conditions. Stunting as a result of overpopulation commonly occurs. Few yellow perch exceed a length of 12 inches or a weight of a pound, but weights up to 5 pounds have been reported.

Bluestripe Darter

Percina cymatotaenia (Gilbert and Meek)

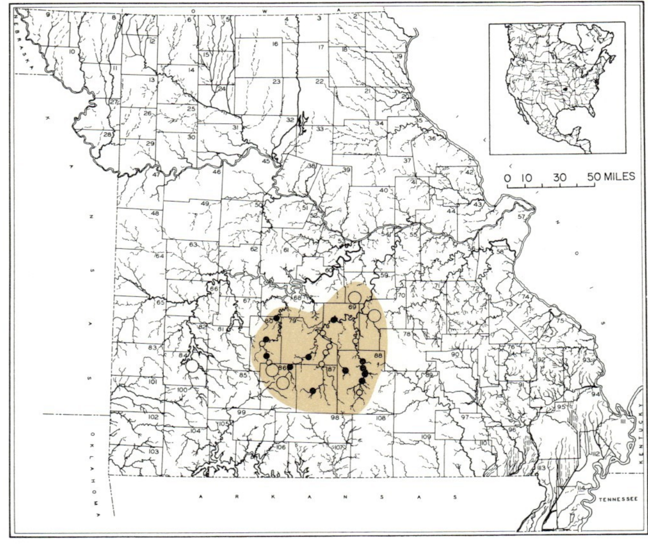

DESCRIPTION

Illustration: Page 282, 11a.

Characters: A slender darter with a broad continuous dark stripe extending along the midside, ending in a small, jet-black spot at base of tail fin. One or more enlarged and modified scales present between bases of pelvic fins; breast and belly otherwise covered with scales of normal size and shape. Gill covers not broadly connected by membrane across throat; distance from membrane notch to front of upper lip much less than distance from notch to front of pelvic fin base. Lateral line complete, containing 68 to 73 scales. Spinous dorsal with 11 to 13 spines. Anal fin with 2 spines and 11 or 12 rays.

Life colors: Back and upper sides dark brown with pale lengthwise streaks; underparts creamy yellow with scattered dark specks. Stripe along midside black with a greenish tinge. Fins faintly barred by narrow brownish lines.

Size: Adults are commonly 2.5 to 3.5 inches long to a maximum of about 4 inches.

Scientific name: *Percina,* "a small perch"; *cymatotaenia,* from the Greek, *cymato,* meaning "wave," and *taenia,* meaning "band" or "ribbon," a reference to the wavy black stripe along the midside.

DISTRIBUTION AND HABITAT

The bluestripe darter has a localized distribution in streams of the Osage and Gasconade systems of the northern Ozarks. It is not known to occur outside of Missouri, but is represented in the uplands of western Kentucky by a closely related species that is still without a valid scientific name. The bluestripe darter is one of the rarest Missouri fishes. Perhaps it was more common before the turn of the century than it is today. One early collector reported the bluestripe darter as "abundant in the Niangua, Osage Fork, and Sac River systems."[220] Today it is not abundant in any of these streams and has not been collected in the Sac River since Gilbert made his collections. Another early collector reported this darter from the Maries River near Dixon and the Little Piney River at Newburg,[88] but these streams evidently no longer support populations.

In recent collections the bluestripe darter has occurred only in Ozark rivers of medium size. Early collectors found it more frequently in small headwater streams. This darter inhabits quiet pools and backwaters having a sandy bottom and abundant cover in the form of submergent vegetation or deposits of sticks and leaves.

HABITS AND LIFE HISTORY

Bluestripe darters that I have kept in aquaria spent considerable time swimming about or hovering in midwater, suggesting that this species is less specialized for a bottom-dwelling life than other darters. It is carnivorous, probably feeding principally on insects and other small aquatic invertebrates. Spawning evidently occurs in May over gravelly riffles, since an adult male in breeding condition was collected at that time and place.

Blackside darter

Percina maculata (Girard)

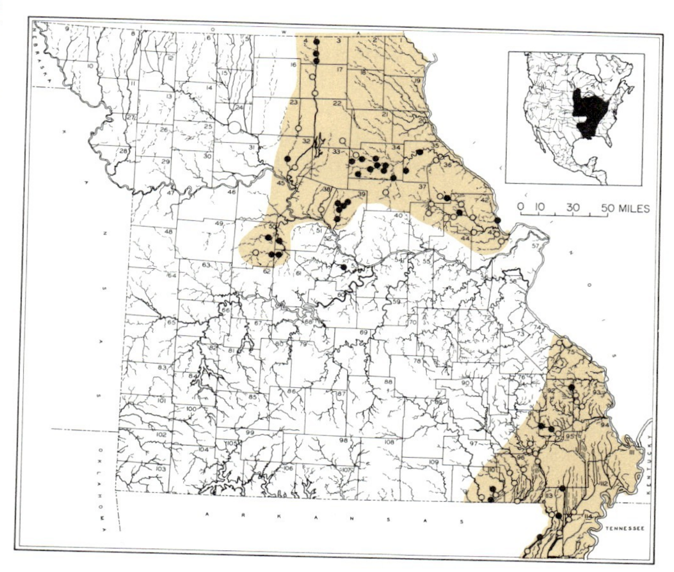

DESCRIPTION

Illustration: Page 284, 15a.

Characters: A moderately slender darter with 7 to 9 dark blotches along the midside and a narrow, dusky vertical bar beneath the eye. Blotches confined to side and somewhat connected along lateral line. One or more enlarged and modified scales are present between pelvic fin bases; breast and forward part of belly otherwise naked or with a series of enlarged and modified scales. Gill covers not broadly connected by membrane across throat; distance from membrane notch to front of upper lip much less than distance from notch to front of pelvic fin base. Lateral line complete, containing 62 to 68 scales. Dorsal fins with 13 to 15 spines and 12 to 14 rays. Anal fin with 2 spines and 10 or 11 rays.

Life colors: Back and upper sides brown with about 9 irregular dark cross-bars and numerous dark wavy lines, separated from creamy white underparts by a series of blackish blotches. Base of tail fin with a small black spot (most prominent in small individuals). A dusky vertical bar extends downward from eye and another extends forward from eye onto snout. Dorsal fin and tail fin dusted with blackish specks and barred with narrow brown lines; lower fins clear or yellowish-white.

Size: Adults are commonly 2 to 4 inches long to a maximum of about 4.3 inches.

Scientific name: *Percina,* "a small perch"; *maculata,* Latin, meaning "spotted."

DISTRIBUTION AND HABITAT

The blackside darter has two centers of occurrence in Missouri. One of these is in the ditches and streams of the Lowlands; the other is in the Prairie and Ozark border streams of central and northeastern Missouri. Five specimens of the blackside darter were collected from Grand River in Livingston County in 1854, but no specimens have subsequently been collected from that drainage. It probably was more widespread in the Prairie streams of northwestern Missouri in the past than is now the case. It is not abundant anywhere within its Missouri range.

The blackside darter is characteristic of small to medium-sized streams having low or moderate gradients, permanent flow, and gravelly or sandy bottoms. It tolerates more turbid and warmer waters than most darters. Adults are usually found on gravelly riffles in a slight current or in short, gravelly pools adjacent to riffles. The young commonly occur in backwaters, among accumulations of sticks, leaves, and other debris.

HABITS AND LIFE HISTORY

The blackside is less a bottom fish than many darters, swimming for extended periods in midwater and sometimes rising to the surface or jumping clear of the water for flying insects.[94] An Iowa study reveals that aquatic insects make up the bulk of its diet.[221] In Iowa the blackside darter averages 1.5 inches in length when a year old, and 2, 2.6, and 3.1 inches by the end of succeeding years.

The blackside spawns in Illinois from April to June.[222] Adults in spawning condition have been collected in Missouri during May. Spawning is sometimes preceded by upstream migrations.[223]It spawns over a bottom of sand or gravel in water about a foot deep having a moderate current.[224] The eggs are released and fertilized as the female comes to rest in a depression after a short pursuit by one or more males. During the spawning act the male is reported to undergo a striking color change, with much of the head and body becoming yellow-gold or emerald green. The blackside darter does not practice parental care, abandoning the eggs after spawning. Some females mature and spawn as yearlings but others do not spawn for the first time until they are 2 years old.[222]

Dusky Darter

Percina sciera (Swain)

DESCRIPTION

Illustration: Page 284, 14a.

Characters: A moderately slender darter with a series of 8 to 10 dark blotches along the midside. A character shared with no other Missouri darter is that the free margin of the preopercle (bone just ahead of gill cover) is often weakly saw-toothed (serrate.) Another characteristic feature is the presence of 3 roundish black spots—the lower 2 often connected—extending vertically across body at base of tail fin. One or more enlarged and modified scales are present between pelvic fin bases; breast and forward part of belly otherwise naked or with a series of enlarged and modified scales. Gill covers rather broadly connected by membrane across throat; distance from membrane notch to front of upper lip equal to or greater than distance from notch to front of pelvic fin base. Lateral line complete, containing 59 to 68 scales. Dorsal fins with 11 to 14 spines and 13 or 14 rays. Anal fin with 2 spines and 9 to 11 rays.

Life colors: Back and upper sides brown with about 9 indistinct dark cross-bars, separated from creamy-white underparts by a lengthwise series of black blotches. Fins mostly dusky-olive; soft dorsal and tail fin often barred by narrow brown lines. Males are darker and less definitely blotched than females, the blotches along midside less connected and more squarish in outline.

Size: Adults are commonly 2 to 4 inches long to a maximum of about 4.2 inches.

Scientific name: *Percina,* "a small perch"; *sciera,* Greek, meaning "dusky."

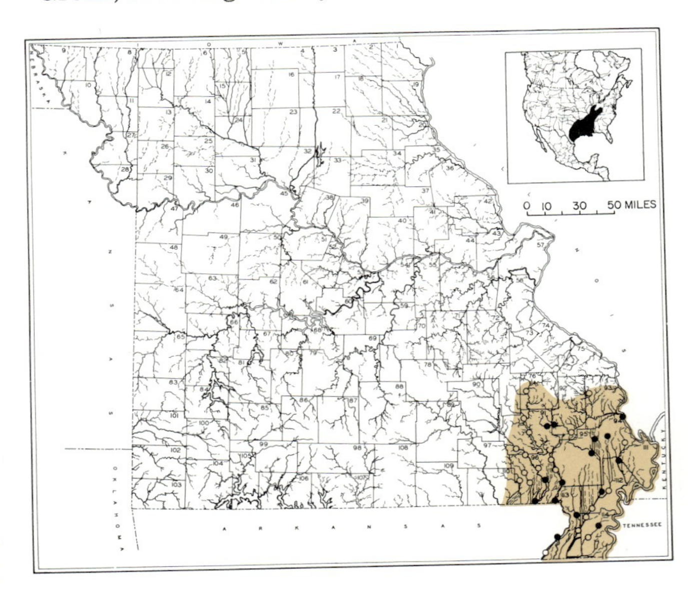

DISTRIBUTION AND HABITAT

This Lowland darter is common in the streams and ditches of southeastern Missouri and penetrates into the adjacent Ozarks along streams entering the Lowlands.

The habitat requirements of the dusky darter

are much like those of the blackside darter. It is characteristic of clear, low-gradient streams having strong flow and sand or gravel bottoms. It is usually found on sluggish gravel-bottomed riffles, but also occurs in quiet backwaters having silt-free bottoms and accumulations of leaves, sticks, or other organic debris.

HABITS AND LIFE HISTORY

The following information on the dusky darter is from an Illinois study.[225] The diet of this darter consists entirely of the immature stages of aquatic insects (midges, caddisflies, black flies, snipe flies, mayflies, and stoneflies). Midges are the major food item for small darters; larger darters feed principally on caddisflies.

The spawning period of the dusky darter evidently varies from year to year, depending on flooding and other factors. June appears to be the preferred month for spawning in Illinois, although some spawning occurs from May into July. The spawning habits of this darter are not known in detail, but the available evidence suggests that the eggs are scattered over a gravelly substrate and then abandoned.

In the Embarras River, Illinois, the dusky darter averages 2.3, 2.9, and 3.2 inches standard length when 1, 2, and 3 years of age respectively. Males grow more rapidly and attain a larger size than females. Both sexes become mature during the spring following hatching. Few individuals live more than 3 years.

Slenderhead Darter

Percina phoxocephala (Nelson)

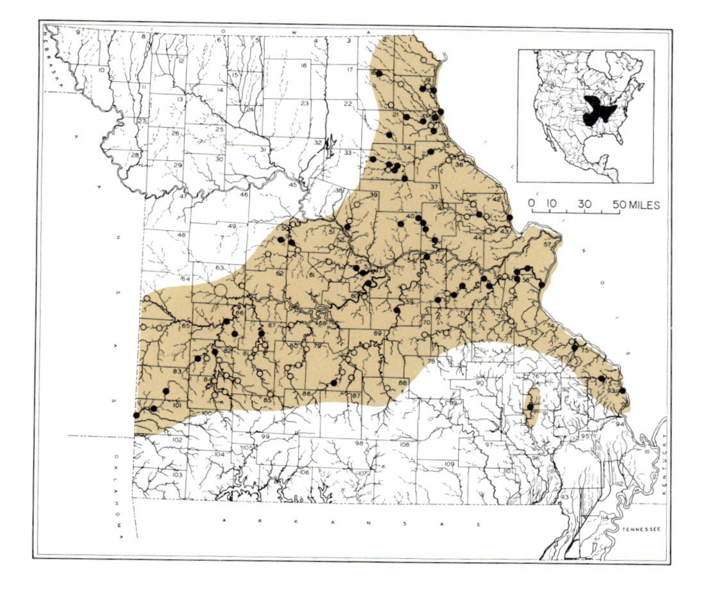

DESCRIPTION

Illustration: Page 282, 10a.

Characters: A slender darter with a series of 10 to 15 small, indistinct dark blotches or bars along midside. Head long and slender, its length going 3.5 times or less into standard length. One or more enlarged and modified scales between pelvic fin bases; breast naked except for a few enlarged and modified scales; belly with a series of enlarged and modified scales along midline (males), or with scales of normal size and shape (females). Gill covers broadly connected by membrane across throat; distance from membrane notch to front of upper lip much greater than distance from notch to front of pelvic fin base. Lateral line complete, containing 62 to 74 scales. Dorsal fins with 11 to 13 spines and 11 to 14 rays. Anal fin with 2 spines and 9 or 10 rays.

Similar to longnose darter, page 302, but with a shorter snout, its length about equal to distance from back of eye to rear margin of preopercle. Also, the slenderhead darter has 6 branchiostegal rays (slender, curving bones in membrane at lower margin of gill cover), as is typical of most darters.

Life colors: Back and upper sides yellowish-brown mottled and spotted with darker brown; lower sides and belly creamy white. Midside with a series of small dusky blotches, ending at base of tail fin in a small black spot. Spinous dorsal dusky with an outer orange band; soft dorsal and tail fin faintly banded with brownish lines.

Size: Adults are commonly 2 to 3.8 inches long to a maximum of about 4 inches.

Scientific name: *Percina,* "a small perch"; *phoxocephala,* Greek, meaning "tapering head."

DISTRIBUTION AND HABITAT

The range of the slenderhead darter in Missouri extends in a broad band from Spring River in Jasper County northeastward into the upper Mississippi River and its tributaries. This darter also occurs at scattered localities southward along the Mississippi River. Within its area of occurrence it is one of the commonest darters in large streams.

The slenderhead darter inhabits medium-sized creeks to large rivers having gravelly or rocky bottoms and permanent strong flow. It does best in streams that are transitional in character between the Ozarks and Prairies. The slenderhead darter is most often found on gravelly or rocky riffles in moderate to swift current.

HABITS AND LIFE HISTORY

In the Embarras River, Illinois, the slenderhead darter feeds principally on immature aquatic insects, along with lesser quantities of amphipods, fish eggs, and terrestrial insects.[226] Midges and blackflies are the principal insects eaten.

The slenderhead spawns in central Missouri from late April into May over swift-flowing gravelly riffles. The spawning habits are not known in detail. In the Des Moines River, Iowa, the slenderhead darter attains a length of about 1.4 inches by the end of its first year of life, and averages 1.9, 2, and 2.3 inches in length in succeeding years.[221] All males and most females are sexually mature during the first spring following hatching.[226]

Longnose Darter

Percina nasuta (Bailey)

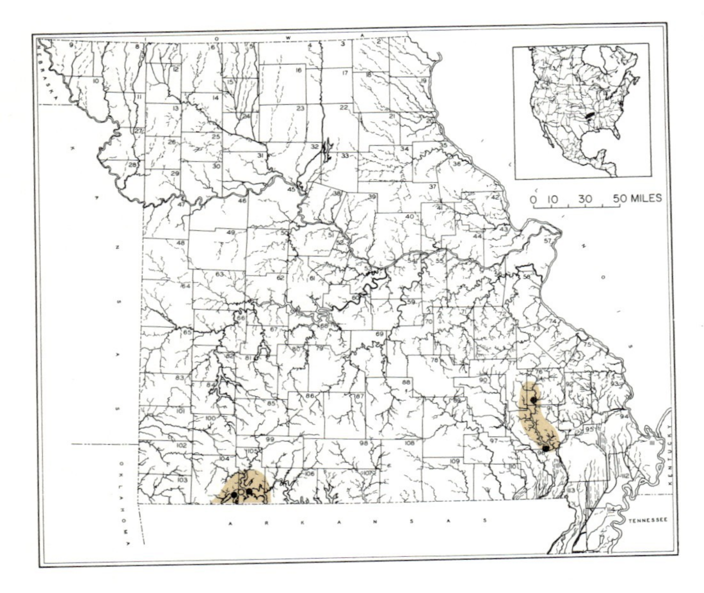

DESCRIPTION

Illustration: Page 282, 10b.

Characters: A slender darter with a series of 10 to 15 small, indistinct dark blotches or bars along midside. Head very long and slender, its length going less than 3.5 times into standard length. One or more enlarged and modified scales between pelvic fin bases; breast naked except for a few enlarged and modified scales; belly with a series of enlarged and modified scales along midline (males) or with scales of normal size and shape (females). Gill covers broadly connected by membrane across throat; distance from membrane notch to front of upper lip much greater than distance from notch to front of pelvic fin base. Lateral line complete, containing 64 to 79 scales. Dorsal fins with 11 to 13 spines and 13 or 14 rays. Anal fin with 2 spines and 8 or 9 rays.

Similar to slenderhead darter, page 301, but with a longer snout, its length much greater than distance from back of eye to rear margin of preopercle. Also, the longnose darter often has 7 branchiostegal rays (slender, curving bones in membrane at lower margin of gill cover), not 6 as is typical of darters.

Life colors: Similar to those of slenderhead darter, page 301.

Size: About as in slenderhead darter.

Scientific name: *Percina,* "a small perch"; *nasuta,* Latin, meaning "large-nosed."

DISTRIBUTION AND HABITAT

The longnose darter has been collected in Missouri only from the White River in Stone and Taney counties and the St. Francis River and Lake Wappapello in Madison and Wayne counties. The section of White River where specimens were collected is now covered by Table Rock Lake and the longnose darter has not been collected there since impoundment. Six specimens were reported in a rotenone sample obtained by Department of Conservation biologists from Asher Cove, Lake Wappapello, in 1949. Evidently no specimens were preserved. However, I have examined two adult specimens labeled "Lake Wappapello, 1953" (exact locality unknown) that were also collected by Department biologists. In 1969 two juvenile longnose darters were collected from the St. Francis River in Madison County by Dr. Jamie E. Thomerson and students. This locality was sampled on two subsequent occasions, but no more specimens were obtained. At present the longnose darter is rare in Missouri waters and may be restricted to the upper St. Francis River.

It is an inhabitant of medium-sized to large Ozark rivers. It has been collected on riffles and also in quiet backwaters near thick growths of aquatic vegetation. Occurrence of the longnose darter in collections from Lake Wappapello suggests that it is one of the few darters able to persist in impoundments.

HABITS AND LIFE HISTORY

Nothing is known about the biology of this fish.

Logperch

Percina caprodes (Rafinesque)

DESCRIPTION

Illustration: Page 281, 8a.

Characters: Readily separated from other Missouri darters by having the mouth overhung by the distinctly conical snout. Another distinctive feature is the color pattern consisting of 15 to 20 narrow, vertical dark bars on a light background. Bars alternating in length, with every other bar extending only about to lateral line while the bar on either side extends nearly to belly. One or more enlarged and modified scales between pelvic fin bases; breast and midline of belly otherwise naked or with enlarged and modified scales. Gill covers not broadly connected by membrane across throat; distance from membrane notch to front of upper lip much less than distance from notch to front of pelvic fin base. Lateral line complete, containing 73 to 91 scales. Dorsal fins with 13 to 16 spines and 15 to 17 rays. Anal fin with 2 spines and 9 to 12 rays.

Life colors: Back and sides pale yellowish-olive with numerous narrow, brown bars; belly creamy-white. Usually with a dusky bar beneath eye and a small black spot at base of tail fin. Spinous dorsal fin dusky at base, with an orange band in males; soft dorsal and tail fins faintly banded with brown lines.

Size: The largest of the darters. Adults are commonly 4 to 6 inches in length, occasionally reaching a length of 7 inches or more.

Scientific name: *Percina,* "a small perch"; *caprodes,* Greek for "resembling a pig," in reference to the snout.

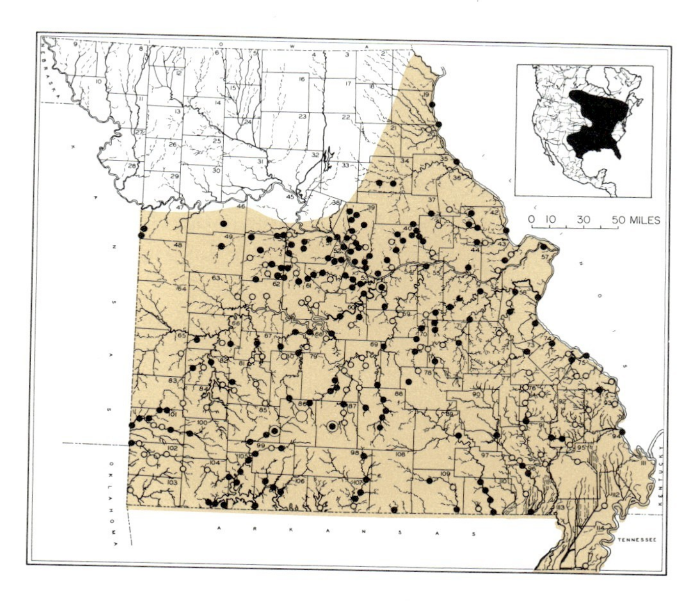

DISTRIBUTION AND HABITAT

The logperch occurs throughout the Ozarks and at scattered localities elsewhere in the state. It achieves its greatest abundance along the border between the Ozarks and Prairie Region where it is one of the most common darters. It is one of the few Missouri darters to persist in impoundments.

This darter inhabits a variety of stream types but penetrates into headwater creeks only if they maintain large, permanent pools. It avoids streams that are continuously turbid or excessively silty, or that lack well defined gravelly riffles. It is most often found in the deeper and more sluggish sections of riffles, but also occurs in pools if the bottom is mostly free of silt. In reservoirs the logperch occurs along gravelly wave-swept shores.

HABITS AND LIFE HISTORY

The logperch spends much of its time on the bottom in typical darter fashion. It uses its conical snout to turn over rocks in search of food. Rocks several times larger than the darter's head are overturned with ease, after which the logperch carefully examines the undersurface of the rock and picks off the small invertebrates thus exposed. Immature stages of aquatic insects, along with small crustaceans and snails, make up the bulk of this darter's diet.[42, 227]

The logperch spawns in Missouri in April and May. At that time the males gather in loose aggregations, consisting of a few to a hundred or more individuals, on clean, gravelly or sandy riffles. Females congregate in deeper water nearby, entering the aggregations of males only when ready to spawn. Although the female is often pursued by several males, only one normally participates in the spawning act. The spawning fish vibrate rapidly until buried in the bottom, at which time the eggs are laid and fertilized.[223] About 10 to 20 eggs are deposited at each spawning, and a female may repeat the spawning act many times before her full complement of eggs is laid.

Early growth of the logperch is rapid, and 60 to 70 percent of the adult size is reached in one year.[222] This darter averages 2.9 inches in length after one year, and 4.2 inches and 4.8 inches at the end of succeeding years. Few individuals live more than 3 years.

Gilt Darter

Percina evides (Jordan and Gilbert)

DESCRIPTION

Illustration: Page 284, 15b.

Characters: A moderately slender darter with a series of 7 to 9 dark blotches along the midside and a narrow, dusky vertical bar beneath the eye. Blotches vertically elongated and continuous with dark cross-bars on back. One or more enlarged and modified scales between pelvic fin bases; breast and midline of belly otherwise naked or with enlarged and modified scales. Gill covers not broadly connected by membrane across throat; distance from membrane notch to front of upper lip much less than distance from notch to front of pelvic fin base. Lateral line complete, containing 64 to 76 scales. Dorsal fins with 11 to 13 spines and 12 or 13 rays. Anal fin with 2 stiff spines and 10 rays.

Life colors: Back brownish-olive with squarish dark cross-bars. Sides orange-yellow with greenish-black blotches. A well developed dusky bar beneath eye. Fins dusky or clear, without definite

markings. Breeding males with lower surface of head and throat orange-red and the body and fins tinged with orange; these colors often somewhat developed in nonbreeding males and in females.
Size: Adults are commonly 2.3 to 3.3 inches long to a maximum of about 3.5 inches.
Scientific name: *Percina,* "a small perch"; *evides,* Greek, meaning "comely."

DISTRIBUTION AND HABITAT

The gilt darter is common and widespread in the eastern and southern Ozarks. It has been collected only once from the Osage River system, and does not occur in the Elk and Spring rivers.

This darter inhabits clear, medium-sized to large streams with clean, silt-free bottoms and permanent strong flow. It is most often found in the gravelly sections of riffles and pools, in a slight or moderate current.

HABITS AND LIFE HISTORY

Little is known concerning the habits of this fish. Brilliantly colored males were taken from Current River the third week of June, suggesting a late or prolonged spawning season.

River Darter

Percina shumardi (Girard)

DESCRIPTION

Illustration: Page 285, 16a.
Characters: A moderately stout darter with a series of 9 to 12 dark blotches or bars along midside and a narrow dusky vertical bar beneath the eye. A characteristic feature is the two prominent black blotches in spinous dorsal, one at front of fin and the other near base of last 3 spines. Characters useful in separating this species from the rather similar stargazing darter are the fully scaled cheek and the absence or near-absence of scales from nape (region of body in front of dorsal fin). One or more enlarged and modified scales between pelvic fin bases; breast and most of belly otherwise naked or with a few enlarged and modified scales. Gill covers moderately well connected by membrane across throat; distance from membrane notch to front of upper lip about equal to distance from notch to front of pelvic fin base. Lateral line complete, containing 47 to 56 scales. Dorsal fins with 9 or 10 spines and 13 to 15 rays. Anal fin with 2 spines and 11 or 12 rays. Males with anal fin greatly enlarged, a character shared only with stargazing darter.

Life colors: Back brownish-olive with 6 or 7 squarish dark brown cross-bars. Sides yellowish with a series of black blotches that become deeper and narrower toward head. Head with a prominent black bar extending vertically downward from eye and another extending forward from eye onto snout. Spinous dorsal with 2 prominent black blotches; soft dorsal and anal fin faintly banded by narrow brown lines.
Size: Adults are commonly 2.3 to 3.3 inches long to a maximum of about 3.5 inches.

Scientific name: *Percina,* "a small perch"; *shumardi,* named for Dr. G.C. Shumard, surgeon of the U.S. Pacific Railroad Survey.

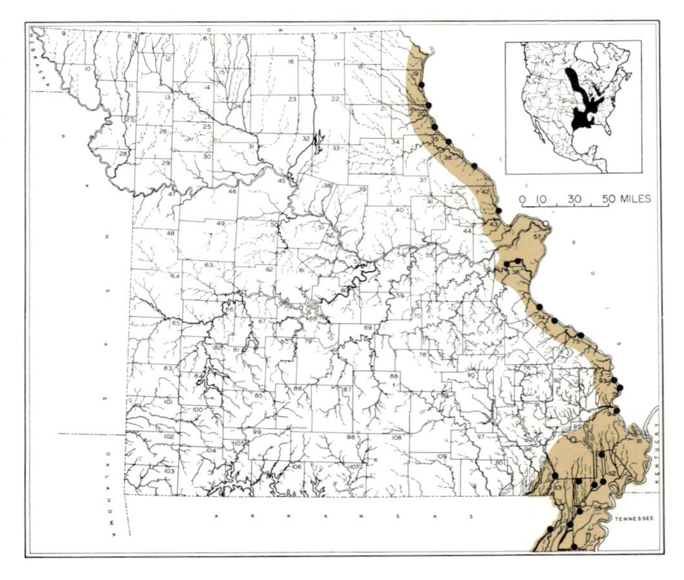

DISTRIBUTION AND HABITAT

The river darter is the most common darter in the Mississippi River and is common in the larger ditches and streams of the Lowlands. It is almost invariably found in deep chutes and riffles where the current is swift and the bottom is composed of coarse gravel or rock. It seems more tolerant of continuous turbidity than most darters, as indicated by its presence in the lower Mississippi River.

HABITS AND LIFE HISTORY

An Illinois study revealed that the diet of the river darter consists principally of midge and caddisfly larvae.[222] This study also indicated that this darter spawns in April and May. The spawning habits of the river darter are not known, but the enlarged anal fin of the male is probably of some significance in spawning. In Illinois, this darter averages about 1.9 inches at one year of age and is about 2.6 inches long when 2 years old.

Stargazing Darter

Percina uranidea (Jordan and Gilbert)

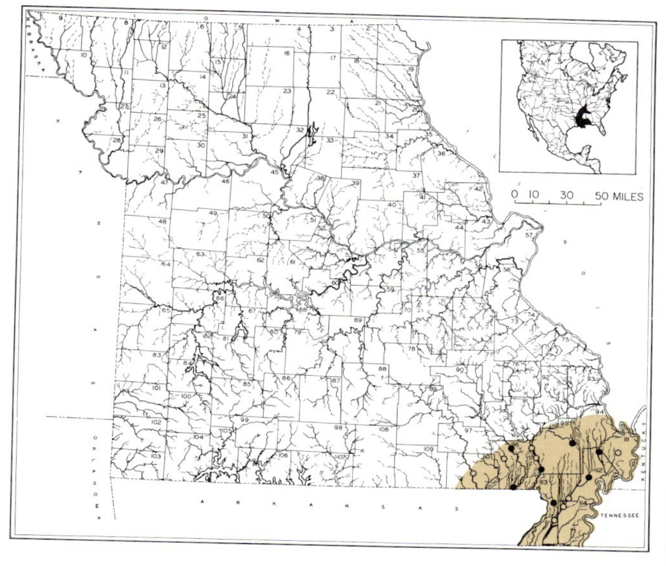

DESCRIPTION

Illustration: Page 285, 16b.

Characters: A slender or moderately stout darter with a series of 8 to 10 dark blotches along midside and a narrow, dusky vertical bar beneath eye. Characters useful in separating this species from the rather similar river darter are the absence or near-absence of scales from the cheek and the fully scaled nape (upper surface of body in front of dorsal fin). One or more enlarged and modified scales between pelvic fin bases; breast and midline of belly otherwise naked or with a few enlarged and modified scales. Gill covers moderately well connected by membrane across throat; distance from membrane notch to front of upper lip about equal to distance from notch to front of pelvic fin base. Lateral line complete, containing 51 to 56 scales. Dorsal fins with 9 to 11 spines and 14 or 15 rays. Anal fin with 2 spines and 10 or 11 rays. Males with anal fin greatly enlarged, a character shared only with river darter.

Life colors: Back brownish-olive with 4 or 5 squarish dark brown cross-bars. Sides yellowish with 8 to 10 oblong black blotches that are somewhat connected along the lateral line. Head with a prominent black bar extending vertically downward from eye and another extending forward from eye onto snout. Soft dorsal and tail fin faintly banded by narrow brown lines; fins otherwise without definite markings.

Size: Adults are commonly 2.2 to 3.3 inches long to a maximum of about 3.5 inches.

Scientific name: *Percina,* "a small perch"; *uranidea,* Greek, meaning "sky-looking" in reference to the orientation of the eyes.

DISTRIBUTION AND HABITAT

This species is confined to the Lowlands where its distribution and abundance is much like that of the related river darter. The two species seem similar in their requirements but are seldom abundant at the same locality. Possibly they compete intensively and at any given locality conditions favor one species over the other. The favored species is thus able to largely replace its rival.

HABITS AND LIFE HISTORY

Nothing is known of the habits of this species.

Channel Darter

Percina copelandi (Jordan)

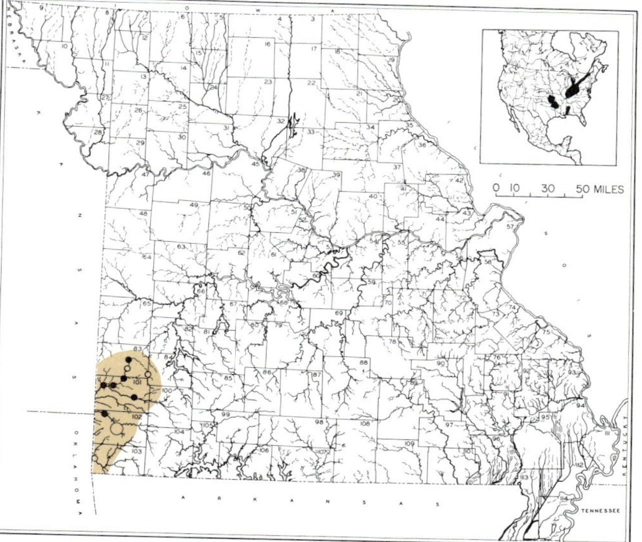

DESCRIPTION

Illustration: Page 283, 12a.

Characters: A slender darter with a series of

about 10 to 15 small oblong dark blotches along midside. A useful character for identifying this species is the continuous deep groove separating upper lip from snout. In most other darters the upper lip and snout are joined at midline by a bridge of skin (frenum). One or more enlarged and modified scales are present between pelvic fin bases; breast and midline of belly otherwise naked or with enlarged and modified scales. Gill covers not broadly connected by membrane across throat; distance from membrane notch to front of upper lip much less than distance from notch to front of pelvic fin base. Lateral line complete, containing 51 to 56 scales. Dorsal fins with 11 to 13 spines and 12 rays. Anal fin with 2 spines and 8 or 9 rays.

Life colors: Back yellowish-olive with about 8 indistinct brown cross-bars and scattered brown X and W-shaped markings. Sides yellow with a series of somewhat connected black blotches that form an interrupted horizontal stripe. Often with a dusky bar or spot beneath eye and a dusky bar extending forward from eye onto snout. Fins without prominent markings. Breeding males darker, the throat, breast, and pelvic fins nearly black.

Size: Adults are commonly 1.6 to 2.3 inches long to a maximum of about 2.5 inches.

Scientific name: *Percina,* "a small perch"; *copelandi,* named for its discoverer, H.E. Copeland.

DISTRIBUTION AND HABITAT

The channel darter occurs in Missouri only in Spring River and its large tributaries of the southwestern Ozarks. In these streams it is fairly common on sluggish riffles and in pools having enough current to create silt-free gravelly or rocky bottoms. Populations of the channel darter in southwestern Missouri are widely separated from the main range of the species to the northeast. Perhaps the Missouri populations date from a southwestward movement of the species during one of the glacial advances of the Pleistocene ice age.

HABITS AND LIFE HISTORY

The channel darter takes its food mostly from the bottom and its diet consists principally of midge larvae and other immature aquatic insects.[227, 228] Spawning has been observed in Michigan in July.[228] The spawning season is probably earlier in Missouri. Males guard spawning territories over stony bottoms where there is noticeable current, but there is no parental care of eggs or young. Females move through the territories, spawning successively with many males. Growth of the channel darter has not been studied.

Crystal Darter

Ammocrypta asprella (Jordan)

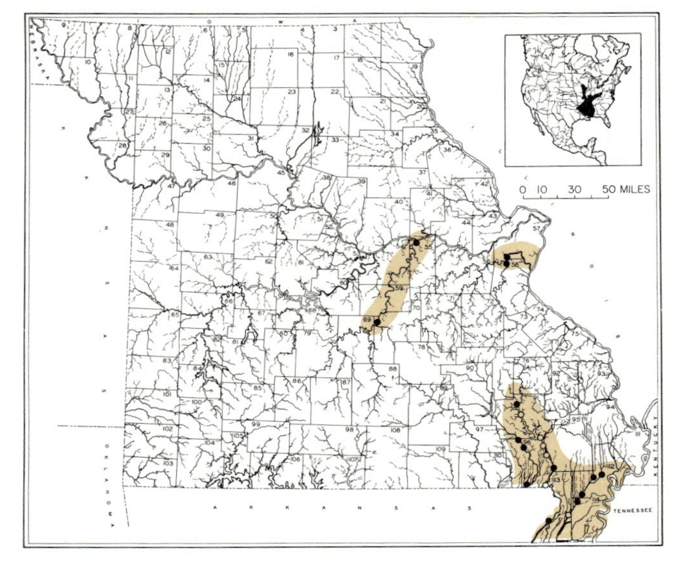

DESCRIPTION

Illustration: Page 279, 5a; **47.**

Characters: A pale, very slender darter with 4 or 5 dark cross-bars that extend obliquely forward from back onto sides. Body depth going more than 7 times into standard length. Upper lip not separated from snout by a deep groove, but joined at midline by a narrow bridge of skin (frenum). Body fully scaled except for breast and belly. Lateral line complete, containing 81 to 98 scales. Anal fin with 1 flexible spine and 12 to 14 rays. Tail fin rather deeply forked.

Life colors: Back and upper sides pale yellow with 4 or 5 brown cross-bars; underparts silvery-white. Midside with a series of oblong dusky blotches. Fins without definite markings.

Size: Adults are commonly 2.2 to 3.8 inches long to a maximum of about 4 inches.

Scientific name: *Ammocrypta,* Greek, meaning "sand concealed," in reference to the habit of lying buried in the sand; *asprella,* a diminutive of *aspro,* a European genus of perch.

DISTRIBUTION AND HABITAT

The crystal darter is confined principally to the larger ditches and rivers of the Lowlands, but penetrates into the southeastern Ozarks along the Black and St. Francis rivers. It is also known from the Meramec and Gasconade rivers. This darter is not abundant anywhere in Missouri.

The crystal darter occurs in the open stretches of large, clear streams with low or moderate gradients. It is generally found over a bottom of sand or small gravel, in a slight current.

HABITS AND LIFE HISTORY

Nothing is known of the habits of this distinctive darter.

Western Sand Darter

Ammocrypta clara Jordan and Meek

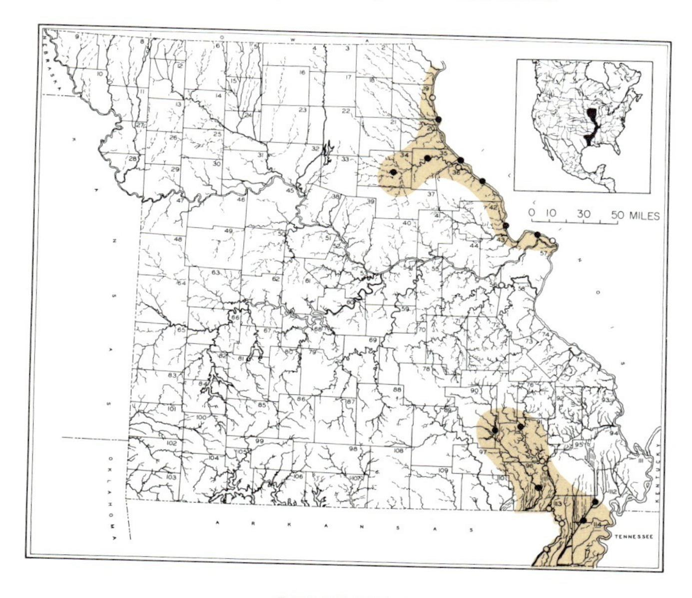

DESCRIPTION

Illustration: Page 280, 6a.

Characters: A pale, very slender darter without prominent markings except for a series of dark spots along the back. Body depth going more than 7 times into standard length. Upper lip separated from snout by a continuous groove, not connected at midline by a narrow bridge of skin (frenum). Lateral line complete, containing 66 to 78 scales. Anal fin with 1 flexible spine and 8 or 9 rays. Tail fin only slightly forked.

Very similar to scaly sand darter, but with the following differences: body naked except for scales on caudal peduncle and forward along midside; spine near rear margin of gill cover long and prominent, its length much greater than width of its base; dusky blotches along midside absent or very indistinct.

Life colors: Back a translucent yellow with a series of dusky spots; sides and belly silvery-white. Sometimes with a series of indistinct dusky blotches along midside. Fins without definite markings.

Size: Adults are commonly 1.8 to 2.3 inches long to a maximum of about 2.5 inches.

Scientific name: *Ammocrypta,* Greek, meaning "sand concealed," in reference to the habit of lying buried in the sand; *clara,* Latin, meaning "clear," in reference to the translucent appearance of the species.

DISTRIBUTION AND HABITAT

The western sand darter is not abundant anywhere in Missouri but occurs most commonly in the upper Mississippi River and in Lowland ditches of the southeast. In the Lowlands it is less common than the scaly sand darter.

True to its name, this darter is invariably found over a sandy bottom. It avoids strong currents, occupying the quiet margins of the stream channel and shallow backwaters. It seems intolerant of excessive siltation and turbidity

HABITS AND LIFE HISTORY

When not actively foraging over the bottom this darter lies buried in the sand with only the eyes and snout showing. The sharp nose and slender form are evidently adaptations for burrowing, which is accomplished by rapid swimming motions. Because of its pale, translucent coloration the western sand darter blends well with the uniformly light color of its habitat. The food habits and spawning habits of the western sand darter have not been studied.

Scaly Sand Darter

Ammocrypta vivax Hay

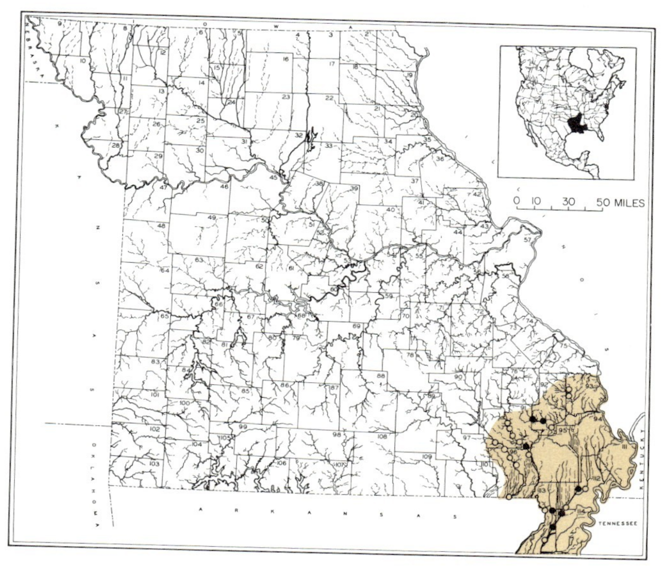

DESCRIPTION

Illustration: Page 280, 6b.

Characters: A pale, very slender darter with a series of irregularly shaped dark spots on back and several dusky blotches on midside. Body depth going more than 7 times into standard length. Upper lip separated from snout by a continuous groove, not connected at midline by a bridge of skin. Lateral line complete, containing 64 to 78 scales. Anal fin with 1 flexible spine and

8 or 9 rays. Tail fin only slightly forked.

Very similar to western sand darter but with the following differences: body mostly scaled except for breast and belly; spine near rear margin of gill cover rather short and broad, its length about equal to width of its base; dusky blotches along midside more prominent.

Life colors: Like those of western sand darter except with rather distinct dusky blotches along midside and faint, dusky lines in fins.

Size: Adults are commonly 1.8 to 2.3 inches long to a maximum of about 2.5 inches.

Scientific name: *Ammocrypta,* Greek, meaning "sand concealed," in reference to the habit of lying buried in the sand; *vivax,* Latin, meaning "vivacious."

DISTRIBUTION AND HABITAT

The scaly sand darter is a Lowland species, confined in Missouri to streams and ditches of the southeast. It is not abundant but is more common within its Missouri range than the western sand darter. The habitats of the two species are much alike.

HABITS AND LIFE HISTORY

The habits of this darter, as far as is known, are not notably different from those of the western sand darter.

Johnny Darter

Etheostoma nigrum Rafinesque

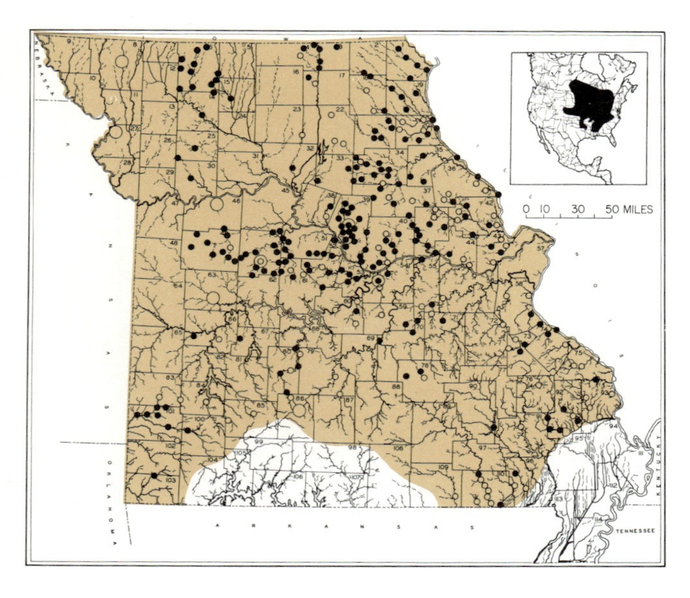

DESCRIPTION

Illustration: Page 286, 19a.

Characters: A slender, straw-colored darter with about 6 dark cross-bars on back, and small W and X-shaped markings scattered over back and sides. Upper lip and snout separated by a continuous groove, not connected at midline by a narrow bridge of skin as in many darters. Midline of belly without enlarged and modified scales. Gill covers not broadly connected by membrane across throat; distance from membrane notch to front of lower lip equal to or less than distance from notch to front of pelvic fin base. Anal fin with 1 thin, flexible spine and 7 to 10 rays. Spinous dorsal with 9 or 10 spines.

Similar to bluntnose darter, but with the following differences: snout less bluntly rounded; dark streak extending forward onto snout from eye not meeting its opposite on tip of snout; cheek without scales or with a few scales behind eye; soft dorsal with 12 or 13 rays; lateral line complete or nearly so, extending to behind soft dorsal; dorsal fins only slightly separated.

Life colors: Back and upper sides yellow with about 6 dark brown cross-bars and scattered zigzag brown lines; lower parts yellowish-white. Gill cover with a metallic-green luster. A black streak extends forward from eye and often there is a black bar or spot beneath eye. Dorsal and tail fins faintly banded by brown lines. Breeding males are often nearly black towards head and have fleshy white tips on some fins.

Size: Adults are commonly 1.6 to 2.8 inches long to a maximum of about 3 inches.

Scientific name: *Etheostoma,* from the Greek *etheo,* "to strain," and *stoma,* "mouth"; *nigrum,* Latin, meaning "black".

DISTRIBUTION AND HABITAT

The johnny darter is one of the common Missouri darters, occurring over most of the state except for the Lowlands, the south-central Ozarks, and parts of the western Prairies. It is most abundant in the Prairie and Ozark border streams of central and northeastern Missouri. Westward in the Prairie Region it becomes increasingly spotty in distribution but is locally abundant.

This darter inhabits streams of all sizes but is more abundant in creeks than in rivers. It is more tolerant of turbidity than most darters, but avoids streams that are excessively turbid and silty, and those with high gradients or continuous strong flow. Unlike many darters, it is more often found in quiet pools than in riffles. Perhaps the johnny darter is excluded from the Lowlands by competition from the related bluntnose and speckled darters.

HABITS AND LIFE HISTORY

The johnny darter feeds principally on the immature stages of aquatic insects.[42, 221] Food is located primarily by sight, with odor possibly playing a minor role.[229]

The johnny darter deposits its eggs on the underside of flat rocks or other objects lying near the bottom and the male fish attends the eggs until they hatch.[223] Nest sites are selected by the male who cleans off the underside of the selected rock by the action of his fins. The eggs are laid while the spawning pair are in an upside down position. A single nest may contain over 1,100 eggs. More than one female may spawn in a nest and a single female may deposit several clutches of eggs in a single season. In Missouri spawning occurs in April and May.

In the Des Moines River, Iowa, the johnny darter averages 1.2 inches in length by the end of its first year of life, and attains lengths of 1.8, 2.2, and 2.4 inches in succeeding years.[221]

Bluntnose Darter

Etheostoma chlorosomum (Hay)

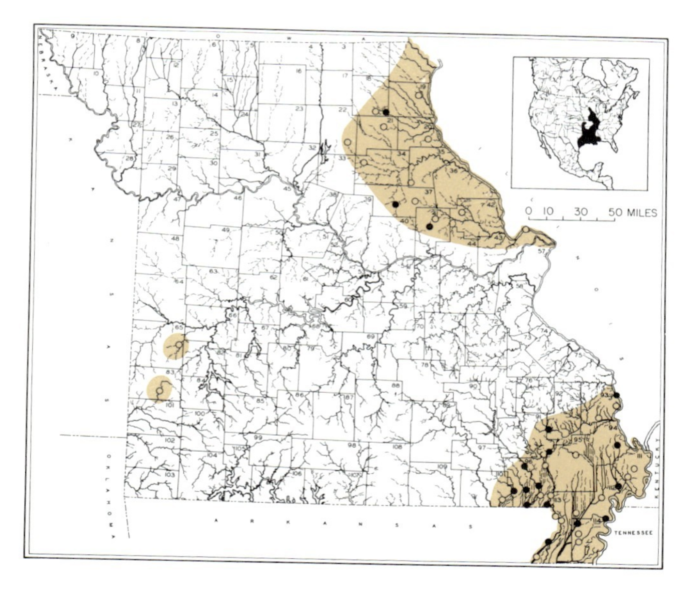

DESCRIPTION

Illustration: Page 286, 19b.

Characters: A slender, straw-colored darter with about 6 dark cross-bars on the back and small W and X-shaped markings scattered over back and sides. Upper lip and snout separated by a continuous groove, not connected at midline by a bridge of skin as in many darters. Midline of belly without enlarged and modified scales. Gill covers not broadly connected by membrane across throat; distance from membrane notch to front of lower lip equal to or less than distance from notch to front of pelvic fin base. Anal fin with 1 thin, flexible spine and 7 to 9 rays. Spinous dorsal with 9 or 10 spines.

Similar to johnny darter, but with the following differences: snout more bluntly rounded; dark streak extending forward onto snout from eye meeting its opposite on tip of snout; cheek fully scaled; soft dorsal with 10 or 11 rays; lateral line incomplete, usually ending beneath soft dorsal; dorsal fins more widely separated than in johnny darter.

Life colors: Like those of johnny darter, page 308, except as noted under *Characters*.

Size: A smaller fish than the johnny darter, not exceeding a length of 2 inches.

Scientific name: *Etheostoma,* from the Greek *etheo,* "to strain," and *stoma,* "mouth"; *chlorosomum,* Greek, meaning "greenish-yellow."

DISTRIBUTION AND HABITAT

The bluntnose darter has two principal centers of occurrence in Missouri. One of these is in the Lowland streams and ditches of the southeast; the other is in the Prairie streams of northeastern Missouri. This darter is also known from one locality in the upper Osage River system and another just across the divide in the Spring River system. The bluntnose darter seems to have declined in abundance in Missouri during the past 30 years, but remains fairly common in the Lowlands.

It inhabits the sluggish streams of lowlands and of level, undissected uplands. It is found in pools and backwaters without noticeable current where the bottom is composed of sand and organic debris. Increased siltation has probably been a factor in the decline of the bluntnose darter in the intensively cultivated prairies of northeastern Missouri.

HABITS AND LIFE HISTORY

The habits of this fish have not been studied but are probably like those of the johnny darter.

Speckled Darter

Etheostoma stigmaeum (Jordan)

DESCRIPTION

Illustration: Page 287, 20a.

Characters: A slender, straw-colored darter with about 6 dark cross-bars on back and small W and X-shaped markings scattered over back and sides. Upper lip and snout separated by a continuous deep groove, not connected at midline by a narrow bridge of skin as in many darters. Differs from johnny and bluntnose darters in having 2 spines in anal fin and 11 or 12 spines in spinous dorsal. Midline of belly without enlarged and modified scales. Gill covers not broadly connected by membrane across throat; distance from membrane notch to front of lower lip equal to or less than distance from notch to front of pelvic fin base. Lateral line incomplete, usually ending beneath soft dorsal. Scales in lengthwise series along midside 43 to 53.

Life colors: Back and upper sides yellow with dark brown cross-bars and scattered brown zigzag lines; lower parts yellowish-white. A dusky bar or spot beneath eye and a black bar extending forward from eye onto snout. Dorsal and tail fins faintly banded by brown lines. Breeding males are darker: about 8 squarish blue or green bars are present along side of body; side of head blue or green; spinous dorsal black with a narrow orange band; other fins, except pectorals, dark, faintly tinged by orange.

Size: Adults are commonly 1.4 to 2 inches long to a maximum of about 2.2 inches.

Scientific name: *Etheostoma,* from the Greek *etheo,* "to strain," and *stoma,* "mouth"; *stigmaeum,* Greek, meaning "speckled."

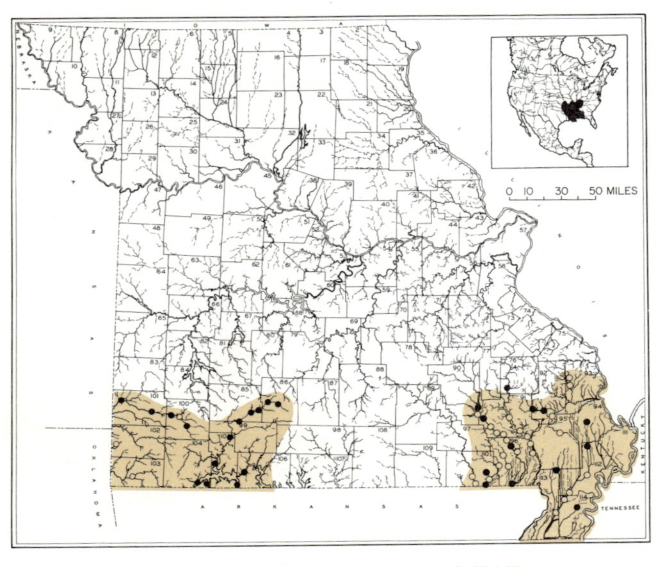

DISTRIBUTION AND HABITAT

The speckled darter has two distribution centers in the state. One is in the Lowlands and adjacent sections of the southeastern Ozarks; the other is in the southwestern Ozarks.

The habitat of this darter is much like that of the johnny and bluntnose darters, except that it occurs more often in clear, high-gradient streams. It occupies sluggish riffles when spawning, but at other times is found in quiet pools and backwaters having sandy or rocky bottoms.

HABITS AND LIFE HISTORY

The speckled darter spawns in Missouri over gravelly riffles in April and May. The eggs are buried in the gravel in a manner similar to the orangethroat and rainbow darters.[223] Nothing else is known of its habits.

Missouri Saddled Darter

Etheostoma tetrazonum (Hubbs and Black)

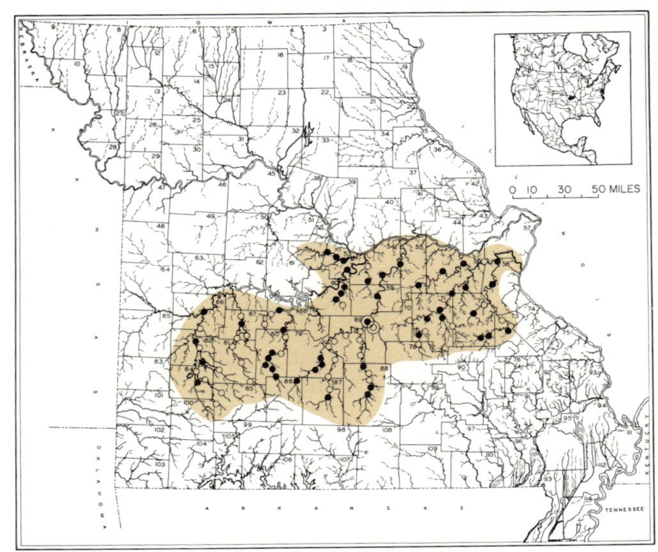

DESCRIPTION

Illustration: Page 290, 26a; **48.**

Characters: A stout darter with 4 equally prominent dark cross-bars on the back. Upper lip attached to snout at midline by a narrow bridge of skin (frenum). Midline of belly without enlarged and modified scales. Gill covers broadly connected by membrane across throat; distance from membrane notch to front of lower lip much greater than distance from notch to front of pelvic fin base. Lateral line complete. Dorsal fins with 11 to 13 spines and 12 to 14 rays. Anal fin with 2 stiff spines and 8 to 10 rays.

Similar to Arkansas saddled darter but with a stouter body. Also, there are usually 46 to 57 scales in lateral line and 5 or 6 scales above lateral line.

Life colors: Back and upper sides mottled olive-brown with 4 dark brown saddle bars that extend obliquely down and forward to lateral line. Midside vaguely mottled with orange and with a series of indistinct green blotches or bars. Spinous dorsal with a broad dusky band; soft dorsal, tail fin, and pectoral fins with faint orange dots and faintly banded by brown lines.

Breeding males very brilliantly colored. Sides with scattered red dots and a series of alternating blue-green and reddish-orange bars; lower sides rust-red; breast blue-black. Spinous dorsal dusky at base, a blue-green band through middle and an orange-red band along outer margin; soft dorsal and tail fins dusky blue-green with rows of red dots; pectoral fins golden-yellow with red dots; pelvic and anal fins blue-green, the tips of pelvic fins thickened and whitish.

Size: Adults are commonly 2 to 3.3 inches long to a maximum of about 3.5

Scientific name: *Etheostoma,* from the Greek *etheo,* "to strain," and *stoma,* "mouth"; *tetrazonum,* Greek, meaning "four-banded," in reference to the four dark saddle markings.

DISTRIBUTION AND HABITAT

This darter occurs only in Missouri where it is restricted to streams of the northern Ozarks from the Moreau and Osage stream systems east to the Meramec. In this area it is one of the most abundant darters.

The Missouri saddled darter is characteristic of clear, high-gradient streams having continuous strong flow. It avoids small headwater creeks, achieving greatest abundance in moderately large Ozark rivers. It lives in the deeper, swifter riffles over a bottom of coarse gravel and rock.

HABITS AND LIFE HISTORY

Little is known of the habits of this darter. It is specialized for life on the bottom in swift currents and probably feeds on the immature stages of caddisflies, stoneflies and other insects that occupy the riffle habitat. It spawns on rocky riffles in late April and May.

Arkansas Saddled Darter

Etheostoma euzonum (Hubbs and Black)

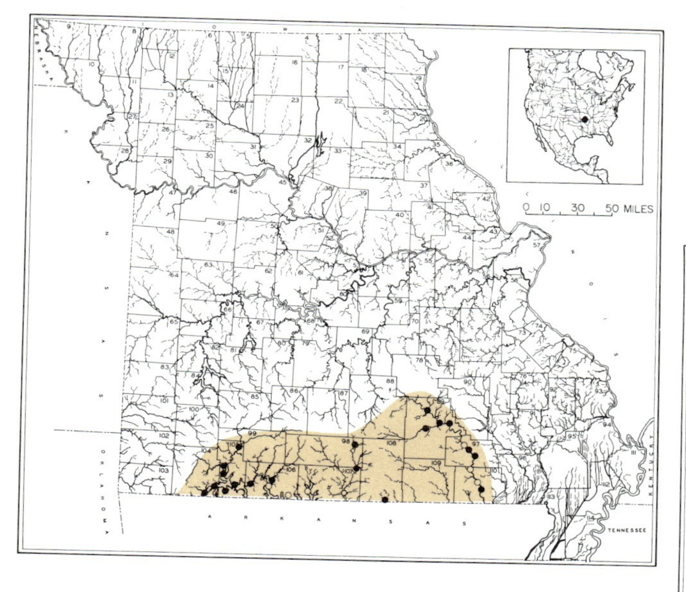

DESCRIPTION

Illustration: Page 290, 26b.

Characters: A stout darter with 4 equally prominent dark cross-bars on the back. Upper lip attached to snout at midline by a bridge of skin (frenum). Midline of belly without enlarged and modified scales. Gill covers broadly connected by membrane across throat; distance from membrane notch to front of lower lip much greater than distance from notch to front of pelvic fin base. Lateral line complete. Dorsal fins with 12 to 15 spines and 14 or 15 rays. Anal fin with 2 stiff spines and 9 to 11 rays.

Similar to Missouri saddled darter, but with a more slender body. Also, there are usually 60 to 73 scales in lateral line and 7 or 8 scales above lateral line.

Life colors: Like those of Missouri saddled darter, page 310.

Size: A somewhat larger fish than Missouri saddled darter, attaining a length of 4.3 inches or more.

Scientific name: *Etheostoma,* from the Greek *etheo,* "to strain", and *stoma,* "mouth"; *euzonum,* Greek, meaning "well zoned," in reference to the prominent saddle markings.

DISTRIBUTION AND HABITAT

The Arkansas saddled darter occurs in the White and Current River systems of the southern Ozarks. In that area it is one of the most abundant darters in large streams.

It replaces the closely related Missouri saddled darter in streams of the southern Ozarks and the habitat of the two species is not recognizably different.

HABITS AND LIFE HISTORY

The habits of this darter have not been studied.

Banded Darter

Etheostoma zonale (Cope)

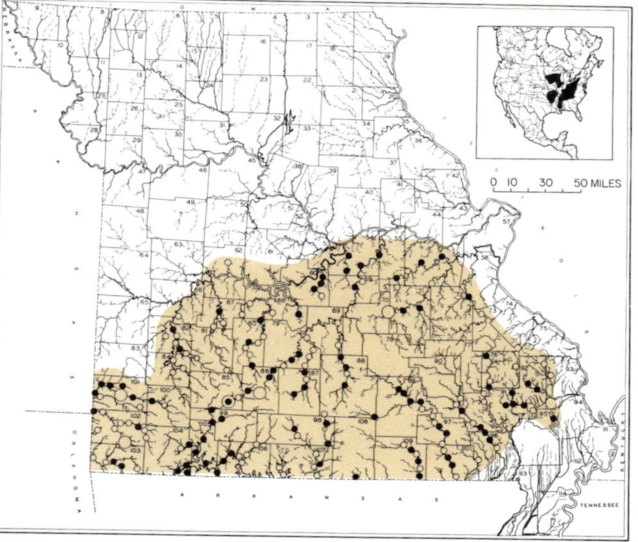

DESCRIPTION

Illustration: Page 291, 29b.

Characters: A moderately slender darter with 6 or 7 dark cross-bars on the back. Upper lip connected to snout at midline by a narrow bridge of skin (frenum). Midline of belly without enlarged and modified scales. Gill covers broadly connected by membrane across throat; distance from membrane notch to front of lower lip much greater than distance from notch to front of pelvic fin base. Lateral line complete, containing 44 to 54 scales. Anal fin with 2 stiff spines and 7 or 8 rays.

Similar to harlequin darter, page 312, but with the following differences: second and fourth dark cross-bars on back about equal in width to adjacent bars; body at base of tail fin with a vertical series of 3 or 4 small dark spots; spinous dorsal with 11 or 12 (occasionally 10) spines. Pectoral fins shorter than in harlequin darter, extending backward only about to tips of pelvic fins.

Life colors: Back and upper sides mottled olive-brown with 6 or 7 dark brown cross-bars. Midside with a series of dark green blotches or bars. Lower parts yellowish-white with scattered dusky markings. A dusky spot or bar beneath eye and another extending forward from eye onto snout. Spinous dorsal rust-red at base; all fins prominently marked by narrow brown lines. Breeding males have about 10 bright green bars encircling body; lower surface of head and breast blue-green; dorsal fins each with a brick-red band at base; fins otherwise a rather uniform dusky green.

Size: Adults are commonly 1.6 to 2.8 inches long to a maximum of about 3 inches.

Scientific name: *Etheostoma,* from the Greek *etheo,* "to strain", and *stoma,* "mouth"; *zonale,* Latin, meaning "banded."

DISTRIBUTION AND HABITAT

The banded darter is one of the common and widespread darters of the Ozarks, where it occurs in all of the principal stream systems. Elsewhere in Missouri it has been collected only from a Lowland ditch in Stoddard County.

This darter inhabits clear, high-gradient streams having permanent strong flow. It is common on rocky riffles but is more often observed clambering about over algae-covered boulders in pools having enough current to prevent deposition of silt. Young of the banded darter commonly occur in quiet water around aquatic plants or in accumulations of leaves, sticks, and other organic debris.

HABITS AND LIFE HISTORY

The banded darter lives on the bottom in typical darter fashion. Its food probably consists mainly of immature aquatic insects gleaned from the bottom. Spawning occurs in Missouri from mid-April into May. The banded darter begins spawning somewhat later than the greenside darter but has similar habits, attaching its eggs to strands of filamentous algae and aquatic mosses. This species generally spawns in a slower current over sparser vegetation than the greenside darter. In western Pennsylvania males of the banded darter average 1.2, 1.6, 1.9, and 2.2 inches standard length by the end of their first through fourth summers of growth.[230] Females grow more slowly and do not attain as large a size as males. Some individuals mature at one year of age, but most do not mature until they are 2 years old. Only a few individuals survive their fourth summer of life.

Harlequin Darter

Etheostoma histrio Jordan and Gilbert

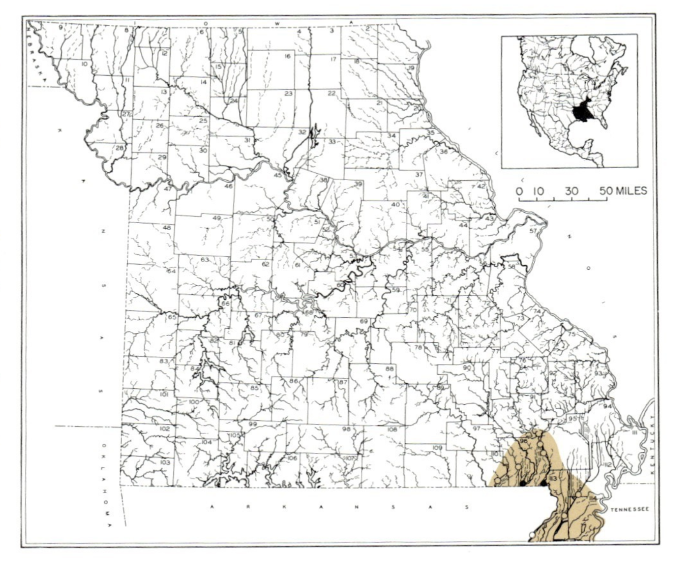

DESCRIPTION

Illustration: Page 291, 29a.

Characters: A moderately slender darter with 6 or 7 dark cross-bars on the back. Upper lip often separated from snout at midline by a continuous shallow groove. Forward half of belly without scales; back half covered by scales of normal size and shape. Gill covers broadly connected by membrane across throat; distance from membrane notch to front of lower lip much greater than distance from notch to front of pelvic fin base. Lateral line complete, containing 45 to 58 scales. Anal fin with 2 stiff spines and 6 to 8 rays.

Similar to banded darter, page 311, but with the following differences: second and fourth dark cross-bars on back narrower than adjacent bars; body at base of tail fin with large blotches; cheek and gill cover usually without scales; spinous dorsal with 9 (occasionally 10) spines; pectoral fins very long, extending backward past tips of pelvic fins.

Life colors: Back and upper sides mottled green with 6 or 7 dark brown cross-bars. Midside with a series of dark green blotches. Lower parts yellowish-white with scattered dusky spots or blotches. All fins prominently marked by narrow brown lines and spots. Males more brightly colored and more boldly marked than females.

Size: Adults are commonly 1.5 to 2.7 inches long to a maximum of about 3 inches.

Scientific name: *Etheostoma,* from the Greek *etheo,* "to strain," and *stoma,* "mouth"; *histrio,* Latin, meaning "a harlequin."

DISTRIBUTION AND HABITAT

This Lowland species has been collected in Missouri only from the larger streams and ditches of the southeast. It is one of the rarest Missouri darters and seems to have declined in abundance over the past 30 years.

The harlequin darter exhibits a definite preference for sandy bottoms where logs, sticks and other organic debris are present.[231] In Missouri young of the harlequin darter have been collected from among finely divided tree roots and in beds of organic debris along the quiet margins of pools.

HABITS AND LIFE HISTORY

In Texas, adults of the harlequin darter in spawning condition have been collected in February.[231] Spawning probably is somewhat later than this in Missouri. Nothing else is known concerning the biology of this darter.

Greenside Darter

Etheostoma blennioides Rafinesque

DESCRIPTION

Illustration: Page 287, 20b; **47.**

Characters: A moderately slender darter with 6 or 7 dark cross-bars on the back and a bluntly rounded snout that projects ahead of the mouth. Differing from other Missouri darters in having a prominent, nipple-like extension at middle of upper lip (nipple poorly developed in small individuals). Upper lip separated from snout at midline by a deep, continuous groove. Midline of belly without enlarged and modified scales. Gill covers broadly connected by membrane across throat; distance from membrane notch to front of lower lip much less than distance from notch to front of pelvic fin base. Lateral line complete, containing 57 to 78 scales. Anal fin with 2 stiff spines and 6 to 9 rays.

Life colors: Back and upper sides light yellowish-olive with scattered orange-red spots and 6 or 7 brown cross-bars. Lower sides with a series of V or W-shaped green blotches. A dusky vertical bar beneath eye and another extending forward from eye to front of upper lip. Dorsal fins rusty-red at base; all fins, except pelvics, faintly banded by brown lines. Breeding males have much bright green and blue-green on head, body, and fins, and have about 8 dark green bars encircling back half of body; spots on upper part of body and basal parts of dorsal fins more intensely red than in other adults.

Size: One of the largest darters, attaining a length of at least 5.4 inches. Most adults are 2.5 to 4.5 inches long.

Scientific name: *Etheostoma,* from the Greek *etheo,* "to strain," and *stoma,* "mouth"; *blennioides,* "like the blenny," a marine fish.

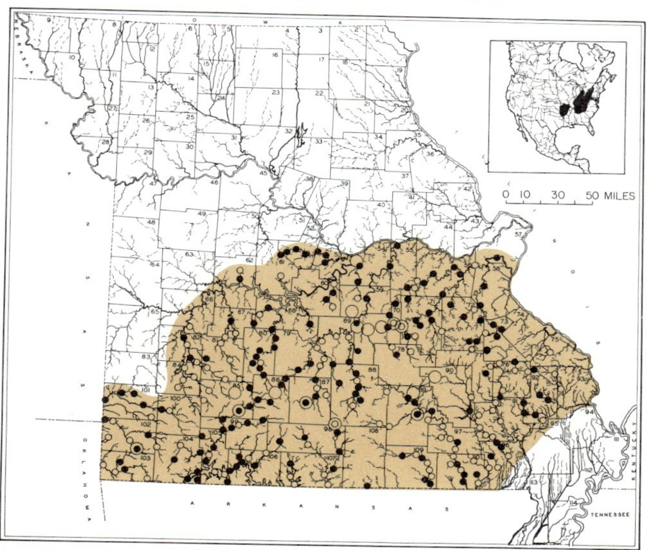

DISTRIBUTION AND HABITAT

The greenside is one of the most abundant and widespread darters in the Ozarks, but has never been taken elsewhere in Missouri. No two Missouri fishes are more closely associated than the greenside and banded darters. The distribution pattern of the two is strikingly similar, differing notably only in the absence of the banded darter from the Moreau River in central Missouri. The greenside darter is the more abundant of the two species at most localities.

There seems to be no significant difference in the habitat requirements of the greenside and banded darters. The greenside is most abundant on swift, gravelly or rocky riffles, but is often observed foraging over boulders or submerged logs in pools having slight current. The young commonly occur in quiet water among growths of aquatic vegetation or in accumulations of leaves, sticks, and other organic debris.

HABITS AND LIFE HISTORY

Except as noted, the following information is from a detailed report of the life history of the greenside darter in New York.[232] The greenside spends most of the daylight hours foraging slowly over the bottom. At rest, the weight of the body is distributed on the pelvic and caudal fins and the base of the caudal peduncle. The food of young greensides during the first few weeks of life is not known; juveniles and adults feed almost exclusively on the immature stages of midges, caddisflies, mayflies and other aquatic insects. Nearly all of the insects eaten are of the types found clinging to rocks in riffles.

The greenside spawns earlier than most Missouri darters. Spawning is usually underway by late March and is completed by the end of April. Like the banded darter, the greenside attaches its eggs to strands of filamentous algae and aquatic mosses. The males occupy and defend territories. The eggs are laid about 40 at a time; a female may spawn successively with different males and deposit her eggs over a period of several days. The eggs hatch in 18 days at a temperature of 55° to 58° F.

Males grow more rapidly and attain a larger maximum size than females. About 60% of the total growth is achieved during the first growing season. Males reach a standard length of about 1.9, 2.5, 2.8, and 3 inches by the end of growing seasons one through four. All males and females mature and spawn in the spring of the year following hatching and most survive only three growing seasons. Among Missouri darters, only the logperch attains a larger size than the greenside.

Niangua Darter

Etheostoma nianguae Gilbert and Meek

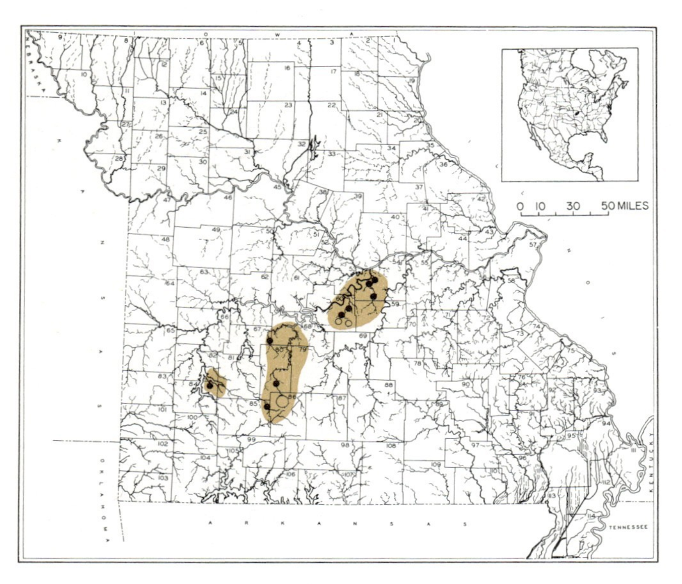

DESCRIPTION

Illustration: Page 288, 22a; **48.**
Characters: A slender darter with about 8 dark cross-bars on the back. Readily distinguished from other Missouri darters by the presence of 2 small jet-black spots at base of tail fin. Head very long and slender, its length going 3.5 times or less into standard length. Gill covers not broadly connected by membrane across throat; distance from membrane notch to front of lower lip about equal to distance from notch to front of pelvic fin base. Midline of belly without enlarged and modified scales. Lateral line complete, containing 72 to 81 scales. Anal fin with 2 stiff spines and 11 or 12 rays.
Life colors: Back light yellowish-olive with scattered orange spots and about 8 rather prominent dark brown cross-bars. Sides with a series of V-shaped dark green blotches alternating with narrow orange bars. A dark streak extends forward and another backward from eye. Two small jet-black spots at base of tail fin. Spinous dorsal dusky with deep red spots at base and a narrow orange fringe on outer margin; soft dorsal, tail and pectoral fins alternately banded with orange and black spots. Breeding males with all colors much brighter than in females and nonbreeding males.
Size: Adults are commonly 3 to 4 inches long to a maximum of about 4.2 inches.
Scientific name: *Etheostoma,* from the Greek *etheo,* "to strain," and *stoma,* "mouth"; *nianguae,* named for the Niangua River, from which it was first collected.

DISTRIBUTION AND HABITAT

This distinctive darter has a very localized distribution, occurring only in a few tributaries of the Osage River in central Missouri. It is not abundant anywhere, but is more common in the Maries River and Tavern Creek than elsewhere. In 1971 four specimens of this darter were collected from Arbell Creek, Dade County, just upstream from the rising waters of Stockton Lake.[233] This represents the only known occurrence for the Niangua darter in the Sac River drainage. There have been no noticeable changes in the distribution or abundance of the Niangua darter within the last 25 or 30 years. Its status before that is unknown, but there is no evidence that would suggest a more widespread distribution before 1900 than now.

The Niangua darter is characteristic of clear, small to medium-sized streams with permanent flow and clean, gravelly or rocky bottoms. It is most often found in the deeper sections of riffles, but also occurs in rocky pools having no perceptible current.

HABITS AND LIFE HISTORY

The Niangua darter behaves in a manner typical of darters, remaining most of the time on the bottom and moving about in short, quick dashes. It probes for food in crevices between rocks with its long, slender snout. However, it does not overturn rocks with its snout as does the logperch. The diet of the Niangua darter has not been studied but almost certainly consists principally of immature aquatic insects. It has been observed spawning over swift gravelly riffles in early April following an abrupt increase in stream temperature from the 50's to near 65° F. The males precede the females to the spawning sites and occupy territories. When a female enters the territory of a male he begins following her. As the male comes near the female often engages in a rapid "head-bobbing" display. Just prior to the spawning act the female plunges head first into the gravel and comes to rest with only her head and tail visible. The male takes a position above her and vibrates rapidly as the eggs are released and fertilized. The female then emerges from the gravel and the eggs are left to complete their development without further attention. Burying the eggs in this manner provides a measure of protection against predation. The female repeats the spawning act with the same or a different male until her full complement of eggs has been deposited.

The Niangua darter achieves a length of about 2.1 to 2.7 inches by the end of its first year of life. Most individuals do not become sexually mature until they are 2 years of age and 3 inches or more in length.

Redfin Darter

Etheostoma whipplei (Girard)

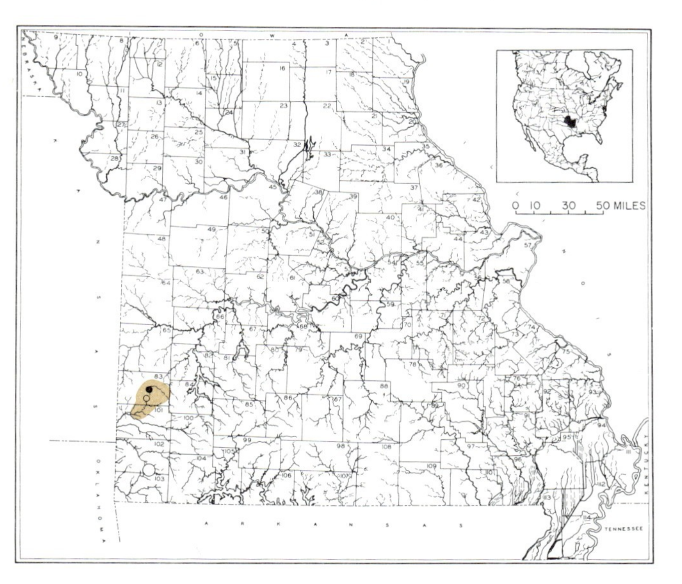

DESCRIPTION

Illustration: Page 292, 30a.

Characters: A moderately stout darter with about 12 indistinct dark cross-bars on back (cross-bars often not evident). An enlarged black scale is present above base of pectoral fin; cheek beneath eye with a prominent dusky vertical bar. Gill covers broadly connected by membrane across throat; distance from membrane notch to front of lower lip greater than distance from notch to front of pelvic fin base. Belly scaled, but scales often small and inconspicuous. Lateral line incomplete, usually ending beneath soft dorsal. Scales in a length-wise series along midside 59 to 67. Spinous dorsal with 10 to 12 spines, and about equal in height to soft dorsal. Anal fin with 2 stiff spines and 7 to 9 rays.

Life colors: Back mottled olive-brown, the cross-bars (if present) dark brown. Sides light brown with scattered pale spots and an enlarged black scale just above base of pectoral fin. Belly white with scattered dusky specks. A dusky bar beneath eye and another extending forward from eye onto snout. Dorsal, tail, and anal fins with faint brown bands. Breeding males have scattered red spots on body; spinous and soft dorsal dusky basally, orange-red outward, and blue along outer margin; tail fin similar in color to dorsal fins and with two orange-red spots at base; lower fins dusky blue.

Size: Adults are commonly 1.8 to 2.5 inches in length to a maximum of about 2.8 inches.

Scientific name: *Etheostoma,* from the Greek *etheo,* "to strain," and *stoma,* "mouth"; *whipplei,* named for Lieutenant A. W. Whipple, in command of the survey by which the species was discovered.

DISTRIBUTION AND HABITAT

The redfin darter has been collected in Missouri only from the Spring and Elk River systems. An early collector reported it from the North Fork of White River,[88] but this report may have resulted from a misidentification. The only recent collections of the redfin darter are from the North Fork of Spring River, Barton County.

This fish is reported to inhabit the gravelly riffles of streams having moderate or low gradients.[42]

HABITS AND LIFE HISTORY

Reproduction of the redfin darter occurs in April in Kansas.[42] Nothing else is known of its habits.

Mud Darter

Etheostoma asprigene (Forbes)

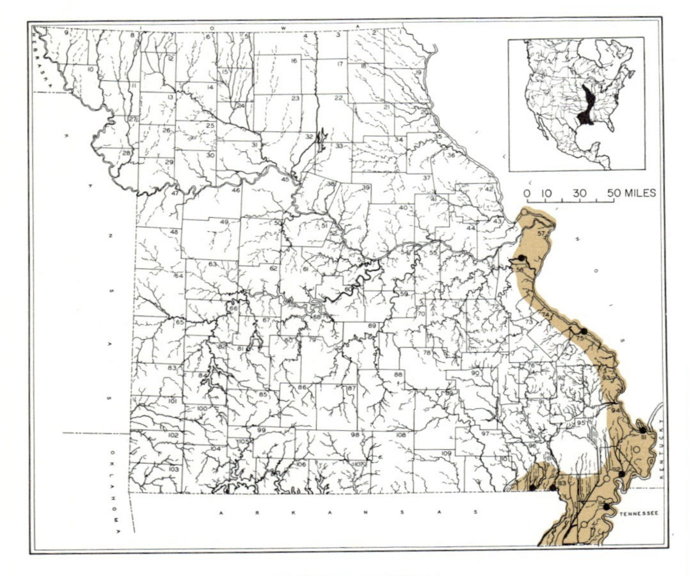

DESCRIPTION

Illustration: Page 294, 34a.

Characters: A moderately stout darter with 8 to 10 indistinct dark cross-bars on back (bars often not evident). Spinous dorsal with a broad blackish band at base; cheek beneath eye with a prominent dusky vertical bar. Gill covers not broadly connected by membrane across throat; distance from membrane notch to front of lower lip less than distance from notch to front of pelvic fin base. Midline of belly without enlarged and modified scales. Gill cover and cheek fully scaled. Lateral line incomplete, usually ending beneath soft dorsal. Scales in a lengthwise series along midside 44 to 52. Spinous dorsal with 10 or 11 spines. Anal fin with 2 stiff spines and 8 or 9 rays.

Life colors: Back mottled olive-brown, often with about 8 to 10 indistinct dark brown cross-bars. Sides mottled brown, the back half marked by alternating bars of greenish-brown and orange-yellow. A dusky bar beneath eye and another extending forward from eye onto snout. Spinous dorsal with a broad blackish band at base, pale orange outward, and black along outer margin; soft dorsal and tail fins faintly banded by brown lines. Breeding males have alternating red and blue-green bars on sides and a red band in spinous dorsal.

Size: Adults are commonly 1.6 to 2.3 inches long to a maximum of about 2.5 inches.

Scientific name: *Etheostoma,* from the Greek *etheo,* "to strain," and *stoma,* "mouth"; *asprigene* from *Asper,* a European genus of perch, and *genos,* Greek for "a race" or "kind."

DISTRIBUTION AND HABITAT

The mud darter occurs at scattered localities in the Lowlands and northward along the Mississippi River. It is locally common at some localities in the Lowlands. It inhabits Lowland lakes and ponds and the sluggish riffles and pools of large, low-gradient streams.

HABITS AND LIFE HISTORY

Nothing is known about the habits of this darter.

Yoke Darter

Etheostoma juliae Meek

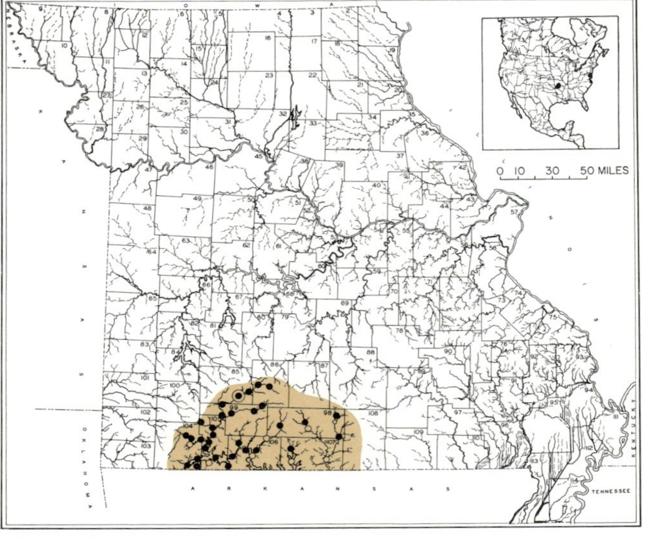

DESCRIPTION

Illustration: Page 289, 25a.

Characters: A stout-bodied darter with a prominent dark cross-bar on the back ahead of spinous dorsal, followed by 3 less distinct cross-bars. Upper lip attached to snout at midline by a bridge of skin. Gill covers broadly connected by membrane across throat; distance from membrane notch to front of lower lip much greater than distance from notch to front of pelvic fin base. Midline of belly without enlarged and modified scales. Breast without scales. Lateral line complete or nearly so, extending behind soft dorsal. Scales in a lengthwise series along midside 51 to 62. Spinous dorsal with 11 spines. Anal fin with 2 stiff spines and 7 or 8 rays.

Life colors: Back mottled brown with 4 darker brown cross-bars, the first much more prominent and longer than the others, extending downward to base of pectoral fin. Sides lighter brown, thickly spotted with yellow, and with an enlarged blue-green scale above pectoral fin base. Belly yellowish-white. A blackish vertical bar beneath eye; lower surface of head thickly sprinkled with black specks. Spinous dorsal fin dusky on lower half; fins otherwise pale yellow. Breeding males similar in color but with fins bright yellowish-orange.

Size: Adults are commonly 1.8 to 2.5 inches long to a maximum of about 2.8 inches.

Scientific name: *Etheostoma,* from the Greek *etheo,* "to strain," and *stoma,* "mouth"; *juliae,* named for Mrs. J. H. Gilbert.

DISTRIBUTION AND HABITAT

The yoke darter occurs only in the White River system of southern Missouri and northern Arkansas. In this area it is one of the most abundant darters.

It inhabits clear high-gradient streams having strong permanent flow. It is restricted primarily to riffles having swift current and coarse gravel or rock bottoms. This is often the only darter in the swiftest sections of such riffles.

HABITS AND LIFE HISTORY

The yoke darter spawns on swift riffles in May. Nothing else is known of its habits.

Arkansas Darter

Etheostoma cragini Gilbert

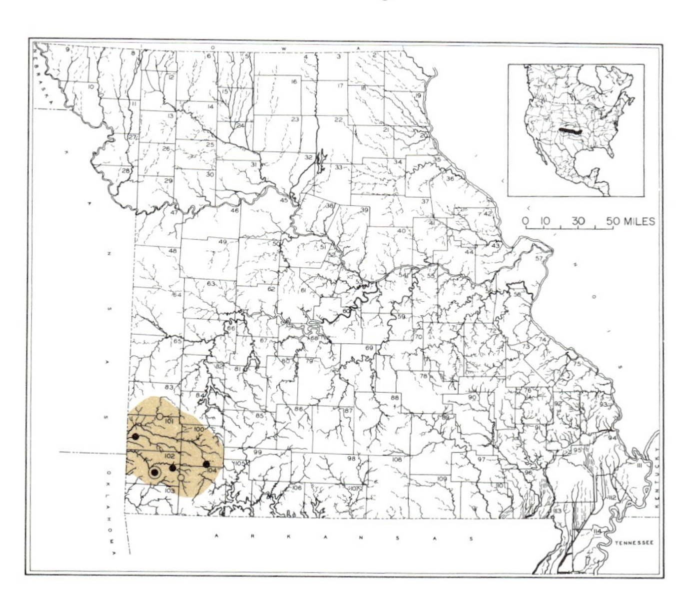

DESCRIPTION

Illustration: Page 293, 33a.

Characters: A moderately stout darter with 6 to 8 indistinct dark cross-bars on the back (cross-bars often not evident). Body and head thickly sprinkled with fine black specks; cheek beneath eye with a narrow dusky vertical bar. Gill covers not broadly connected by membrane across throat; distance from membrane notch to front of lower lip much less than distance from notch to front of pelvic fin base. Midline of belly without enlarged and modified scales. Lateral line incomplete. Spinous dorsal with 9 or 10 spines. Anal fin with 2 stiff spines and 6 to 8 rays.

Similar to stippled darter, page 318, but with the following differences: lateral line shorter, usually not extending to behind base of spinous dorsal; scales in a lengthwise series along midside 45 to 55; soft dorsal with 11 to 13 (occasionally 14) rays; snout more blunt, and shorter than eye.

Life colors: Similar to those of stippled darter, page 318, but often with a series of horizontally oblong dusky blotches along midside, forming an interrupted stripe. In breeding males the gill membranes, belly, and underside of caudal peduncle are orange.

Size: Adults are commonly 1.6 to 2.2 inches long to a maximum of about 2.5 inches.

Scientific name: *Etheostoma,* from the Greek *etheo,* "to strain," and *stoma,* "mouth"; *cragini,* named for Prof. F. W. Cragin, then director of Washington College Laboratory.

DISTRIBUTION AND HABITAT

The Arkansas darter is known in Missouri only from the Spring River system of the southwestern Ozarks. Because of its specialized habitat this darter is spotty in distribution but is often quite common where it does occur.

It inhabits the quiet pools of the smallest spring branches and spring-fed creeks where it is most often found along the margins of riffles and pools, associated with thick growths of water cress. Although the stippled darter and Arkansas darter both occur in southwestern Missouri, they are rarely collected at the same locality. Where both occur in the same area, the stippled darter tends to occupy larger and warmer streams than the Arkansas darter.

HABITS AND LIFE HISTORY

Adults of the Arkansas darter that apparently were spawning were collected in Colorado on March 25.[234] When frightened these darters swam a short distance and plunged head first into the silt, completely burying themselves and concealing their location by the cloud of muddy water created by this activity. Spawning evidently takes place in shallow water over a bottom of coarse gravel.

Stippled Darter

Etheostoma punctulatum (Agassiz)

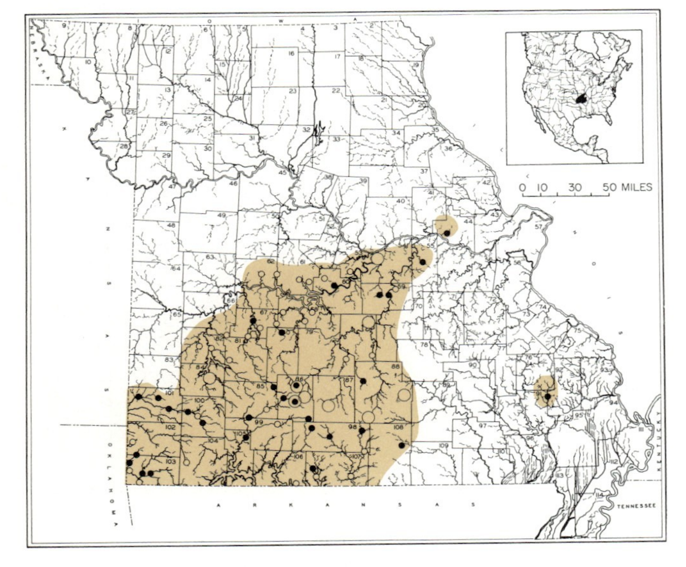

DESCRIPTION

Illustration: Page 293, 32a.

Characters: A moderately stout darter with 6 or 7 indistinct dark cross-bars on the back (bars often not evident). Body and head thickly sprinkled with fine black specks; cheek beneath eye with a narrow dusky vertical bar. Gill covers not broadly connected by membrane across throat; distance from membrane notch to front of lower lip much less than distance from notch to front of pelvic fin base. Midline of belly without enlarged and modified scales. Lateral line incomplete. Spinous dorsal with 10 to 12 spines. Anal fin with 2 stiff spines and 7 to 9 rays.

Similar to Arkansas darter, page 317, but with the following differences: lateral line longer, usually extending to behind base of soft dorsal; scales in a lengthwise series along midside 58 to 80; soft dorsal with 14 to 15 (occasionally 13) rays; snout more pointed and longer than eye.

Life colors: Back and sides mottled light brown, often with a series of faint dark brown cross-bars or blotches. Almost entire head and body thickly sprinkled with fine black specks. A dusky bar beneath eye. Spinous dorsal with a dusky band at base; other fins dusky, often faintly banded by brown lines. Breeding males brightly colored: throat and belly bright orange-red; side with a broad, blue-green stripe and a short blue-green vertical bar across base of pectoral fin; spinous dorsal with a broad blue-green band at base, a bright orange band outward, and a narrow black fringe; soft dorsal and tail fins dusky with rays yellowish; anal and pelvic fins black with large tubercles along rays.

Size: Adults are commonly 2.4 to 3.2 inches long to a maximum of about 3.5 inches.

Scientific name: *Etheostoma,* from the Greek *etheo,* "to strain," and *stoma,* "mouth"; *punctulatum,* Latin, meaning "with little points," in reference to the numerous black specks.

DISTRIBUTION AND HABITAT

The stippled darter is locally common and widely distributed over the western half of the Ozarks. It is rare in the southeastern Ozarks where it may be less common than before 1900.

This darter is most often found in small creeks and spring branches having clear water, permanent flow, and silt-free bottoms. Except when spawning, it is found in quiet pools and backwaters where it hides around large rocks or in beds of organic debris.

HABITS AND LIFE HISTORY

Little is known about the habits of this darter. It apparently spawns on rocky riffles in April and May, but males still in breeding color have been taken as late as July.

Goldstripe Darter

Etheostoma parvipinne Gilbert and Swain

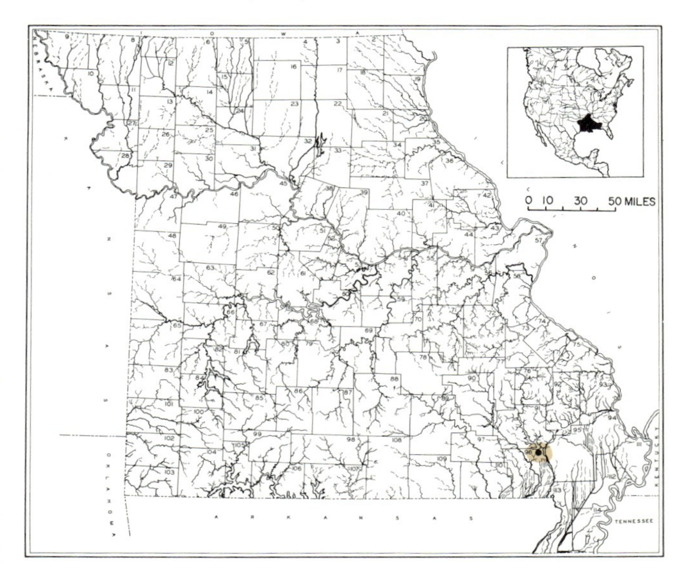

DESCRIPTION

Illustration: Page 291, 28a.

Characters: A rather stout, mottled-brown darter without definite cross-bars on the back. A useful character for identifying this species is the pale stripe that is usually evident along the lateral line. Cheek beneath eye with a dusky vertical bar. Gill covers broadly connected by membrane across throat; distance from membrane notch to front of lower lip much greater than distance from notch to front of pelvic fin base. Midline of belly without enlarged and modified scales. Lateral line complete or nearly so, extending well behind soft dorsal. Lateral line scales usually 48 to 57. Dorsal fins with 9 to 11 spines and 9 to 12 rays. Anal fin with 1 or 2 stiff spines and 7 to 9 rays.

Life colors: Back a more or less uniform light brown contrasting with the dark brown and more definitely mottled sides. Belly yellowish. Eye with a dusky bar beneath; lateral line often marked by a pale streak. All fins except pectorals banded with brown lines. Breeding males are without bright colors.

Size: Adults are usually 2.3 to 2.9 inches long to a maximum of about 3.2 inches.

Scientific name: *Etheostoma,* from the Greek *etheo,* "to strain," and *stoma,* "mouth"; *parvipinne,* Latin, meaning "small fin."

DISTRIBUTION AND HABITAT

The goldstripe darter has been collected in Missouri only from a small spring in Butler County. This spring originates at the base of a low hill along the bluff line separating the Ozarks from the Lowlands and flows into the Lowlands. Four specimens of the goldstripe darter have been collected at this locality and all were obtained in a single collection made in 1971. Efforts to locate other springs in the area that might be inhabited by this darter were unsuccessful.

This Lowland darter is reported to inhabit small springs and spring branches having an abundance of aquatic vegetation.[235] The Butler County spring in which the goldstripe darter was collected contains much water cress *(Nasturtium).* All specimens were collected from the first riffle below the spring source, over a rocky bottom covered by a layer of silt.

HABITS AND LIFE HISTORY

Nothing has been written concerning the habits and life history of the goldstripe darter.

Rainbow Darter

Etheostoma caeruleum Storer

DESCRIPTION

Illustration: Page 294, 35a; **49.**

Characters: A stout-bodied darter with 3 dark cross-bars on back, often interspersed with 1 to 7 less distinct bars. Gill covers not broadly connected by membrane across throat; distance from membrane notch to front of lower lip about equal to distance from notch to front of pelvic fin base. Midline of belly without enlarged and modified scales. Lateral line incomplete, usually ending beneath soft dorsal. Scales in a lengthwise series along midside 38 to 54. Dorsal fins with 9 or 10 spines and 12 to 14 rays. Anal fin with 2 stiff spines and 6 to 8 rays.

Similar to orangethroat darter, page 320, but with the following differences: body usually deepest beneath spinous dorsal; sensory canal encircling lower half of eye continuous (not interrupted beneath eye); pectoral fin with 13 to 15 rays; breeding males, in life, with red in anal fin and with red over entire undersurface of head.

Life colors: Back mottled brown with a series of dark brown cross-bars or blotches. Sides lighter brown with a series of blue-green bars (best developed on back half of body). Spinous dorsal dusky at base; soft dorsal and tail fin faintly banded by brown lines. Breeding males brilliantly colored: body encircled by 8 to 11 bright blue-green bars, the spaces between bars orange-red; cheek and breast blue-black and lower surface of head orange-red; fins variously banded and blotched with blue-green and orange-red.

Size: Adults are commonly 1.3 to 2.7 inches long to a maximum of about 3 inches.

Scientific name: *Etheostoma,* from the Greek, *etheo,* "to strain," and *stoma,* "mouth"; *caeruleum,* Latin, meaning "blue."

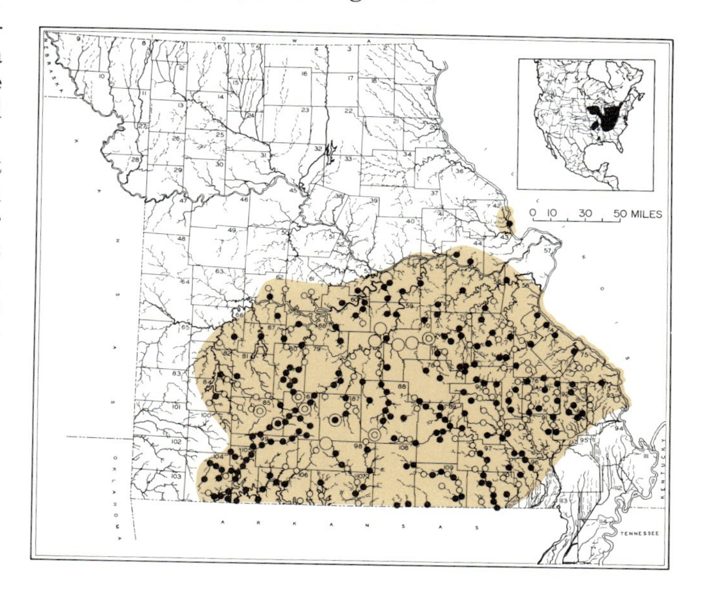

DISTRIBUTION AND HABITAT

The rainbow darter is one of the most abundant and characteristic darters of the Ozarks, where it occurs in all the principal stream systems except the Spring and Elk.

This darter inhabits rocky and gravelly riffles of clear, high-gradient streams having permanent, strong flow. It is less tolerant of turbidity and intermittent flow than the related orangethroat darter. Where the two species occur together the rainbow darter occupies deeper, swifter water than the orangethroat.

HABITS AND LIFE HISTORY

The rainbow darter is strictly a bottom dweller, spending much of its time lurking under the edge of an overhanging rock or foraging over the bottom in search of small invertebrates. Small crustaceans are the first food of the young; larger individuals feed on insect larvae, snails, and crayfish.[227]

Spawning occurs in Missouri from late March into May. Breeding adults congregate in large numbers in riffle sections where the gravelly bottom provides a substrate suitable for egg deposition. The larger males—those two or more years old—defend territories, while the yearling males and the females move about randomly over the spawning area.[236] When a female ready to spawn enters the territory of a large male, a pursuit follows which ends when the female stops and buries the lower half of her body in the gravel. She accomplishes this by driving her head into the gravel and moving forward with vigorous strokes of the tail fin. The male takes a position above her and the eggs are fertilized and buried in the gravel as both vibrate rapidly. Yearling males are rarely successful in attracting females but often take a position near the spawning pair and also vibrate.

Males of the rainbow darter usually attain a larger size than females. Breeding females range in length from about 1.3 to 2 inches; breeding males are mostly 1.6 to 2.6 inches long.

Orangethroat Darter

Etheostoma spectabile (Agassiz)

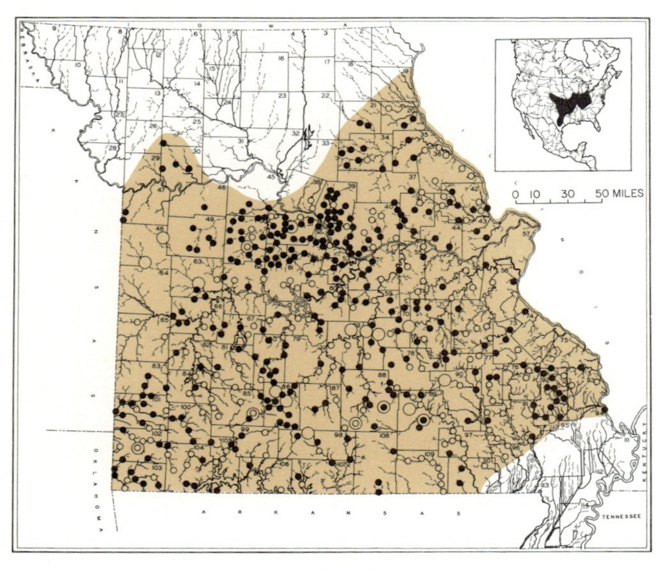

DESCRIPTION

Illustration: Page 294, 35b; **48.**

Characters: A moderately stout darter with 6 to 10 indistinct dark cross-bars on the back. Sides often prominently streaked by dark horizontal lines. Gill covers not broadly connected by membrane across throat; distance from membrane notch to front of lower lip less than or nearly equal to distance from notch to front of pelvic fin base. Midline of belly without enlarged and modified scales. Lateral line incomplete, ending beneath soft dorsal. Scales in lengthwise series along midside 38 to 57. Dorsal fins with 9 to 11 spines and 12 or 13 rays. Anal fin with 2 spines and 6 to 8 rays.

Similar to rainbow darter, page 319, but with the following differences: body usually deepest ahead of spinous dorsal; sensory canal encircling lower half of eye interrupted beneath eye; pectoral fin with 11 or 12 rays; breeding males, in life, without red in anal fin and with red on undersurface of head confined to the gill membranes.

Life colors: Back mottled yellowish-brown with indistinct dark brown cross-bars. Sides lighter brown, often with narrow, blue-green vertical bars (best developed towards tail) or brown horizontal streaks. Spinous dorsal with faint dusky bands; soft dorsal and tail fin faintly banded by narrow brown lines. Breeding males very brilliantly colored: sides with series of alternating blue-green bars and brick-red blotches; gill membranes bright orange and remainder of undersurface of head blue-green; belly with a patch of red in some populations; fins variously banded and spotted by blue-green and red.

Variation: The orangethroat darter varies considerably from one stream system to another; four subspecies have been recognized in Missouri.[237] The most striking differences involve the coloration of breeding males, particularly the banding of the spinous dorsal, the development of blue-green bars along the side, and the presence or absence of red on the belly.

Size: Adults are commonly 1.2 to 2 inches long to a maximum of about 2.5 inches.

Scientific name: *Etheostoma,* from the Greek *etheo,* "to strain", and *stoma,* "mouth"; *spectabile,* Latin, meaning "conspicuous."

DISTRIBUTION AND HABITAT

The orangethroat darter is one of the most widespread Missouri darters, occurring throughout the Ozarks and northern Ozark border and penetrating westward in tributaries of the Missouri River to Clay and Jackson counties. In the smallest creeks and spring branches of the Ozarks and the Prairie and Ozark border streams of central Missouri it is the most abundant darter. In larger Ozark streams it is replaced by the rainbow darter.

This darter is characteristic of small creeks and spring branches where it is most often found over a gravelly or rocky bottom on sluggish riffles, or in pools having enough current to prevent the deposition of silt. The orangethroat darter is more tolerant of turbidity than many darters but is most abundant in clear streams. It inhabits streams of all sizes in the Prairie and Ozark border, but is uncommon in the larger streams of the central Ozarks. This results from a tendency to avoid streams with continuous strong flow where conditions favor the related rainbow darter.

HABITS AND LIFE HISTORY

In most respects the habits of the orangethroat darter are not notably different from those of the rainbow darter. The orangethroat begins spawning earlier in the spring than the rainbow darter, perhaps because the small streams in which it occurs warm rapidly. Males move onto gravelly riffles and occupy territories as early as February. Spawning is often underway by mid-March, and is completed by the last of May. Frequently early spawning is interrupted by cold snaps. Orangethroats desert the riffles when the temperature drops below 40° F. They generally spawn in slower current and lay their eggs in finer gravel than the rainbow darter.[223] Eggs hatch in about 9 or 10 days.

An interesting feature of the early life history of this darter in the Missouri Ozarks is that the fry move into pools after hatching and become associated with nests of the smallmouth bass.[238] Many bass nests literally swarm with darters; 638 darter fry were siphoned from one nest, and this figure probably represents less than half the total number present. The darters probably benefit because they are protected from predators by the male bass who will not himself feed on such "small fry." Another possible benefit is that small crustaceans and other animal life that are the food of small orangethroats seem to be more abundant on bass nests than elsewhere on the stream bottom. The fry of other darters that spawn at the same time as the smallmouth bass (*e.g.* rainbow and fantail darters) do not utilize bass nests in this way.

Most breeding adult orangethroat darters are in their second or third summer of life and few survive beyond their fourth summer. Males attain a larger size than females.

Fantail Darter

Etheostoma flabellare Rafinesque

DESCRIPTION

Illustration: Page 292, 30b.
Characters: A slender darter with 8 to 15 indistinct dark cross-bars on the back, or without definite cross-bars. Lower jaw usually projecting beyond upper jaw. Sides often prominently streaked with dark horizontal lines. Spinous dorsal less elevated than in any other Missouri darter, its height less than half the height of soft dorsal. Gill covers broadly connected by membrane across throat; distance from membrane notch to front of lower lip much greater than distance from notch to front of pelvic fin base. Midline of belly without enlarged and modified scales. Lateral line incomplete, ending beneath soft dorsal. Scales in lengthwise series along midside 40 to 57. Spinous dorsal with 6 to 8 spines. Anal fin with 2 stiff spines and 6 to 8 rays.

Life colors: Back olive-brown, often with 8 to 15 dark brown cross-bars. Sides yellowish-brown, variably marked by dark brown horizontal streaks or vertical bars. An enlarged and blackened scale on side just above pectoral fin base. Tail fin prominently banded by dark brown lines; other fins yellowish or dusky, without definite markings. Breeding males darker, sometimes nearly black on head; spinous dorsal with a prominent fleshy knob at tip of each spine.

Size: Adults are commonly 1.3 to 2.8 inches long to a maximum of about 3 inches.

Scientific name: *Etheostoma,* from the Greek *etheo,* "to strain," and *stoma,* "mouth"; *flabellare,* Latin, meaning "like a fan," from the form of the tail.

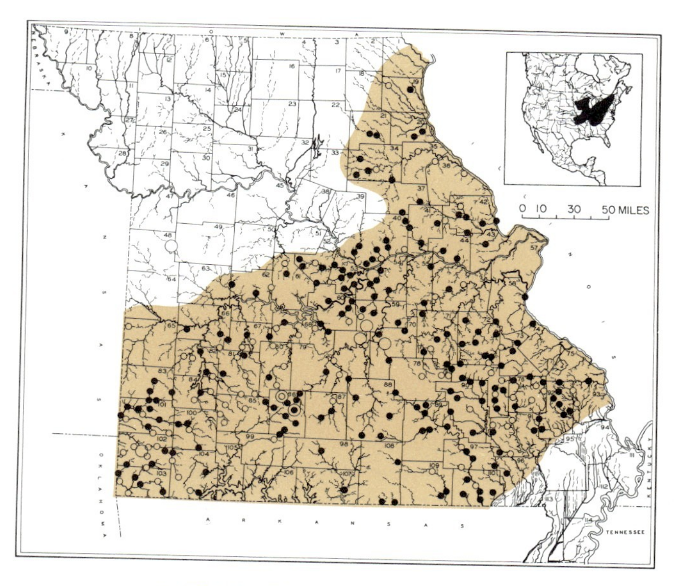

DISTRIBUTION AND HABITAT

The fantail darter occurs over most of the Ozarks and northeastward into tributaries of the upper Mississippi River. It is one of the most abundant darters over much of its Missouri range but is rare and highly localized in distribution in the White River system.

The fantail inhabits the rocky and gravelly

riffles of permanent-flowing streams ranging in size from small creeks to moderately large rivers. It is more tolerant of turbidity and organic pollution than most darters.

HABITS AND LIFE HISTORY

The fantail darter lives on the bottom, utilizing the narrow spaces between rocks as protection from predators and from the direct force of stream currents. It feeds principally on the immature stages of aquatic insects that occupy the riffle habitat.

Spawning occurs in Missouri during April and May. The spawning habits of the fantail darter have been described in detail.[239] Breeding males seek out and occupy cavities beneath rocks. Cavities about one-half to three-fourths of an inch in height and with only a few places of possible entrance are preferred. A female ready to spawn swims from stone to stone until she finds one with a male. She then enters and deposits a clutch of eggs that adhere in a single layer to the underside of the rock. The female is then chased out by the male, who remains with the eggs until they hatch, cleaning and aerating them by his movements in the confined space of the nest. The thickened, fleshy knobs on the dorsal spines of the male are apparently of special importance in cleaning the lower surface of the rock prior to spawning and in keeping the eggs free of silt and other fine material. A female deposits about 45 eggs at each spawning and may spawn as many as five times in a season. Eggs hatch in 14 to 35 days, depending on temperature. At 70° F. the incubation period is about 21 days.

In Iowa the fantail darter attains lengths of 0.8, 1.4, and 1.8 inches during the first through third years of life.[240] Males grow more rapidly and attain a larger size than females.

Slough Darter

Etheostoma gracile (Girard)

DESCRIPTION

Illustration: Page 292, 31a.

Characters: A slender darter, distinguished from all other Missouri species in having the lateral line arched upward, separated by only 3 scale rows from the spinous dorsal. Back without definite dark cross-bars or with 9 or 10 very indistinct bars. Gill covers not broadly connected by membrane across throat; distance from membrane notch to front of lower lip slightly less than distance from notch to front of pelvic fin base. Belly covered with scales of normal size and shape near anus but with a naked strip behind pelvic fins. Lateral line incomplete, ending beneath spinous dorsal. Scales in lengthwise series along midside 40 to 56. Spinous dorsal with 8 to 10 spines. Anal fin with 2 stiff spines (the first shorter and not distinctly stouter than the second), and 5 to 7 rays.

Life colors: Back mottled brown, often with 9 or 10 indistinct dark brown cross-bars. Sides lighter brown with greenish blotches or bars (best developed towards tail fin) and dark brown zigzag lines. Lateral line marked by a characteristic narrow pale streak. Eye red with 4 short dark lines radiating outward from it. Spinous dorsal blackish at base and with a narrow reddish band or row of red dots outward; soft dorsal and tail fin faintly banded by dark brown lines. Breeding males more brightly colored and with basal half of spinous dorsal blue-black.

Size: Adults are commonly 1.6 to 2.1 inches long to a maximum of about 2.3 inches.

Scientific name: *Etheostoma,* from the Greek, *etheo,* "to strain," and *stoma,* "mouth"; *gracile,* Latin, meaning "slender" or "thin".

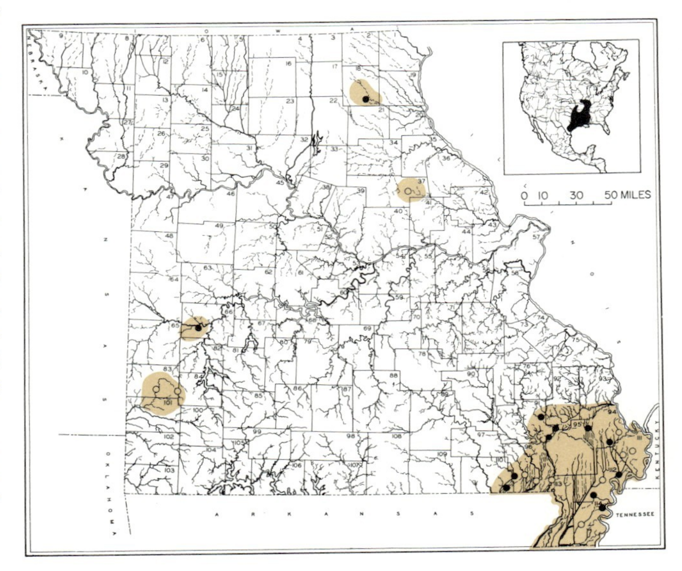

DISTRIBUTION AND HABITAT

The slough darter is common in the Lowlands of southeastern Missouri and occurs rarely in tributaries of the upper Mississippi River and the Osage and Spring River systems of the southwest.

It is well named for it is characteristic of oxbows and other overflow waters along the flood plains of streams. It also occurs in the pools of sluggish streams and ditches of lowlands and of level upland prairies. The habitats in which the slough darter occurs are characterized by moderately clear, warm water without noticeable current and with soft bottoms including much organic debris. Often thick growths of submergent aquatic plants are present. The requirements of the slough darter are similar to those of the bluntnose darter, and the patterns of distribution of the two species are strikingly similar.

HABITS AND LIFE HISTORY

The following remarks concerning the slough darter are from an Illinois study.[241] Like virtually all darters, this species feeds primarily on insect larvae and small crustaceans. Midge larvae make up the bulk of its diet in late winter. In spring a larger variety of food is eaten, and by May mayfly larvae are the most important food. Adults feed heavily in the spring but apparently feed very little from July through September.

Spawning occurs in late May and is complete within a period of 1 or 2 days. Egg deposition is preceded by courtship during which the male follows the female about, stroking her with his pectoral fins and rubbing his enlarged chin tubercles over the top of her head and snout. The eggs are laid and fertilized, one at a time, usually in neat rows along a stick or the stem of a leaf. Development is more rapid than in most darters and the eggs hatch in 5 days at 73° F.

Early growth is rapid and almost half of the first year's growth is completed in a week. Females and males grow at about the same rate, reaching adult size and spawning at one year of age.

Least Darter

Etheostoma microperca Jordan and Gilbert

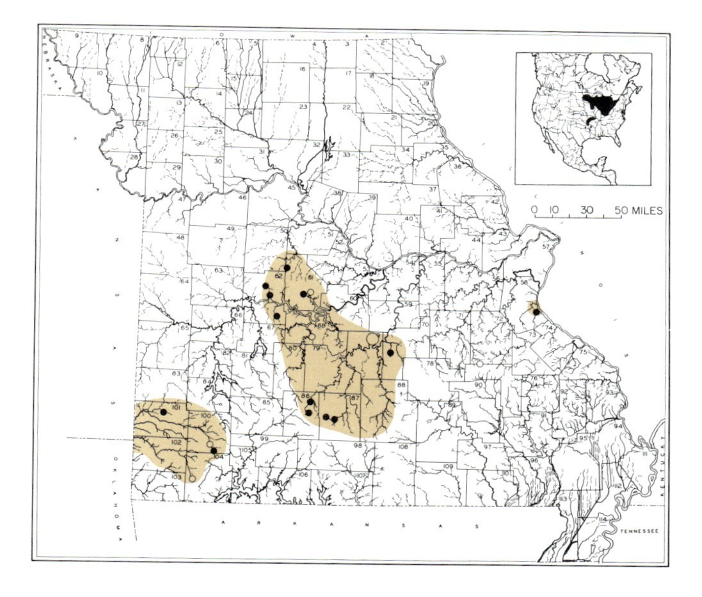

DESCRIPTION

Illustration: Page 295, 36b.

Characters: A small, rather slender darter with the lateral line entirely lacking. No definite dark cross-bars on back. Gill covers rather broadly connected by membrane across throat; distance from membrane notch to front of lower lip equal to or greater than distance from notch to front of pelvic fin base. Belly without scales or with a few scales of normal size and shape just in front of anus. Scales in a lengthwise series along midside 32 to 38. Anal fin with 2 stiff spines and 5 or 6 rays.

Similar to cypress darter, page 324, but with the following differences: cheek without scales; gill cover with few or no scales; lateral line usually absent; dorsal fins usually with 6 or 7 spines and 9 or 10 rays; mouth smaller, upper jaw extending only to or slightly behind front of eye.

Life colors: Back and sides olive-brown with scattered dark brown specks and zigzag markings. Midside with a series of small dusky blotches. Four short dusky bars radiate outward from eye. Dorsal and tail fins splotched and banded with dark brown; other fins without definite markings. Breeding males have reddish spots along base of spinous dorsal and have much longer pelvic fins than females.

Size: Adults are commonly 1 to 1.6 inches long to a maximum of about 1.8 inches.

Scientific name: *Etheostoma,* from the Greek, *etheo,* "to strain," and *stoma,* "mouth"; *microperca,* Greek, meaning "small perch."

DISTRIBUTION AND HABITAT

The least darter is widely distributed along the northern and western margin of the Ozarks. Because of its specialized habitat requirements it tends to occur as isolated colonies, but is often abundant where it occurs.

The least darter is invariably found in clear, quiet, heavily vegetated waters such as pools of small creeks having permanent flow, and spring pools and seeps along the flood plains of larger streams.

HABITS AND LIFE HISTORY

This underwater acrobat spends much of its time off of the stream bottom, clambering about among the leaves and stems of aquatic plants. Microcrustaceans and the immature stages of aquatic insects probably make up the bulk of its food.

The breeding habits of the least darter are much like those of the slough darter.[242] The eggs are deposited singly, usually on the bottom or sides of the stems and leaves of aquatic plants. The enlarged pelvic fins of the male function in clasping the back of the female during the spawning act. Spawning evidently occurs in Missouri during May or early June.

The least darter and the closely related cypress darter are the smallest Missouri fishes, maturing at a length of about one inch.

Cypress Darter

Etheostoma proeliare (Hay)

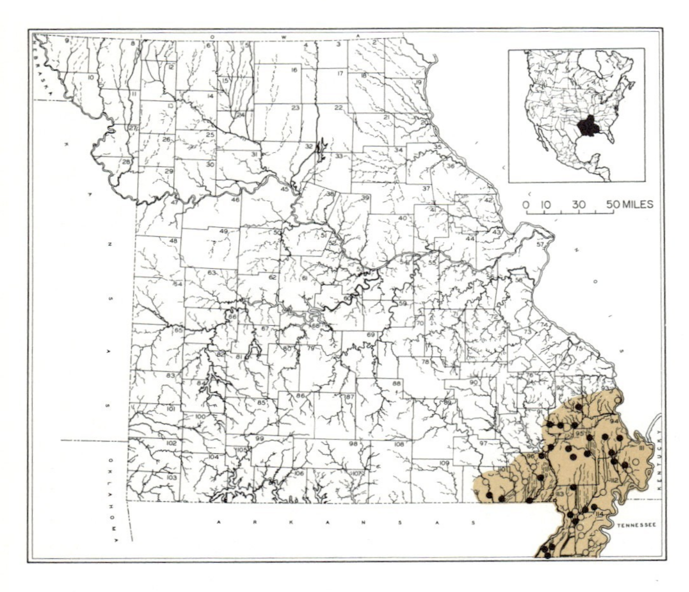

DESCRIPTION

Illustration: Page 295, 36a.

Characters: A small, rather slender darter with the lateral line very short, represented by only a few pored scales just behind head. No definite dark cross-bars on back. Gill covers rather broadly connected by membrane across throat; distance from membrane notch to front of lower lip equal to or greater than distance from notch to front of pelvic fin base. Belly without scales or with a few scales of normal size and shape just in front of the anus. Scales in a lengthwise series along midside 32 to 38. Anal fin with 1 or 2 stiff spines and 5 or 6 rays.

Similar to least darter, page 323, but with the following differences: cheek and gill cover scaled; lateral line usually present (represented by a few pores near head); dorsal fins usually with 7 or 8 spines and 10 or 11 rays; mouth larger, upper jaw extending distinctly behind front of eye.

Life colors: Similar to those of least darter, page 323.

Size: Adults are usually 1 to 1.6 inches long to a maximum of about 1.8 inches.

Scientific name: *Etheostoma,* from the Greek *etheo,* "to strain," and *stoma,* "mouth"; *proeliare,* Latin, pertaining to battle, the species being found on the Civil War battlefield of Corinth in Mississippi.

DISTRIBUTION AND HABITAT

The cypress darter is the most common and widespread darter in the Lowlands of southeastern Missouri. The largest populations of this darter occur in clear, sluggish ditches having much submergent vegetation. In swifter and less sparsely vegetated ditches the cypress darter is restricted largely to the margins where cover is provided by organic debris, or the undercut roots of terrestrial plants.

HABITS AND LIFE HISTORY

The habits of this darter have not been studied but are probably much like those of the least darter.

DRUMS

Sciaenidae

This family contains many species, most of which are marine. Many reach a large size and are highly valued as food and game fishes. Only a single species occurs in Missouri. The name for the family comes from the peculiar grunting or croaking sounds produced by some species.

Freshwater Drum

Aplodinotus grunniens Rafinesque

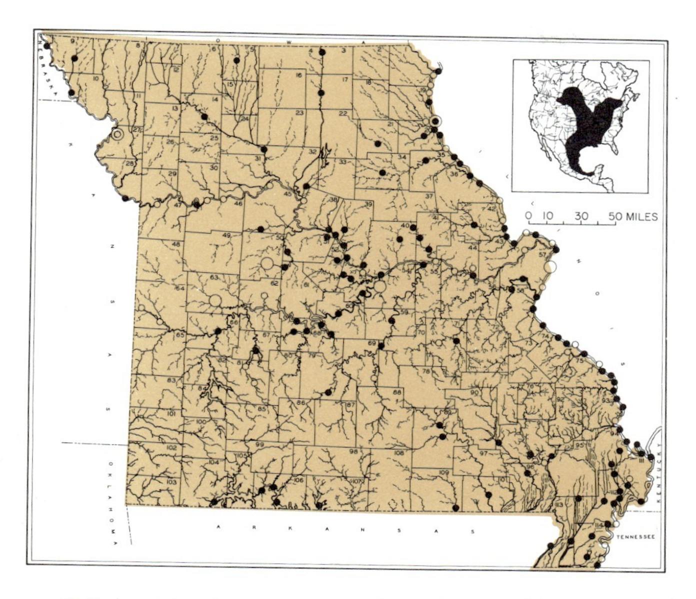

Other common names: Croaker, White perch, Rock perch, Sheepshead.

DESCRIPTION

Illustration: Page 33, 25b; **50.**

Characters: A silvery, deep-bodied fish with a long dorsal fin that is divided into two distinct parts. Head and body sloping steeply upward from snout to dorsal fin, resulting in a distinctive hump-backed appearance. Body and upper part of head covered with rough-edged (ctenoid) scales. Dorsal fin usually with 10 stiff spines and 29 to 32 rays; soft dorsal very long, about twice the length of spinous dorsal. Anal fin with 2 spines at front; second spine much longer and stouter than first. Pelvic fin with 1 spine and 5 rays; outer ray elongated into a slender filament.

Life colors: Back gray with blue and purple reflections. Side silvery. Belly, undersurface of head, and lips milk-white. Dorsal, tail, and anal fins dusky; pelvic fins white, often tinged with orange; pectoral fins clear.

Size: Adults are commonly 12 to 20 inches long and weigh 12 ounces to 5 pounds. The largest specimen known from Missouri weighed 34 pounds.

Scientific name: *Aplodinotus,* Greek, meaning "single back," in reference to the dorsal fin; *grunniens,* Latin, meaning "grunting," in reference to the sounds produced by this species.

DISTRIBUTION AND HABITAT

The freshwater drum occurs in large streams over much of the state but is most abundant in the Missouri and Mississippi rivers and the downstream sections of their major tributaries. In a survey of the commercial and sport fishes of the Mississippi River it ranked as the second most abundant species.[32] It is scarce in Ozark streams but is rather common in the large reservoirs of that region.

This fish is characteristic of large rivers, lakes, and impoundments. In streams it is usually found in the larger pools; in reservoirs it often occurs at depths of 30 feet or more. It avoids strong current but is tolerant of high turbidity.

HABITS AND LIFE HISTORY

The freshwater drum lives most of the time on or near the bottom. It has long been considered to be a mollusc feeder, principally because the heavy throat-teeth appear to be adapted for crushing mollusc shells. However, studies of its food habits indicate that fish, crayfish, and immature aquatic insects comprise the bulk of its diet.[243, 244, 245] It feeds by grubbing in the bottom, often moving rocks with its snout to capture the insects and other small aquatic life thus disturbed.[94]

Spawning of the freshwater drum has not been observed, but apparently takes place in open water and the eggs float until hatching.[244] The "drumming" sound for which this fish is named may be associated with spawning activities.[246] In a Wisconsin lake researchers detected drumming only between early May and August, with a peak in June. The drum spawns in Missouri in late April or May. Spawning is preceded by movements of adults out of large rivers and reservoirs into tributary streams.

In Missouri streams they average 4.4 inches in length by the end of the first year of life and 8.1, 10.6, 12.4, 13.9, and 14.9 inches in succeeding years.[52] Growth is slightly more rapid in Lake Wappapello.[192] On the average, a 13-inch drum weighs about a pound and a 16-inch specimen weighs 2 pounds. Most drum caught by fishermen weigh 2 pounds or less. The maximum life span is at least 13 years.

IMPORTANCE AND ANGLING

The freshwater drum is an important sport and commercial fish along the Missouri and Mississippi rivers and makes up a small part of the hook-and-line catch in other large streams and reservoirs of Missouri.

Most drum are taken on live bait fished on the bottom. Worms, crayfish, and small minnows are favorite baits. Occasionally they are taken on small artificial lures such as spinners and fly and spinner combinations.

GLOSSARY OF TERMS

Adipose fin — A small, fleshy, rayless structure situated on the midline of the back behind the dorsal fin.

Air bladder — A gas filled sac lying above the intestine.

Anal fin — The single fin situated on the midline of the lower body surface behind the anus.

Barbel — A fleshy, flap-like or cylindrical and tapering projection (quite small and inconspicuous in some minnows) found near the mouth.

Belly — The undersurface of the body from a point immediately behind the pectoral fins to the front of the anal fin.

Body cavity — The space containing the intestine and associated internal organs.

Body depth — The greatest vertical distance between the midline of the back and the midline of the belly, exclusive of the fins and associated structures.

Body width — The greatest distance from one side of the body to the other.

Breast — The undersurface of the body between the junction of the gill covers and a point immediately behind the pectoral fins.

Caudal peduncle — The part of the body between the base of the anal fin and the base of the tail fin.

Concave — Curved or rounded inward.

Convex — Curved or rounded outward.

Ctenoid scales — Scales having a patch of small prickles on the exposed rear part.

Cycloid scales — More or less rounded scales without prickles.

Dorsal fin — A fin (or fins) situated on the midline of the back and having spines or rays.

Ear flap — A flattened, flexible structure extending back from the rear margin of the gill cover. Best developed in some sunfishes.

Eye diameter — As used here, the greatest distance from one fleshy rim of the eye socket to the other.

Fin ray — A slender rod-shaped structure supporting the fin membranes. *Soft rays* are jointed (crossed by grooves or striations), often branched, and flexible near their tips. *True spines* are unjointed (not marked by grooves or striations), unbranched, and usually sharp and stiff all the way to their tips. The spines of sculpins are soft and flexible. The hardened soft rays of fishes such as the carp and catfishes are referred to as spines.

Fin ray count — In most fishes only *principal* soft rays are counted, including all branched rays and one unbranched ray at the front of the fin. Often the two main branches of the last ray are separated to their bases, but they are still counted as one ray. In catfishes there is no definite break in size between principal rays and small, poorly developed, *rudimentary* rays, and all fin rays are counted. All *spines* are counted, regardless of size.

Gill arches — The series of curved, bony structures lying beneath the gill cover and supporting the gill rakers and gill filaments.

Gill cover — The large, flat bone on the side of the head, beneath which the gills are located.

Gill rakers — The knob-like or comb-like projections on the front edge of the gill arch.

Gill opening — In higher fishes, the single slit-like opening between the gill cover and the side of the head.

Head length — The distance from the tip of the snout or upper lip to the furthermost point on the membrane along the back of the gill cover.

Head depth — The vertical distance from the occiput (point where the head joins the back) to the undersurface of the head or breast.

Head width — The greatest width of the head when the gill covers are closed.

Lateral line — A series of sensory tubes and pores that extends back from the head along the side of the body. The lateral line may be *complete* (extending to the base of the tail fin), *incomplete* (terminating before reaching the base of the tail fin), or absent.

Lateral line scales — The scales bearing the tubes of the lateral line.

Lateral line scale count — Begins with the first lateral line scale behind the head and extends back along the lateral line to the hidden base of the tail fin, as indicated by the crease formed when the tail fin is bent to one side. Scales behind the crease are not counted, even if a tube is present. A scale over the crease is counted if most of its exposed surface is ahead of the crease. If the lateral line is incomplete or absent the count is of a series of scales along the midside in the position that would be occupied by the lateral line if it were present. In fishes without a lateral line this count is referred to as *scales in lateral series.*

Measuring — See *proportional measurements.*

Muscle bands — In lampreys, a series of ridge-like bulges of muscle situated along the side. Each muscle band is separated from adjacent bands by definite grooves.

Paired fins — The pectoral and pelvic fins, occupying approximately the same position in fishes as the fore-limbs and hind-limbs of higher animals.

Pectoral fin — The farthest forward or uppermost of the paired fins.

Pelvic fin — The paired fin situated beneath or behind the pectoral fin.

Pharyngeal arches — The pair of curved bones located in the throat just behind the last pair of gill arches, and bearing the throat teeth.

Preopercle — The bone just ahead of the gill cover.

Proportional measurements — Measurements in which the length of one body part is expressed as a proportion of the length of another body part. The most accurate method for determining proportional measurements is to obtain the length of each body part with dividers, transfer these lengths to a ruler to determine their numerical values, and divide one value by the other. An easier and more rapid method which will usually suffice is to obtain the length of one body part with dividers and "step it off" by rotating the dividers stepwise along the length of the other body part.

Scales above lateral line — This count begins with the scale at the front of the dorsal fin (spinous dorsal if both spinous and soft dorsals are present), and includes all scales in an oblique series downward and backward to (but not including) the lateral-line scale.

Scales in lateral series — See *lateral line scale count.*

Sensory canal — As used here, one of the branches of the lateral line that extends onto the head.

Snout — The part of the head in front of the eye (exclusive of the lower jaw).

Snout length — The distance from the most forward point on the head (exclusive of the lower jaw) to the front of the bony socket of the eye.

Soft dorsal — A dorsal fin containing only soft rays, or the soft-rayed hind part of the dorsal fin if both spines and soft rays are present.

Soft ray — See *Fin rays.*

Spine — See *Fin rays.*

Spinous dorsal — A dorsal fin containing only spines, or the forward spiny part of the dorsal fin if both spines and soft rays are present.

Standard length — The straight-line distance from the most forward point on the head (exclusive of the lower jaw) to the hidden base of the tail fin, as indicated by the crease formed when the tail fin is bent to one side.

Throat (pharyngeal) teeth — Teeth borne on the two curved bones comprising the left and right pharyngeal arches. The number and shape of these teeth are useful characters for the identification of certain fishes, especially minnows and suckers. Suckers always have a single row of teeth on each arch; minnows may have one or more rows. When the teeth occur in a single row, the number of teeth on one arch (left) is indicated by a number separated by a dash from the count for the other arch (right). Thus, a count of 4-4 indicates that there is a single row of four teeth on each arch. When there are two rows, as in many minnows, the formula is written as follows: 2,4-4,2. This indicates that there are two rows of teeth on the left arch (the numbers to the left of the dash) with two teeth in the outer row and four teeth in the inner row. The numbers following the dash apply to the right arch, and also indicate four teeth in the inner row and two teeth in the outer row. The pharyngeal arches must be removed to examine the throat teeth. To accomplish this, the fleshy ligaments by which the upper and lower ends of the arch are attached must be severed with a scalpel or other sharp instrument. Great care is required in removing the arch to avoid breaking off the fragile teeth.

Total length — The straight-line distance from the most forward point on the head to the end of the tail fin, when the mouth is closed and the lobes of the tail fin are squeezed together.

REFERENCES CITED

1. Pflieger, W. L. 1971. A distributional study of Missouri fishes. Mus. Nat. Hist., Univ. Kansas, Publ. 20(3):225-570.
2. Gerking, S. D. 1953. Evidence for the concepts of home range and territory in stream fishes. Ecology, 34(2):347-365.
3. Funk, J. L. 1955. Movements of stream fishes in Missouri. Trans. Am. Fish. Soc., 1957:39-57.
4. Sigler, W. F. 1958. The ecology and use of carp in Utah. Utah State Univ., Agric. Exper. Sta., Bull. 405, 63 pp.
5. Purkett, C. A., Jr. 1963. The paddlefish fishery of the Osage River and Lake of the Ozarks, Missouri. Trans. Am. Fish. Soc., 92(3):239-244.
6. Robinson, J. W. 1969. Twilight for two rivers. Missouri Conserv., 30(4):4-5.
7. Fleener, G. G. 1971. Recreational use of the Platte River, Missouri (pp. 63-78 *In* Stream channelization: A symposium. E. Scheneberger and J. L. Funk, ed.). North Central Div., Am. Fish. Soc., Spec. Publ. No. 2.
8. Hubbs, C. L. and K. F. Lagler. 1958. Fishes of the Great Lakes Region. Cranbrook Inst. Sci., Bull. 26:1-213.
9. Lagler, K. F. 1956. Freshwater fishery biology (2nd ed.). Wm. C. Brown Co., Dubuque, Iowa, 421 pp.
10. Cross, F. B. 1962. Collecting and preserving fishes. Univ. Kansas Misc. Publ. No. 30:41-44.
11. Leach, W. J. 1940. Occurrence and life history of the northern brook lamprey, *Ichthyomyzon fossor*, in Indiana. Copeia, 1940(1):21-34.
12. Hall, J. D. 1963. An ecological study of the chestnut lamprey, *Ichthyomyzon castaneus* Girard, in the Manistee River, Michigan. Diss. Abstr., 24(2):901-902.
13. Case, B. 1970. Spawning behavior of the chestnut lamprey *(Ichthyomyzon castaneus)*. J. Fish. Res. Bd. Canada, 27(10):1872-1874.
14. Hall, G. E. and G. A. Moore. 1954. Oklahoma lampreys: their characterization and distribution. Copeia, 1954(2):127-135.
15. Dendy, J. S. and D. C. Scott. 1953. Distribution, life history, and morphological variations of the southern brook lamprey, *Ichthyomyzon gagei*. Copeia, 1953(3):152-162.
16. Seversmith, H. F. 1953. Distribution, morphology and life history of *Lampetra aepyptera*, a brook lamprey, in Maryland. Copeia, 1953(4):225-232.
17. Okelberg, P. 1921. The early history of the germ cells in the brook lamprey, *Entosphenus wilderi* (Gage) up to and including the period of sex differentiation. J. Morph., 35:1-15.
18. Dees, L. T. 1961. Sturgeons. U. S. Bur. Commerc. Fish., Fish. Leaflet 526:1-7.
19. Priegel, G. R. and T. L. Wirth. 1971. The lake sturgeon, its life history, ecology and management. Wisc. Dept. Nat. Res., Publ. 240-70, 20 pp.
20. Hoopes, D. T. 1960. Utilization of mayflies and caddisflies by some Mississippi River fish. Trans. Am. Fish. Soc., 89:32-34.
21. Held, J. W. 1969. Some early summer foods of the shovelnose sturgeon in the Missouri River. Trans. Am. Fish. Soc., 98(3):514-517.
22. Coker, R. E. 1930. Studies of common fishes of the Mississippi River at Keokuk. Bull. U. S. Bur. Fish., 45:141-225.
23. Helms, D. R. 1973. Progress report on the second year study of shovelnose sturgeon in the Mississippi River. Annual Progress Report, Proj. 2-156-R-2, 33 pp.
24. Forbes, S. A. and R. E. Richardson. 1920. The fishes of Illinois (2nd ed). Ill. Nat. Hist. Surv., 3:1-357.
25. Robinson, J. W. 1966. Observations on the life history, movement, and harvest of the paddlefish, *Polyodon spathula*, in Montana. Montana Acad. of Sci., 26:33-44.
26. Stockard, C. R. 1907. Observations on the natural history of *Polyodon spathula*. Am. Nat., 41:753-766.
27. Eddy, S. and P. H. Simer. 1928. Notes on the food of the paddlefish and the plankton of its habitat. Ill. State Acad. Sci., 21:59-68.
28. Fitz, R. B. 1966. Unusual food of the paddlefish *(Polyodon spathula)* in Tennessee. Copeia, 1966(2):356.
29. Purkett, C. A., Jr. 1961. Reproduction and early development of the paddlefish. Trans. Am. Fish. Soc., 90(2):125-129.

30. Ballard, W. W. and R. G. Needham. 1964. Normal embryonic stages of *Polyodon spathula* (Walbaum). J. Morph., 114(3):465-478.

31. Purkett, C. A., Jr. 1963. Artificial propagation of paddlefish. Progr. Fish-Cult., 25(1):31-33.

32. Barnickol, P. G. and W. C. Starrett. 1951. Commercial and sport fishes of the Mississippi River between Caruthersville, Missouri, and Dubuque, Iowa. Bull. Ill. Nat. Hist. Sur., 25(5):267-350.

33. Raney, E. C. 1942. Alligator gar feeds on birds in Texas. Copeia, 1941(1):50.

34. Goodyear, C. P. 1967. Feeding habits of three species of gars, *Lepisosteus,* along the Mississippi Gulf Coast. Trans. Am. Fish. Soc., 96(3):297-300.

35. May, E. B. and A. A. Echelle. 1968. Young-of-year alligator gar in Lake Texoma, Oklahoma. Copeia, 1968(3):629-630.

36. Lagler, K. F., C. B. Obrecht, and G. V. Harry. 1942. The food habits of gars (*Lepisosteus* spp.) considered in relation to fish management. Invest. Ind. Lakes and Streams, 2:117-135.

37. Potter, G. E. 1927. Ecological studies of the short-nosed gar-pike *(Lepidosteus platystomus)* Univ. Iowa Stud. in Nat. Hist., 11(9):17-27.

38. Redmond, L. C. 1964. Ecology of the spotted gar *(Lepisosteus oculatus* Winchell) in southeastern Missouri. Unpubl. M.A. Thesis, Univ. of Missouri, 144 pp.

39. Netsch, N. E. 1964. Food and feeding habits of the longnose gar in central Missouri. Proc. 18th Ann. S. E. Assoc. Game and Fish. Comm.:506-511.

40. Netsch, N. F. and A. Witt, Jr. 1962. Contributions to the life history of the longnose gar, *(Lepisosteus osseus)* in Missouri. Trans. Am. Fish. Soc., 91(3):251-262.

41. Fisher, H. J. 1962. Some fishes of the lower Missouri River. Am. Midl. Nat., 68(2):424-429.

42. Cross, F. B. 1967. Handbook of fishes of Kansas. Univ. Kans. Mus. Nat. Hist., Misc. Publ. 45:1-357.

43. Holland, H. T. 1964. Ecology of the bowfin *(Amia calva* Linnaeus) in southeastern Missouri. Unpubl. M.A. Thesis, Univ. of Missouri, 89 pp.

44. Reighard, J. 1940. The natural history of *Amia calva* Linnaeus. Mark Anniversary Volume, 4:57-108.

45. Funk, J. L. 1969. Missouri's state-wide general creel census. Mo. Dept. Cons., D-J Ser. No. 6, 275 pp.

46. Schmidt, J. 1925. The breeding places of the eel. Smithson. Rept. for 1924:279-316.

47. Smith, D. G. 1968. The occurrence of larvae of the American eel, *Anguilla rostrata,* in the straits of Florida and nearby areas. Bull. Marine Science, 18(2):280-293.

48. Evermann, B. W. 1902. Description of a new species of shad *(Alosa ohiensis),* with notes on other food-fishes of the Ohio River. Rept. U. S. Fish. Comm., (1901):273-288.

49. Moore, G. A. 1957. Fishes. (pp. 31-210 *In* Vertebrates of the United States, by W. F. Blair *et. al.).* McGraw-Hill Book Co., New York.

50. Laurence, G. C. and R. W. Yerger. 1966. Life history studies of the Alabama shad, *Alosa alabamae,* in the Apalachicola River, Florida. Proc. 20th Ann. S. E. Assoc. Game and Fish Comm.:260-273.

51. Bodola, A. 1964. Life history of the gizzard shad, *Dorosoma cepedianum* (Le Sueur) in western Lake Erie. U. S. Fish and Wildl. Serv., Fish. Bull. 65(2):391-425.

52. Purkett, C. A., Jr. 1958. Growth rates of Missouri stream fishes. Mo. Cons. Comm., D-J Ser. No. 1, 46 pp.

53. Miller, R. V. 1967. Food of the threadfin shad, *Dorosoma petenense,* in Lake Chicot, Arkansas. Trans. Am. Fish. Soc., 96(3):243-246.

54. Bryant, H. E. and A. Hauser. 1968. Growth of threadfin shad in Bull Shoals Reservoir. Proc. 22nd Ann. Conf. S. E. Assoc. Game and Fish Comm.:275-283.

55. Battle, H. J. and W. M. Sprules. 1960. A description of the semi-buoyant eggs and early developmental stages of the goldeye, *Hiodon alosoides* (Rafinesque). J. Fish. Res. Bd. Canada, 17(2):245-266.

56. Martin, M. 1954. Age and growth of the goldeye *Hiodon alosoides* (Rafinesque) of Lake Texoma, Oklahoma. Okla. Acad. Sci., 33(1952):37-49.

57. Van Oosten, J. 1961. Records, ages, and growth of the mooneye, *Hiodon tergisus,* of the Great Lakes. Trans. Am. Fish. Soc., 90(2):170-174.

58. Maynard, H. J. 1889. Rainbow trout in southwestern Missouri. Bull. U. S. Fish Comm., 7(1887):55-56.

59. Brigham, W. U. 1973. Nest construction of the lamprey, *Lampetra aepyptera.* Copeia, 1973(1):135-136.

60. Brynildson, O. M., *et. al.* 1963. Brown trout, its life history, ecology, and management. Wisc. Cons. Dept., Publ. 234:1-15.

61. Ming, A. D. 1968. Life history of the grass pickerel, *Esox americanus vermiculatus,* in Oklahoma. Okla. Fish. Res. Lab., Bull. 8, 66 pp.

62. Call, R. E. 1887. Memoranda on a collection of fishes from the Ozark Region of Missouri. Proc. Davenport Acad. Nat. Sci., 5:73-80.

63. Wich, K. and J. W. Mullan. 1958. A compendium of the life history and ecology of the chain pickerel *Esox niger* (Le Sueur). Mass. Div. Fish. and Game, Fish. Bull. 22, 27 pp.

64. Threinen, C. W. *et. al.* 1966. The northern pike, its life history, ecology, and management. Wisc. Cons. Dept., Publ. 235, 16 pp.

65. Oehmcke, A. A. *et. al.* 1965. The Wisconsin muskellunge, its life history, ecology, and management. Wisc. Cons. Dept., Publ. 225:1-12.

66. Sneed, K. E. 1971. A controversial biological control. Am. Fish. Farmer, May, 1971:6-9.

67. Forbes, S. A. 1883. The food of the smaller fresh-water fishes. Bull. Ill. State Lab. Nat. Hist., 6:65-94.

68. Dobie, J., O. L. Meehean, S. F. Sniezko, and G. N. Washburn. 1956. Raising bait fishes. U. S. Fish and Wildl. Serv., Cir. 35, 124 pp.

69. Kramer, R. H. and L. L. Smith, Jr. 1960. Utilization of nests of largemouth bass, *Micropterus salmoides,* by golden shiners, *Notemigonus crysoleucas.* Copeia, 1960(1):73-74.

70. Cooper, G. P. 1936. Age and growth of the golden shiner *(Notemigonus crysoleucas)* and its suitability for propagation. Pap. Mich. Acad. Sci., Arts, and Lett., 21(1935):587-597.

71. Starrett, W. C. 1950. Food relationships of the minnows of the Des Moines River, Iowa. Ecology, 31(2):216-233.

72. Dinsmore, J. J. 1962. Life history of the creek chub, with emphasis on growth. Iowa Acad. Sci., 69:296-301.

73. Reighard, J. 1910. Methods of studying the habits of fishes, with an account of the breeding habits of the horned dace. Bull. U. S. Bur. Fish., 28(1908):1111-1136.

74. Smith, B. G. 1908. The spawning habits of *Chrosomus erythrogaster* Rafinesque. Biol. Bull., 15:9-18.

75. Davis, B. J. and R. J. Miller. 1967. Brain patterns in minnows of the genus *Hybopsis* in relation to feeding habits and habitat. Copeia, 1967(1):1-39.

76. Lachner, E. A. 1950. The comparative food habits of the cyprinid fishes *Nocomis biguttatus* and *Nocomis micropogon* in western New York. J. Wash. Acad. Sci., 40(7):229-236.

77. Botrell, C. E., R. H. Ingersol, and R. W. Jones. 1964. Notes on the embryology, early development, and behavior of *Hybopsis aestivalis tetranemus* (Gilbert). Trans. Am. Micr. Soc., 83:391-399.

78. Starrett, W. C. 1951. Some factors affecting the abundance of minnows in the Des Moines River, Iowa. Ecology, 32(1):13-27.

79. Olund, L. J. and F. B. Cross. 1961. Geographic variation in the North American cyprinid fish, *Hybopsis gracilis.* Univ. Kans. Mus. Nat. Hist. Publ., 13(7):323-348.

80. Fuchs, E. H. 1967. Life history of the emerald shiner, *Notropis atherinoides,* in Lewis and Clark Lake, South Dakota. Trans. Am. Fish. Soc., 96(3):247-256.

81. Flittner, G. A. 1964. Morphometry and life history of the emerald shiner, *Notropis atherinoides* Rafinesque. Diss. Abstr., 25:37,59.

82. Pfeiffer, R. A. 1955. Studies on the life history of the rosyface shiner, *Notropis rubellus.* Copeia, 1955(2):95-104.

83. Reed, R. J. 1958. The early life history of two cyprinid fishes, *Notropis rubellus* and *Campostoma anomalum pullum.* Copeia, 1958(4):325-326.

84. Reed, R. J. 1957. Phases of the life history of the rosyface shiner, *Notropis rubellus,* in northwestern Pennsylvania. Copeia, 1957(4):286-290.

85. Hunter, J. R. and A. D. Hasler. 1965. Spawning association of the redfin shiner, *Notropis umbratilis,* and the green sunfish, *Lepomis cyanellus.* Copeia, 1965(3):265-285.

86. Jordan, D. S. and S. E. Meek. 1885. List of fishes collected in Iowa and Missouri in August, 1884, with descriptions of three new species. Proc. U. S. Natl. Mus., 8:1-17.

87. Raney, E. C. 1940. The breeding behavior of the common shiner, *Notropis cornutus* (Mitchell). Zoologica, 25(1):1-14.

88. Meek, S. E. 1891. Report of explorations made in Missouri and Arkansas during 1889, with an account of the fishes observed in each of the river basins examined. Bull. U. S. Bur. Fish., 9(1889):113-141.

89. Harlan, J. R. and E. B. Speaker. 1956. Iowa fish and fishing (3rd ed.). Iowa Cons. Comm., Des Moines, 324 pp.

90. Marshall, N. 1947. Studies on the life history and ecology of *Notropis chalybaeus* (Cope). Florida Acad. Sci., 9(1946):163-188.

91. McCann, J. A. 1959. Life history studies of the spottail shiner of Clear Lake, Iowa, with particular reference to some sampling problems. Trans. Am. Fish. Soc., 88(4):336-343.

92. Smith, L. L., Jr. and R. H. Kramer. 1964. The spottail shiner in Lower Red Lake, Minnesota. Trans. Am. Fish. Soc., 93(1):35-45.

93. Griswold, B. L. 1963. Food and growth of spottail shiners and other forage fishes of Clear Lake, Iowa. Iowa Acad. Sci. Proc., 70:215-223.

94. Trautman, M. B. 1957. The fishes of Ohio. Ohio State Univ. Press, 683 pp.

95. Pflieger, W. L. 1965. Reproductive behavior of the minnows, *Notropis spilopterus* and *Notropis whipplei.* Copeia, 1965(1):1-8.

96. Winn, H. E. and J. F. Stout. 1960. Sound production by the satinfin shiner, *Notropis analostanus,* and related fishes. Science, 132:222-223.

97. Delco, E. A., Jr. 1960. Sound discrimination by males of two cyprinid fishes. Texas J. Sci., 12:48-54.

98. Outten, L. M. 1958. Studies of the life history of the cyprinid fishes *Notropis galacturus* and *rubricroceus.* J. Elisha Mitchell Sci. Soc., 74(2):122-134.

99. Gibbs, R. H., Jr. 1961. Cyprinid fishes of the subgenus *Cyprinella* of *Notropis.* IV. The *Notropis galacturus-camurus* complex. Am. Midl. Nat., 66(2):337-354.

100. Cook, F. A. 1959. Freshwater fishes in Mississippi. Miss. Fish and Game Comm., 1-239.

101. Black, J. D. 1945. Natural history of the northern mimic shiner *Notropis volucellus volucellus* Cope. Invest. Ind. Lakes and Streams, 2(18):449-469.

102. Hoyt, R. D. 1970. Food habits of the silverjaw minnow, *Ericymba buccata* Cope, in an intermittent stream in Kentucky. Am. Midl. Nat., 84(1):226-236.

103. Hoyt, R. D. 1971. The reproductive biology of the silverjaw minnow, *Ericymba buccata* in Kentucky. Trans. Am. Fish. Soc., 100(3):510-519.

104. Hoyt, R. D. 1971. Age and growth of the silverjaw minnow, *Ericymba buccata* Cope, in Kentucky. Am. Midl. Nat., 86(2):257-275.

105. Raney, E. C. 1939. The breeding habits of the silvery minnow, *Hybognathus regius* Girard. Am. Midl. Nat., 21(3):674-680.

106. Parker, H. L. 1964. Natural history of *Pimephales vigilax* (Cyprinidae). Southwest. Nat., 8(4):228-235.

107. Kraatz, W. C. 1928. Study of the food of the blunt-nosed minnow, *Pimephales notatus.* Ohio J. Sci., 28(2):86-98.

108. Hubbs, C. L. and G. P. Cooper. 1936. Minnows of Michigan. Cranbrook Inst. Sci., Bull. 8:1-84.

109. Westman, J. R. 1938. Studies on the reproduction and growth of the bluntnose minnow, *Hyborhynchus notatus* (Rafinesque). Copeia, 1938(2):57-6l.

110. Coyle, E. E. 1930. The algal food of *Pimephales promelas* (fathead minnow). Ohio J. Sci., 30(1):23-35.

111. Wynne-Edwards, V. C. 1933. The breeding habits of the black-headed minnow *(Pimephales promelas* Raf.). Trans. Am. Fish. Soc., 62(1932):382-383.

112. Markus, H. C. 1934. Life history of the blackhead minnow *(Pimephales promelas).* Copeia, 1934(3):116-122.

113. Carlson, D. R. 1967. Fathead minnow, *Pimephales promelas* Rafinesque, in the Des Moines River, Boone County, Iowa, and the Skunk River drainage, Hamilton and Story Counties, Iowa. Iowa State J. Sci., 41(3):363-374.

114. Moore, G. A. and F. B. Cross. 1950. Additional Oklahoma fishes with validation of *Poecilichthys parvipinnis* (Gilbert and Swain). Copeia, 1950(2):139-148.

115. Starostka, V. J. and R. L. Applegate. 1970. Food selectivity of bigmouth buffalo, *Ictiobus cyprinellus,* in Lake Poinsett, South Dakota. Trans. Am. Fish. Soc., 99(3):571-576.

116. Schoffman, R. J. 1943. Age and growth of gourdhead buffalo in Reelfoot Lake. J. Tenn. Acad. Sci., 18(1):36-46.

117. Brady, L. and A. Hulsey. 1959. Propagation of buffalo fishes. Proc. 13th Ann. Conf. S. E. Assoc. Game and Fish Comm.:80-90.

118. Yeager, L. E. 1936. An observation on spawning buffalofish in Mississippi. Copeia, 1936(4):238-239.

119. Greer, J. K. and F. B. Cross. 1956. Fishes of El Dorado City Lake, Butler County, Kansas. Trans. Kans. Acad. Sci., 59(3):358-363.

120. McComish, T. S. 1967. Food habits of bigmouth and smallmouth buffalo in Lewis and Clark Lake and the Missouri River. Trans. Am. Fish. Soc., 96(1):70-74.

121. Schoffman, R. J. 1944. Age and growth of the smallmouth buffalo in Reelfoot Lake. J. Tenn. Acad. Sci., 19(1):3-9.

122. Brezner, J. 1958. Food habits of the northern river carpsucker in Missouri. Progr. Fish-Cult., 20(4):170-174.

123. Behmer, D. J. 1965. Spawning periodicity of the river carpsucker, *Carpiodes carpio.* Iowa Acad. Sci., 72:253-262.

124. Vanicek, D. 1961. Life history of the quillback and highfin carpsuckers in the Des Moines River. Proc. Iowa Acad. Sci., 68:238-246.

125. Stewart, N. H. 1927. Development, growth, and food habits of the white sucker, *Catostomus commersoni* Le Sueur. Bull. U. S. Bur. Fish., 42(1926):147-184.

126. Purkett, C. A., Jr. 1958. Growth of fishes in the Salt River, Missouri. Trans. Am. Fish. Soc., 87(1957):116-131.

127. Raney, E. C. and E. A. Lachner. 1946. Age, growth, and habits of the hog sucker, *Hypentelium nigricans* (Le Sueur), in New York. Am. Midl. Nat., 36(1):78-86.

128. Bowman, M. L. 1970. Life history of the

black redhorse, *Moxostoma duquesnei* (Le Sueur) in Missouri. Trans. Am. Fish. Soc., 99(3):546-559.

129. Meyer, W. H. 1962. Life history of three species of redhorse *(Moxostoma)* in the Des Moines River, Iowa. Trans. Am. Fish. Soc., 91(4):412-419.

130. Hackney, P. A., W. M. Tatum, and S. L. Spencer. 1967. Life history study of the river redhorse, *Moxostoma carinatum* (Cope), in the Cahaba River, Alabama, with notes on the management of the species as a sport fish. Proc. 21st Ann. Conf. S. E. Assoc. Game and Fish Comm.:324-332.

131. Jackson, S. W., Jr. 1957. Comparison of the age and growth of four fishes from Lower and Upper Spavinaw Lakes, Oklahoma. Proc. 11th Ann. Conf. S. E. Assoc. Game and Fish. Comm.:232-249.

132. Hankinson, T. L. 1919. Notes on life-histories of Illinois Fish. Trans. Ill. State Acad. Sci., 12:132-150.

133. Lewis, W. M. and D. Elder. 1953. The fish population of the headwaters of a spotted bass stream in southern Illinois. Trans. Am. Fish. Soc., 82(1952):193-202.

134. Ewers, L. A. and M. W. Boesel. 1935. The food of some Buckeye Lake fishes. Trans. Am. Fish. Soc., 65:57-70.

135. Moen, T. 1953. Food habits of the carp in northwest Iowa lakes. Iowa Acad. Sci., 60:665-686.

136. Cooper, G. P. 1935. Some results of forage fish investigations in Michigan. Trans. Am. Fish. Soc., 65:132-142.

137. Forney, J. L. 1955. Life history of the black bullhead, *Ameiurus melas* (Rafinesque), of Clear Lake, Iowa. Iowa State Coll. J. Sci., 30(1):145-162.

138. Houser, A. and C. Collins. 1962. Growth of black bullhead catfish in Oklahoma. Oklahoma Fish. Res. Lab., Report No. 79:1-18.

139. Raney, E. C. and D. A. Webster. 1940. The food and growth of the young of the common bullhead, *Ameiurus nebulosus nebulosus* (Le Sueur), in Cayuga Lake, N. Y. Trans. Am. Fish. Soc., 69(1939):205-209.

140. Breder, C. M. 1935. The reproductive habits of the common catfish, *Ameiurus nebulosus* (Le Sueur), with a discussion of their significance in ontogeny and phylogeny. Zoologica, 19:143-185.

141. Breder, C. M. 1939. Variations in the nesting habits of *Ameiurus nebulosus* (Le Sueur). Zoologica, 24(3):367-368.

142. Todd, J. H., J. Atema, and J. E. Bardach. 1967. Chemical communication in social behavior of a fish, the yellow bullhead. Science, 158(3801):672-673.

143. Schoffman, R. J. 1955. Age and rate of growth of the yellow bullhead in Reelfoot Lake, Tennessee. J. Tenn. Acad. Sci., 30(1):4-7.

144. Bailey, R. M. and H. M. Harrison. 1948. Food habits of the southern channel catfish *(Ictalurus lacustrus punctatus)* in the Des Moines River, Iowa. Trans. Am. Fish. Soc., 75(1948):110-138.

145. Marzolf, R. C. 1957. The reproduction of channel catfish in Missouri ponds. J. Wildl. Mgt., 21(1):22-28.

146. Davis, J. 1959. Management of channel catfish in Kansas. Univ. Kans. Mus. Nat. Hist., Misc. Publ. 21:1-56.

147. Marzolf, R. C. 1955. Use of pectoral spines and vertebrae for determining age and rate of growth of the channel catfish. J. Wildl. Mgt., 19(2):243-249.

148. Jordan, D. S. and B. W. Evermann. 1916. American food and game fishes. Doubleday, Page & Co., New York, 572 pp.

149. Brown, B. E. and J. S. Dendy. 1961. Observations on the food habits of the flathead and blue catfish in Alabama. Proc. 15th Ann. Conf. S. E. Assoc. Game and Fish. Comm.:219-222.

150. Jenkins, R. M. 1956. Growth of blue catfish *(Ictalurus furcatus)* in Lake Texoma. Southwest. Nat., 1(4):166-173.

151. Bean, T. H. 1880. Description of a new species of *Amiurus (A. ponderosus)* from the Mississippi River. Proc. U. S. Natl. Mus. (1879)2:286-290.

152. Fisher, H. J. 1954. Fishing the wild Missouri. Missouri Conserv., 15(4):10-16.

153. Evermann, B. W. and H. W. Clark. 1920. Lake Maxinkuckee, a physical and biological survey. Ind. Dept. Cons. Publ., 1:1-660.

154. Adams, C. C. and T. L. Hankinson. 1928. The ecology and economics of Oneida Lake fish. Roosevelt Wild Life Annals. 1 (3 and 4):235-548.

155. Fowler, H. W. 1917. Some notes on the breeding habits of local catfishes. Copeia 42:32-36.

156. Taylor, W. R. 1969. A revision of the catfish genus *Noturus* Rafinesque, with an analysis of higher groups in the Ictaluridae. U. S. Natl. Mus., Bull. 282:1-315.

157. Greeley, J. R. 1929. Fishes of the Erie-Niagara Watershed. *In* A biological survey of the Erie-Niagara System. Suppl. to 18th Ann. Rept. N. Y. State Cons. Dept., 3(6):150-179.

158. Carlson, D. R. 1966. Age and growth of the stonecat, *Noturus flavus* Rafinesque, in the Vermillion River. Proc. South Dakota Acad. Sci., 45:131-137.

159. Minckley, W. L. and J. E. Deacon. 1959. Biology of the flathead catfish in Kansas.

Trans. Am. Fish. Soc., 88:344-355.

160. Fontain, P. A. 1944. Notes on the spawning of the shovelhead catfish, *Pylodictis olivaris* (Rafinesque). Copeia, 1944(1):50-51.

161. Magnuson, J. J. and L. L. Smith, Jr. 1963. Some phases in the life history of the trout-perch. Ecology, 44(1):83-95.

162. Lawler, G. H. 1954. Observations on the trout-perch *Percopsis omiscomaycus* (Walbaum) at Heming Lake, Manitoba. J. Fish. Res. Bd. Canada, 11(1):1-4.

163. Eddy, S. and T. Surber. 1943. Northern fishes. Univ. Minn. Press, 276 pp.

164. Hall, G. E. and R. M. Jenkins. 1954. Notes on the age and growth of the pirate perch, *Aphredoderus sayanus,* in Oklahoma. Copeia, 1954(1):69.

165. Poulson, T. L. 1963. Cave adaptation in amblyopsid fishes. Am. Midl. Nat., 70(2):257-290.

166. Eigenmann, C. H. 1909. Cave vertebrates of America. A study in degenerative evolution. Carnegie Inst. Wash. Publ. 104.

167. Robins, C. R. and E. E. Deubler, Jr. 1955. The life history and systematic status of the burbot, *Lota lota lacustris* (Walbaum), in the Susquehanna River system. New York State Mus., Circ. 39:1-49.

168. Cahn, A. R. 1936. Observations on the breeding of the lawyer, *Lota maculosa.* Copeia, 1936(3):163-165.

169. Hall, G. E. 1956. Additions to the fish fauna of Oklahoma, with a summary of introduced species. Southwest. Nat., 1(1):16-26.

170. McCaskill, M. L., J. T. Thomerson, and P. R. Mills. 1972. Food of the northern studfish, *Fundulus catenatus,* in the Missouri Ozarks. Trans. Am. Fish. Soc., 101(2):375-377.

171. Bonham, L. E. 1962. Ecology of a saline spring, Boone's Lick. Unpubl. M. A. Thesis, Univ. of Mo., 89 pp.

172. Koster, W. J. 1948. Notes on the spawning activities and the young stages of *Plancterus kansae* (Garman). Copeia, 1948(1):25-33.

173. Hunt, B. P. 1953. Food relationships between Florida spotted gar and other organisms in the Tamiami Canal, Dade County, Florida. Trans. Am. Fish. Soc., 82(1952):13-33.

174. Leitholf, E. 1917. *Fundulus chrysotus.* Aquatic Life, 2(11):141-142.

175. Mayer, F. 1931. *Fundulus sciadicus.* Aquatic Life, 15(2):40,57.

176. Goodyear, C. P. 1970. Terrestrial and aquatic orientation in the starhead topminnow, *Fundulus notti.* Science, 168:603-605.

177. Rice, L. A. 1942. The food of seventeen Reelfoot Lake fishes in 1941. J. Tenn. Acad. Sci., 17(1):4-13.

178. Atmar, G. L. and K. W. Stewart. 1972. Food, feeding selectivity and ecological efficiencies of *Fundulus notatus* (Cyprinodontidae). Am. Midl. Nat., 88(1):76-89.

179. Carranza, J. and H. E. Winn. 1954. Reproductive behavior of the blackstripe topminnow, *Fundulus notatus.* Copeia, 1954(4):273-278.

180. Barnickol, P. G. 1941. Food habits of *Gambusia affinis* from Reelfoot Lake, Tennessee, with special reference to malarial control. Rept. Reelfoot Lake Biol. Sta. 5:5-13.

181. Krumholz, L. A. 1948. Reproduction of the western mosquitofish, *Gambusia affinis affinis* (Baird and Girard), and its use in mosquito control. Ecol. Monogr., 18(1):1-43.

182. Cahn, A. R. 1927. An ecological study of southern Wisconsin fishes. The brook silversides *(Labidesthes sicculus)* and the cisco *(Leucichthys artedi)* in their relations to the region. Illinois Biol. Monogr., 11(1):1-151.

183. Nelson, J. S. 1968. Life history of the brook silverside, *Labidesthes sicculus,* in Crooked Lake, Indiana. Trans. Am. Fish. Soc., 97(3):293-296.

184. Hubbs, C. L. 1921. An ecological study of the life-history of the fresh-water Atherine fish *Labidesthes sicculus.* Ecology,2:262-276.

185. Mense, J. B. 1967. Ecology of the Mississippi silversides, *Menidia audens* Hay, in Lake Texoma. Okla. Fish. Res. Lab., Bull. 6:1-32.

186. Hubbs, Clark, B. Sharp, and J. F. Schneider. 1971. Developmental rates of *Menidia audens* with notes on salt tolerance. Trans. Am. Fish. Soc., 100(4):603-610.

187. Koster, W. J. 1937. The food of sculpins (Cottidae) in central New York. Trans. Am. Fish. Soc., 66(1936):374-382.

188. Smith, B. G. 1923. Notes on the nesting habits of *Cottus.* Pap. Mich. Acad. Sci., Arts, and Lett., 2:221-222.

189. Bailey, J. E. 1952. Life history and ecology of the sculpin, *Cottus bairdi punctulatus* in southwestern Montana. Copeia, 1952(4):243-255.

190. Sigler, W. F. 1949. Life history of the white bass, *Lepibema chrysops* (Rafinesque) of Spirit Lake, Iowa. Iowa State Coll. Res. Bull., 366:201-244.

191. Riggs, C. D. 1955. Reproduction of the white bass, *Morone chrysops.* Invest. Ind. Lakes and Streams, 4:87-110.

192. Patriarche, M. H. 1953. The fishery in Lake Wappapello, a flood-control reservoir on the St. Francis River, Missouri. Trans. Am. Fish. Soc., 87:240-258.

193. Scruggs, G. D., Jr. 1955. Reproduction of resident striped bass in Santee-Cooper Reservoir, South Carolina. Trans. Am. Fish. Soc., 85:144-159.

194. Stevens, R. E. 1958. The striped bass of the Santee-Cooper Reservoir. Proc. 11th Ann. Conf. S. E. Assoc. Game and Fish. Comm.:253-264.

195. May, D. D. and J. C. Fuller. 1962. A study on striped bass egg production in the Congaree and Wateree Rivers. Proc. 16th Ann. S. E. Assoc. Fish and Game Comm.:285-301.

196. Collier, J. E. 1959. Changes in fish populations and food habits of yellow bass in North Twin Lake, 1956-1958. Proc. Iowa Acad. Sci., 66:518-522.

197. Welker, B. D. 1963. Summer food habits of yellow bass and black bullheads in Clear Lake. Proc. Iowa Acad. Sci., 69:286-295.

198. Burnham, C. W. 1909. Notes on the yellow bass. Trans. Am. Fish. Soc., 39:103-108.

199. Schoffman, R. J. 1958. Age and rate of growth of the yellow bass in Reelfoot Lake, Tennessee, for 1955 and 1957. J. Tenn. Acad. Sci., 33(1):101-105.

200. Fajen, O. F. 1962. The influence of stream stability on homing behavior of two smallmouth bass populations. Trans. Am. Fish. Soc., 91(4):346-349.

201. Pflieger, W. L. 1966. Reproduction of the smallmouth bass *(Micropterus dolomieui)* in a small Ozark stream. Am. Midl. Nat., 76(2):410-418.

202. Smith, P. W. and L. M. Page. 1969. The food of spotted bass in streams of the Wabash River drainage. Trans. Am. Fish. Soc., 98(4):647-651.

203. Kramer, R. H. and L. L. Smith, Jr. 1962. Formation of year classes in largemouth bass. Trans. Am. Fish. Soc., 91(1):29-41.

204. Larimore, R. W. 1957. Ecological life history of the warmouth (Centrarchidae). Ill. Nat. Hist. Surv. Bull., 27(1):1-83.

205. Carr, M. H. 1946. The breeding habits of the eastern stumpknocker, *Lepomis punctatus punctatus* (Cuvier). Quart. J. Fla. Acad. Sci., 9:101-106.

206. Huish, M. T. 1957. Food habits of three Centrarchidae in Florida. Proc. 11th Ann. Conf. S. E. Assoc. Game and Fish Comm.:293-302.

207. Schoffman, R. J. 1939. Age and growth of the red-eared sunfish in Reelfoot Lake, Tennessee. J. Tenn. Acad. Sci., 14(1):61-71.

208. Barney, R. L. and Anson, B. J. 1923. Life history and ecology of the orangespotted sunfish, *Lepomis humilis.* Appendix XV, Rept. U. S. Comm. Fish., 1922:1-16.

209. Witt, A., Jr. and R. C. Marzolf. 1954. Spawning and behavior of the longear sunfish, *Lepomis megalotis megalotis.* Copeia, 1954(3):188-190.

210. Huck, L. E. and G. E. Gunning. 1967. Behavior of the longear sunfish, *Lepomis megalotis* (Rafinesque). Tulane Stud. in Zool., 14(3):121-131.

211. Hunter, J. R. 1963. The reproductive behavior of the green sunfish, *Lepomis cyanellus.* Zoologica, 48(2):13-24.

212. Burress, R. M. 1949. The growth rates of bluegills and largemouth black bass in fertilized and unfertilized ponds in central Missouri. Unpubl. M. A. Thesis, Univ. of Missouri, 79 pp.

213. Burress, R. M. 1965. A quantitative creel census on two arms of Bull Shoals Reservoir, Missouri. Proc. 16th Ann. Conf. S. E. Assoc. Game and Fish Comm.:387-398.

214. Conley, J. M. 1966. Ecology of the flier, *Centrarchus macropterus* (Lacépède) in southeast Missouri. Unpubl. M. A. Thesis, Univ. of Missouri, 119 pp.

215. Barney, R. L., and B. J. Anson. 1920. Life history and ecology of the pygmy sunfish, *Elassoma zonatum.* Ecology, 1(4):241-256.

216. Eschmeyer, P. 1950. The life history of the walleye in Michigan. Mich. Dept. Cons., Inst. for Fisheries Research, Bull. 3:1-99.

217. Niemuth, W., W. Churchill, and T. Wirth. 1966. The walleye, its life history, ecology, and management. Wisc. Cons. Dept., Publ. 227:1-14.

218. Vasey, F. W. 1967. Age and growth of walleye and sauger in Pool 11 of the Mississippi River. Iowa State J. Sci., 41(4):447-466.

219. Carufel, L. H. 1963. Life history of saugers in Garrison Reservior. J. Wild. Mgt., 27(3):450-456.

220. Gilbert, C. H. 1888. Descriptions of new and little known etheostomids. Proc. U. S. Natl. Mus., 10:47-64.

221. Karr, J. R. 1963. Age, growth, and food habits of johnny, slenderhead and blacksided darters of Boone County, Iowa. Proc. Iowa Acad. Sci., 70:228-236.

222. Thomas, D. L. 1970. An ecological study of four darters of the genus *Percina* (Percidae) in the Kaskaskia River, Illinois. Ill. Nat. Hist. Surv., Biol. Notes No. 70:1-18.

223. Winn, H. E. 1958. Observations on the reproductive habits of darters (Pisces-Percidae). Am. Midl. Nat., 59(1):190-212.

224. Petravicz, W. P. 1938. The breeding habits of the black-sided darter, *Hadropterus maculatus* Girard. Copeia, 1938(1):40-44.

225. Page, L. M. and P. W. Smith. 1970. The life history of the dusky darter, *Percina sciera,* in the Embarras River, Illinois. Ill. Nat. Hist. Surv., Biol. Notes No. 69:1-15.

226. Page, L. M. and P. W. Smith. 1971. The life history of the slenderhead darter, *Percina* *phoxocephala,* in the Embarras River, Illinois. Ill. Nat. Hist. Surv., Biol. Notes No. 74:1-14.

227. Turner, C. L. 1921. Food of the common Ohio darters. Ohio J. Sci., 22(2):41-62.

228. Winn, H. E. 1953. Breeding habits of the percid fish *Hadropterus copelandi* in Michigan. Copeia, 1953(1):26-30.

229. Roberts, N. J. and H. E. Winn. 1962. Utilization of the senses in feeding behavior of the johnny darter, *Etheostoma nigrum.* Copeia, 1962(3):567-570.

230. Lachner, E. A., E. F. Westlake, and P. S. Handwerk. 1950. Studies on the biology of some percid fishes from western Pennsylvania. Am. Midl. Nat., 43(1):92-111.

231. Hubbs, Clark and J. Pigg. 1972. Habitat preferences of the harlequin darter, *Etheostoma histrio,* in Texas and Oklahoma. Copeia, 1972(1):193-194.

232. Fayhy, W. E. 1954. The life history of the northern greenside darter, *Etheostoma blennioides blennioides* Rafinesque. J. Elisha Mitchell Sci. Soc., 70(2):139-205.

233. Taber, C. A. and R. F. Wilkinson, Jr. 1972. *Etheostoma nianguae* in the Sac River drainage, Missouri. Am. Midl. Nat., 89(1):251-252.

234. Ellis, M. M. and B. B. Jaffa. 1918. Notes on Cragin's darter, *Catonotus cragini* (Gilbert). Copeia, 59:73-75.

235. Smith-Vaniz, W. F. 1968. Freshwater fishes of Alabama. Auburn Univ. Agric. Exper. Sta., 211 pp.

236. Reeves, C. D. 1907. The breeding habits of the rainbow darter (*Etheostoma caeruleum* Storer), a study in sexual selection. Biol. Bull., 14:35-59.

237. Distler, Donald D. 1968. Distribution and variation of *Etheostoma spectabile* (Agassiz) (Percidae, Teleostei) Univ. Kans. Sci. Bull., 48(5):143-208.

238. Pflieger, W. L. 1966. Young of the orangethroat darter *(Etheostoma spectabile)* in nests of the smallmouth bass *(Micropterus dolomieui).* Copeia, 1966(1):139-140.

239. Lake, C. T. 1936. The life history of the fantailed darter. Am. Midl. Nat., 17:816-830.

240. Karr, J. R. 1964. Age, growth, fecundity and food habits of fantail darters in Boone County, Iowa. Iowa Acad. Sci. Trans., 71:274-280.

241. Braasch, M. E., and P. W. Smith. 1967. Life history of the slough darter, *Etheostoma gracile* (Pisces, Percidae). Ill. Nat. Hist. Surv., Biol. Notes No. 58:1-12.

242. Petravicz, J. J. 1936. The breeding habits of the least darter, *Microperca punctulata* Putnam. Copeia, 1936(2):77-82.

243. Moen, T. 1955. Food of the freshwater drum, *Aplodinotus grunniens* Rafinesque, in four Dickinson County, Iowa, lakes. Proc. Iowa Acad. Sci., 62:589-598.

244. Daiber, F. C. 1953. The life history and ecology of the sheepshead, *Aplodinotus grunniens* Rafinesque, in western Lake Erie. Diss. Abstr., 64:131-136.

245. Priegel, G. R. 1967. Food of the freshwater drum, *Aplodinotus grunniens,* in Lake Winnebago, Wisconsin. Trans. Am. Fish. Soc., 96(2):218-220.

246. Schneider, H. and A. D. Hasler. 1960. Laute und lauterzeugung beim süsswassertrommler *Aplodinotus grunniens* Rafinesque. (Sciaenidae, Pisces). Zeitschr. Vergleich. Physiol., Berlin, 43(5):499-517.

247. Hoy, P. R. 1872. Journal of an exploration of western Missouri in 1854, under the auspices of the Smithsonian Institution. Smithsonian Inst. Ann. Rept. for 1864:431-438.

248. Kraatz, W. C. 1923. A study of the food of the minnow *Campostoma anomalum.* Ohio J. Sci., 23:265-283.

249. Lachner, E. A. 1952. Studies of the biology of the cyprinid fishes of the chub genus *Nocomis* of the northeastern United States. Am. Midl. Nat., 48(2):433-466.

250. Lane, C. E., Jr. 1954. Age and growth of the bluegill, *Lepomis m. macrochirus* (Rafinesque), in a new Missouri impoundment. J. Wildl. Mgt., 18(3):358-365.

251. Purkett, Charles A., Jr. 1966. Missouri's fish cultural program. American Fishes and U.S. Trout News, Nov.—Dec.:5.

252. Cowel, B. C. and B. S. Barnett. 1974. Life history of the taillight shiner, *Notropis maculatus,* in central Florida. Amer. Midl. Nat., 91(2):282-293.

INDEX

Illustration
Description
Color plate

About the Author

William L. Pflieger was born in Columbus, Ohio in 1932. He holds Bachelor of Science and Master of Science degrees from Ohio State University, where he received his early training in Ichthyology under the guidance of Milton B. Trautman. He also attended the University of Michigan, and received the Doctor of Philosophy degree from the University of Kansas in 1969.

Dr. Pflieger joined the fisheries research staff of the Missouri Department of Conservation in 1961. Over the past 14 years he has conducted research on a variety of topics relating to the biology of Missouri fishes. His most recent studies have been of fish distribution, reproduction and hybridization in the black basses, and trout-food production in Lake Taneycomo. He has also been active in the Department's programs for preservation of natural areas and rare and endangered species.

He is a research associate at the University of Missouri, and is a member of the Society of Sigma Xi, the American Fisheries Society, and the American Society of Ichthyologists and Herpetologists. He has authored several scientific papers, and a companion volume to this book, "A Distributional Study of Missouri Fishes".

His hobbies include bee keeping, bird watching, underwater photography, and canoeing and camping along Missouri streams with wife Jo Ann and daughters Patricia and Cynthia.

Dr. James R. Karr

Topography of a Fish

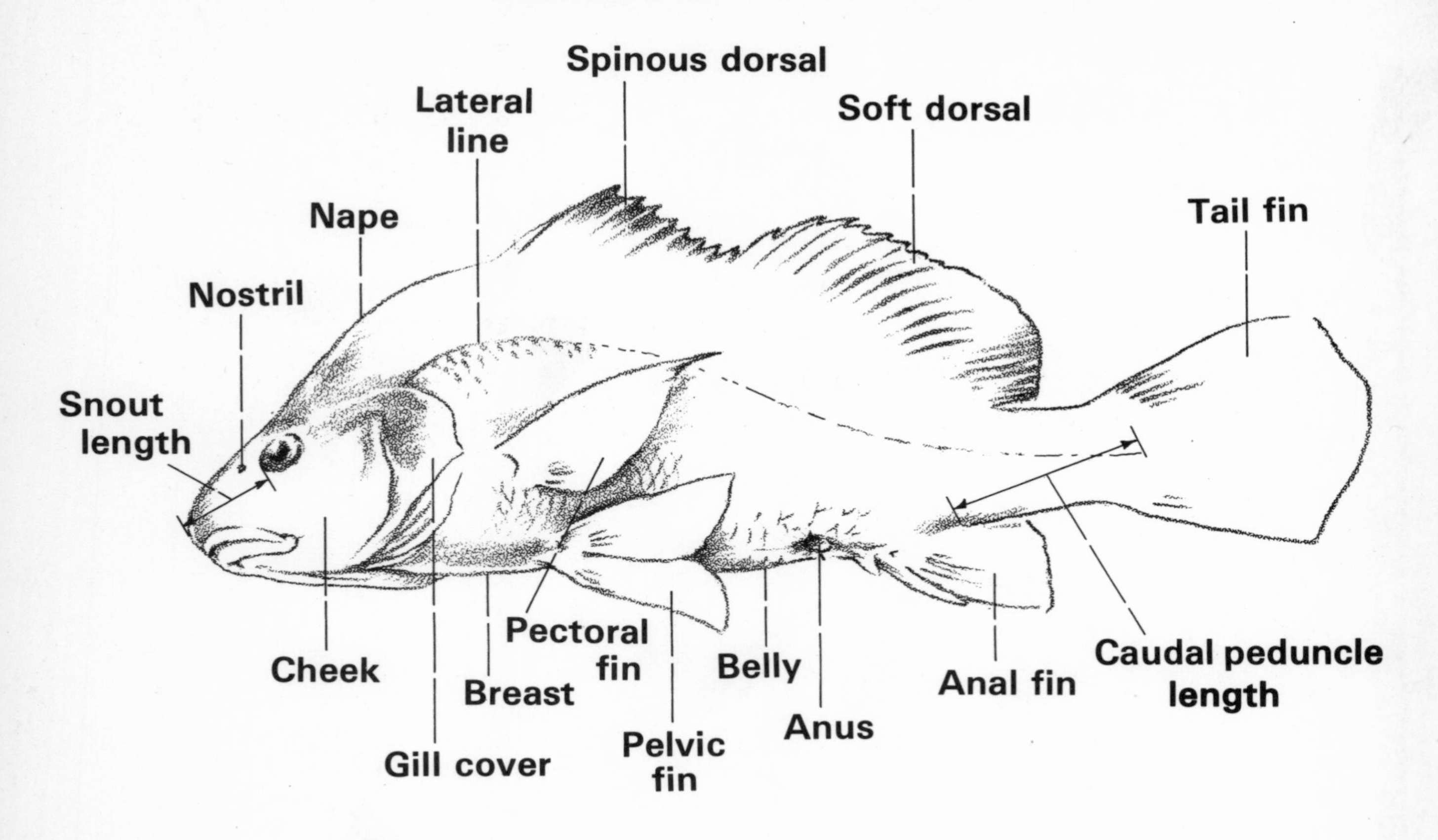

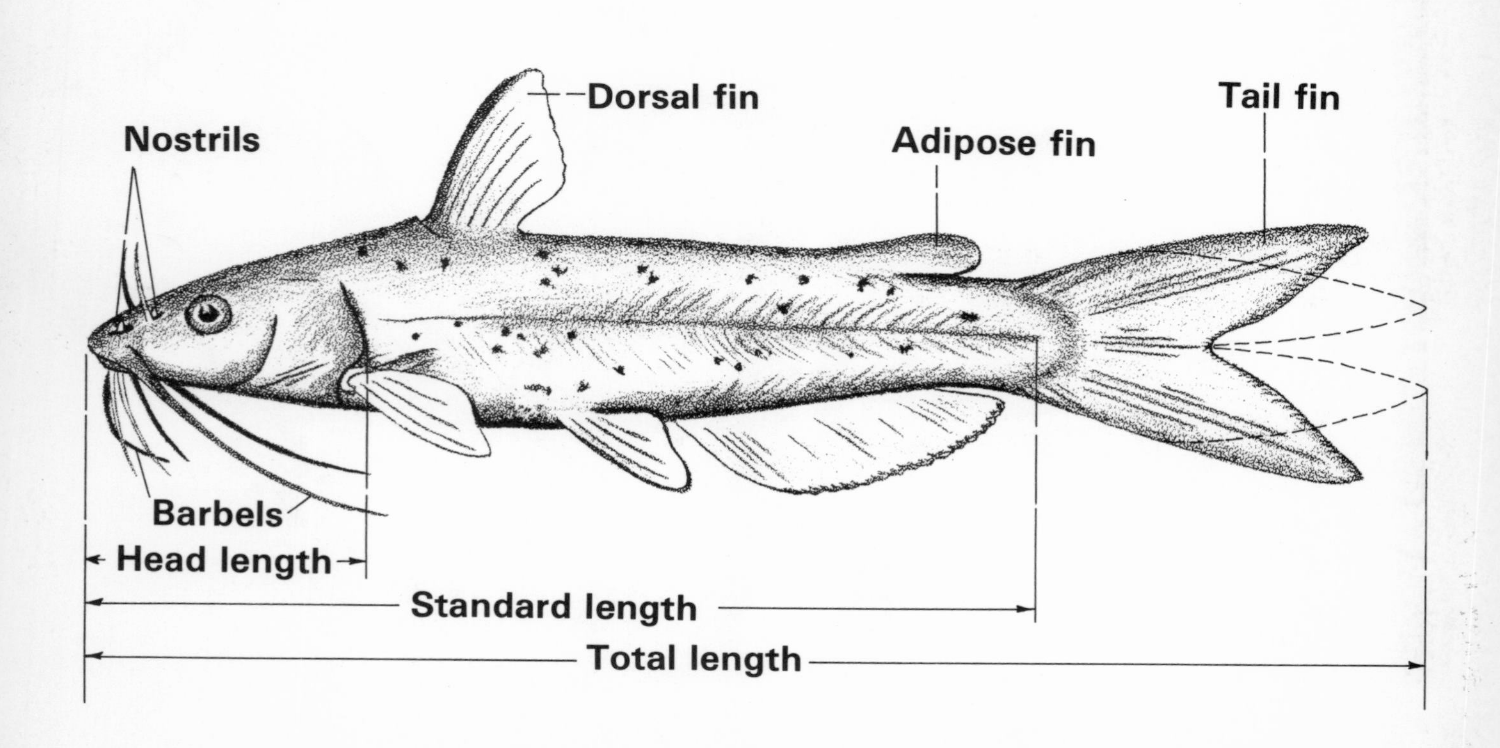